Table of Contents

CHAPTER 1

Introduction to Chemistry

1.1 THE SCOPE OF CHEMISTRY

Chemistry is one of the most exciting and relevant areas of study because all aspects of life are to some degree related to chemistry. From this textbook you will learn the most fundamental chemical concepts in a form that will allow you to apply them to your specific areas of interest. To begin our study, let's state a simplified working definition of chemistry. The study of **chemistry** is concerned with the composition of matter, the changes that matter undergoes, and the relation between these changes in matter and changes in energy. A **chemist** is a person who studies the composition, structure, and properties of matter and seeks to explain the changes that matter undergoes.

But what is matter? Put simply, matter is anything that has mass and occupies space. The earth, and everything on it, is composed of matter. We use terms such as substances, materials, objects, and bodies when referring to matter. Examples of matter are as far ranging as the air you breathe, the food you eat, the objects that you own, and the ground upon which you walk. As we will discover, and as we will stress throughout the textbook, matter is closely associated with energy; in fact, in some instances it cannot be easily distinguished from energy. At this time we will defer our discussion of matter and energy to complete our brief look at the scope of chemistry.

Chemistry overlaps with and is an integral part of the other sciences (Fig. 1.1). Chemistry is sometimes called the **central science** because it is closely tied to all of the other sciences.

Biology, the study of living systems, applies chemical principles to help understand the functioning of cells, the basic units of life. Geology, the study of the earth, incorporates chemical observations in order to elucidate the processes that occur on earth.

Physics and chemistry, both physical sciences, overlap to a large degree since physics also deals with matter, energy, and the interaction of the two. Physics is the natural science that deals with subjects such as light, heat, motion electricity, optics, and the most basic structure of matter. The principal difference between physics and chemistry is that physicists are more interested in the most fundamental components and regularities of nature and how they fit together to yield our universe. Chemists and physicists make use of the same laws of nature to gain a better understanding of the properties and behavior of matter.

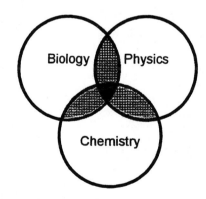

Figure 1.1
Science is divided into three major overlapping disciplines: chemistry, physics, and biology

The study of chemistry may be separated into artificial divisions or branches that categorize the most significant areas of study. These overlapping divisions include (1) analytical, (2) inorganic, (3) organic, (4) biological, (5) physical, and (6) geological chemistry. An insight into each division is gained by considering what the various types of chemists study.

Analytical chemists examine matter to find the identity and amount of its components. Most chemists use analytical procedures and techniques to some degree in their studies. **Inorganic chemists** study the properties, structures, and reactions of all elementary substances. As we will discover, one of these substances, carbon, has a special set of properties. Therefore, a division of chemistry is entirely devoted to this vast topic. It is called organic chemistry. **Organic chemists** investigate the properties of carbon-containing substances, and produce new ones, in the laboratory. **Biological chemists**, also called **biochemists**, study the compounds that compose living things and the ways they interact to produce living systems. **Physical chemists** apply the concepts of physics to the behavior of matter in an effort to better understand that behavior. For example, physical chemists propose theories to why certain substances undergo chemical reactions and others do not. Finally, **geochemists** investigate the structures, properties, and reactions of substances found in the earth's crust, atmosphere, and oceans.❖

REVIEW EXERCISES
1.1 Use a dictionary to find the definitions of each of the following:
(a) chemistry

(b) physics

(c) biology

(d) geology

1.2 List and describe the major divisions of chemistry.
(a)

(b)

(c)

(d)

(e)

1.2 THE EARLY HISTORY OF CHEMISTRY

Ancient People
The birth of chemistry coincides with the first time people became aware that they could improve upon what nature offered. By observing lightning, fire, decay, and other natural phenomena, primitive people eventually discovered that the properties of objects could be changed.

After harnessing fire, ancient people solved day to day problems more efficiently. Pottery or bricks were formed from baked clay. Through trial and error, ceramics, glazes, and glasses were discovered. Advances in the "chemistry" of these times helped people develop the foundation for civilization.

During this early period of history, now called the stone age, people found that they could improve their lives by developing new materials. The search for new substances to replace their stone tools led to the discovery of metals. Metals added a new dimension to life. Unlike stone, metals could be hammered and shaped into a multitude of forms. Weapons created from metals remained sharper longer than stone counterparts, and metal weapons could be resharpened. Copper, gold, and tin were the first metals used—a copper cooking pan was found in an Egyptian tomb dating back to 3200 B.C.

Sometime around 3000 B.C. a startling discovery was made. If copper and tin ores were heated and mixed, a new metal (an alloy) was formed which was much harder than either copper or tin. The metal, bronze, ushered in a new era—the bronze age.

A thousand years elapsed before the bronze age ended. It was common knowledge throughout the world that a superior metal, iron, existed. But it was rare, and no method for extracting the iron from its ore was readily available. In approximately 1500 B.C. the Hittites, a group of people who lived in Asia Minor, found a means of liberating iron from its ore, using a method that is a forerunner of our present day smelting process. By chance, the Hittites heated iron ore in a charcoal (a form of carbon) smelter, producing an iron-carbon mixture that resembles steel. Thus the world was thrust into the iron age about 1000 B.C.

During the iron age, other practical chemical advances were made. In Egypt, various chemicals were incorporated into all aspects of life and death. The ancient Egyptians made alcoholic beverages by the fermentation of fruits, concocted embalming fluids to preserve the dead, and developed pigments, dyes, and paints that have lasted to modern times.

> Steel is an alloy of iron that contains other metals and less than 0.5% carbon. Alloys are most frequently produced when two or more metals are mixed

The Ancient Greeks

The ancient Greeks, in about 600 B.C., were one of the first peoples to pose important questions about why matter behaved as it did. They wanted to know the effect of heat on metals; what were the most basic forms of matter; and if one metal could be changed into another. Greek scholars sought to determine the composition of the universe.

Thales of Miletus (640-546 B.C.) was one of the first Greek philosophers to conceive the idea of "elements." Thales suggested that elements were the most fundamental forms of matter. Other Greek thinkers looked to nature and speculated that the entire universe was composed of four elements: earth, air, fire, and water (Fig. 1.2).

Aristotle (384-322 B.C.), one of the greatest

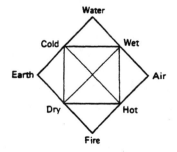

Figure 1.2
The ancient Greeks believed that all matter was composed of four "elements:" Earth, air, fire, and water.

ancient Greek philosophers, accepted and advanced the four-element theory. He suggested that in addition to the four basic elements there could be two pairs of opposite qualities: hot-cold and wet-dry. Aristotle also believed that each element had its own set of

> Aristotle was the most famous student of Plato. Plato thought that Aristotle was "the intelligence of the school"

properties; e.g., earth should fall and fire should rise. With each modification of the four-element theory, a greater number of plausible explanations were proposed to questions and problems that had puzzled people for centuries.

Today, some people might think of these ideas as humorous or simple-minded solutions to complex problems. Nevertheless, the four-element theory, in a variety of forms, lasted for approximately 2000 years. In part, the longevity of this theory can be attributed to its simplicity. Many problems of nature are explained effortlessly in terms of earth (solid), air (gas), fire (energy), and water (liquid).

Ancient Greek philosophers also attempted to understand the problem of the decomposition of matter into smaller parts. If a stone was broken or crushed, could the fragments of stone be further subdivided? If so, was there a limit beyond which the fragment could no longer be divided? About 450 B.C. **Leucippus** and his disciple **Democritus** proposed the idea of the *atom*. The word "atom" is derived from the Greek term for "indivisible." Democritus suggested that the smallest particle of matter was an atom—a unit of matter that was indivisible.

> To understand the very large, we must understand the very small.
> -Democritus

Democritus also speculated that atoms in different substances varied with respect to size and shape. This was an incredible proposition, considering that Democritus was a philosopher—one who proposes ideas about nature through logic—rather than a true scientist—one who conducts controlled systematic experiments based on observable facts.

The Alchemists

From approximately A.D. 300 to A.D. 1100 the Dark Ages prevailed in Europe and chemical advancements almost came to a standstill. However, in Africa and the Middle East, Arab cultures continued to make significant chemical contributions during this period. A small group of Arabs tried to find a way to convert (they said "transmute" cheap, abundant metals to gold. This period in the history of chemistry is now known for these dedicated men who searched for gold—the **alchemists**.

As part of their quest for a way to change base metals to gold, the alchemists sought to find the magic elixir of life, or as it is sometimes called, the philosopher's stone. They thought that the magic elixir could rid one's body of disease and was the key to eternal life. Thousands of alchemists searched in vain for gold and the magic elixir. Even though they never achieved their principal goals, they did uncover a vast amount of chemical knowledge. Various contemporary laboratory techniques and glassware are traced to the alchemists. Some historians believe that the term "chemistry" is derived from the alchemists' term for the mixing of chemicals. The practice of alchemy continued for more than 2000 years, from the period before the birth of Christ until the eighteenth century. Alchemy died and chemistry emerged because curious people started to ask more probing questions about matter. What explains the behavior of matter? Is matter composed only of earth, air, fire, and water? Do all substances act in a predictable, regular manner?

Early Scientists

Robert Boyle, an Irishman who lived from 1627 to 1691, saw the shortcomings of alchemy and decided to apply what is now known as scientific reasoning to the study of chemistry. Boyle followed the lead of other great scientific investigators of his time: Galileo Galilei (1564-1642), Jan Baptista Van Helmont (1577-1644), Evangelista Torricelli (1608-1647), and Otto von Guericke (1602-1686).

Boyle's exacting studies of gases and their properties supported the idea proposed 1000 years before by certain Greek philosophers—that matter is composed of atoms. In his famous book *The Sceptical Chymist,* published in 1661, Boyle attacked the idea that matter is composed of only four elements. Instead, Boyle proposed that if a substance thought to be an element is capable of being broken down into simpler forms, then it is not an element. One of the most significant outcomes of Boyle's work is the idea of careful experimentation as a vital component of science—the idea that any propositions regarding matter must be supported by reproducible observations.

Other scientists of the seventeenth century were concerned with the nature of energy, which they called "fire." Their interest was spurred by the invention of the steam engine and the possibility of developing more efficient engines capable of performing heavy work. Scientists wanted the answers to questions like these: Why do certain substances burn while others do not? How is heat transferred from one object to an other? What is the nature of the combustion process?

A German physician and chemist, **Georg Ernest Stahl** (1660-1734), proposed the phlogiston theory to help answer some of these questions about "fire." The term "phlogiston" was derived from the Greek term that means "to set on fire." Stahl's phlogiston theory described combustible

> Stahl was physician to King Frederick William I of Prussia. Besides advancing the phlogiston theory, Stahl was a leading proponent of vitalism the idea that a different set of natural laws governs living systems.

objects as those that contain a large quantity of phlogiston. As an object burned, Stahl suggested, phlogiston flowed from the object; the object stopped burning when all of the phlogiston was released. A log burned because it contained phlogiston. The resulting ashes lacked phlogiston; consequently, ashes were noncombustible.

Joseph Priestley's (1733-1804) discovery of oxygen as a component of air and of its ability to support combustion (burning), brought about the end of the phlogiston theory. Priestley informed the French scientist **Antoine Laurent Lavoisier** (1743-1794) of his discovery of oxygen. Lavoisier immediately repeated Priestley's experiments and found that oxygen was truly formed when he performed them. But Lavoisier saw something much more

> Priestley, a Unitarian minster, befriended Ben Franklin and Thomas Jefferson in the United States after leaving England because of religious persecution.

important—that mathematics could explain the decomposition of matter. When dealing with matter, Lavoisier found that the whole equaled the sum of its parts. He then conducted a classic experiment, heating mercury and oxygen to conclusively show that oxygen and not phlogiston supported combustion.

Lavoisier is considered the father of modern chemistry. His textbook, *Elementary Treatise on Chemistry*, published in 1789, indicated to the world that chemistry was a science based on theories supported by reproducible experiments. In the *Treatise* he discussed 33 elements known at that time. To his credit, all but two, caloric and light, are considered elements today. Lavoisier's contributions to chemistry are comparable to those of Isaac Newton to physics. Lavoisier possessed a rare talent found in few people who have ever lived: he correctly organized and interpreted a large body of facts, yielding a completely new area of human concern, that of modern chemistry. Figure 1.3 shows a time line of the history of chemistry.❖

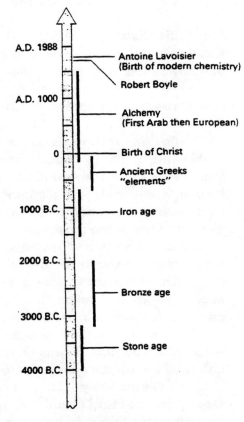

Figure 1.3 A time line of the history of chemistry.

Lavoisier's text was published in the year that the French Revolution began. He was arrested and tried for crimes against the people. Lavoisier pleaded that he was a scientist and not an aristocrat. The reply from the revolutionaries was "The Republic has no need for scientists." He was guillotined on May 8, 1794.

REVIEW EXERCISES

1.3 Write a brief explanation of how the following materials changed the lives of people:

(a) stone during the stone age

(b) bronze during the bronze age

(c) iron during the iron age

1.4 What contributions did the ancient Greeks make to the advancement of people's understanding of matter?

1.5 Write the name of the scientist responsible for each of the following:

(a) phlogiston theory

(b) discovery of oxygen

(c) proposition that matter was not solely composed of the four elements.

1.6 What were the main goals of the alchemists?

1.3 CHEMISTRY IN THE MODERN WORLD

Advances in chemistry make a valuable contribution to our modern lifestyle. For example, deadly diseases are controlled by potent antimicrobial agents (commonly called antibiotics). Tetracyclines, sulfa drugs, penicillins, and cephalosporins control diseases that were incurable 70 years ago. Many people take for granted that no matter what illness we contract, it can be treated with a drug.

We see chemistry in action every day in our homes. The "art" of cooking involves chemical techniques for frying, baking, roasting, and boiling. Cleaning involves selecting the appropriate soap, detergent, or cleaning fluid to best remove dirt and stains. Waxes are rubbed or sprayed on surfaces to protect and beautify. Pesticides are used to rid our houses and gardens of insect pests, and herbicides remove unwanted plants from our lawns.

Home recreation incorporates many advances in chemical technology. Picture tubes in television sets contain substances called phosphors that glow various colors when struck by an electron beam. Magnetic recording tape is manufactured by affixing specific metallic substances to a strong plastic tape that does not stretch or shrink. Advances in the chemical processes used to manufacture transistors and integrated circuits (ICs) have resulted in personal computers, videotape recorders, giant television screens, electronic games, digital high-fidelity stereophonic sound systems, and modern telecommunications.

Modern means of transportation also rely on the chemical industry. For example, passenger jets can fly faster and carry more people economically as a result of strong new metals and plastics used in the bodies of aircraft. Plastic parts have been developed that are superior in many ways to the heavier, more costly metal parts they replace. In part, the increased gas mileage of new cars is due to the decreased weight of the cars, a result of the replacement of heavier metal parts with lighter plastic parts.

Modern society has become very dependent upon the continuing advances in chemistry. To a degree, many people expect chemists to rescue them from the clutches of life's problems and annoyances. But, unfortunately, for each new advance we must pay some price. Environmental problems result from by-products of the chemical industry. New health problems are caused by lifesaving drugs. Pesticides used to protect our crops accumulate in our bodies, causing serious health problems.❖

REVIEW EXERCISES

1.7 List three ways in which your life would change if all plastic goods were no longer available.

1.8 Write a short paragraph describing the role of chemists in the modern world.

1.4 A STRATEGY FOR LEARNING CHEMISTRY

In order to be most successful in your study of chemistry, you should have some sort of learning strategy or plan. Consider the following steps as a model for developing your own strategy.

1. Approach the study of chemistry in a positive way. If you think chemistry is hard or impossible and that you are going to fail—you will! Instead, try to regard chemistry as an important, central subject that will not only assist you in obtaining your educational goals but will give you a deeper understanding of yourself and your environment.

2. Begin your study of each new chemistry topic by quickly reading the material in the textbook before attending the lecture. It is not important to memorize new terms or solve problems at this time. Use the *Study Guidelines* found at the end of each chapter to identify the most significant topics in the chapter.

3. After attending the lecture and obtaining a good set of lecture notes—the highlights of what your professor thinks is most important— reread the chapter, paying careful attention to those topics discussed in the lecture. While doing this second reading, answer all *Review Exercise* questions; these are located at the end of most chapter sections. Strive to understand as much as possible of one section of the textbook before proceeding to the next one. On some occasions you may want to answer appropriate *Review Exercises* at the end of the section before moving to the next section.

4. After you have reread the chapter and answered the *Review Exercises*, complete all assigned *Exercises* at the end of each chapter. **The only way to successfully learn chemistry is to do chemistry by solving problems and answering questions.** If you can solve the problems and answer the questions at the end of the chapter, then, and only then, will you have an adequate knowledge of the material in the chapter. Some helpful hints to consider when solving problems are:
   (a) Read each problem carefully and determine if you understand what the problem asks. If not, reread the appropriate section in the chapter or refer to your lecture notes.
   (b) Determine what is to be found (what is unknown), and write it on paper.
   (e) Extract from the problem all relevant information, and write it below your statement of what is to be found.
   (d) Use the factor-label method (discussed in Chap. 2), when appropriate, to solve the problem. When the factor-label method cannot be used, you must rely on logic or knowing the correct relationship or equation. Also, **never forget units.** Knowing what unit belongs with a number is usually more important than knowing the number itself.
   (e) If possible, check to see if the answer corresponds to the correct answer listed with the problem and in Appendix D. If the answer is incorrect, check for arithmetic errors, and if none are found, compare the numbers used to those

given and carefully examine the units for possible errors.

(f) Instead of wasting a lot of time on a problem that you are unable to solve at the moment, leave the problem and try others. Come back to the unsolved problem later, perhaps in a few days. After returning to the problem, you may find that you can solve it with ease (brains work in mysterious ways).

(g) Seek help any time you are unable to solve a problem after a reasonable attempt to obtain the correct answer. Do not be afraid to ask questions; this is one of the most effective ways to learn chemistry.

5. To ascertain how well you understand the material presented in the chapter, carefully go through the *Study Guidelines* listed at the beginning of the chapter to see if you have learned the material completely.

> The important thing is to not stop questioning
> -*Albert Einstein*

The list above outlines only a suggested learning strategy. Although it is not necessary to follow each step given here exactly, it is necessary to develop a successful strategy for learning chemistry, whatever that strategy may be. If you do not have a better method, use the one presented until you have developed your own plan.

A few words concerning your **lecture notes** are in order. Lecture notes are very important because they give an added perspective (your professor's) on the material in the textbook. But, in your zeal to obtain a complete set of notes, do not forget to listen to what the professor is saying. Listening is a critical skill to learn. Shortly after each lecture, rewrite your lecture notes. Rewriting your notes will allow you to rethink what was said, correct errors, clear up undecipherable passages, and add any extra thoughts.

Repetition is another key to learning chemistry efficiently. The amount of study time necessary for learning chemistry is normally greater than that needed for many other subjects. A large proportion of your study time should be spent working and reworking problems and transferring thoughts from your brain to paper. Correctly solving a problem once does not guarantee that you have totally learned how to solve problems of this type. Work many similar problems before proceeding to new problems. When learning new ideas, definitions, concepts, or rules, write them down on paper, over and over again. Chemistry is best learned through repetition!

To maximize your achievement, plan to spend time each day studying chemistry. Cramming at the last minute rarely works in chemistry. Shorter, less intense periods of study spread out over a longer time are most effective. Using this technique, you will not get bored as readily, and you will not be frustrated by trying to accomplish too much at the last moment.

Finally, you must learn that when studying chemistry, you must know and understand the previously introduced concepts before you can tackle new material. Failure to learn more basic material will prevent you from understanding new topics. thus, if you find yourself in this situation, go back and learn the more fundamental concepts before trying to comprehend the new concepts.❖

1.5 World Wide Web and WorldWideWolfe

World Wide Web

Most people know of the existence of a computer network called the Internet, and perhaps to some extent one component of the Internet called the **World Wide Web** (WWW). The WWW was first conceived at the European Laboratory for Particle Physics (CERN) in 1989 and first implemented in late 1990. It was developed to easily obtain and transmit scientific information. In those early days, it was only used by scientists. This is no longer true. It is possible that some day most people on Earth will be connected to the Internet to access information on the WWW!

In the early days of the Internet less convenient means such **FTP** and **Gopher** were used to transfer information. The emergence of the WWW was in part due to its graphical means of transferring information. The WWW system uses a file transfer method called **HTTP** (Hypertext Transfer Protocol). At its simplest, the WWW system is a "web" of linked hypertext documents. Hypertext means that clicking the mouse on highlighted text in a document causes the computer to retrieve and display some new document. Once the user's computer is linked in some way to the Internet, the user can make effective use of the WWW system with little more knowledge of computers other than how to use a mouse.

A document obtained through a hypertext link might reside on a completely different computer to the first document. This basic concept of hypertext is now extended so that the WWW has evolved into an online hypermedia system. **Hypermedia documents** are hypertext documents that contain embedded graphics, movie clips, and sound clips, in addition to plain text.

In order to read documents on the WWW, the user's computer must be connected to the Internet. In many institutions such connections are through a local area network (LAN), while the home user may have to resort to a modem connection through a telephone line. The user also requires a computer program called a **browser** in order to view the WWW documents. Good examples of such programs are Netscape Navigator and Internet Explorer.

A document being read by a user has links (usually color coded). When the mouse cursor is clicked on a link something happens. Typically, the user is taken to a different document. This is the basic concept of "hypertext." The key feature of a WWW hypertext document is its linking to other documents which might well be written by completely different authors in a different country. In a sense, clicking a link is like having instant access to another document.

Besides obtaining a new document, clicking on a link may cause a file to be transferred (downloaded) automatically to the user's computer or it will allow the user to search a database for documents containing specific words chosen by the user. The user is required to fill in a box in an online "form" with a short piece of text and then must click on the "Search" button. The remote computer program does the rest. Even when searching databases on another continent, the search usually only takes a few seconds.

Some people believe online hypertext books will replace printed books. This seems somewhat unlikely in the next few years, simply on grounds of convenience. However, online hypertext documents do have some advantages over the printed word. Hypertext documents contain text, but can also contain embedded graphics (such as a reaction mechanism), movie clips (perhaps for animating molecular motions), and even sound clips (good for chemistry lectures). Such documents are called multimedia documents. If nothing else, multimedia makes the document more interesting and informative. At the user's choice, the graphics are displayed automatically. The sounds and movie clips are activated with a single mouse click on an appropriate link. Display and use of these features requires fast computers because the time required to transfer sound and graphics files is often long.

No programming experience is required to construct documents to be placed on a WWW server. Documents on the WWW are written in a "markup language" called **HTML** (Hypertext Markup Language). These documents are plain text files which any word or text processor is capable of writing to the hard drive. The links and various formatting options such as headings or emphasized text are just text strings (called tags or elements) contained between <angle> brackets within the document. If you are interested, many online tutorials and guides for writing HTML are available.

One of the most important components in HTML is the anchor tag—a text string that defines a link. The information that describes this link is called the **Uniform Resources Locator** or URL, for short. The URL specifies the location of a document on the Internet. The general form of a URL is as follows.

http://{computer server}/{address of document}

The part of the URL before the colon (http in this case) specifies an access method or protocol. The "http" (**h**ypertext **t**ransport **p**rotocol) means to access a WWW document. The part of the URL after the two slashes and before the first single slash is the Internet address of the computer server that contains the document of interest. The remaining part is the address of the file on that computer server. For example, the URL for WorldWideWolfe (the web site for this textbook) is

http://www.mindspring.com/~drwolfe/WWWolfe_hcc.htm

The computer server with the information is "www.mindspring.com" and the actual HTML page on this server is called "WWWolfe_hcc.htm."

Chemistry and World Wide Web

What chemistry information can be found on the WWW? A vast amount of chemistry information already exists on the Internet and each day more information is added. Let us consider some of the general types of chemistry information that can be obtained. Do not be concerned if you do not understand each of the following because these are topics that will be discussed in the course.

1. Periodic Tables

If you want to know information about an element, you would link to one of the many interactive periodic tables. After reaching the periodic table, you just click on the element of interest to access the information available. One of the most comprehensive periodic table sites is called WebElements.

2. Chemical Databases

A chemical database contains information about compounds. For example, you may want to know the formula, structure, toxicity, or solubility of a compound. This information can be found in chemical databases throughout the WWW. An excellent site to find such information is the NIST WebBook.

3. Molecular Structures

A molecule has a three-dimensional shape called its molecular geometry. If you want to see the shape of a molecule, you have a wide selection of WWW sites to accomplish this. With the proper software, you can rotate the molecule and change they way it is represented. A good site to view the shapes of molecules is WebMolecules.

4. Beginning Chemistry

If you are a student it is important to obtain information about the new topics that you are studying. The WWW has a vast amount of information for beginning chemistry students. You can find online textbooks that are equal to or better than your own textbook, animations of chemical principles, descriptions of laboratory procedures, practice tests, problem sets, simulations of chemical phenomena, and much more. The best place for HCC students to find beginning chemistry information is **WorldWideWolfe**. At this site you will find links to all of the topics covered in CHM 1025, CHM1045, and CHM1046.

5. Search Engines

If you do not know where to go to find chemistry information (or any information), the best place to start is a **WWW search engine**. What is a search engine? It is a WWW site that allows you to search for information on the WWW. Many search engines can be found on the WWW. For example, some of the more popular ones include Excite, HotBot, InfoSeek, and Lycos. At each of these sites you can type in the key words that you want to know more about. Typically, one of the aforementioned search engines will give you hundreds or thousands of hits. A "hit" is a document that contains the key words that you submitted. To further narrow the search you can search by adding additional words and only search the initial hits.

WorldWideWolfe

While this textbook will be your principal source of information, definitions, examples problems, summaries, review problems, and chapter pretests, WorldWideWolfe is the online component of this textbook. You can access the section of WorldWideWolfe devoted to begining chemistry students at the following URL.

http://www.mindspring.com/~drwolfe/WWWolfe_hcc.htm

For each chapter in this book, you can access information from many sites including

WorldWideWolfe. The URL for the beginning chemistry links is

http://www.mindspring.com/~drwolfe/WWWolfe_hcc_1025_links.htm

Depending upon which browser you use, add the above two URLs to either your Bookmarks (Netscape) or your Favorites (Internet Explorer). Each time you want to return to these pages just select them from your Bookmarks or Favorites.

Starting in Chapter 2, the section that follows the chapter text is called **WorldWideWolfe Links**. In this section, you will find recommended sections of WorldWideWolfe and World Wide Web links to chemistry sites that will help you with the material in the chapter. If you encounter problems with these links, you can contact the author at his email address: **drwolfe@mindspring.com**. ❖

SUMMARY

The study of **chemistry** is concerned with the composition of matter, the changes that matter undergoes, and the relation between the changes in matter and changes in energy. Six major **divisions of chemistry** are analytical chemistry, inorganic chemistry, organic chemistry, physical chemistry, biochemistry, and geochemistry. Chemistry is sometimes considered the central science because all other sciences, to a degree, deal with matter. Chemistry's domain extends into every aspect of life, from birth to death.

Chemistry began in ancient times, when people saw that matter could be changed and used to improve the quality of life. Discoveries at this time were made through trial-and-error methods, leading people through the stone, bronze, and iron ages. The ancient Egyptians and Greeks were among the first civilizations to question why matter behaved as it did. Early Greek philosophers proposed explanations for the composition and structure of matter. About 450 B.C. **Democritus** suggested that matter was composed of tiny particles called atoms.

Modern chemistry grew out of the pseudoscience called alchemy. **Alchemists** searched for methods to convert base metals to gold. **Robert Boyle** was one of the first scientists to suggest that ideas and thoughts about matter must be supported by reproducible experiments. **Antoine Lavoisier** is credited with being the father of modern chemistry as a result of his pioneering experiments on the properties of matter.

STUDY GUIDELINES

After completing Chapter 1 you should be able to

1. Write a simple definition of chemistry and explain the relationship of chemistry to the other sciences

2. Define and give examples of different types of matter

3. Identify and describe the main divisions of chemistry

4. Explain the role that the discovery of new materials like bronze and iron played in the development of civilization

5. Discuss the contributions of the ancient Greek philosophers to the development of a better understanding of the nature of matter

6. Describe the contributions made by the alchemists to the development of chemistry

7. Identify the scientific contributions of Boyle, Stahl, Priestley, and Lavoisier

8. List contributions by chemists to modern society

9. Begin to develop your own successful strategy for learning chemistry

EXERCISES*

Scope of Chemistry

1.9   (a) What is the dictionary definition of chemistry? (b) Compare the dictionary definition of chemistry to the one proposed in the chapter.

1.10 (a) What is the name of the discipline in which chemistry overlaps with biology? (b) What are some topics that might be studied in this discipline?

1.11 What are 10 different examples of matter found in your house?

1.12 List two different areas that each of the following might study: (a) chemists, (b) biologists, (c) physicists, (d) geologists.

1.13 Explain how the sciences of physics and chemistry are similar and different.

1.14 Explain what each of the following chemists investigates: (a) analytical, (b) inorganic, (c) organic, (d) biological, (e) physical, (f) geological.

1.15 What type of chemist would study the following: (a) rocks and minerals, (b) synthesis of a new carbon compound, (c) antibiotics, (d) structure of metals, (e) amount of pollution in the air?

1.16 List five household consumer products that help simplify the task of living.

History of Chemistry

1.17 What effect did the harnessing of fire by early peoples have on their development of civilization?

1.18 For prehistoric peoples, what advantages were afforded by the discovery of metals to replace stone objects?

1.19 What chemical advances were made during the: (a) bronze age, (b) iron age?

1.20 (a) What metals were used by ancient peoples? (b) Why did the discovery of iron (actually steel) significantly change the course of history?

1.21 What are the four elements of matter suggested by the Greeks?

1.22 Explain how Aristotle modified the four-element theory.

1.23 The four-element theory was used for thousands of years. List two plausible reasons for its longevity.

1.24 How do philosophers differ from scientists when approaching and solving problems?

1.25 (a) Who is credited with the idea that matter is composed of small particles called atoms? (b) What term did he use to describe atoms?

1.26 What contributions did the alchemists

make to modern chemistry?

1.27 What was the importance of the magic elixir to the alchemists?

1.28 Propose a reason why Boyle entitled his book *The Sceptical Chymist*.

1.29 Who investigated the following: (a) application of mathematics to chemical changes, (b) release of phlogiston when objects burned, (c) divisibility of particles, (d) properties of gases?

1.30 How did the early scientists explain the loss of weight by an object when it burns?

1.31 Why is Antoine Lavoisier considered the father of modern chemistry?

1.32 If human beings still exist in A.D. 3000, what label (stone age, bronze age, iron age, ...) might they attach to the middle to late twentieth century and early twenty first century?

Additional Exercises

1.33 (a) Go through a current issue of the newspaper and list all topics that directly concern chemistry or closely related topics. (b) Explain how the topics found in part (a) affect your life.

1.34 List and discuss three ways in which chemical advances have produced environmental or societal problems.

1.35 Use newspaper and magazine articles to obtain information on how chemistry affects you within the community in which you live. Write a summary of the information that you find.

1.36 Compare the learning strategy for studying chemistry presented in Sec. 1.4 to that which you presently use for other subjects. (a) How are they similar and different? (b) What changes must you make to most effectively learn chemistry?

1.37 Go to the library and find out what the most important scientific accomplishments of each of the following scientists were: (a) Galileo Galilei (1564-1642), (b) Jan Baptista Van Helmont (1577-1644), (c) Evangelista Torricelli (1608-1647), (d) Otto von Guericke (1602-1686).

1.38 Define each of the following Internet terms: (a) World Wide Web, (b) http, (c) hypermedia, (d) hypertext, (e) html, (f) url, and (g) browser.

1.39 How can the World Wide Web be used in the study of chemistry?

1.40 What is the name of the Web page that is associated with this textbook?

Chapter 1 Pretest Assignment

1. Complete each of the following statements with the correct word, number, or phase.

    a. _____ is the study of matter and its interactions.
    b. _____ is the division of chemistry that is concerned with the quantities and amounts of the components of matter.
    c. _____ were the group of men who attempted to find a potion that would change base metals to gold.
    d. _____ wrote the The Sceptical Chymist and did not believe that matter was composed of earth, air, fire, and water.
    e. _____ is the division of chemistry concerned with all noncarbon compounds.
    f. _____ are chemists that study the substances that make up the earth.
    g. _____ was the first person to propose the idea of atoms.
    h. _____ proposed the idea that burning substances released phlogiston.

2. Write a paragraph that explains why chemistry can be consider to be the central science.

3. List three ways in which chemistry helps improve your daily life.

    a.
    b.
    c.

4. Write a paragraph that describes the importance of Lavoisier's contribution to chemistry.

5. Write a definition of chemistry.

6. How can the World Wide Web be used to better learn chemistry?

7. What is the meaning of each of the following?

    a. HTTP
    b. URL
    c. HTML
    d. WWW

CHAPTER 2

Problem Solving in Chemistry

2.1 TECHNIQUES FOR SOLVING SCIENTIFIC PROBLEMS

A systematic, logical procedure called the **scientific method** is used by scientists to solve problems. In reality, no one method applies in all cases. You should think of the scientific method as a general set of rules that guide scientists when they pursue a problem. Not all of the rules are followed all of the time, but in general the steps are as follows:

1. State the problem precisely in terms of the most relevant variable factors.
2. Obtain facts pertinent to the problem through carefully controlled experiments.
3. Organize, analyze, and evaluate the collected facts, keeping in mind the problem being solved, and try to find a pattern in the facts. If no pattern exists, reevaluate the problem; possibly the wrong problem is being investigated, or the problem is not stated clearly.

WWWolfe 1
(See WWWolfe section at the end of the chapter.)

4. Propose an explanation (hypothesis) to account for the pattern found in the data.
5. Conduct experiments to determine if the proposed hypothesis applies in similar situations.
6. If the experiments support the hypothesis, publish the findings to inform the rest of the world; however, if the experiments do not support the hypothesis, then modify the hypothesis, experimental procedures, or problem and start again.

Let's take a closer look at each step of the scientific method (Fig. 2.1). The first step is to state the problem precisely, in terms of what it is you are trying to solve. An exact statement of the problem should indicate the direction to follow when solving the problem. A large quantity of information (facts, laws, and theories) is collected. This information is organized, evaluated, and analyzed prior to stating the problem.

After the problem is defined, one or more experiments are performed to collect additional facts (data) that will be used to help solve the problem. A **fact** is an accepted truth—something that everyone accepts as correct. Data are facts collected during an experiment; from the data, the problem is solved.

When collecting data, experimenters are careful to

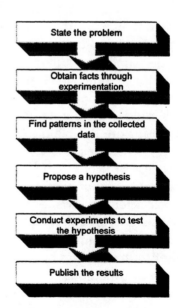

Figure 2.1 Typical steps followed when investigating scientific problems.

manipulate, or change, one variable quantity at a time. In other words, they do a **controlled experiment.** The variable of interest, called the **independent variable**, is changed, and the effect on the outcome, or **dependent variable** is observed. All other potentially variable quantities are held constant; i.e., they are not allowed to change. By performing controlled experiments the investigator can discover relationships that exist between two variables.

After all of the data are collected, they are analyzed to find regularities and patterns. Experimenters then ask themselves what accounts for the regularities in the data. After answering this question, they formulate a **hypothesis,** which is a tentative guess that explains the patterns in the data. Outcomes are then predicted for new experiments that will test the hypothesis. New experiments are conducted and their results analyzed to determine if the hypothesis is supported or not. If it is supported, the hypothesis is labeled valid; if not, the hypothesis is modified.

A hypothesis or a group of closely related hypotheses that are supported through tight, controlled experiments may be elevated to the level of a **theory.** It is important to note that a theory mainly differs from a hypothesis in that a theory to some degree has been substantiated through good experiments and is generally more broad and encompassing than a hypothesis.

Theories are sometimes called **models** because they are used to create "pictures" of phenomena that cannot be observed directly. For example, a theory is used by chemists to explain the behavior and structure of atoms, which are infinitesimal bodies that cannot be seen clearly. From this theory a model of the atom has been developed. Biologists propose theories to explain the behavior of animals, and physicists propose theories to explain the origin of the universe.

Theories are generally regarded as useful or not useful, rather than right or wrong. Once they are published, theories are subject to scientific scrutiny and criticism. Good theories stand up under the most severe testing; theories that are not so good fall apart under similar conditions. Useful theories have fewer assumptions and exceptions than inferior theories. In chemistry, many phenomena—atoms, molecules, physical states, and chemical changes—are understood through the application of generally accepted theories. It should also be noted that these theories evolve in light of new evidence. Good scientific theories are flexible and can be modified to accommodate new discoveries.

Theories also explain scientific laws. A **scientific law** is a statement as to how a process or event in the universe occurs given a particular set of conditions. There are only a few basic scientific laws; each one explains some consistency of behavior in the natural world. For example, the law of conservation of matter states that matter cannot be created or destroyed under normal conditions. We will discuss this and other laws of conservation in Chap. 4. When applying a scientific law, one is confident of its universality—laws have few, if any, exceptions.

> Nature's laws affirm instead of prohibit. If you violate her laws you are your own prosecuting attorney, judge, jury, and hangman.
> -Luther Burbank

Even though the scientific method has passed the test of time and is based on a sound logical foundation, it has some limitations and flaws. The scientific method assumes that nature acts in a consistent, rational, and understandable way. But in some cases the laws of nature only apply to a subset of matter. For example, some laws work for only normal-size objects; they fail miserably when explaining the behavior of extremely small or large objects. Certain "why" questions regarding the universe are unanswerable, and no matter what problem-solving method is used, they will remain unanswered. Finally, the scientific method is based on a foundation of logic that has inherent limitations; consequently, scientific investigators must be careful not to overstep the limits of logical thought or they can logically fabricate incorrect results with a high level of confidence!❖

REVIEW EXERCISES

2.1 List the six basic steps of the scientific method.
(a)
(b)
(c)
(d)
(e)
(f)

2.2 Define each term completely:
(a) fact
(b) data
(c) hypothesis
(d) theory
(e) law
(f) variable quantity
(g) constant quantity

2.3 What are the limitations of the scientific method?

2.2 STUDENT GUIDE TO PROBLEM SOLVING IN CHEMISTRY

To solve chemistry problems successfully, you must employ some of the same procedures used by research scientists. Haphazard attempts to solve problems are generally unproductive, whether they are undertaken in the research laboratory or in the classroom. The "key" that unlocks the mysteries of how to succeed in chemistry is a systematic procedure for approaching and solving chemistry problems.

Before we plunge into the details of learning how to solve chemistry problems, let us consider a simple problem faced by most people: How does one go from one place to another? Solving this problem is easy: (1) Determine where you are located initially; (2) pinpoint the exact location of your destination; (3) using a map or prior knowledge, plan a pathway to follow; and (4) go! Few people would jump into their cars and drive endlessly until they found their destination. Instead, they follow a logical plan.

If you think carefully about this simple problem, it is evident that the problem cannot be solved if you do not know either your location or your destination. How can you go to an unknown place? How can you plan a trip if you do not know where you are starting from? Even if you know where you are located and where you are headed, it is impossible to plan a trip if you lack appropriate knowledge of what lies between the two points. If the destination is a familiar place, then you search your brain for the route that has the smallest number of obstacles such as traffic jams, traffic lights, and stop signs. If you are unfamiliar with the destination, you will probably use a map to plan an expedient route. When reading a map, most people usually look for major highways and the shortest path possible, although on some trips one must use back roads and alternative routes. The situation dictates the pathway.

Thinking about the way you solve the problem of going from one place to another will help you understand how to solve chemistry problems. Chemistry students must also know (1) where they are, (2) where they are going, and (3) what pathway they intend to follow before they can solve a chemistry problem. Too often, in a rush to solve a problem, students forget about following a logical route and, in effect, jump into their cars without a map, to search endlessly for their destinations. Random problem-solving methods usually end in frustration.

Chemistry problem solving begins with a careful reading of the problem to determine what is unknown. **What are you trying to find?** If the answer to this question is not apparent, reread the problem and list any unfamiliar words or terms. Find the exact meanings of the unfamiliar terms by referring to the chapter or glossary in the textbook. If you still cannot decide what is unknown, go back to the chapter and reread appropriate sections, paying attention to the example problems. After you have figured out what is unknown, write it down. Now you know where you are headed.

Continue the chemistry-problem-solving process by listing all relevant information (data) given or known. In other words, answer the question: **What is known?** Write numbers with their labels, or units. A number is meaningless without a label (unless it's unitless). **Units,** or labels, are words that describe the number. For example, 6 dogs, 10 houses, 2 days, and 5 seconds are examples of labeled numbers. In these examples, dogs, houses, days, and seconds describe the numbers to which they are attached. In some problems, besides the data and conversion factors found in the problem, additional information may be required. Such information is found in tables or charts located in the chapter and appendixes. After completing this second step in chemistry problem solving, you know where you are located.

Now you must develop a logical plan for traveling from the location to the destination. The logical plan comes from an understanding of the chemistry principles that pertain to the problem. Ask yourself: What is the connection between what is known and what is unknown? One of the most important procedures applied to the solution of chemistry problems is the **factor-label method** that is sometimes called the **unit-conversion method.**

The factor-label method is an orderly procedure in which known, labeled numbers are converted to new numbers with new labels. For example, 14 days can be changed to 2 weeks once we know that 1 week equals 7 days, or 3 dozen doughnuts can be changed to 36 doughnuts using our knowledge that there are 12 doughnuts in a dozen. The specifics of the factor-label method are discussed and illustrated in the next section. At this point, it is important for you to realize that some systematic, logical procedure such as the factor-label method is required if you are to solve chemistry problems. A systematic procedure is the "map" that guides you to your destination.

A chemistry problem is finally solved when you **perform the indicated**

mathematical operations. This final step is purely mechanical. Using the correct setup, all numbers and their associated units are added, subtracted, multiplied, or divided to yield the final numerical answer with its units. After you have obtained an answer always ask we yourself: **Is this a reasonable answer to the problem?** If the answer is not reasonable, go back and look for mistakes that you may have made. Too often students submit unreasonable answers because they blindly accept an answer without giving thought to its validity.

When possible, check your answer with the correct answer. If you have successfully solved the problem, your answer should agree with the correct answer. If your answer does not agree, check to see if you made an arithmetic error. If no arithmetic error is detected, assume you have made an error in logic. Analyze the reasoning that you used originally, or attempt to work back from the correct answer. A word of caution is in order: Do not rely totally on this last method; the correct answer is not available during quizzes and exams!

In summary, the four steps most commonly followed when solving chemistry problems are:

1. Carefully read the problem and determine what it asks. On paper, write down exactly what you are trying to find—the unknown quantity.
2. Extract from the problem all information that is given, and obtain any other information that is necessary to solve the problem.
3. Apply appropriate chemistry principles, logic, and the factor-label method to convert the known information to what is desired.
4. Perform the indicated mathematical operations and find the answer to the problem. If possible, check to see that the answer is correct. If the answer is incorrect, repeat any steps as required.

WWWolfe 2
(See WWWolfe
section at the end of
the chapter.)

Before proceeding, it is extremely important to understand and learn all four chemistry-problem-solving steps. **Possibly the most important thing learned in an introductory chemistry course is how to approach and solve problems.**❖

REVIEW EXERCISES

2.4 List all things that must be known before a problem can be solved.

2.5 What are the four principal steps used to solve chemistry problems?
(a)

(b)

(c)

(d)

2.3 THE FACTOR-LABEL METHOD

Numerous problems encountered in chemistry are conveniently solved using the factor-label method. In the factor-label method, one or more conversion factors are used to change the given units to the desired units. A **conversion factor** is an exact relationship between two quantities expressed as a fraction. For example, one dozen objects is defined as 12 objects.

$$1 \text{ dozen objects} = 12 \text{ objects}$$

The correct way to express this equality as a conversion factor is

$$\frac{12 \text{ objects}}{1 \text{ dozen objects}} \quad \text{or} \quad \frac{1 \text{ dozen objects}}{12 \text{ objects}}$$

In a **conversion factor,** the fraction line is read as "per." So the above pair of expressions is read as "12 objects per 1 dozen objects or 1 dozen objects per 12 objects."

Mathematically, conversion factors are obtained by dividing both sides of the equality by one of the quantities. Dividing both sides of the equality 1 dozen objects = 12 objects by 1 dozen objects yields

$$\frac{\cancel{1 \text{ dozen objects}}}{\cancel{1 \text{ dozen objects}}} = \frac{12 \text{ objects}}{1 \text{ dozen objects}}$$

and canceling the 1 dozen objects gives us the conversion factor

$$1 = \frac{12 \text{ objects}}{1 \text{ dozen objects}}$$

To obtain the inverted form of the conversion factor, divide the equality by "12 objects,"

$$\frac{1 \text{ dozen objects}}{12 \text{ objects}} = \frac{\cancel{12 \text{ objects}}}{\cancel{12 \text{ objects}}}$$

and then cancel the "12 objects."

$$\frac{1 \text{ dozen objects}}{12 \text{ objects}} = 1$$

Note that a conversion factor always equals 1. Therefore, if a quantity is multiplied by a conversion factor, the value of the quantity is unchanged, even though the number and units change. Multiplying 1 times any number does not alter the value of the number.

Other examples of conversion factors are

> The value of a number is unchanged when it is multiplied by 1. Consider the following examples: $4 \times 1 = 4$, $10 \times 1 = 10$, $85 \times 1 = 85$.

$$\frac{60 \text{ seconds}}{1 \text{ minute}} \quad \frac{12 \text{ inches}}{1 \text{ foot}} \quad \frac{4 \text{ quarts}}{1 \text{ gallon}}$$

Each of these conversion factors was obtained from exact relationships between the two units. For example, by definition 60 seconds elapse per 1 minute (60 seconds = 1 minute). After dividing both sides by 1 minute, the above conversion factor is obtained. If we had divided by 60 seconds, the reciprocal of this factor would have been obtained: 1 minute/60 seconds. Similarly, the reciprocals of the other two conversion factors are 1 foot/12 inches and 1 gallon/4 quarts.

Conversion factors are used to change the units associated with a number to another set of units. This is accomplished by multiplying the conversion factor times the given quantity, so that the given unit cancels and yields the desired unit.

$$\text{Given unit} \times \underbrace{\frac{\text{desired unit}}{\text{given unit}}}_{\text{Conversion factor}} = \text{desired unit}$$

For example: How many dozen eggs is 120 eggs?

$$120 \text{ eggs} \times \frac{1 \text{ dozen eggs}}{12 \text{ eggs}} = 10 \text{ dozen eggs}$$

In this case, we see that the given unit, eggs, is canceled by the unit eggs in the denominator of the conversion factor, yielding dozen eggs, the unit in the numerator of the conversion factor. Thus, 120 eggs equals 10 dozen eggs.

Study the following examples of simple factor-label conversions used to solve nonscientific problems. The purpose of these problems is to show the mechanics of the factor-label method.

Example Problem 2.1
A builder constructs 50 houses of 10 rooms each. How many rooms are there in all 50 houses?

Solution
1. What is unknown?   Number of rooms in 50 houses
2. What is known? 10 rooms/1 house; 50 houses
3. Apply the factor-label method.

Because the problem asks for the number of rooms, and we know the number of houses and the number of rooms per house, we write the conversion factor with rooms in the numerator (top) and houses in the denominator (bottom). When houses are multiplied by rooms per house, the houses cancel, leaving the number of rooms.

$$\text{houses} \times \frac{10 \text{ rooms}}{1 \text{ house}} = \text{? rooms}$$

4. Perform the indicated math operations.

$$50 \text{ \sout{houses}} \times \frac{10 \text{ rooms}}{1 \text{ \sout{house}}} = \textbf{500 rooms}$$

In this example, we have applied the basic principles of problem solving: (1) identifying what is unknown, (2) identifying what is known, (3) applying the factor-label method to find the desired units, and (4) performing the indicated arithmetic operations.

Exercise
One nautical mile is 6076 feet. How many feet in 0.75 nautical miles? (4557 feet)

Example Problem 2.2
A soup company packages 30 cans of soup per box. How many boxes are needed to hold 8700 soup cans?

Solution
1. What is unknown?   Number of boxes that hold 8700 soup cans
2. What is known? 30 soup cans/1 box; 8700 soup cans
3. Apply the factor-label method.

$$\text{\sout{Soup cans}} \times \frac{1 \text{ box}}{30 \text{ \sout{soup cans}}} = \text{? boxes}$$

To obtain the number of boxes and cancel soup cans, we invert the conversion factor, placing the desired unit, boxes, in the numerator and the unit soup cans in the denominator.
4. Perform the indicated math operations.

$$8700 \text{ \sout{soup cans}} \times \frac{1 \text{ box}}{30 \text{ \sout{soup cans}}} = \textbf{290 boxes}$$

The factor-label setup shows that 30 is divided into 8700 to obtain the correct answer, 290 boxes.

Exercise
One quart holds 57.75 cubic inches. What is the volume in quarts of 25 cubic inches? (0.43 quarts)

Example Problems 2.1 and 2.2 are simple, almost trivial, nonchemical examples that illustrate the general procedure for solving chemistry problems. Most chemistry problems are as easy to solve as these, once the techniques of problem solving and the factor-label method are learned. Use the factor-label method to solve the following Review Exercises before going on to the next section.

REVIEW EXERCISES

2.6 An orange crate holds 66 oranges.
(a) How many crates are needed to hold 2310 oranges?

(b) How many oranges are contained in 175 full crates?

2.7 One brand of gasoline costs $1.15 per gallon.
(a) How many gallons can be purchased with $16.10?

(b) What is the cost of exactly 11 gallons of this gasoline? (c) How many gallons can be purchased with $1.00?

2.6 (a) 35 crates, (b) 11,550 oranges; 2.7 (a) 14 gallons, (b) 12.65 dollars, (c) 0.870 gallons.

Often, more than one conversion factor is utilized to solve a problem. Let's consider the problem of converting a given number of years to hours. Most people do not know an exact relationship between years and hours, and such a relationship is generally not found in a table. But application of the rules regarding problem solving and conversion factors efficiently gives us the correct answer.

Knowing that we want to find the number of hours, given the number of years, and that there are 365 days/year and 24 hours/day we write

$$\text{Years} \times \frac{365 \text{ days}}{1 \text{ year}} \times \frac{24 \text{ hours}}{1 \text{ day}} = \text{hours}$$

The number of years is first multiplied by the conversion factor that relates days to years. The years cancel, giving the number of days. Days are then converted to hours by multiplying by the conversion factor that equates hours and days. In a similar manner the days cancel, yielding the number of hours.

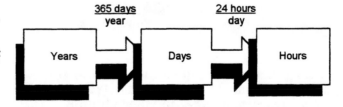

Figure 2.2 To convert years to hours, multiply the given number of years by the conversion factor that equates years to days, and then multiply the result by the conversion factor that equates days to hours.

Figure 2.2 illustrates the pathway followed to find the number of hours in a given number of years. Because a direct path is not available, an indirect route, obtaining the number of days, is followed.

Conversion factors are introduced successively until the desired unit is found. Any number of conversion factors may be used to solve a problem. Example Problems 2.3 and 2.4 illustrate time conversions that require more than one conversion factor.

Example Problem 2.3
How many seconds elapse in exactly 4 hours?

Solution
1. What is unknown?   Number of seconds
2. What is known? 4 hours; 60 minutes/hour; 60 seconds/minute
3. Apply the factor-label method.

$$\text{Hours} \times \frac{60 \text{ minutes}}{1 \text{ hour}} \times \frac{60 \text{ seconds}}{1 \text{ minute}} = ? \text{ seconds}$$

Hours are first converted to minutes, using the conversion factor 60 minutes per 1 hour. In a similar manner, minutes are converted to seconds with the conversion factor 60 seconds per 1 minute. The first conversion factor cancels hours, yielding minutes; the second conversion factor cancels minutes, giving seconds, the units of the answer. This pathway is represented diagrammatically in Fig. 2.3.
4. Perform the indicated math operations.

$$4 \text{ hours} \times \frac{60 \text{ minutes}}{1 \text{ hour}} \times \frac{60 \text{ seconds}}{1 \text{ minute}} = \textbf{14,400 seconds}$$

Exercise
How many seconds elapse in one day? (86,400 seconds)

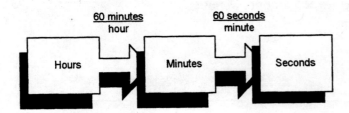

Figure 2.3 To change hours to seconds multiply the given number of hours by the conversion factor that equates hours to minutes and then multiply the result by the conversion factor that equates minutes to seconds.

Example Problem 2.4
Convert exactly 3600 minutes to days.

Solution
1. What is unknown?   Number of days
2. What is known? 3600 minutes; 60 minutes/hour; 24 hours/day
3. Apply the factor-label method.

$$\text{Minutes} \times \frac{1 \text{ hour}}{60 \text{ minutes}} \times \frac{1 \text{ day}}{24 \text{ hours}} = ? \text{ days}$$

Because we start with minutes, we must invert the conversion factor that equates minutes to hours so that minutes cancel when we multiply. Hours are converted to days by inverting the conversion factor that equates hours and days, and canceling hours when we multiply.
4. Perform the indicated math operations.

$$3600 \text{ minutes} \times \frac{1 \text{ hour}}{60 \text{ minutes}} \times \frac{1 \text{ day}}{24 \text{ hours}} = \textbf{2.5 days}$$

A common error when performing arithmetic operations of this type is to forget that both conversion factors require division—both 60 minutes and 24 hours are divided into 3600 minutes.

Exercise
How many years elapse in one second? (3.17×10^{-8} years)

After completing a conversion using the factor-label method, look at the answer and ask yourself if it is reasonable or not. When you convert small units to larger units, the numerical value decreases. Conversely, when you change large units to smaller units, the numerical value increases. For example, if you change years, a larger time unit, to seconds, a smaller time unit, the numerical value for the number of seconds will be significantly larger. As we saw in Example Problem 2.4, 3600 minutes elapse in 2.5 days. Thus, changing a unit of smaller magnitude to one of larger magnitude results in a decrease in the size of the number. Do not let your use of the factor-label method become entirely a mechanical operation. **Apply the factor-label method prudently, considering where you are coming from and where you are heading.**

WWWolfe 3
(See WWWolfe
section at the end of
the chapter.)

Occasionally you may need to calculate the value of a conversion factor. For example, if we know the number of hours per day and the number of days per week, we can calculate the number of hours per week by multiplying the conversion factors in such a way as to cancel the number of days. This is accomplished in the following manner:

$$\frac{24 \text{ hours}}{1 \text{ day}} \times \frac{7 \text{ days}}{1 \text{ week}} = \frac{168 \text{ hours}}{1 \text{ week}}$$

We find that 168 hours elapse during 1 week. Example Problem 2.5 gives another example of the calculation of a new conversion factor.

Example Problem 2.5
One mile is 5280 feet, and the surveyor's unit called a link is exactly 7.92 inches. Calculate the number of links per mile.

Solution
1. What is unknown?   Number of links per mile
2. What is known? 5280 feet/mile; 7.92 inches/link; 12 inches/foot
We must know the relationship between inches and feet because no common units are found in the first two conversion factors (the ones given in the problem).
3. Apply the factor-label method.

$$\frac{5280 \text{ feet}}{\text{mile}} \times \frac{12 \text{ inches}}{\text{foot}} \times \frac{1 \text{ link}}{7.92 \text{ inches}} = \frac{? \text{ links}}{\text{mile}}$$

In the factor-label setup, the number of feet per mile is first converted to inches per mile, and then it is converted to links per mile, the desired conversion factor.
4. Perform the indicated math operations.

$$\frac{5280 \text{ feet}}{\text{mile}} \times \frac{12 \text{ inches}}{\text{foot}} \times \frac{1 \text{ link}}{7.92 \text{ inches}} = \frac{\mathbf{8000 \text{ links}}}{\mathbf{mile}}$$

We find that one mile is exactly 8000 links.
Exercise
One mile is 5280 feet and 8 furlongs. How many feet per furlong? (660 feet)

REVIEW EXERCISES
2.8 Convert exactly 8 days to:
(a) hours

(b) minutes

(c) seconds

(d) years.

2.9 Convert exactly 12 centuries to decades (100 years = 1 century; 10 years = 1 decade)

2.10 Calculate the numerical value for each of the following conversion factors:

(a) seconds/year

(b) centuries/day

(c) days/millennium (1 millennium = 1000 years).

2.8 (a) 192 hours, (b) 11,520 minutes, (c) 691,200 seconds, (d) 0.02192 years; 2.9 120 decades; 2.10 (a) 31,536,000, (b) 0.0000274, (c) 365,000

WorldWideWolfe CHEMISTRY LINKS

Connect to WorldWideWolfe at

http://www.mindspring.com/~drwolfe/WWWolfe_hcc_1025_links.htm

and link to the following sites.

1. Scientific Method

A series of slides that review the basic principles of the scientific method.

2. Factor-Label Method

A brief discussion of the factor-label method.

3. Basic Math Concepts

On this page you can learn how to express numbers using scientific notation and how to determine the number of significant figures. Additionally, you can review basic algebra including formulas and graphs. Finally, it reviews the metric system.

SUMMARY

A systematic set of procedures, called the **scientific method,** is more or less followed in modern scientific research. The heart of the scientific method is the collection of facts and data in order to propose a **hypothesis,** a suggested explanation of the problem. A **controlled experiment** is then conducted to determine if the hypothesis is valid or not. Experiments provide evidence to support hypotheses.

The best way to study chemistry is to follow a systematic plan. Solving problems and answering questions is the most effective way to learn Chemistry. You must know what you are looking for and what information is available before mapping out a strategy for solving a problem. Once the problem is solved, check to see if you have obtained the correct answer. If not, go back and try again.

Many chemistry problems are solved using the **factor-label method.** This is a systematic procedure for converting a number with one unit to a new number with another unit using conversion factors, i.e., fractions that express an equality. Conversion factors are multiplied in such a way that the given unit is canceled and the desired unit is retained.

STUDY GUIDELINES

After completing Chapter 2, you should be able to

1. List and explain the six principal steps of the scientific method

2. Define fact, data, hypothesis, theory, and law

3. Distinguish among facts, theories, and laws

4. Discuss limitations of the scientific method

5. Develop a personal strategy for approaching and solving chemistry problems

6. List and apply all steps required to solve a given chemistry problem

7. Write conversion factors, given equalities.

8. Apply the factor-label method in solving unit-conversion problems.

EXERCISES*

Scientific Method

2.11 List reasons why it is useless to conduct an uncontrolled experiment.

2.12 Why is it important to spend a significant amount of time in stating precisely the problem to be solved?

2.13 (a) How is a fact different from a law? (b) How is a theory different from a law? (c) How is a hypothesis different from a theory?

2.14 Give three examples of theories from everyday life.

2.15 Why are theories labeled valid and invalid, no right and wrong?

2.16 if you were conducting the following experiments, what variables should you control a produce the most valid results? (a) Which of two insecticides is most effective in killing roaches? (b) Which of two automobiles is most fuel efficient? (c) What pain reliever is most effective a controlling headaches?

2.17 Classify each of the following as a fact, theory or law:
(a) Grass is green.
(b) Whatever goes up must come down.
(c) Human beings evolved from apes.
(d) The earth revolves around the sun.
(e) Matter is composed of atoms.
(f) Diamonds are forever.

* The answers to Exercises in boldface type are found in Appendix D

(g) The harder an object is pushed, the faster it accelerates.

2.18 Why can't an experiment be conducted to measure "love"?

2.19 Outline a complete experiment (all six steps that might be used to determine the effectiveness of a newly synthesized antimicrobial agent, i.e., a drug that fights disease.

Factor-Label Method

2.20 A small economy car, when cruising on a highway, gets exactly 47 miles per gallon. (a) How many miles can the economy car travel on exactly 12 gallons of gasoline? (b) How many gallons of gas are consumed in this car during a trip of 164.5 miles?

2.21 Perform the following conversions:
   (a) 8 minutes= ? seconds
   (b) 253 days= ? years
   (c) 9 decades = ? centuries
   (d) 5184 apples = ? dozen apples

2.22 (a) How many hours would it take to travel 462 miles if a constant speed of exactly 55 miles per hour were maintained? (b) How far can you travel at 55 miles per hour in 16.4 minutes?

2.23 How many seconds elapse during each of the following time intervals: (a) 5.00 minutes, b) 0.850 minute, (c) 1.25 hours, (d) 3.1 days?

2.24 What is the age of a 25-year-old person in (a) days, (b) hours, (c) minutes, (d) seconds?

2.25 Perform each of the following time conversions:
   (a) 9641 hours= ? years
   (b) 6505 days= ? decades
   (c) 12 centuries = ? days
   (d) 915,000 seconds = ? days
   (e) 100,000 days= ? millennia (1 millennium = 1000 years)

2.26 In typography, one pica equals twelve points, and one point equals 0.013837 inch exactly. (a) How many inches are there per pica? (b) How many picas per inch?

2.27 In the avoirdupois system of weights, 16 drams equal 437.5 grains, 16 ounces equal one pound, and 16 drams equal one ounce. (a) How many drams are there per pound? (b) How many grains per pound? (c) How many drams per grain?

2.28 Excellent long distance runners run 25 miles in 2 hours. (a) Assuming they run at the same pace throughout the 2 hours, how many miles will they travel in 0.75 hour? (b) How many feet are traveled in 0.75 hour? (5280 feet= 1 mile) (c) How long would it take a runner to travel 10,000 feet at this pace?

2.29 Nine bananas weigh 2.9 pounds, and bananas cost $0.35 per pound. (a) What is the cost of six bananas? (a) How many dozen of bananas can be bought for $12.40? (b) How many dozen of bananas can be bought for $12.40? (c) What is the cost of one banana?

2.30 On a trip from New York to Miami, 1317 miles, an automobile consumed exactly 49 gallons of gasoline costing $1.05 per gallon. (a) What was the average number of miles traveled per gallon? (b) How many gallons of gasoline were consumed per mile? (c) What was the cost of gasoline per 100 miles? (d) What was the total cost of gasoline for the trip?

2.31 A box that contains 100 paper clips costs $0.79; each paper clip weighs 0.0013 pounds. (a) What is the cost of 34 paper clips? (b) What is the cost of a single paper clip? (c) What is the cost of paper clips per pound? (d) How many boxes must be emptied to produce 8 pounds of paper clips? (e) How many pounds of paper clips can be purchased with $54?

2.32 Convert exactly 50,000 seconds to (a) centuries, (b) days, (c) decades.

2.33 The approximate life-span of an American is 75 years. Convert the life-span to (a) seconds, (b) decades, (c) days.

2.34 A furlong is a unit of length equal to 660 feet. Another unit of length, the rod, is equal to 198 inches. (a) How many rods are there per furlong. (b) If a centimeter is 0.394 inch, how many furlongs are there in 1 million centimeters? (c) A fathom is exactly 6 feet. How many rods are there in a fathom? (d) One chain equals exactly 792 inches. If a link equals 0.04 rod, how many yards are there in a link?

Additional Exercises

2.35 Explain specifically how you might solve one of your personal problems making use of the scientific method.

2.36 (a) Propose a means by which a study could be conducted to determine if one brand of toothpaste with fluoride is more effective in preventing the development of dental caries (cavities) than a second brand that is essentially the same but does not contain fluoride. (b) What are the dependent and independent variables? (c) What hypothesis might be stated for such a study? (d) What variables must be held constant in such a study to give validity to the results?

2.37 Light travels at 186,000 miles per second. Light from the sun takes about 0.23 days to travel to the planet Pluto. (a) What is the distance from the sun to Pluto? (b) How far does light travel in 1 year?

2.38 Two ancient Roman units of length were the cubit and the stadium. One cubit is exactly 17.5 inches, and one stadium is 202 yards. (a) How many cubits are there per stadium? (b) How many stadia (plural of *stadium*) are there per cubit?

2.39 Alaska has an area of approximately 571,000 square miles. An acre is equal to 43,560 square feet. (a) If one mile is 5280 feet, calculate the area of Alaska in acres. (b) Calculate the area of Alaska in square feet. (c) Calculate the area of Alaska in square inches.

Chapter 2 Pretest Assignment

1. Complete each of the following statements with the correct word, number, or phase.

    a. _____ is the manipulated variable in an experiment.
    b. _____ are used to create "pictures" of phenomena that cannot be observed directly.
    c. _____ is a statement as to how a process or event in the universe occurs given a particular set of conditions.
    d. _____ is an exact relationship between two quantities expressed as a fraction.
    e. _____ is an orderly procedure in which known, labeled numbers are converted to new numbers with new labels.
    g. _____ is an example of a conversion factor for time units.

2. List the six basic steps of the scientific method.

    a. _____
    b. _____
    c. _____
    d. _____
    e. _____
    f. _____

3. Show all steps in problem solving to convert 2.5 days to years.

4. Light travels at 186,000 miles per second. If a millisecond is one-thousandth of a second, how many feet will light travel in 0.25 milliseconds?

5. A furlong is a unit of length equal to 660 feet. Another unit of length, the rod, is equal to 198 inches. Derive a conversion factor for converting rods to furlongs.

CHAPTER 3

Chemical Measurement

When chemists conduct experiments, they usually make many different measurements. The taking of a **measurement** is a procedure in which an unknown quantity is compared with a known quantity. Usually, the known quantity is obtained from a device calibrated to display the correct value. For example, when you measure your weight, you stand on a scale constructed to display the weight of a person in pounds. As we have discussed previously, each measurement consists of two parts, a *number* and a unit. Because all measurements are uncertain to some degree, chemists making measurements in the laboratory are also concerned with the *reliability* of the measurements. To show how reliable a measurement is, chemists express it to the correct number of significant figures.

In this chapter, we will first discuss uncertainty in measurements and the rules that govern the use of significant figures, and then move to the International System of Units, which is the measurement system used by scientists throughout the world.

3.1 UNCERTAINTY IN MEASUREMENTS

Whenever chemical measurements are made, both precision and accuracy are considered. The **accuracy** of a measurement is how close the obtained value is to a standard, or "true," value. A more accurate measurement is one closer to the standard value than a less accurate measurement. Accuracy is measured in terms of the deviation of the measurement (called the error) from the "true" value. The most common way to measure accuracy is **percent error** or **percent deviation**, which is calculated by dividing the actual value into the deviation (measured value – actual value) times 100.

$$\text{Percent error} = \frac{(\text{measured value} - \text{actual value})}{\text{actual value}} \times 100$$

Precision, on the other hand, refers to how closely repeated measures are grouped, i.e., how reproducible the measurements are. The smaller the range of values obtained when measuring the same quantity, the greater the precision. Most often, good precision is an indication of high accuracy, but not always, as we will see.

The game of darts provides an analogy that is helpful in understanding the terms "accuracy" and "precision." A dart player attempts to "hit the bull's-eye," as a chemist tries to "hit" the true value when measuring matter. Consider Fig. 3.1a; the first dart landed far from the bull's-eye—not an accurate throw. In Fig. 3.1b, the dart is inside the bull's-eye—a more accurate throw. Fig. 3.1c represents a dart board after six throws; notice that the six attempts are grouped closely, which is an indication of good precision, and in the bull's-eye, which shows good accuracy. In contrast, the dart distribution in Fig. 3.1d shows good precision but poor accuracy. Finally, Fig. 3.1e shows poor accuracy and poor precision.

WWWolfe 1
(See WWWolfe
section at the end of
the chapter.)

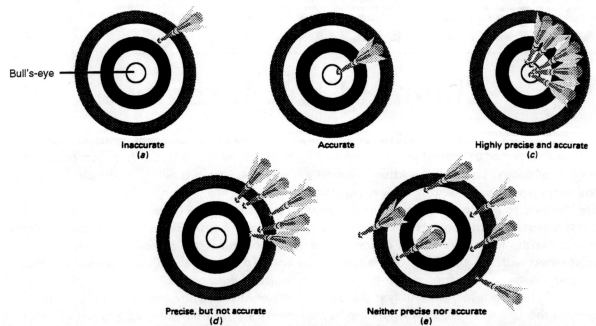

Figure 3.1 The distribution of darts on a dart board can be used as an analogy to understand the terms "precision" and "accuracy." Precise measurements are closely grouped together. Less precise measurements are more spread out. The accuracy of a measurement is related to how close a measurement is to the actual value

Measurement errors account for the range of different values obtained when making the same measurement repeatedly. Two types of errors are generally found in chemical measurements: systematic errors and random errors.

Systematic errors result from (1) poor procedures and methods, (2) malfunctioning and uncalibrated instruments, (3) human error, (4) impure samples, and (5) some unrecognized factors that influence the results. For example, suppose that you measure the weight of an object on a scale but fail to adjust the scale to the zero point before weighing the object. The measurement will be either high or low, depending on the initial incorrect setting of the scale. Systematic errors are reduced by finding their causes and eliminating them.

> Systematic errors can usually be eliminated if they are identified

Random errors occur in all chemical measurements. Even if every precaution is taken to avoid systematic errors, small deviations, or random errors, arise that are unavoidable and not identifiable. Random errors, by definition, are impossible to illustrate. If random errors could be identified, they would be corrected, and thus would not be considered random errors.

> Random errors tend to cancel out and thus do not seriously affect the uncertainty of measurements.

Collectively, systematic and random errors introduce uncertainty—or lack of confidence—into all measured values. Thus, for all reported measurements, the scientist should indicate the degree of certainty and uncertainty in the measurement. In chemistry, this is most frequently accomplished by using significant figures, which is described in the following section.❖

REVIEW EXERCISES

3.1 (a) Write definitions for precision and accuracy.

(b) Can accurate measurements be made without precision? Explain.

3.2 (a) What can be said about 10 measurements known to be highly precise?

(b) Does this mean that these measurements are accurate? Explain.

3.3 The true value for the length of an object is 2.91 meters. What statement may be made regarding the precision of the following length measurements of the object: 2.02 meters, 3.07 meters, 2.87 meters, and 3.17 meters?

3.4 (a) Explain the difference between systematic and random measurement errors.

(b) Give two examples of systematic errors.

(c) Why is it impossible to give an example of a random error?

3.2 SIGNIFICANT FIGURES

Significant figures are the measured digits in a number known with certainty plus one uncertain digit. Stated differently, the significant figures are all known digits plus the first doubtful or estimated digit.

Before we begin our discussion, it is important to note that significant figures apply only to *measured* values, not to exact numbers. For example, if you correctly count the number of students in a small classroom, the value obtained is absolutely accurate (an exact number) with no uncertainty. When we discuss mass in Sec. 3.4, we will define the kilogram as 1000 grams (1 kg

> Significant figures include all measured digits plus one uncertain, or estimated digit.

= 1000 g), which is an exact relationship; consequently, significant figures do not apply. Significant figures apply only to measurements that are to some degree uncertain.

To illustrate significant figures, let us consider Fig. 3.2a, which shows a liquid in a graduated cylinder (a type of glassware used to measure volume). If you measure the level of the liquid relative to the scale etched on the cylinder, the volume of the liquid may be found. The volume shown is 35.5 milliliters, because the liquid level (always read the bottom of the meniscus, the concave upper surface of a liquid in a small container) is about halfway between the 35-milliliter line and the 36-milliliter line. This measurement, 35.5 milliliters, represents three significant figures—the 35 is directly measured (these are the digits that are certain), and the .5 is a good estimate from a careful reading of the graduated cylinder (it is the first uncertain digit).

Usually, the last significant figure is considered uncertain by ±1. In the above example, by stating the volume as 35.5 milliliters, we suggest that the measured volume is at most 35.6 (+0.1) and at least 35.4 (–0.1). If the same liquid is totally transferred to a more precise volumetric instrument—let's say one that has a scale with 0.1-milliliter marks etched accurately on the side—it is possible to obtain an additional significant figure. In Fig. 3.2b we can read the volume to one-hundredth of a milliliter, giving us the value 35.58 milliliters. The first three digits (35.5) are certain, and the last digit (8) is uncertain. Again, the range of uncertainty is ±1 in the last significant figure, giving a range for our measurement of 35.59 to 35.57 milliliters.

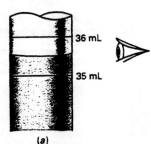

(a)

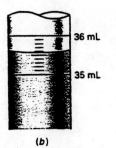

(b)

If, using the same graduated cylinder, you read the volume as 35.5872389 milliliters, you are exceeding the limits of this measuring device. No way exists to be certain of the second decimal place, and it is impossible to measure the third or fourth decimal places—they are meaningless numbers, especially if you consider that the uncertainty is ±0.01 milliliter. **Never report more significant figures than the measuring device is capable of providing.**

Whenever you encounter a measurement, always remember that besides the numerical value and units, the number also indicates the precision with which the measurement was made, or, stated differently, the number of significant figures in the measurement. Consider the following measurements and the number of significant figures indicated by each.

Figure 3.2 (a) With 1-mL graduations, he volume of a liquid can be estimated to within ±0.1 mL. In this case the volume is reported as 35.5 mL; this is three significant figures. (b) With 0.1-mL graduations, he volume can be estimated to within ±0.01 mL. Using his more precisely calibrated graduated cylinder, we report the volume as 15.58 mL; this is four significant figures.

1.25 meters indicates three significant figures (1, 2, 5)
(range: 1.26 – 1.24 meters)

434.56 Kelvins indicates five significant figures (4, 3, 4, 5, 6)
(range: 434.57 – 434.55 Kelvins)

3 grams indicates one significant figure (3)
(range: 4 – 2 grams)

8.913477 centimeters indicates seven significant figures (8, 9, 1, 3, 4, 7, 7)
(range: 8.913478 – 8.913476 centimeters)

When writing measured quantities, always asked you: **Did I report the correct number of significant figures?**

All nonzero numbers in measurements are always significant, but zeros pose a special problem because a zero that acts as a placeholder in a number is *not* significant.

Placeholders are not measured quantities; therefore, by definition, they are not significant figures.

The following rules summarize and illustrate all possible cases in which zeros are found in measurements.

Rule 1
Zeros in the middle of a number. Always, zeros in the middle of a number are significant. In each of the following, the zero is a significant figure.

> 10.004 grams indicates five significant figures (1, 0, 0, 0, 4)
> 47,000.15 milliliters indicates seven significant figures (4, 7, 0, 0, 0, 1, 5)
> 103 square centimeters indicates three significant figures (1, 0, 3)

Zeros in the middle of measured quantities are measured digits and are not placeholders; accordingly, they are significant in all cases.

Rule 2
Zeros in front of a number. Zeros in front of numbers are usually to the right of the decimal point. These zeros act as placeholders (they are not measured), so they are not significant figures. Consider each of the following examples of such cases.

> .0005 liter indicates one significant figure (5)
> .0000477 meter indicates three significant figures (4, 7, 7)
> .000000091 kilogram indicates two significant figures (9, 1)

If these examples are converted to scientific notation, you can readily see the insignificance of the zeros.

$$5 \times 10^{-4} \text{ liter} \qquad 4.77 \times 10^{-5} \text{ meter} \qquad 9.1 \times 10^{-8} \text{ kilogram}$$

In each case the zeros are dropped because they act only as placeholders. Sometimes a zero is placed in front of the decimal point to show that no other digit is present. Similarly, this zero is not significant. The following examples serve to illustrate this point.

> 0.00831 millimeter indicates three significant figures (8, 3, 1)
> 0.1 milliliter indicates one significant figure (1)

Rule 3
Zeros after a number to the right of the decimal point. For this specific case, the zero is either a measured quantity (certain) or a good estimate (the first uncertain digit); consequently, zeros after a number and to the right of the decimal point are all significant. Three examples of this case are as follows:

> .650 decimeter indicates three significant figures (6, 5, 0)
> .178300 millisecond indicates six significant figures (1, 7, 8, 3, 0, 0)
> .3550000 kilometer indicates seven significant figures (3, 5, 5, 0, 0, 0, 0)

For each of the above measurements, the zeros were measured by some instrument. All of the zeros are certain except the last zero, which is uncertain but still significant.

Rule 4

Zeros after a number to the left of the decimal point. Zeros found after a number and to the left of the decimal point are significant if they are measured, and are not significant if they are placeholders. Suppose you see a statement that an object has a measured mass of 800 grams. The measurement 800 grams has a questionable number of significant figures; more information is required to determine what the correct number of significant figures is. The measurement, 800 grams, has three significant figures only if the second zero (units' place)is the first uncertain figure. It has two significant figures if the first zero (tens' place) is the first uncertain figure. A third possibility exists in which the 8 could be the uncertain digit. If this is the case, the measurement has only one significant figure.

To avoid the confusion generated by the ambiguous nature of zeros to the left of decimal points, chemists commonly express such measurements in **scientific notation** (see Appendix A for a complete discussion of scientific notation), in which the decimal factor represents the correct number of significant figures. Thus, 800 grams is expressed as 8×10^2 grams (one significant figure) or 8.0×10^2 grams (two significant figures) or 8.00×10^2 grams (three significant figures), depending on what the actual number of significant figures is.

Let's look at a second example. The measurement 45,000 millimeters is expressed as 2, 3, 4, or 5 significant figures as follows:

4.5×10^4 millimeters represents two significant figures (4, 5)
4.50×10^4 millimeters represents three significant figures (4, 5, 0)
4.500×10^4 millimeters represents four significant figures (4, 5, 0, 0)
4.5000×10^4 millimeters represents five significant figures (4, 5, 0, 0, 0)

REVIEW EXERCISE

3.5 What is the purpose of expressing measurements to the correct number of significant figures?

3.6 What is the number of significant figures indicated by each of the following measurements?
(a) 219,977 grams
(b) 0.2198 centimeter
(c) 5000.020 liters
(d) 0.0005000 kilogram
(e) 5.0110×10^{12} milligrams
(f) 0.0000000070 meter
(g) 27,333,000.00080000 nanometers
(h) 0.2 second

3.6 (a) 6, (b) 4, (c) 7, (d) 4, (e) 5, (f) 2, (g) 16, (h) 1

Normally, after measurements are made, they are used in subsequent calculations. Specific rules are followed so that results of the calculations also have the proper number of significant figures. Two different rules are followed, depending on the arithmetic operation performed. The rules for handling significant figures when adding and subtracting are different from those used when multiplying and dividing. Attempt to learn each rule, and try not to confuse one with the other.

Addition and Subtraction of Significant Figures

When measured quantities are added and subtracted, the answer can have no more digits to the right of the decimal point than does the measured quantity with the least number of decimal places. If, for instance, we add the masses 2.0965 grams and 1.41 grams, the answer can only have two decimal places. First calculate the sum of the two numbers:

$$2.0965 \text{ grams} + 1.41 \text{ grams} = 3.5065 \text{ grams}$$

Then round off to the correct number of decimal places. Because the second mass was measured only to two decimal places, the answer cannot have more than two decimal places.

When you round off, look at the first nonsignificant figure (6 in our example). The first nonsignificant figure is the figure one place to the right of the least significant figure (0, in our example). The *least significant figure is* the last digit in the number retained when rounding off. Then apply the following three rules for rounding off.

Rule 1

If the value of the first nonsignificant figure is greater than 5, add 1 to the least significant figure and drop all nonsignificant digits.

Rule 2

If the value of the first nonsignificant figure is less than 5, retain the least significant figure and drop all nonsignificant digits.

Rule 3

If the first nonsignificant figure is 5 and it is followed by nonzero digits, increase the value of the least significant figure by 1 and drop all nonsignificant digits. If the first nonsignificant figure is 5 and it is followed by zeros or nothing, add 1 to the least significant figure if it is an odd number and drop all nonsignificant digits; however, if the least significant figure is an even number, retain the least significant figure and drop all nonsignificant figures.

> Many people use this simplified version of the rounding rules: "Round up" if the first nonsignificant figure is 5 or greater, and "round down" if the first nonsignificant digit is less than 5.

In our mass example above, the first nonsignificant figure is 6, so 1 is added to 0, giving 1 as the second decimal place. The final answer is expressed as 3.51 grams. Any other answer is incorrect.

3.5065 grams

Least significant figure   First nonsignificant figure

3.506<u>5</u> grams

Add 1 ⤵ ⬅—Drop

Example Problem 3.1 is another illustration of how to apply the rules for adding measurements and expressing the answer to the correct number of significant figures.

Example Problem 3.1
What is the sum of 10.0043 milliliters + 5.5 milliliters + 9.250 milliliters?

Solution

$$
\begin{array}{ll}
10.0043 \text{ milliliters} & \text{(Four decimal places)} \\
5.5 \text{ milliliters} & \text{(One decimal place)} \\
\underline{+ \ 9.250 \text{ milliliters}} & \text{(Three decimal Places)} \\
24.7543 \text{ milliliters} & \text{(Round to one decimal place)}
\end{array}
$$

The least significant figure is 7 and the first nonsignificant figure is 5. We must round off our answer, 24.7543 milliliters, to one decimal place because the second measured quantity, 5.5 milliliters, has only one decimal place. Because the first nonsignificant figure is a 5 followed by nonzero digits we add 1 to the least significant figure, 7, and drop all nonsignificant digits. This gives a final answer of **24.8 milliliters.**

Exercise
(a) What is the difference between 9.0075 g and 8.9955 g? (b) How many significant figures are in the difference? ((a) 0.0120 g, (b) Three significant figures)

Multiplication and Division of Significant Figures
When measurements are multiplied and divided, the answer cannot have more significant figures than the measurement with the least number of significant figures. If two numbers are multiplied, one with six and the other with three significant figures, the answer can have only three significant figures. The following example is an illustration of such a case.

$$
\begin{array}{ll}
5.82131 \text{ centimeters} & \text{(Six significant figures)} \\
\underline{\times \ 4.11 \quad \text{centimeters}} & \text{(Three significant figures)} \\
23.9255841 \text{ square centimeters (cm}^2) &
\end{array}
$$

The first nonsignificant digit in the answer is 2, which is less than 5; thus, Rule 2 is applied, and the answer is rounded off to 23.9 square centimeters (three significant figures).

> When you are doing calculations with a calculator remember that it does not keep track of the number of significant figures. It is your job to round the numbers on calculator displays to the correct number of significant figures.

    The multiplication and division rule results from the fact that, when an uncertain figure—the last figure—is multiplied or divided, it produces uncertain numbers. An answer can have only one certain figure, so all other uncertain figures are dropped. Example Problem 3.2 shows another example of how to multiply and divide measured quantities.❖

Example Problem 3.2

Perform the indicated arithmetic operations and express the answer to the correct number of significant figures.

$$\frac{7.290 \text{ meters} \times 2.0400 \text{ meters}}{0.95 \text{ meters}} =$$

Solution

Notice that the denominator has a measurement with only two significant figures; this limits the answer to two significant figures. Perform the indicated math operations and round off the resulting answer to two significant figures.

$$\frac{7.290 \times 2.0400 \text{ meters}}{0.95 \text{ meters}} = 15.65431579 \text{ meters} = \textbf{16 meters}$$

meters

The first nonsignificant figure is 6; hence, the answer is rounded off by adding 1 to 5 and dropping the nonsignificant figures, which leaves 16 meters as the answer.

It is common to perform calculations in which both addition and multiplication are required. Example Problem 3.3 shows how to solve such problems.

Exercise

Perform the following and express to the correct number of significant figures. (1.3)

$$8.9 \text{ g}/(50.55 \text{ g} \times 0.1333 \text{ g}) =$$

Example Problem 3.3

Perform the indicated arithmetic operations and express the answer to the correct number of significant figures.

$$(11.2050 \text{ mm} - 10.322 \text{ mm}) \times 6.030000 \text{ mm} =$$

Solution

Both rules regarding significant figures apply in this example; first, after subtracting we can only have three decimal places in the answer because 10.322 millimeters has only three decimal places.

$$11.2050 \text{ mm} - 10.322 \text{ mm} = 0.8830 \text{ mm} = 0.883 \text{ mm}$$

Apply the multiplication rule when you multiply 0.883 mm (three significant figures) by 6.030000 mm (seven significant figures). Three significant figures are the maximum number allowed in the answer.

$$0.883 \text{ mm} \times 6.030000 \text{ mm} = 5.32449 \text{ square millimeters} = \textbf{5.32 mm}^2$$

Subtracting values that have magnitudes close to each other usually results in a loss of significant figures. In this problem, a measurement with five significant figures is subtracted from a measurement with six significant figures and gives an answer with only three significant figures.

Exercise

Perform the following calculation and express the answer to the correct number of significant figures:

(0.0455 g – 0.0399 g)/(0.0555 mL – 0.0113 mL) =

(0.13 g/mL)

REVIEW EXERCISE

3.7 Perform the indicated additions and subtractions and express the answers to the correct number of significant figures:

(a) 32.55 grams - 1.9889 grams =

(b) 0.02 milliliter + 0.183 milliliter =

(c) 554.1864 meters + 42.94 meters =

(d) 34.0000 seconds – 11.01108 seconds + 55.3458702 seconds =

(e) 3.0977×10^{23} atoms + 9.2112×10^{22} atoms =

3.8 Perform the indicated multiplications and divisions and express the answers to the correct number of significant figures:

(a) 83.22 grams/5.4 milliliters =

(b) 123.001 meters × 5.0 meters =

(c) 0.39 centimeter × 6.388 centimeters × 16.5495 centimeters =

(d) 706.0 liters/0.00017613 liter =

(e) 51,087.00 milligrams × 12.7 milligrams =

3.9 Perform the indicated arithmetic operations and express the answers to the correct number of significant figures:

(a) (13.983 meters – 12.98551 meters) × 8.319 meters =

(b) (28.08 grams – 28.0694 grams)/(5.623 seconds + 25.1343 seconds) =

(c) $[(6.200 \times 10^5 \text{ centimeters}) \times (2.5 \times 10^{-6} \text{ centimeter})]/[(3.00000 \times 10^4 \text{ centimeters}) \times$
$(8.3901 \times 10^{-15} \text{ centimeter})]$ =

3.7 (a) 30.56 g, (b) 0.20 mL, (c) 597.13 m, (d) 78.3348, (e) 4.0188×10^{23} atoms; 3.8 (a) 15 g/mL, (b) 6.2 $\times 10^2$ m^2, (c) 41 cm^3, (d) 4.008×10^6, (e) 6.49×10^5 mg^2; 3.9 (a) 8.30 m^2, (b) 3×10^{-4} g/s, (c) 6.2×10^9.

3.3 INTERNATIONAL SYSTEM OF UNITS (MODERNIZED METRIC SYSTEM)

The measurement system utilized by scientists and most countries in the world is the metric system. It was first developed by the French Academy of Sciences in 1790 in response to a request by the French National Assembly for a simple and organized system of weights and measures.

The metric system has evolved since 1790, but its basic structure has remained the same. The metric system is a decimal system, one that requires only the movement of the decimal point to change larger to smaller units or vice versa.

A conference held in 1960 made significant modifications in the metric system; the changes were important enough that the name "metric system" was

> The measurement system used in the United States is called the U.S. Customary System of Units (USCS). It was developed from the old English system of measurement

dropped. The revised system is called Le Systeme International d'Unites or **International System of Units (SI)**. Though we commonly speak of the metric system, in actuality we are usually referring to the International System.

Throughout this book, SI units are used along with some non-SI units still employed frequently by the scientific community.

CHEM TOPIC: Metrification in the United States

Of all of the industrialized countries of the world, the United States is the only one that has not adopted a metric system of weights and measures. However, very slowly the United States is moving toward metrification. In 1975 Congress passed the Metric Conversion Act, but it stipulated that metrification be voluntary. Unfortunately, the 17-member United States Metric Board established by the Metric Conversion Act was abolished in 1982 because of federal budget cuts.

In spite of the federal governments attitude toward metrification, many industries have metrified. The automobile industry is one; it metrified because it uses parts from automobile companies from around the world. You see the results of metrification when considering the displacement volume of an engine, which is expressed in liters instead of cubic inches. If you work on autos, you know that you must use your metric wrenches. When you buy tires for your car, you now must specify the metric dimensions.

As you shop in the supermarket, you also see many metric measurements. Volumes of soft-drink containers are given in liters, and the masses of a variety of food packages are given in grams. On reaching the pharmacy section, you find that the contents of pills are given in milligrams, and the volume of liquid medicines is shown in milliliters. For many years, the alcoholic beverage industry has used metric volume measurements to replace measurements such as the fifth (a fifth of a gallon).

At the present time, it seems as if the United States is on hold with respect to metrification, but let us hope that in the upcoming years we will adopt a system consistent with that used by the rest of the world.

The seven base units of the International System are

1. **Meter** (m)—unit of length
2. **Kilogram** (kg)—unit of mass
3. **Second** (s)—unit of time
4. **Kelvin** (K)—unit of temperature
5. **Mole** (mol)—unit of amount of substance
6. **Ampere** (A)—unit of electric current
7. **Candela** (cd)—unit of luminous intensity

All other SI units are created from combinations of these base units. Examples of derived SI units include the square meter (area), the cubic meter (volume), kilograms per cubic meter (density), and meters per second (velocity).

WWWolfe 2
(See WWWolfe section at the end of the chapter.)

Prefixes are placed in front of the base SI unit to change the size of the unit. We will use the meter as an example; the meter is a unit of length approximately equal to 39.4 inches. While it is convenient to measure the dimensions of a room in meters, it is unwieldy to express distances between cities in meters. To magnify the meter 1000 times, it is only necessary to add the prefix *kilo,* meaning "1000 times," in front of *meter,* which produces the unit *kilometer, km.*

$$1 \text{ kilometer} = 1000 \text{ meters}$$

For measuring small distances the meter is an awkward unit. Thus, a prefix is added to specify a unit smaller than a meter. The two most commonly used prefixes are *centi,* "one-hundredth," and *milli,* "one-thousandth." When we add these to the unit *meter,* we get two small units of length, the centimeter and millimeter. One meter contains 100 centimeters:

$$1/100 \text{ meter} = 1 \text{ centimeter}$$
$$100 \times 1/100 \text{ meter} = 100 \times 1 \text{ centimeter}$$
$$1 \text{ meter} = 100 \text{ centimeters}$$

and one meter contains 1000 millimeters:

$$1/1000 \text{ meter} = 1 \text{ millimeter}$$
$$1000 \times 1/1000 \text{ meter} = 1000 \times 1 \text{ millimeter}$$
$$1 \text{ meter} = 1000 \text{ millimeter}$$

Common prefixes encountered in chemistry are

mega (M) =	1,000,000 × =	10^6 ×
kilo (k) =	1000 × =	10^3 ×
deci (d) =	0.1 × =	10^{-1} ×
centi (c) =	0.01 × =	10^{-2} ×
milli (m) =	0.001× =	10^{-3} ×

$$\text{micro } (\mu) = \quad 0.000001 \times = \quad 10^{-6} \times$$

$$\text{nano } (n) = \quad 0.000000001 \times = \quad 10^{-9} \times$$

$$\text{pico } (p) = \quad 0.000000000001 \times = \quad 10^{-12} \times$$

$$\text{femto } (f) = \quad 0.000000000000001 \times = \quad 10^{-15} \times$$

Because these prefixes are used frequently in chemistry, you should learn them. Table 3.1 provides a complete listing of SI prefixes.❖

TABLE 3.1 SI PREFIXES

Prefix	Symbol	Meaning
exa	E	10^{18}
peta	P	10^{15}
tera	T	10^{12}
giga	G	10^{9}
mega	M	10^{6}
kilo	k	10^{3}
hecto	h	10^{2}
deca	da	10^{1}
–	–	$10^{0} = 1$
deci	d	10^{-1}
centi	c	10^{-2}
milli	m	10^{-3}
micro	μ	10^{-6}
nano	n	10^{-9}
pico	p	10^{-12}
femto	f	10^{-15}
atto	a	10^{-18}

REVIEW EXERCISES

3.10 List the seven base SI units and what they measure.

3.11 What is the difference between base and derived SI units? Give an example of each.

3.12 What is the meaning of each of the following prefixes?
(a) milli
(b) mega
(c) micro
(d) nano
(e) kilo

3.13 What prefix indicates each of the following?
(a) 10^{-12}
(b) 10^{-15}
(c) 10^{3}
(d) 10^{-9}
(e) 10^{6}
(f) 10^{-1}
(g) 10^{-3}

3.12 (a) $10^{-3} \times$, (b) $10^{6} \times$, (c) $10^{-6} \times$, (d) $10^{-9} \times$, (e) $10^{3} \times$, 3.13 (a) pico, (b) femto, (c) kilo, (d) nano, (e) mega, (f) deci, (g) milli

3.4 BASE SI UNITS: METER, KILOGRAM, AND KELVIN

Length

The base SI unit of length is the **meter.** Before 1960, the meter was defined as the distance between two marks on a platinum-iridium rod located in France. These etched marks were separated by one ten-millionth the distance from the equator to the north pole on a line going through Sevres, France. After 1960, the meter was redefined in terms of a more universal standard. Today, one meter is 1,650,763.73 wavelengths of a specific light emitted by the gaseous element krypton, ^{86}Kr. Just why the meter is defined in terms of light emitted from krypton gas is beyond the scope of this discussion, but note that this standard is more reproducible than the old standard. Light released by krypton is not affected by temperature or pressure changes, and, with the proper equipment, its wavelength can be measured anywhere.

A meter equals 39.3701 inches, which makes it longer (by 9%) than a yard (one yard equals 36 inches). Fig. 3.3 shows the relationship between a meter and a yard. While the meter is a convenient day-to-day measurement, it is generally too large to use for length measurements in chemistry because chemists deal with infinitesimal (minute) objects like atoms and molecules. Therefore, various prefixes are added to the meter to produce more useful units of length.

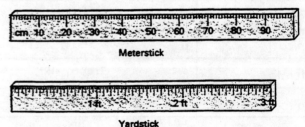

Figure 3.3 One meter is 1.093 yards, or 3.280 feet, or 39.37 inches

A centimeter is 0.01 meter and a millimeter is 0.001 meter. Even these units are gigantic when one is measuring dimensions of objects as small as atoms. A prefix commonly added to meter when considering atomic dimensions is *nano*, or 10^{-9}. One nanometer equals 0.000000001 meter. To give you an idea of how small a nanometer is, we can apply the factor-label method to calculate what fraction of an inch is 1.000 nm. We know that a nanometer is 10^{-9} meter and a meter is 39.37 inches:

$$1.000 \text{ nm} \times \frac{10^{-9} \text{ m}}{1 \text{ nm}} \times \frac{39.37 \text{ in}}{1 \text{ m}} = 3.937 \times 10^{-8} \text{ in}$$

We find that 1.000 nm is only 3.937×10^{-8} in. Additional multiples of the meter are shown in Fig. 3.4 along with the approximate sizes of objects in our universe.

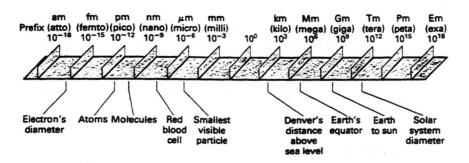

Figure 3.4 Multiples of a meter

Mass

The kilogram is the SI unit of mass. Mass is the quantity of matter contained in an object. A more massive object, as a result of containing more matter, has a smaller acceleration than a less massive object when both are pushed by equal forces (Fig. 3.5).

The terms "mass" and "weight" are frequently confused. **Weight** is the gravitational force of attraction that acts on a mass. The mass of a body is constant no matter where it is located, whereas weight is a variable quantity that depends on where the object is in the universe. For example, if people travel to the moon, their masses remain the same but their weights are approximately one-sixth of their weights on earth because the gravitational attraction on the moon is one-sixth that on earth. On the earth, the gravitational field is nonuniform because it is greater at the poles than at the equator. Thus, the weight of a person changes slightly as he or she travels from the equator to the north pole; but the person's mass remains constant.

Mass and weight measurements require different instruments. Mass is measured with a balance, and weight with a scale. Because a balance operates in a gravitational field, there must be a way to cancel the effects of gravity. Consider a double-pan balance (Fig. 3.6a): An unknown mass is placed on one pan, and known masses are successively added to the other until the pointer returns to its original setting. Gravity is canceled because it is exerted equally on both sides of the balance. Thus, the unknown mass is equal to the sum of the known masses.

In contrast, a scale—the device for measuring weight—is sensitive to gravitational changes. Consider the common spring scale in Fig. 3.6b. A spring scale has a hook attached to a spring, and the spring has a pointer affixed to it that indicates the weight. When an object is hung on the hook, the spring expands and the pointer indicates how much the spring has expanded. Because the effects of gravity are not canceled, as they are in a balance, a spring scale gives the weight of the object.

The standard kilogram, a block of platinum-iridium alloy from which all mass measurements are compared, is located in France. A kilogram is equivalent to 2.2046 pounds. The kilogram is too massive for most routine chemical laboratory measurements; consequently, smaller multiples of the kilogram are used. **Grams (g), milligrams (mg), and microgram (μg)** are the most commonly used units of mass in chemistry labs. Inexpensive triple beam balances are used to measure masses to within 0.01 g, or 1 cg, and more expensive analytical balances easily allow chemists to determine masses to the nearest 0.0001 g, or 0.1 mg (100 μg).

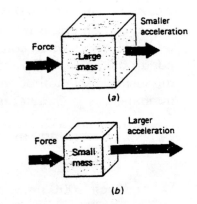

Figure 3.5 If forces of equal magnitude are applied to a large mass (a) and a small mass (b), the acceleration of the smaller mass is greater than the acceleration of the larger mass. The mass of an object is inversely proportional to its acceleration for a constant applied force.

Even with expensive balances, the small mass of an individual atom or molecule is undetectable. A staggering quantity of atoms is needed to give a measurable mass on a sensitive analytical balance. For example, it can be calculated that 3.0×10^{17} gold atoms (rather large atoms, as atoms go) is the smallest number of gold atoms detectable on a balance that has a sensitivity of 0.1 mg.

Most mass measurements taken in the laboratory use the unit grams, but on many occasions grams must be changed to some other unit. Example Problem 3.4 shows how to do a mass-conversion problem.

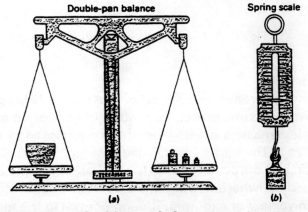

Figure 3.6 (a) A double-pan balance is an instrument for measuring the mass of an object by comparing with known masses. (b) A spring scale is an instrument for measuring the weight of an object.

Example Problem 3.4

A chemistry student does an experiment in which the mass of a sample in milligrams must be determined. The student first measures the mass of an empty beaker and finds that it is 54.389 g. The combined mass of the sample and beaker is then measured and found to be 55.147 g. What is the mass of the sample in milligrams?

Solution

1. What is unknown?   mg

2. What is known? Mass of beaker and sample = 55.147 g; mass of beaker = 54.389 g; 1000 mg/g

To find the mass of the sample in g, the mass of the beaker is subtracted from the mass of the beaker and sample.

Mass of sample = mass of beaker and sample – mass of beaker
Mass of sample = 55.147 g – 54.389 g = 0.758 g

3. Apply the factor-label method.

$$0.758 \text{ g sample} \times \frac{1000 \text{ mg sample}}{1 \text{ g sample}} = ? \text{ mg sample}$$

4. Perform the indicated math operations.

$$0.758 \text{ g sample} \times \frac{1000 \text{ mg sample}}{1 \text{ g sample}} = \textbf{758 mg sample}$$

Exercise
Convert 8.5 lbs to mg. (3.9×10^6 mg)

Temperature

Temperature is a measure of hotness of matter. If an object at a higher temperature contacts an object at a lower temperature, the temperature of the hot object decreases and the temperature of the colder object increases until the temperatures of both objects equalize. We say that heat transfers from the hotter object to the colder object. Heat is a form of energy detected only when objects of different temperatures are in contact with each other. Figure 3.7 shows the relationship between temperature and heat. We will discuss heat in more detail in Chap. 4.

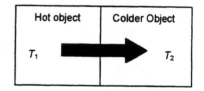

Figure 3.7 Heat always transfers spontaneously from hotter to colder objects. Heat transfer continues until T_1 equals T_2 when the two objects are in thermal equilibrium (at the same temperature).

Chemists use both the **Celsius** and **Kelvin** temperature scales. In 1742, Anders Celsius, a Swedish astronomer, developed the Celsius scale. He set up his scale so that the freezing point of water was assigned the value 0.0 degrees, and the normal boiling point of water was assigned the value of 100 degrees; thus, 100 divisions, or degrees, separate the freezing and boiling points of water. On the Celsius scale, room temperature is 25 degrees, and average human body temperature is approximately 37 degrees.

The SI unit of temperature was named after Lord Kelvin, the title given to William Thomson (1824-1907), a brilliant British physicist. The Kelvin temperature scale employs units called *kelvins* that have the same magnitude as Celsius degrees but are displaced by 273 degrees (actually 273.15 degrees) along the Celsius scale. Thus, the zero point on the Kelvin scale, called absolute zero, is equivalent to –273.15°C. Because absolute zero is the lowest possible temperature, no negative values are in the Kelvin scale.

To change Celsius degrees to kelvins, it is only necessary to add 273.15 to the Celsius temperature:

$$K = °C + 273.15$$

On the Kelvin scale, the freezing and boiling points of water are 273.15 K and 373.15 K, respectively.

$$\text{Freezing point (H}_2\text{O)} = 0°C + 273.15 = 273.15 \text{ K}$$

$$\text{Boiling point (H}_2\text{O)} = 100°C + 273.15 = 373.15 \text{ K}$$

While the Celsius and Kelvin scales are universally used in science, in the United States the Fahrenheit scale predominates among non-scientists. The Fahrenheit temperature scale was proposed by the German scientist Gabriel Fahrenheit in 1714. He decided on 180 divisions between the freezing and boiling points of water, and placed the zero point at the coldest temperature that he could attain his laboratory using salt solutions (salts lower the freezing point of water). The resulting scale fixed the freezing point of pure water at 32 degrees and the boiling point at 212 degrees (exactly 180 degrees above the freezing point).

Figure 3.8 shows the relative magnitudes of the freezing and boiling points of common substances on the three temperature scales: Kelvin, Celsius, and Fahrenheit.

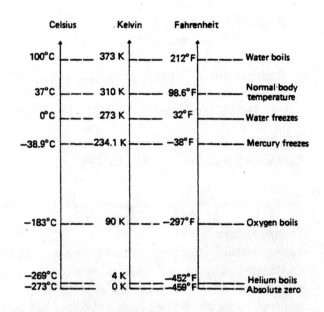

Figure 3.8 Comparisons of the Celsius, Kelvin, and Fahrenheit temperature scales are shown.

Thermometers are used for most laboratory temperature measurements. While many different types of thermometers exist, the mercury thermometer is the laboratory "workhorse." A mercury thermometer has a glass bulb that houses the mercury, a liquid metal. Attached to the bulb is a thin glass tube from which the air has been removed (Fig. 3.9). As the bulb is heated, the mercury expands into the tube. The principal reason mercury is often used in thermometers is that it expands nearly uniformly when heated.

Sometimes temperatures in Fahrenheit degrees must be converted to Celsius degrees and then to Kelvin or vice versa. Temperature conversions are efficiently made using algebraic conversion formulas. To convert a Fahrenheit temperature to a Celsius temperature, the following formula is used:

$$°C = \frac{5}{9} (°F - 32)$$

That is, given a Fahrenheit temperature first subtract 32 from it and then multiply by 5/9 to obtain the equivalent Celsius temperature. For example, when 212°F is substituted into the equation, 100°C is obtained; when 32°F is substituted, 0°C results.

$$°C = 5/9(212°F - 32) = 100°C$$

$$°C = 5/9(32°F - 32) = 0°C$$

If a Celsius temperature is being converted to Fahrenheit, the equation is rearranged and solved for °F. First multiply both sides by 9/5 to eliminate 9/5 from the right side of the equation, giving

$$9/5 \ °C = 5/9(°F - 32) \ 9/5$$

Add 32 to both sides to isolate °F on the right side:

$$32 + 9/5 \ °C = °F - 32 + 32$$

This yields

$$9/5°C + 32 = °F \ \text{ or } \ °F = 9/5°C + 32$$

The three temperature conversion equations,

$$K = °C + 273$$

$$°C = 5/9(°F - 32)$$

$$°F = 9/5°C + 32$$

are used to convert any given temperature in one scale to a temperature on any other scale.

Always remember that the 273 in the Celsius to Kelvin formula is not an exact number but the 32 in the Celsius and Fahrenheit formula is exact. Example Problem 3.5 is an illustration of a temperature-conversion problem.❖

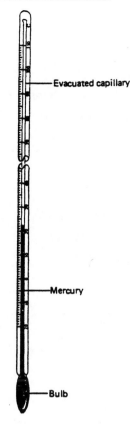

Figure 3.9 Mercury thermometers are the most commonly used temperature-measuring devices in chemistry laboratories. When the bulb containing mercury is heated, the mercury expands uniformly and moves up in the evacuated capillary tube.

Example Problem 3.5
Convert 300.0 K to Fahrenheit.

Solution
1. What is unknown?   °F
2. What is known? 300.0 K
3. Apply the appropriate temperature conversion formulas. First convert K to °C, and then convert to °F.
(a) Convert 300.0 K to °C. To find the °C, first rearrange the equation and substitute the Kelvin temperature in the equation.

$$K = °C + 273.15$$
$$°C = K - 273.15$$
$$°C = 300.0 - 273.15 = 26.8°C$$

The answer, 26.8°C, must be rounded to one decimal place because the temperature was measured to one decimal place.

(b) Convert 26.8°C to °F.

$$°F = 9/5 °C + 32$$
$$°F = 9/5(26.8°C) + 32 = \textbf{80.2°F}$$

The answer, 80.2°F, is equivalent to 300.0 K.
Exercise
Convert 99.9°F to K. (310.9 K)

REVIEW EXERCISES

3.14 What are the base SI units for length, mass, and temperature?

3.15 What standards are used for the units of length and mass?

3.16 Use the factor-label method and scientific notation to perform the following conversions:

(a) 9150 m = ? mm
(b) 0.1005 ft = ? cm
(c) 805 g = ? lb
(d) 337.6 kg = ? ng

3.17 (a) What is the difference between mass and weight?

(b) What is the difference between temperature and heat?

3.18 Perform each of the following temperature conversions:

(a) 55°C = ? K
(b) –91.4°C = ? K
(c) 2010°F = ? °C
(d) –0.287°C = ? °F

3.16 (a) 9.150×10^6 mm, (b) 3.06 cm, (c) 1.77 lb, (d) 3.376×10^{14} ng; 3.18 (a) 328 K, (b) 181.8 K, (c) 1099°C, (d) 31.483°F

3.5 DERIVED SI UNITS OF MEASUREMENT: VOLUME AND DENSITY

Derived SI units are combinations of the base SI units. While many derived units are in use, only volume and density units are discussed here because of their importance in measuring and describing matter.

Volume

Volume is space occupied by matter. All matter occupies some space and therefore has volume. The amount of space taken by a given amount of matter is measured in cubic units—a cubic unit being a unit of length raised to the third power. For example, the volume V of a rectangular object is calculated by multiplying the object's length, l, times its width, w, times its height, h (Fig. 3.10).

$$V = lwh$$

The base unit of length is the meter; thus, one SI unit of volume is the cubic meter: 1 m × 1 m × 1 m, or 1 m³. One cubic meter contains approximately 264 gallons, and for most chemical measurements the cubic meter is much too large.

Instead of working with such an enormous unit as the cubic meter, chemists frequently use a small fraction of this unit, the cubic decimeter. *Deci is* the prefix that means 1/10; thus a decimeter is 0.1 meter (3.937 inches). The cubic decimeter is exactly equivalent to a non-SI unit, the liter (L). Both the cubic decimeter and the liter are equivalent to 0.001 cubic meter. The cubic decimeter is not frequently encountered because of the popularity of the liter. Therefore, the liter is most frequently used throughout this book. Just remember that 1 L and 1 dm³ are different expressions for the same volume, 0.001 m³.

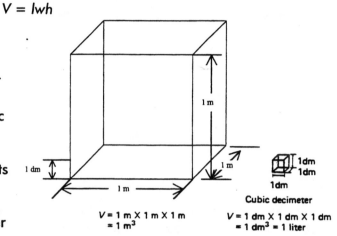

Figure 3.10 One cubic meter (1 m³) is a very large unit of volume; it contains 1000 dm³. One cubic decimeter equals the same volume as the non-SI volume unit called the liter.

$$1 \text{ L} = 1 \text{ dm}^3$$

A liter is approximately equal in volume to a quart (Fig. 3.11). One liter is 1.057 quarts, which means it is larger than a quart. Example Problem 3.6 shows a volume conversion to liters.

Example Problem 3.6

How many liters of gasoline must be purchased to exactly fill a 15.0-gal gasoline tank?

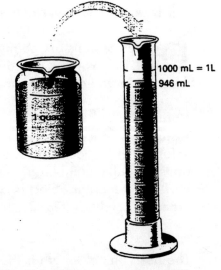

Solution

1. What is unknown?   L
2. What is known?   15.0 gal; 1.057 qt/L; 4 qt/gal
3. Apply the factor-label method.

$$15.0 \text{ gal} \times \frac{4 \text{ qt}}{1 \text{ gal}} \times \frac{1 \text{ L}}{1.057 \text{ qt}} = ? \text{ L}$$

4. Perform the indicated math operations.

$$15.0 \text{ gal} \times \frac{4 \text{ qt}}{1 \text{ gal}} \times \frac{1 \text{ L}}{1.057 \text{ qt}} = \textbf{56.8 L}$$

Figure 3.11 One quart is 0.940 liter, and one liter is 1.06 quart.

1000 mL = 1L
946 mL

A 15.0-gal tank holds a maximum of 56.8 L of gasoline.

Exercise

How many liters, L, in one quart? (0.946 L)

Even the liter is too large for most routine laboratory volume measurements so the milliliter or the cubic centimeter (cm³, also written cc), is regularly used in chemistry. The milliliter and the cubic centimeter are measurements for the same volume, 0.001 L.

> Pipets, burets, graduated cylinders, graduated beakers, volumetric flasks, and syringes are used to measure volumes in the laboratory

$$1 \text{ mL} = 1 \text{ cm}^3 = 1 \text{ cc} = 0.001 \text{ L}$$

Sometimes, very small volumes must be measured; in such cases the microliter, μL, is used. Example Problem 3.7 shows how to find the number of microliters in 1.00 m³.

Example Problem 3.7

How many microliters, μL, are in 1.00 m³?

Solution

1. What is unknown?, μL
2. What is known?   1.00 m³; 1 dm³/0.001 m³; 1 dm³/L; 1 μL/1 × 10⁻⁶ L
3. Apply the factor-label method.

$$1.00 \text{ m}^3 \times \frac{1 \text{ dm}^3}{0.001 \text{ m}^3} \times \frac{1 \text{ L}}{1 \text{ dm}^3} \times \frac{1 \text{ } \mu\text{L}}{1 \times 10^{-6} \text{ L}} = ? \text{ } \mu\text{L}$$

4. Perform the indicated math operations.

$$1.00 \; \cancel{m^3} \quad \times \quad \frac{1 \; dm^3}{0.001 \; \cancel{m^3}} \quad \times \quad \frac{1 \; \cancel{L}}{1 \; \cancel{dm^3}} \times \frac{1 \; \mu L}{1 \times 10^{-6} \; \cancel{L}} = 1 \times 10^9 \; \mu L$$

Exercise
How many pL are in 50.0 cm^3? (5.00 $\times$ 10^{10} pL)

A common problem encountered when dealing with volumes is calculating a volume unit from a given length unit. For example, if we wanted to know the relationship between cubic millimeters and cubic centimeters, we would start by comparing the relationships between meters and millimeters, and meters and centimeters.

$$1 \; m = 1000 \; mm = 10^3 \; mm$$
$$1 \; m = 100 \; cm = 10^2 \; cm$$

Cubing both sides of the equations gives the respective volume units associated with 1 mm and 1 cm relative to 1 m^3.

$$1 \; m^3 = (10^3 \; mm)^3 = 10^9 \; mm^3$$
$$1 \; m^3 = (10^2 \; cm)^3 = 10^6 \; cm^3$$

Knowing the relation of both 1 mm^3 and 1 cm^3 to 1 m^3, we find after dividing these two equalities, that 1 cm^3 contains 10^3 mm^3.

$$\frac{1 \; \cancel{m^3}}{1 \; \cancel{m^3}} = \frac{10^9 \; mm^3}{10^6 \; cm^3}$$

$$1 = 10^3 \; mm^3/cm^3$$

Example Problem 3.8 presents another case in which a length unit is converted to a volume unit.

Example Problem 3.8
An automobile engine has a displacement of 3.80 L. What is its displacement in cubic inches?

Solution
1. What is unknown?   in^3
2. What is known?   3.80 L; 1 L/1 dm^3; 10 dm/1 m; 39.37 in/1 m

To convert L to in^3 we must know the conversion factors for L and dm^3, dm and m, and in and m. To find the relationships between dm^3 and m^3, and in^3 and m^3, cube the conversion factors 10 dm/1 m and 39.37 in/1 m as follows:

$$\frac{(10 \text{ dm})^3}{(1 \text{ m})^3} = \frac{10^3 \text{ dm}^3}{1 \text{ m}^3}$$

$$\frac{(39.37 \text{ in})^3}{(1 \text{ m})^3} = \frac{6.102 \times 10^4 \text{ in}^3}{1 \text{ m}^3}$$

3. Apply the factor-label method.

$$3.80 \text{ L} \times \frac{1 \text{ dm}^3}{1 \text{ L}} \times \frac{1 \text{ m}^3}{10^3 \text{ dm}^3} \times \frac{6.102 \times 10^4 \text{ in}^3}{1 \text{ m}^3} = ? \text{ in}^3$$

4. Perform the indicated math operations.

$$3.80 \text{ L} \times \frac{1 \text{ dm}^3}{1 \text{ L}} \times \frac{1 \text{ m}^3}{10^3 \text{ dm}^3} \times \frac{6.102 \times 10^4 \text{ in}^3}{1 \text{ m}^3} = \mathbf{232 \text{ in}^3}$$

A 3.80-L engine displacement is equivalent to a displacement of 232 in^3.

Exercise
Convert 3.5 cm^3 to nm^3. (3.5×10^{21} nm^3)

REVIEW EXERCISES
3.19 (a) What is the SI unit of volume?

(b) What other volume units are used in chemistry?

3.20 Perform each of the following volume conversions:

(a) 2.59 L = ? mL = ? cm^3 = ? dm^3 = ? m^3
(b) 8.16 × 103 μL = ? m^3 = ? L = ? mL = ? mm^3

3.21 A barrel is a unit of volume used to measure crude oil. One barrel contains 44 gallons.

(a) How many liters of oil are there in a barrel?
(b) How many cubic centimeters of oil are there in a barrel?
(c) How many barrels of oil are required to fill a tank with a volume of 8.77 × 10^6 mL?

3.22 (a) Calculate the displacement of an engine in liters if it has a displacement of 425 in^3.

(b) What is the displacement of an engine in cubic inches if it is a 1.8-L engine?

3.20 (a) 2.59 × 10^3 mL = 2.59 × 10^3 cm^3 = 2.59 dm^3 = 2.59 × 10^{-3} m^3; (b) 8.16 × 10^{-6} m^3 = 8.16 × 10^{-3} L = 8.16 mL = 8.16 × 10^3 mm^3 ; 3.21 (a) 1.7 × 10^2 L, (b) 1.7 × 10^5 cm^3, (c) 53 barrels; 3.22 (a) 6.96 L, (b) 1.1 × 10^2 in^3 .

Density

Density is an important property of matter. The **density** of a substance describes how much mass is contained in a unit volume.

$$\text{Density} = \frac{\text{mass}}{\text{volume}}$$

Substances with higher densities have more mass packed into equivalent volumes than those with lower densities. For example, 1.0 mL of gold has a mass of 19 g; in contrast, 1.0 mL of water has a mass of only 1.0 g. If equal masses of gold and water are compared, the gold occupies one-nineteenth the volume of the water.

A density can be thought of as a conversion factor that equates the mass and volume of a substance.

Densities of substances are measured by finding the mass of a known volume of the substance. Mass is most commonly measured in grams, and volume is measured in milliliters or cubic centimeters and in liters. For the more compact forms of matter, liquids and solids, densities are expressed in grams per cubic centimeter or grams per milliliter. For less dense forms of matter, mainly gases, densities are expressed in grams per liter and grams per cubic decimeter.

Each substance has a characteristic density; for example, the density of water at 4°C is 1.00 g/cm³, which means that 1.00 g of water occupies a volume of 1.00 cm³ at 4°C. Table 3.2 lists the densities of common materials.

When the temperature of a sample of matter changes, typically its volume also changes; consequently, the density of a substance depends on its temperature. The density of water is 1.00 g/cm³ only at 4°C. At room temperature, 25°C (298 K), the density of water decreases to 0.997 g/cm³. When the temperature is raised to 80°C, the density of water decreases to 0.971 g/cm³. Therefore, the temperature must be stated whenever a density is given.

Densities may be used to compare masses of substances that have the same volume. It is incorrect to say, "Gold is a heavier metal than iron." Properly, one says, "Gold is more dense than iron." Table 3.2 shows that the density of gold is 19.3 g/cm³, which is higher than the density of iron, 7.86 g/cm³. Relative volumes of substances with the same mass are shown in Fig. 3.12.

TABLE 3.2 DENSITIES OF SELECTED MATERIALS

Liquids and solids	Density, g/cm³ (25°C)	Gases	Density, g/dm³ (1 atm, 0°C)
Aluminum(s)	2.7	Air	1.29
Benzene(l)	0.86	Ammonia, NH_3	0.72
Ethanol(l)	0.78	Carbon dioxide, CO_2	1.98
Gold(s)	19.3	Chlorine, Cl_2	3.21
Iron(s)	7.86	Hydrogen, H_2	0.090
Lead(s)	11.4	Krypton, Kr	3.71
Mercury(l)	13.6	Nitrogen, N_2	1.25
Osmium(s)	22.6	Oxygen, O_2	1.43
Phosphorus(s)	1.8	Radon, Rn	9.7
Platinum(s)	21.4	Xenon, Xe	5.90
Potassium(s)	0.86		
Silicon(s)	2.3		
Sodium(s)	0.97		
Water(l)	1.0		
Uranium	18.9		

In the laboratory, densities are measured by finding the mass of a known volume. Liquid densities are easily obtained. A volumetric instrument such as a graduated cylinder or volumetric flask is weighed, filled to a specific volume level, and reweighed. If we subtract the mass of the container from the mass of the container plus the liquid, we get the mass of the liquid (Fig. 3.13).

Mass of liquid = mass of container and liquid – mass of container

Density varies with temperature because substances expand and contract when heated and cooled. To find the density of the liquid, its volume is divided into the mass. A typical density determination for a liquid is found in Example Problem 3.9.

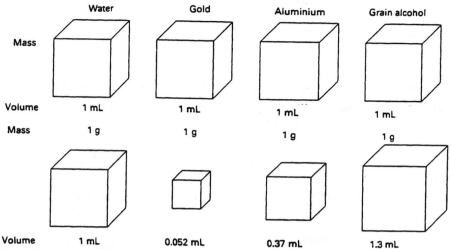

Figure 3.12 If you consider equal volumes of matter, substances with higher densities have greater masses than those with smaller densities. If you consider equal masses of matter, substances with higher densities have smaller volumes than those with smaller densities.

$$d_{liq} = \frac{\text{mass of liquid}}{\text{volume of liquid}}$$

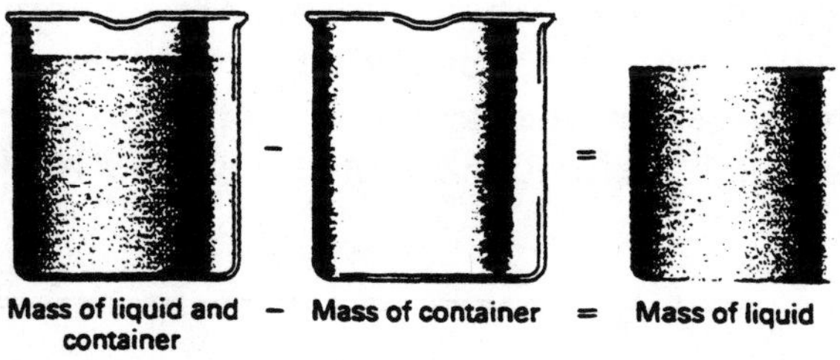

Mass of liquid and — Mass of container = Mass of liquid
container

Figure 3.13 To find the mass of a liquid measure the mass of the container that holds the liquid and then measure the mass of the container plus the liquid. The mass of the liquid is the difference between the two masses.

Example Problem 3.9

An empty 10-mL graduated cylinder has a mass of 53.24 g. When 10.0 mL of an unknown liquid is added to the cylinder, the total mass is 63.12 g. Calculate the density of the unknown liquid.

Solution

1. What is unknown?   Density of the unknown liquid, g/cm^3
2. What is known?   Volume = 10.0 mL; mass of empty graduated cylinder = 53.24 g; mass of liquid plus graduated cylinder = 63.12 g, 1 cm^3/1 mL

$$d_{liquid} = \frac{\text{mass of liquid}}{\text{volume of liquid}}$$

3. To find the density of a substance, it is necessary to measure the mass of a known volume of the substance. The mass of the unknown liquid is found by subtracting the mass of the graduated cylinder from the mass of the graduated cylinder and liquid.

Mass of liquid = 63.12 g – 53.24 g = 9.88 g

4. Divide the mass of the liquid by its volume, 10 mL, which is equal to 10 cm^3.

$$d = \frac{\text{mass}}{\text{volume}} = \frac{9.88 \text{ g}}{10.0 \text{ cm}^3} = \textbf{0.988 g/cm}^3$$

The density of the unknown liquid is 0.988 g/cm^3.

Exercise
The mass of a flask is 54.338 g. When 23.5 mL of a liquid is added to the flask, the combined mass of the flask and liquid is 93.104 g. What is the density of liquid? (1.65 g/cm^3)

Densities are helpful quantities when working in the laboratory. Sometimes it is inconvenient to measure the mass of a substance directly. If the volume and density of a substance are known, the mass can be calculated. Think of the density of an object as another conversion factor, mass/volume. Example Problem 3.10 shows how density is applied as a conversion factor.

Example Problem 3.10
A student places 25.0 cm^3 of decane in a graduated cylinder. If the density of decane is 0.730 g/cm^3, what is the mass of decane in the cylinder?

Solution
1. What is unknown?   Mass of decane in g
2. What is known?   Volume of decane = 25.0 cm^3 ; density of decane = 0.730 g/cm^3
3. Apply the factor-label method

$$25.0 \ \cancel{\text{cm}^3 \text{ decane}} \times \frac{0.730 \text{ g decane}}{1 \ \cancel{\text{cm}^3 \text{ decane}}} = ? \text{ g decane}$$

4. Perform the indicated math operations.

$$25.0 \ \cancel{\text{cm}^3 \text{ decane}} \times \frac{0.730 \text{ g decane}}{1 \ \cancel{\text{cm}^3 \text{ decane}}} = \textbf{18.3 g decane}$$

Exercise
The density of aluminum, Al, is 2.70 g/cm^3. What is the volume of 1.00 kg of aluminum? (370 cm^3)

Other Derived SI Units

Many other derived SI units of measurement are used in chemistry, including measures of (1) energy, (2) force, (3) power, (4) electric charge, and (5) pressure. We will investigate some of these in later chapters.❖

REVIEW EXERCISES

3.23 (a) An unknown solid is found to have a mass of 133.1 g and a volume of 11.68 cm³. What is the density of the solid?

(b) If the unknown solid is one of those listed in Table 3.2, what is the unknown solid?

3.24 (a) What is the volume of 937 g of aluminum?

(b) What is the mass of 3.91 L of aluminum? (The density of aluminum is found in Table 3.2.)

3.25 An empty 25.0-cm³ graduated cylinder has a mass of 98.24 g.
(a) If 25.0 cm³ of an unknown liquid and the graduated cylinder have a total mass of 121.44 g, what is the density of the liquid?

(b) What is the mass of 75.0 mL of the liquid?

3.26 Consider the metals sodium, Na, and iron, Fe, to answer the following.
(a) Considering equal volumes of Na and Fe, which would have the greatest mass?

(b) Considering equal masses of Na and Fe, which would have the greatest volume?

3.23 (a) 11.40 g/cm³, (b) lead, 3.24 (a) 347 cm³, (b) 1.06 × 10⁴ g, 3.25 (a) 0.928 g/cm³, (b) 69.6 g, 3.26 (a) Fe, (b) Na.

WorldWideWolfe CHEMISTRY LINKS

Connect to WorldWideWolfe at

http://www.mindspring.com/~drwolfe/WWWolfe_hcc_1025_links.htm

and link to the following sites.

Problem Solving in Chemistry, Chemical Measurement

1. Introduction to Chemistry

Discusses the most basic principles relating to chemistry. It has Learning Objectives, Lecture Notes, Frequently Asked Questions, References and Resources and Glossary.

2. Measurement

This is the best place to start learning about chemical measurements. It has Learning Objectives, Before You Start, Lecture Notes, References and Resources, Frequently Asked Questions, Glossary, Quiz: Significant Figures, Tutorial: Arithmetic with units, Tutorial: Introduction to unit conversion, and Tutorial: Uncertainty in Measurement.

SUMMARY

All measurements are, to some degree, uncertain because of measurement errors. Systematic and random errors are the two general types of errors found in measurements. **Systematic errors** result from improper techniques, uncalibrated equipment, or human error: they may be corrected. **Random errors** are those that cannot be identified but are present: they cannot be corrected.

Chemists use significant figures to express the degree of certainty of a measurement. **Significant figures** are the measured digits plus one estimated digit. Measurements with a greater number of significant figures are more certain than those with less. When we do calculations involving measurements, we must be careful to follow the rules regarding significant figures so that the results of the calculations have only one uncertain digit.

The **International System of Units** (SI) is the system of measurement used by scientists. All SI units of measurement are either base or derived units. The seven base units SI are the meter, kilogram, kelvin, second, mole, ampere, and candela. All other units are derived from these seven base units; thus, they are called derived SI units. To increase or decrease the magnitude of SI units, it is only necessary to place the appropriate prefix in front of the unit. Frequently encountered SI prefixes are kilo ($1000 \times$), centi ($10^{-2} \times$), mini ($10^{-3} \times$), and micro ($10^{-6} \times$).

Mass is the quantity of matter in an object and is usually measured in kilograms, grams, or milligrams. No matter where an object is found, mass remains constant. **Weight** is the force of gravity on a mass. The weight of an object varies, depending on its location in the universe. **Temperature** is a measure of the hotness of matter. The **kelvin** (K) is the SI unit of temperature. The zero point on the Kelvin scale is absolute zero, the lowest possible temperature. One Kelvin has the same magnitude as one Celsius degree, the non-SI unit of temperature.

Volume is measured in cubic meters, cubic decimeters, or cubic centimeters in SI. These measures of volume are derived from the base units of length—meters, decimeters, and centimeters. Liters and milliliters, two non-SI volume units, are commonly used in chemistry. **Density** is the ratio of mass to volume and is most frequently measured in grams per cubic centimeter or grams per liter.

KEY TERMS

absolute zero	metric system
balance	random error
base units	scale a significant figure
density	specific gravity

a derived unit
international System of Units (SI)
kilogram
mass
measurement uncertainty

systematic error
temperature
volume
weight

STUDY GUIDELINES

After completing Chapter 3, you should be able to

1. Distinguish between precision and accuracy of measurements

2. Distinguish between systematic and random errors in measurements

3. Give a definition of significant figures

4. Determine if a zero in a measured quantity is significant

5. Add, subtract, multiply, and divide measured quantities and ex-press the answer to the correct number of significant figures with the correct units

6. List the seven base SI units and explain what they measure

7. List common prefixes used in the SI and state their meaning

8. Explain the difference between base and derived SI units

9. Convert base SI units to common multiples

10. Distinguish between mass and weight

11. Define temperature and briefly explain how it is different from heat

12. Perform temperature conversions given Kelvin, Celsius, or Fahrenheit temperatures

13. Convert units of volume to multiples and to other units

14. Calculate the density of a substance given its mass and volume

15. Calculate either the mass or volume of an object given its density

EXERCISES

3.27 Define each of the following terms: SI, metric system, base unit, derived unit, kilogram, mass, weight, balance, scale, absolute zero, volume, density, temperature, systematic error, random error, measurement uncertainty, significant figure, specific gravity.

Uncertainty in Measurements

3.28 By what means is the accuracy is a measurement determined?

3.29 What factors decrease the accuracy of the measurement you take of your weight on a bathroom scale?

3.30 What could be said about the precision of the following group of volume measurements for the same object: 144 mL, 163 mL, 155 mL, 182 mL, 159 mL, and 149 mL?

3.31 Select the more precise measuring device in each of the following pairs: (a) centigram balance that measures to one-hundredth of gram or analytical balance which measures to one-tenth of a milligram; (b) pipet or calibrated beaker; (c) large graduated cylinder or small graduated cylinder; (d) volumetric flask or graduated cylinder.

3.32 What systematic errors might influence the measurement of air temperature on an out-door thermometer?

3.33 Why can't random errors be eliminated from measurements?

Significant figures

3.34 How many significant figures are there in each of the following measured quantities?
(a) 24.084   (b) 128.0700
(c) 0.098   (d) 0.0012000
(e) 500.0   (f) 0.00000000191010
(g) 0.00133490   (h) 0.0002
(i) 8.90×10^1 (j) 5×10^{-8}

3.35 For each measurement listed in Exercise 3.34, write the least significant figure.

3.36 Express each measurement listed in Exercise 3.34 with one significant figure.

3.37 Round off each of the following to four significant figures:

(a) 194.645
(b) 10.998
(c) 962.1539
(d) 0.659119999
(e) 999,650,004,000

3.38 Use scientific notation to express 90,000 with (a) one, (b) two, (c) three, (d) four, and (e) five significant figures.

3.39 Add each of the following and express the answer to the correct number of significant figures:
(a) 2.345 g + 2.5 g =
(b) 32.0030 mL + 11.87 mL =
(c) 4.5666 g + 3.2388 g + 10.382 g =
(d) 494.14320 m + 171.579 m + 91.15 m =

3.40 Subtract each of the following and express the answer to the correct number of significant figures:
(a) 154.236 mL – 56.9 mL =
(b) 1.00666 cm – 0.839 cm =
(c) 40.311 g – 40.277 g =
(d) 900.0088 mm – 65.3 mm – 138.5454 mm =

3.41 Multiply each of the following and express the answer to the correct number of significant figures:
(a) 0.077g × 6 g =
(b) 732.2 s × 8.1 s =
(c) 5.5050 cm × 9.9 cm =
(d) 0.009470 kg × 472.0 kg =

3.42 Divide each of the following and express the answer to the correct number of significant figures with the correct units:
(a) 9.233 g/1.4 mL =
(b) 89.08 m/0.509514 m =
(c) $(5.83 \times 10^{14}$ m$)/(4 \times 10^{-6}$ s$) =$
(d) 0.00071000 g/0.93 cm^3 =

3.43 Perform the indicated arithmetic operations and express the answer to the correct number of significant figures:
(a) (133 × 534.00)/(9.1 + 0.4543) =
(b) (154.7325 – 154.7036) × 9.89892 =
(c) [(0.000100/0.0027711) – 0.0000522 +0.00046]/5.198 =

Base SI Units

3.44 Write the base SI unit that corresponds to the following measurements: (a) time, (b) quantity of substance, (c) length, (d) electric current, (e) mass, (f) temperature.

3.45 (a) Use a dictionary to find the meaning of the following English measurement units: dram, scruple, minim, and slug. (b) What difficulties are encountered when using such units that are not encountered when using the International System?

3.46 What prefix is used for each of the following: (a) 0.01 ×, (b) 1,000,000 ×, (c) 10^{-6} ×, (d) 0.1 ×, (e) 1000 ×, (f) 0.001 ×, (g) 10^{-9} ×?

3.47 What is the meaning of each of the following prefixes: (a) milli, (b) deca, (c) giga, (d) pico, (e) nano, (f) deci, (g) kilo, (h) centi, (i) micro, (j) hecto

Length

3.48 Perform each of the following length conversions:
(a) 91 m = ? mm
(b) 1669 cm = ? m
(c) 4.3 km = ? cm
(d) 6.8 km = ? μm
(e) 358.0 mm = ? nm
(f) 74.6 Mm = ? km

3.49 If one mile equals 5280 feet, change each quantity that follows to the designated unit of length:
(a) 1 mi = ? m
(b) 23 mi = ? in
(c) 6.1 mi = ? cm
(d) 56 mi = ? mm
(e) 705 mi = ? km
(f) 486.0 mi = ? Mm

3.50 Change each to the designated SI unit:
(a) 19 in = ? km
(b) 36.9 ft = ? mm
(c) 5 ft 10 in = ? m
(d) 136.0 yd = ? m
(e) 0.0015 in = ? nm
(f) 35.156 mi = ? mm

3.51 The distance from the earth to the sun is 9.3×10^7 mi. Express this distance in (a) kilometers, (b) meters, (c) millimeters, and (d) picometers.

3.52 (a) What is the modern standard of length in the SI? (b) Why did it replace the old standard?

3.53 A person's body measurements are as follows: weight = 130 lbs; height = 5 ft 7 in; chest = 37 in; waist = 30 in; hips = 35 in. Convert the weight measurement to kilograms and the length measurements to centimeters.

Mass

3.54 Assuming that you could travel to Jupiter and make a quick weight measurement, how would your weight there compare to your weight here on earth? (Jupiter is the largest planet in our solar system, with a mass many times that of earth.)

3.55 Perform the following mass conversions:
(a) 58.73 kg = ? mg
(b) 74 mg = ? g
(c) 9.7115×10^{12} μg = ? kg
(d) 12.93 kg = ? pg
(e) 43.8×10^{-4} g = ? μg
(f) 45.2×10^{19} mg = ? Mg
(g) 0.000022 kg = ? dg
(h) 8.395×10^8 g = ? cg

3.56 If there are exactly 16 ounces in a pound and 2000 pounds constitute one ton, change each of the following to the designated SI unit:
(a) 52 lb = ? g
(b) 6186 oz = ? mg
(c) 1.088 tons = ? Mg
(d) 12.033 1b = ? cg
(e) 8.43×10^{-3} 1b= ? ng
(f) 3.94×10^{13} oz = ? dg

Temperature

3.57 Change each Celsius temperature to Kelvin: (a) 11°C, (b) –61°C, (c) –235.6°C, (d) 2.04°C.

3.58 Change each Kelvin temperature to Celsius: (a) 88 K, (b) 314.7 K, (c) 0.388 K, (d) 3221 K.

3.59 Change each Fahrenheit temperature to Celsius: (a) 77.7°F, (b) –77.7°F, (c) 1466°F, (d) –459°F.

3.60 Change each Celsius temperature to Fahrenheit: (a) 77.7°C, (b) –77.7°C, (c) 1466°C, (d) –140.0°C.

3.61 Convert each Kelvin temperature to Fahrenheit: (a) 77.7 K, (b) 98.6 K, (c) 1111.11 K, (d) 0.89 K.

3.62 One temperature has exactly the same numerical value on both the Celsius and

Fahrenheit temperature scales. Use algebra to find this temperature.

3.63 Cesium is a highly reactive metal that melts at 28.7°C. (a) What is the melting point of cesium in degrees Fahrenheit? (b) What is the melting point on the Kelvin scale? (c) If you could hold cesium in your hand, what would happen to it?

3.64 The melting and boiling points of hydrogen are –269.7°C and –268.9°C, respectively. (a) Calculate the melting and boiling points of hydrogen in kelvins. (b) Find the melting and boiling points of hydrogen in Fahrenheit.

Volume

3.65 A block of wood is 2.1 cm long, 0.54 cm wide, and 934 mm high. What is the volume of the block in (a) cubic centimeters, (b) cubic decimeters, (c) milliliters, (d) liters?

3.66 Calculate the volume in liters of a metal block that is 4503 mm long, 439 cm wide, and 0.0229 m high.

3.67 Perform the indicated volume conversions:
(a) $3.98 \text{ dm}^3 = ? \text{ cm}^3$
(b) $12 \text{ mL} = ? \text{ m}^3$
(c) $73.570 \text{ mL} = ? \text{ } \mu\text{L}$
(d) $1.14 \text{ m}^3 = ? \text{ mL}$
(e) $508.2 \text{ L} = ? \text{ m}^3$
(f) $1.2 \times 10^7 \text{ } \mu\text{L} = ? \text{ m}^3$

3.68 Change each to the indicated unit:
(a) $821.0 \text{ mL} = ? \text{ qt}$
(b) $1.000 \text{ m}^3 = ? \text{ mm}^3$
(c) $199 \text{ mL} = ? \text{ qt}$
(d) $3.501 \text{ cm}^3 = ? \text{ ft}^3$
(e) $8.1 \text{ ft}^3 = ? \text{ cc}$

3.69 Change each to the indicated SI unit:
(a) $177 \text{ gal} = ? \text{ m}^3$
(b) $50.45 \text{ pints} = ? \text{ cm}^3$
(c) $3.04 \times 10^{-5} \text{ qt} = ? \text{ dm}^3$
(d) $0.0011 \text{ gallons} = ? \text{ mm}^3$

Density

3.70 Calculate the density of each substance in grams per milliliter, given mass and volume:
(a) Mass = 651 g; volume = 49.9 mL
(b) Mass = 8.32 g; volume = 9.67 mL
(c) Mass = 1.58 kg; volume = 1.677 L

(d) Mass = 7.24 lb; volume = 0.03119ft^3

3.71 Vanadium, an element, has a density of 6.11 g/cm^3. Calculate the mass of vanadium contained in the following volumes: (a) 33 cm³, 3 (b) 544 mL, (c) 211.5 L, (d) 0.289 cm³, (e) 1 qt, (f) 0.000671 m³.

3.72 The density of pure silicon is 2.33 g/cm^3. Calculate the volume of the following masses of silicon: (a) 834.6 g, (b) 900.5 mg, (c) 3.330 kg, (d) 71.9 lb, (e) 9.00 t (1 t = 1000 kg).

3.73 Air has a density of 1.29 g/L. Express the density of air in each of the following units: (a) grams per cubic foot, (b) kilograms per cubic meter, (c) pounds per cubic foot, (d) milligrams per cubic millimeter, (e) kilograms per cubic centimeter.

3.74 The metal platinum has a density of 21.4 g/cm³. If you are given a metal sample weighing 9.29 g that occupies 0.434 cm³, how could you quickly determine if the sample is pure platinum or not? Is it?

3.75 A graduated beaker is used to determine the density of an unknown liquid. The mass of the beaker is 40.1 g. What is the density of the unknown liquid if the beaker and 18.6 mL of the unknown liquid together weigh 69.7 g?

3.76 A 1.28-qt bottle is used to store liquid mercury (density = 13.6 g/cc). What is the mass of the mercury in the bottle in (a) grams, (b) kilograms, and (c) milligrams?

3.77 A 45.045-g graduated cylinder is used to measure the density of a liquid. After 15.0 mL of this liquid is poured into the cylinder, the combined mass of the cylinder and liquid is 69.731 g. Calculate the density of the liquid.

3.78 What is the mass of air in a room that measures 6.1 m × 5.5 m × 4.3 m?

3.79 A bar of osmium, Os, has the following dimensions: 0.35 m × 2.43 cm × 453.9 mm. What is the mass of the osmium bar in kilograms?

Additional Exercises

3.80 Perform the following arithmetic operations and express the answers to the correct number of significant figures with the correct units:

(a) $\dfrac{(0.3441 \text{ g} - 0.3294 \text{ g})}{(8.03 \text{ g} \times 0.0233 \text{ g})}$

(b) $(10.004 \text{ m} \times 7.322 \text{ m}) - 67.9 \text{ m}^2 + (4.558 \text{ m} \times 81.2 \text{ m} \times 16.03 \text{ m})/81.04 \text{ m} =$

(c) $(5.79 \text{ cm}^3/4.220 \text{ cm}^3) \times (203.1 \text{ cm}^3 + 821.9 \text{ cm}^3)/0.00345 \text{ m}^3 =$

3.81 Perform each of the following conversions:
(a) $9.32 \text{ mg} = ? \text{ Mg}$
(b) $0.02445 \text{ cm}^3 = ? \text{ m}^3$
(c) $3.22 \text{ cm} = ? \text{ pm}$
(d) $81.4°C = ? °F$
(e) $9561 \text{ g} = ? \text{ cg}$
(f) $1.63 \text{ g/mL} = ? \text{ kg/dm}^3$
(g) $-248°C = ? \text{ K}$
(h) $451 \text{ nL} = ? \text{ m}^3$

3.82 One pennyweight equals exactly 24 grains, and one grain equals 15.432 grams. (a) How many grams are there in one pennyweight? (b) How many pennyweights are there in 3.699 kg? (c) How many milligrams are there in 9.872 grains?

3.83 A gill is a unit of volume equal to 7.219 cubic inches. (a) What is the volume of a gill in cubic centimeters? (b) The density of xenon is 5.897 kg/m³. What is the mass of 25 gills of xenon?

3.84 The hectare is a unit of area equal to exactly 10,000 square meters. (a) How many square centimeters are there in 1.00 hectare? (b) How many hectares are there in 1.00 km²? (c) How many square miles are there in 1.00 hectare? (One mile equals 5280 feet.)

3.85 (a) One nautical mile (nmi) is equivalent to 6076.1 feet. If a ship travels at 23.0 mi/hr, how many kilometers will the ship travel in 1 day? (b) One statute mile is equivalent to exactly 5280 feet. How fast in statute miles per hour would the same ship have to travel to traverse the distance obtained in part a?

3.86 Commercial airplanes regularly travel in excess of 555 mi/hr. Convert this speed to: (a) kilometers per hour, (b) meters per second, (c) millimeters per nanosecond.

3.87 A cylinder is measured and is found to weigh 124.54 g. Its height is 3.22 cm, and its circular diameter is 1.88 cm. The formula for the volume of a cylinder is $V = \pi r^2 h$. Calculate the density of the cylinder.

3.88 What volume of uranium has the same mass as 93.4 cm³ of mercury? (The densities of uranium and mercury are found in Table 3.2.)

3.89 What size cube—length of each side—can be formed from 961 g of chromium metal? The density of chromium is 7.20 g/cm³. (Hint An equation to find the volume of a cube is $V_{cube} = l^3$, in which l is the length of each side.)

3.90 Automakers express engine displacement in liters. What is the displacement of a 2.0-L engine in (a) cubic inches (b) cubic meters?

3.91 The densities of ethanol and water at 20°C are 0.7894 g/cm³ and 0.9982 g/cm³, respectively. (a) Calculate the density of an ethanol-water mixture that contains 31.24 g of ethanol and 43.11 g of water. (b) Calculate the density of an ethanol-water mixture that contains 472.1 cm³ of ethanol and 93.77 cm³ of water.

3.92 (a) What Fahrenheit temperature is numerically equal to twice the Celsius temperature? (b) What Celsius temperature is numerically equal to twice the Fahrenheit temperature?

3.93 A 32.326-g container is completely filled with water. The mass of the container with the water is found to be 57.205 g. The water is removed, and the container is filled with an unknown liquid. The mass of the container with the unknown liquid in it is 55.223 g. Assume the density of water is 1.000 g/mL and calculate the density of the unknown liquid.

3.94 A small particle is found to have a volume of 8.22 μm³ and a density of 2.39 g/cm³. How many particles with the same volume and density are contained in a 1.33-kg sample?

3.95 The density of mercury is 13.546 g/cm³ at 20°C and is 13.521 g/cm³ at 30°C. What change in volume, occurs when 1.000 g of mercury is heated from 20°C to 30°C, assuming that none of the mercury evaporates?

3.96   The density of thorium, Th, is 11.71 g/cm³. If a sphere of pure Th has a diameter of 4.551 cm, what is the mass of the sphere?

Chapter 3 Pretest Assignment

1.   Complete each of the following statements with the correct word, number, or phase.

   a. _____ is the ratio of mass to volume for an object.
   b. _____ is the number of measured digit plus one estimate.
   c. _____ is the prefix that means 10^{-6} ×.
   d. _____ is the SI unit for temperature.
   e. _____ is the number of significant figures indicated by the following
   measurement

                                 0.0150 g

2. List the base units in the SI system and what they measure.

3. Convert 27.90 in. to nm.

4. Convert –55.1°F to K.

5. Calculate the mass of air that has the same volume as 125 g Fe.

6. Convert 75 mm^3 to pm^3.

7. Explain the difference between random and systematic errors.

8. Convert 25.0 lb to pg.

CHAPTER 4

Matter and Energy

4.1 PROPERTIES OF MATTER

As we discussed in Chap. 3, matter is anything that has mass and occupies space. One of the principal concerns of chemists is to study the composition and structure of matter. **Composition** refers to the identity and quantity of the components (ingredients) of matter. **Structure** refers to the physical arrangement of the components within matter. Collectively, the composition and structure determine the properties, or characteristic traits, of matter.

Each type of matter has its own unique set of properties. Thus, different types of matter are distinguished by their properties, just as people are distinguished by their physical appearance and personality traits. Properties are classified as either physical or chemical. We will begin our study of matter by discussing these two general groups of properties.

WWWolfe 1
(See WWWolfe section at the end of the chapter.)

Physical Properties and Changes

A **physical property** is a characteristic of an individual substance that can be determined without changing the composition of that substance. A physical property that we have already discussed is density. Density is the mass of a unit volume. When density is measured, it is only necessary to find the mass and volume of a sample of the substance—no change in composition occurs when making this measurement.

Examples of physical properties are color, hardness, electrical conductivity, heat conductivity, physical state, melting point, boiling point, and tensile strength. Physical properties are measured by observing what happens when matter interacts with heat, light, electricity, and other forms of energy, or when matter is subjected to various stresses and forces.

A substance has a unique set of physical properties that distinguishes it from all other substances. If two substances

> Tensile strength is the resistance to pulling, and measured by finding the breaking stress.

have the same set of physical properties, the most plausible conclusion is they are the same substance with the same composition and structure.

To illustrate, let's investigate the physical properties of pure gold. Gold is a bright-yellow metal that melts at 1063°C and boils at 2808°C. Its density is 19.3 g/cm^3, which is a very high density for a metal. On a hardness scale of 1 to 10, gold has a value of 2.8, which means it is soft. It shares the common physical property of metals called malleability, i.e., the ability of a substance to be hammered into different shapes or thin foils (called leaf). Gold leaf, 1.3×10^{-5} cm thick, is used in expensive decorations. Gold is one of the best conductors of electricity and is an excellent heat conductor. Table 4.1 lists the physical properties of other selected substances.

TABLE 4.1 PHYSICAL PROPERTIES OF SELECTED SUBSTANCES

Substance	Color	Physical state (25°C)	Density	Melting point, °C
Aluminum, Al	Grayish	Solid	2.70 g/cm^3	660
Bromine, Br_2	Red brown	Gas	3.10 g/dm^3	−7.3
Chlorine, Cl_2	Pale green	Gas	2.98 g/dm^3	−101
Copper, Cu	Red brown	Solid	8.92 g/cm^3	1085
Helium, He	Colorless	Gas	0.178 g/dm^3	−
Water, H_2O	Colorless	Liquid	1.00 g/cm^3	0.00

When the physical properties of a substance are altered but the composition remains the same, we say that a **physical change** has occurred. No new substance forms when a physical change takes place. Examples of physical changes are changes in state, density, shape, magnetic properties, and conductivity. After a physical change, the starting substance is still present but in a modified state (Fig. 4.1). For example, after a rock is crushed, it still has the same composition; only the particle size has changed. When ice melts, it changes from the solid state to the liquid state. When iron is magnetized, it is still iron.

> The composition of a substance remains the same when a physical change occurs.

Chemical Properties and Changes

A **chemical property** describes how the composition of a substance changes or does not change when the substance interacts with other substances or energy forms. Terms used to describe some chemical properties are "reactive," "inert," "unstable" and "combustible." Chemical properties are observed when a substance changes composition. Paper burns in air, iron rusts, silver tarnishes, TNT explodes—these are all illustrations of chemical properties. In each case a new substance is formed, and a **chemical change** occurs.

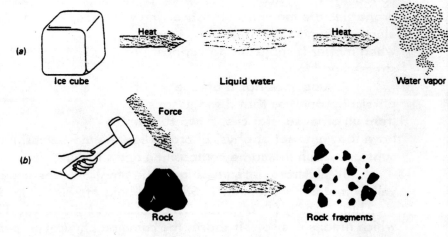

Figure 4.1 (a) After undergoing a physical change, the substance's composition remains the same. Addition of heat to ice changes it to liquid water. Addition of heat to liquid water changes it to water vapor. (b) Only the particle size of the rock changes after being broken into pieces. A change in shape is a physical change.

Chemical changes or chemical reactions are the result of the chemical properties of matter. After a chemical change, the composition of the substance that underwent the change is no longer the same. For each chemical change, we can write a chemical equation that shows what the original substance or substances and those that result from the change. The starting materials, called **reactants**, undergo a chemical change and produce the **products.**

Reactants → products

The arrow that separates the reactants from the products is a symbol meaning "yield" or "produce." In chemical reactions, the reactants combine to yield the products. If only one reactant is present initially, we usually say the reactant "decomposes" or "rearranges" to yield the products.

To monitor chemical changes, we first observe the physical properties of the reactants, and then consider the physical properties of the products. If a chemical change has truly taken place, some or all of the physical properties of the products will be different from those of the reactants.

Examples of everyday chemical changes include the rusting of iron, the cooking of foods, the ignition of gasoline, the explosion of dynamite, and the burning of wood. Each of these examples involves a complex reaction, requiring elaborate equations to explain what happens to the reactants. Let's consider a less complex chemical change, the decomposition, or breakdown, of water using electricity.

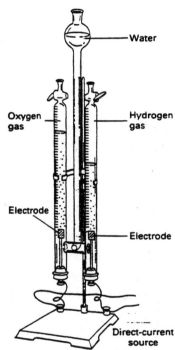

When an electric current passes through water (Fig. 4.2), the water changes to new substances, hydrogen and oxygen. This process is known as the electrolysis of water. A word equation for the decomposition of water reads as follows:

Liquid water → hydrogen gas + oxygen gas

This equation states: "Liquid water decomposes to yield hydrogen and oxygen both of which are gases." Of course, this only occurs when an electric current passes through the water. How do we know that a chemical change rather than a physical change has taken place? First we must consider the physical properties of water: (1) A liquid; (2) normal boiling point is 100°C; (3) melting point is 0°C; (4) flows easily; (5) has a high specific heat; (6) is a poor heat conductor; (7) density equals 1 g/cm^3. These hardly resemble the physical properties of the products, hydrogen and oxygen. Both are gases with boiling and melting points well below 0°C, and their densities are quite small compared with the density of water.

Figure 4.2 Electrolysis occurs when water is decomposed by a direct electric current. During electrolysis, water is changed chemically to hydrogen gas and oxygen gas.

Example Problem 4.1 shows how to predict whether a property of matter is classified as physical or chemical. Study each of the examples.

Example Problem 4.1

For each of the following, determine if a chemical or physical property is described. (a) Heating limestone produces carbon dioxide and calcium oxide. (b) Ice floats on water. (c) Copper can be drawn into thin wires. (d) Milk sours if not refrigerated.

Solution

(a) "Heating limestone produces carbon dioxide and calcium oxide" describes a chemical property of limestone because two new substances form after heating. If a physical change had occurred, limestone would have been present after heating.

(b) "Ice floats on water" describes a physical property. Floating involves no change in physical properties, and thus immediately eliminates the possibility of a chemical change. Ice floats on water because ice has a lower density than water. Density is a physical property. A substance floats on the surface of a fluid of higher density (assuming it does not mix with the fluid).

(c) "Copper can be drawn into thin wires" describes a physical property. Copper's shape is changed when it is drawn into wires; its composition does not change.

(d) "Milk sours" describes a chemical property. A change in the taste of the milk indicates that one or more new substances are present in the sour milk that were not present in the fresh milk. The increase in the concentration of acid produced by microorganisms causes milk to sour.

Exercise

Classify the following as a physical or chemical property.

The antiseptic solution hydrogen peroxide releases bubbles of oxygen gas when it contacts a cut or burn. (Chemical property)

When classifying properties as physical or chemical, ask yourself: Has the composition changed? Can an equation be written that shows the reactants and products? If the answer is "yes" to both questions, the property being described is chemical. Solving problems and answering questions by eliminating possibilities is an effective technique to use. Sort through all given information and discard what you can.

WWWolfe 2
(See WWWolfe
section at the end of
the chapter.)

Example Problem 4.2 shows you how to classify chemical and physical changes. ❖

Example Problem 4.2

For each of the following, determine if a physical or chemical property is described. (a) Liquid water evaporates to produce water vapor. (b) Fermenting grapes produce ethanol. (c) A candle burns.

Solution

(a) "Liquid water evaporates to produce water vapor" describes a physical change. When water evaporates, the composition remains constant. Water is present in two different states; thus, a physical change has occurred.

(b) "Fermenting grapes" is an example of a chemical change. Fermentation is the process in which yeast is added to crushed fruits or grains to produce ethanol, the drinking variety. Ethanol, a new substance, is formed by fermentation, showing that a chemical change has taken place.

(c) "A candle burns" illustrates a chemical change. Whenever a substance is burned, the initial substance, a candle in this example, is changed to new substances with new compositions; accordingly, the change is chemical.

Exercise

Classify the following as either a chemical or physical property. (a) Alcohol dissolves in water, (b) A gas is released when vinegar and baking soda mix. ((a) physical property, (b) chemical property)

REVIEW EXERCISE

4.1 For each of the following, determine if a chemical or physical property is described.

(a) Sulfur is bright yellow.
(b) Silicon is a hard substance.
(c) At low temperatures mercury exists in the solid state.
(d) Cadmium is corroded by acids.
(e) Hydrogen explodes when ignited in the air.

4.2 For each of the following, determine if a chemical or physical change is described.

(a) Paper ignites when placed in a flame.
(b) Sand and water are separated when passed through a filter.
(c) Charcoal burns, leaving ashes.
(d) Dry ice forms a vapor "cloud" upon heating.
(e) Sugar dissolves in water.

4.1 Physical: (a), (b), (c); chemical: (d), (e), 4.2 Physical: (b), (d), (e); chemical: (a), (c).

4.2 STATES OF MATTER

All matter on earth exists in three physical states: **solid, liquid, and gaseous.** Various physical properties distinguish the three states of matter. The properties most often considered are shape, volume, average density, structure, viscosity, and compressibility. Shape, volume, and density have been discussed previously; the last two properties require some explanation.

> A fourth state of matter known as the plasma state also exists. Only matter at temperatures that exceed 100 million degrees is found in the plasma state.

Viscosity is a measure of the resistance to flow. Substances with high viscosities do not flow readily, whereas substances with low viscosities flow more readily. If we are told that water is more fluid than motor oil, we know that the viscosity of water is less than that of motor oil. **Compressibility** is the measure of the decrease in volume of a substance with applied pressure. A substance is deemed compressible if a force exerted on its surface (a pressure) results in a compacting of the substance.

Let's consider each physical state individually, starting with the solid state and proceeding to the liquid and gaseous states. The physical state of a substance depends on its temperature and pressure. Unless otherwise noted, room conditions of 25°C (298 K) and normal atmospheric pressure are assumed. Atmospheric pressure is measured in atmospheres, the atmosphere being a unit of gas pressure. Normal atmospheric pressure is equivalent to one atmosphere, 1 atm.

Solids

Solids have fixed shapes that are independent of their container. The volume of a solid is also fixed, and does not change when a pressure is exerted. Solids are almost completely incompressible. Those that seem compressible, such as foams or corrugated paper, actually are solids that have holes, or empty regions, throughout their volume. When these are "compressed," the solid structure fills into the empty regions: the solid itself is not compressed.

| Pressure results when a force is exerted on an area. One of the most common units of pressure is the atmosphere. |

Of the three states of matter, solids have the highest average density. Densities greater than 1 g/cm^3 are the norm for solids. This is not true for most liquids and gases. A high average density reflects the fact that the particles within solids are usually packed closer than those in liquids or gases. The tightly packed particles of solids are also highly organized (Fig. 4.3). The regular patterns of particles found in solids are not detected in either liquids or gases.

Solids have practically no ability to flow because the particles that compose a solid are very tightly bonded. Stated differently: Solids have very high viscosities.

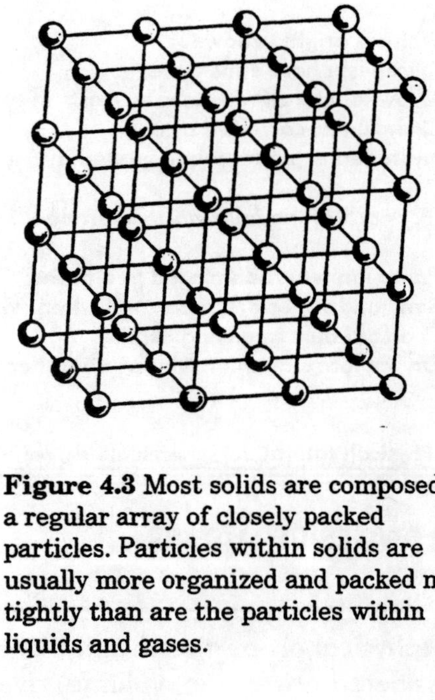

Figure 4.3 Most solids are composed of a regular array of closely packed particles. Particles within solids are usually more organized and packed more tightly than are the particles within liquids and gases.

Liquids

Liquids are different from solids in many respects, but the two share some characteristics. Like solids, liquids are essentially incompressible; pressure exerted on liquids generally produces little, if any, change in their volumes. When placed in a container, liquids assume the shape of the container to the level they fill (Fig. 4.4).

As previously mentioned, the average density of liquids is less than that of solids but greater than that of gases. Liquid particles are not bonded as strongly as those in solids, and they are less orderly— more randomly distributed. Both factors tend to increase the average volume of liquids relative to that of solids. Thus, for equal masses of an average solid and liquid, the volume of the liquid is usually larger than that of the solid, which results in a lower density.

Viscosities of liquids vary over a broad range. Liquids have much lower viscosities than solids; i.e., they are significantly more fluid than solids. However, the viscosities of liquids are greater than those of gases. The gaseous state is the most fluid state of matter.

Figure 4.4 A liquid completely fills and takes the shape of the bottom of its container.

Gases

Gases bear little resemblance to the more-condensed states of matter, solids and liquids. To a degree, the properties of gases are the opposite of those of solids. Gases completely fill the volume of their containers, are compressible (Fig. 4.5), have a completely disorganized structure, possess the lowest average density of the three states, and have the lowest viscosities. Table 4.2 summarizes the properties of the physical states, and Table 4.3 lists examples of common solids, liquids, and gases.

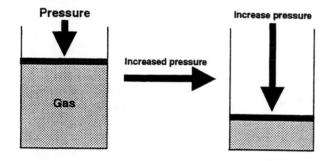

Figure 4.5 Gases are compressible. If he external pressure increases on a gas sample, its volume decreases. Liquids find solids are almost incompressible.

TABLE 4.2 PROPERTIES OF THE THREE PHYSICAL STATES

Property	Solid	Liquid	Gas
Shape	Constant	Variable	Variable
Volume	Constant	Constant	Variable
Density	Highest	Moderately high	Lowest
Structure	Organized	Semiorganized	Random
Viscosity	Highest	High to low	Lowest
Compressibility	Incompressible	Incompressible	Compressible
Particles	Closely packed	Less closely packed	Widely separated

TABLE 4.3 EXAMPLES OF SOLIDS, LIQUIDS, AND GASES (25°C, 1 atm)

Solids	Liquids	Gases
Diamond (Carbon)	Alcohol (C_2H_5OH)	Carbon dioxide (CO_2)
Gold (Au)	Ether ((C_2H_5)$_2$O)	Helium (He)
Ice (solid water)	Kerosene (mixture)	Methane (CH_4)
Iron (Fe)	Mercury (Hg)	Neon (Ne)
Salt (NaCl)	Oils	Nitrogen (N_2)
Sugar ($C_{12}H_{22}O_{11}$)	Water (H_2O)	Water vapor (H_2O)

Changes of State

Matter can change from one physical state to another. For example, when heated, solids change to liquids. The characteristic temperature at which a particular solid changes to a liquid is its **melting point.** At the melting point, the solid and liquid states of the substance coexist. Liquids, in turn, change to solids as they are cooled. The temperature at which a liquid becomes a solid is called the **freezing point.** Freezing and melting occur at the same temperature. In one case, the solid changes into a liquid—it melts. Moving in the other direction, a liquid changes into a solid—it freezes.

$$\text{Solid} \quad \underset{\text{freezing}}{\overset{\text{melting}}{\rightleftharpoons}} \quad \text{liquid}$$

For example, water freezes or melts at 0.0°C. Table 4.4 lists the melting (freezing) points of some common substances.

> The solid and liquid states are in equilibrium at the melting point

TABLE 4.4 NORMAL MELTING AND BOILING POINTS COMMON SUBSTANCES

Substance	Melting point, °C	Boiling point, °C
Aluminum, Al	660	2450
Carbon dioxide, CO_2	–56.2	–78.4
Helium, He	–269.7	–268.9
Hydrogen, H_2	–259.2	–252.7
Iron, Fe	1536	3000
Mercury, Hg	–38.4	357
Oxygen, O_2	–218.8	–183
Sodium, Na	97.8	892
Water, H_2O	0.0	100

Liquids, when heated, change to their vapors. A **vapor** is the gaseous phase of a substance. The transition temperature for this change is termed the **boiling point.** At the boiling point the liquid and vapor states coexist. When a substance boils, vapor bubbles can be seen throughout the liquid phase. The change in the opposite direction, from vapor to liquid, is **condensation.**

$$\text{Liquid} \underset{\text{condensation}}{\overset{\text{boiling}}{\rightleftarrows}} \text{vap}$$

Again, refer to Table 4.4 for examples of boiling points of common substances. A pressure of 1 atm is specified for the boiling points listed in the table because pressure significantly affects the boiling points of liquids. We will discuss the effect of pressure on boiling points in Chap. 13. Many solids change directly to their vapors without going through the liquid state. This state change is called sublimation. At the temperature and pressure at which a substance sublimes, the solid and vapor states coexist.

$$\text{Solid} \overset{\text{sublimation}}{\rightleftarrows} \text{vap}$$

A good example of a solid that sublimes is "dry ice," or solid carbon dioxide. At –78°C (195 K), solid carbon dioxide and gaseous carbon dioxide coexist.

> The liquid and vapor states are in equilibrium at the boiling point. A solid that changes to a vapor is said to sublime

REVIEW EXERCISES

4.3 (a) What is viscosity?

(b) What trend exists in viscosities when considering the solid, liquid, and gaseous states?

4.4 What properties distinguish an average solid from an average liquid? Give specific examples.

4.5 (a) What physical state has the most unorganized structure? (b) What accounts for the unorganized structure?

4.6 What physical states coexist at the following transition points?

(a) melting point
(b) subliming point
(c) freezing point
(d) boiling point

4.5 (a) gas; (b) weak forces between particles, 4.6 (a) solid, liquid; (b) solid, vapor; (c) solid, liquid; (d) liquid, vapor

4.3 CLASSIFICATION OF MATTER

Matter exists in many different forms throughout the earth, and every year thousands of new types of matter are synthesized. When dealing with such a large variety of substances, it is best to divide this enormous group into smaller categories of similar types of matter.

Matter may be grouped into two major classes: **pure substances** and **mixtures**. We will discuss pure substances before we consider the mixtures, which are more complex. Figure 4.6 shows a complete classification of matter.

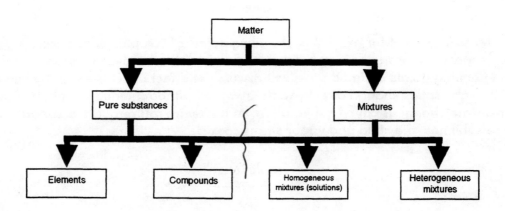

Figure 4.6 All forms of matter may be subdivided into two classes: pure substances and mixtures. Two classes of pure substances exist: elements and compounds. Mixtures are combinations of pure substances. Two classes of mixtures exist: homogeneous mixtures (solutions) and heterogeneous mixtures.

Pure Substances

A pure substance, substance for short, must meet the following three criteria:

1. It has the same composition throughout the sample.
2. Its components are inseparable using physical methods.
3. Changes of state occur at a constant temperature.

Analysis of a pure substance reveals the same composition throughout the sample. All parts of a pure substance contain the same percent of each component. For example, water is a pure substance—all water samples are composed of 11% hydrogen and 89% oxygen by mass. If some other percents are found for hydrogen and oxygen, then the substance is impure water or it is not water at all.

The components of pure substances cannot be separated by physical methods. If the components of pure substances can be separated (not all are), chemical means are required. For example, one way of separating water into its component elements is to pass an electric current through it. This results in the production of hydrogen gas and

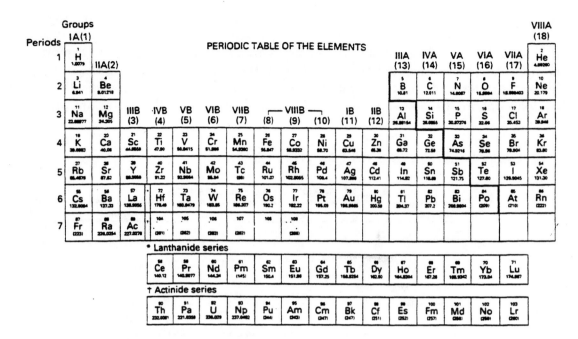

Figure 4.7 All of the elements are listed on the periodic table. Each element is a member of a chemical group, a vertical column of elements, and a period, a horizontal row of elements. In addition, two numbers are found next to each symbol.

oxygen gas. Physical methods, such as filtering or heating at normal temperatures, have no effect on water with respect to separating it into its components. Water passes through filters, and heat changes liquid water to water vapor.

All pure substances undergo state changes at constant temperatures. In contrast, state changes of mixtures occur over broader temperature ranges. Chemists use this property to assess the purity of a substance; a sharper melting point (smaller observable temperature range) indicates a higher level of purity. A broad range in the melting temperature is characteristic of an impure sample, a mixture.

Pure substances may be subdivided into two groups: elements and compounds (Fig. 4.6). Elements are pure substances that cannot be decomposed by chemical changes. Compounds are pure substances that may be chemically decomposed to elements.

Elements
Elements are the basic units of matter. All of the other types of matter contain elements. Today, more than 110 different elements have been identified. Whenever the number of elements is stated, it is necessary to introduce some doubt. New elements are occasionally discovered, and they are added to the list. About 92 elements occur in nature, and the remaining are synthetic. At 25°C, 97 elements are solids, 2 are liquids, and 11 are gases.

All of the known elements are listed, using their symbols, in the **periodic table**, which is probably the most important table in chemistry (Fig. 4.7. Each element is located in a horizontal row called a **period,** and in a vertical column called a **group** (sometimes called a *family*). Each period is numbered consecutively from 1 to 7; each group of elements is assigned either a Roman numeral and a letter or a number from 1 to 18. A periodic table and an alphabetical listing of the elements are found at the end of the textbook.

Chemists use symbols to represent elements. The use of symbols to represent elements dates back to the ancient Greeks, who originally suggested that matter was composed of elements. Table 4.5 lists four of the ancient Greek symbols, those for the elements sulfur, gold, copper, and lead. In addition, the symbols used by the alchemists and by John Dalton, the developer of the first scientific theory of the atom, are given in this table.

TABLE 4.5 ANCIENT SYMBOLS FOR THE ELEMENTS

TABLE 4.5   ANCIENT SYMBOLS FOR THE ELEMENTS

Source	Sulfur	Gold	Copper	Lead
Ancient Greeks	ω	♂	♀	♄
Alchemists	🜍	☉	♀	♄
John Dalton (1808)	⊕	Ⓖ	Ⓒ	Ⓛ
Modern	S	Au	Cu	Pb

Modern symbols are usually derived from the first one or two letters of the name of the element. Twelve of the elements have one-letter symbols that correspond to the first letter of the element's name. They are hydrogen, H; boron, B; carbon, C; nitrogen, N; oxygen, O; fluorine, F; phosphorus, P; sulfur, S; vanadium, V; yttrium, Y; iodine, I; and uranium, U.

> Ytterby, a town in Sweden, has four elements named after it: yttrium, Y; terbium, Tb; terbium, Er; ytterbium, Yb.

Two other elements are designated by one-letter symbols, but these symbols are not the first letter of the elements' English names. K is the symbol for the element potassium. Why K? K is the first letter of the old Latin name for potassium, *kalium,* which means ashes. It is convenient to use K instead of P (phosphorus) or Po (polonium) because other elements have these symbols. Similarly, the symbol for tungsten, W, is derived from its old name, "wolfram." Today, some scientists use this old name and no longer refer to W as tungsten.

Most of the remaining elements are assigned two-letter symbols. The first letter is always an uppercase letter, and the second is a lowercase letter. The symbol for cobalt is Co, not CO. CO is not a symbol; it is the formula of a compound called carbon monoxide. Some symbols are made up of the first two letters of the English name, others are two letters of an old name, and the remainder combine the first letter with some other letter in the name.

Origins of the modern names of elements are interesting. Some derived names from those of great scientists, while some are named for mythological gods and astronomical bodies. Table 4.6 lists the origins of selected elements' names.

TABLE 4.6 ORIGINS OF THE NAMES OF SELECTED ELEMENTS

Symbol and name	Origin
Names derived from a location	
Am, amercium	America
Bk, berkelium	Berkeley, California
Cf, californium	California
Eu, europrium	Europe
Fr, francium	France
Ge, germanium	Germany
Po, polonium	Poland
Sr, strontium	Strontia, Scotland
Names derived from the name of a scientist	
Cm, curium	Marie and Pierre Curie
Es, einsteinium	Albert Einstein
Fm, fermium	Enrico Fermi
Lr, lawrencium	Ernest O. Lawrence
Md, mendelevium	Dmitri Mendeleev
No, nobelium	Alfred Nobel
Names derived from a god or astronomical body	
He, helium	Greek, *helios*, "sun"
Nb, niobium	Niobe, daughter of Tantalus
Np, neptunium	Neptune
Pd, palladium	an asteroid called Pallas
Pu, plutonium	Pluto
Se, selenium	Greek, *Selene*, "moon"
Th, thorium	Thor
U, uranium	Uranus

Atoms are the smallest particles that retain the chemical properties of elements. Atoms are extremely small; 1 g of carbon, C, contains 5×10^{22} C atoms. Placed end to end, approximately 2×10^8 atoms of C are needed to span an inch. Each element is composed of similar atoms. Both the chemical and physical properties of an element are directly related to the composition and properties of its atoms. In Chap. 5 we will investigate this central topic in chemistry.

WWWolfe 3
(See WWWolfe
section at the end of
the chapter.)

Table 4.7 lists the abundances, in percent by mass, of the elements found in the earth's crust and in the entire earth. The crust of the earth is the thin outer layer that surrounds the mantle and core of the earth. Outside the crust is the atmosphere. In the earth's crust, O and Si are the most abundant elements, and they comprise 74.3% of the mass of the crust. Al, Fe, Ca, Na, K, and Mg are the next most abundant elements. Together these six elements compose 24.2% of the mass of the earth's crust. If the whole earth is considered, a different distribution of elements is found. Iron is the most abundant element on earth because it makes up the core of the earth. Iron is followed by O, Si, and Mg; these elements account for 92.0% of the mass of the earth.

TABLE 4.7 ABUNDANCE OF ELEMENTS IN THE EARTH'S CRUST AND THE WHOLE EARTH

Earth's crust		Whole earth	
Element	Abundance, % by mass	Element	Abundance, % by mass
O	46.6	Fe	34.6
Si	27.7	O	29.5
Al	8.1	Si	15.2
Fe	5.0	Mg	12.7
Ca	3.6	S	1.9
Na	2.8	Ni	1.6
K	2.6	Ca	1.1
Mg	2.1	Al	1.1
Ti	0.44	Na	0.57
H	0.14	Cr	0.26
P	0.11	Mn	0.22
Mn	0.095	Co	0.13
F	0.063	P	0.10

REVIEW EXERCISES

4.7 What are the three criteria used to identify pure substances?

4.8 (a) What are the two classes of pure substances? (b) Give an example of each.

4.9 Write the names of each of the following elements: (a) B, (b) Be, (c) Ba, (d) Br, (e) Bi.

4.10 Write the symbols and names for 10 elements whose names begin with C.

4.11 List five elements in which the first letter of the symbol is different from the first letter of the name.

Compounds

Compounds make up the other class of pure substances. They are more complex than elements. Elements undergo chemical reactions to form compounds; thus, **compounds** are chemical combinations of elements. Consequently, compounds can only be separated into their component elements by chemical means. The smallest subdivision of a compound is a **molecule,** which is a chemical combination of atoms.

Formulas are used to represent compounds. Each formula shows the specific composition of a compound. Most people are familiar with the chemical formula of water, H_2O. What information is conveyed by the formula of water? It indicates that all water is composed of two parts hydrogen and one part oxygen. If water is decomposed by electrolysis, two volumes of hydrogen are formed for each volume of oxygen.

$$Water \rightarrow 2 \text{ hydrogen} + 1 \text{ oxygen}$$

Additionally, the formula of a compound gives the ratio of the different types of atoms that make up one molecule of that compound. For example, water molecules are particles that contain two atoms of hydrogen and one atom of oxygen.

In each chemical formula the symbol of each atom is listed with a subscript—a number written to the right of and below the symbol—which indicates the total number of that type of atom in the molecule. If only one atom of a given element is found in the molecule, the subscript is not written; it is understood to be 1. In the formula of the water molecule, H_2O, the subscript 2 is placed next to hydrogen, but no subscript is written next to oxygen because there is only one oxygen atom per molecule. As an additional example, let's consider carbon dioxide, CO_2.

$$CO_2$$
One carbon atom ⟋   ⟍ Two oxygen atoms

A CO_2 molecule contains one carbon atom and two oxygen atoms. When reading the formula, we say "see-oh-two."

Other examples of compounds are NaCl, sodium chloride; NH_3, ammonia; CH_4, methane; and $C_{12}H_{22}O_{11}$, sucrose. NaCl is common table salt. All living systems maintain a balance between the dissolved NaCl and fluids within their cells. An excess amount of NaCl in your diet may lead to problems such as hypertension. NH_3, ammonia, is an ingredient of many common household cleaners. Ammonia is a fertilizer and is used to synthesize many important chemicals. CH_4, methane, is the major component of natural gas, which is an important fuel. Sucrose, $C_{12}H_{22}O_{11}$, also known as table sugar, is the sweetening agent used by most people in the world.

In more complex formulas, parentheses are used to group repeating units. For example, the formula of calcium phosphate is $Ca_3(PO_4)_2$. Calcium phosphate contains two PO_4 (phosphate, which is actually PO_4^{3-}) groups. Instead of writing PO_4 twice, we enclose it in parentheses and write 2 as a subscript to the right. The formula for calcium phosphate indicates that three calcium atoms, two phosphorus atoms, and eight oxygen atoms make up one molecule of calcium phosphate.

> Calcium phosphate is a white powder that melts at 1730°C.

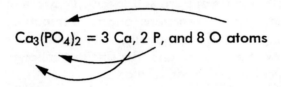

$$Ca_3(PO_4)_2 = 3 \text{ Ca, 2 P, and 8 O atoms}$$

REVIEW EXERCISES

4.12 What information can be obtained from the formula of a compound?

4.13 For each of the following, write the name of each atom and tell how many atoms are in the formula:

(a) KBr
(b) BeF_2
(c) NiO
(d) $Fe(OH)_3$
(e) PCl_3
(f) $Ba(NO_3)_2$
(g) $RbMnO_4$
(h) $(NH_4)_2C_2O_4$
(i) $Ca(H_2PO_4)_2$

4.13   (a) Potassium 1, bromine 1; (b) beryllium 1, fluorine 2; (c) nickel 1, oxygen 1; (d) iron 1, oxygen 3, hydrogen 3; (e) phosphorus 1, chlorine 3; (f) barium 1, nitrogen 2, oxygen 6; (g) rubidium 1, manganese 1, oxygen 4; (h) nitrogen 2, hydrogen 8, carbon 2, oxygen 4; (i) calcium 1, hydrogen 4, phosphorus 2, oxygen 8.

Mixtures

Mixtures make up the second major division of matter. They are more complex than pure substances because mixtures are composed of two or more pure substances that are physically associated. Three criteria are used to classify a mixture:

1. Its composition is variable.
2. Its components may be separated by physical methods.
3. Changes of state occur over a range of temperatures.

Many possibilities exist when a mixture is prepared. Two substances can be mixed in virtually any proportion. For example, a mixture of sugar and water might contain 1 g of sugar in 100 mL of water, or 15 g of sugar in 80 mL of water, or many other possible combinations.

Unlike pure substances, mixtures may be separated into their components by physical methods. For example, a mixture of sugar and water is separated by evaporating the water, leaving the sugar behind. A mixture of iron and aluminum can be separated with a magnet. Iron is attracted to the magnet, leaving the aluminum behind (Fig. 4.8).

When a mixture undergoes a change of state, the observed temperature at which the change takes place is not constant. Usually, a broad range of temperatures is observed from the time when the mixture begins to change state until it is entirely in the new state. Because mixtures are composed of two or more pure substances, each component changes state at a different temperature; this is what produces the wide range.

Milk, gasoline, asphalt, ocean water, granite, and air are some examples of mixtures. The components of milk include such compounds as water, proteins, fats, and vitamins. Gasoline is a mixture of organic

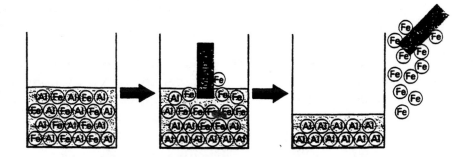

Figure 4.8 Mixtures are separated by physical methods. A mixture of iron and aluminum is separated by placing a magnet into the mixture. Aluminum is not attracted by a magnet, but iron is strongly attracted.

compounds called hydrocarbons because they are chiefly carbon-hydrogen compounds. Asphalt contains tarry substances blended with sand, gravel, glass, and stones. Ocean water is primarily water with a large number of dissolved substances, which include minerals, salts, and gases. Granite is a rock composed of quartz, feldspar, and mica—three common minerals. Finally, air is a mixture of gases, mainly nitrogen and oxygen, with smaller amounts of carbon dioxide, water vapor, argon, and others.

Homogeneous and Heterogeneous Mixtures

Mixtures are divided into two classes, homogeneous mixtures and heterogeneous mixtures. "Homogeneous" is a word derived from the Greek words *homos*, which means "the same" or "equal," and *genus*, which means "kind" or "structure." "Hetero" is a prefix that means "different."

A **heterogeneous mixture** is one that exhibits more than one phase. A phase is an observable region of matter with a composition different from the surrounding regions. The phases can be distinguished from each other by their properties. For example, when sand is added to water, the sand does not dissolve; it just falls to the bottom of the water. When observing sand and water, you see the solid sand phase and the liquid water phase. Oil and water, salt and sand, and granite are all examples of heterogeneous mixtures.

Homogeneous mixtures are also called **solutions.** Only one phase is found in homogeneous mixtures. For example, let's consider a sugar water solution. It is prepared by mixing solid sugar and liquid water. After the sugar dissolves, a homogeneous mixture results. When looking at sugar water, you cannot tell whether it is pure water or a solution.

Other examples of solutions are alcohol and water, air, and most alloys. Ethanol (grain alcohol) and water is a popular beverage throughout the world. The alcohol content of drinks can range from a few percent to as high as 60% alcohol by volume. Air is a gaseous solution. All gaseous mixtures exhibit only one phase; therefore, they are classified as solutions. Most alloys are solutions of metals. Examples of common alloys include sterling silver, which is 92.5% Ag (silver) and 7.5% Cu (copper), and brass, which is 67% Cu (copper) and 33% Zn (zinc).

Mixtures, whether homogeneous or heterogeneous, may be separated into their components by physical methods. A solution of salt and water can be separated by heating, for example. During heating, water changes to a vapor, which is then condensed, leaving the salt behind. This is the basis of the process called **distillation.** Figure 4.9 illustrates a laboratory distillation setup. After crude oil is pumped out of the ground, it is separated into its components by distillation.

Filtration is a method used to separate some heterogeneous mixtures. Such mixtures are poured into a funnel that contains a filter paper, which is paper containing small, uniform openings or pores. The pores block large particles and allow small particles to pass through. Sand and water are separated by pouring the mixture into a filter. The small water molecules easily pass through the filter paper, but the larger particles of sand are blocked by the filter paper (Fig. 4.10).

Wine is filtered to remove particulate matter before it is bottled.

Example Problem 4.3 shows how another simple mixture can be separated.❖

Example Problem 4.3
How can a mixture of sand and salt be separated?

Solution
A combination of sand and salt is a heterogeneous mixture. One contrasting property, the different abilities of the two substances to dissolve in water, provides for a convenient method of separation. Salt dissolves in water, whereas sand does not. Thus, if water is added to the mixture, the salt dissolves, leaving the sand undissolved. The salt water solution that results is filtered. Sand is trapped by the filter paper, while the salt water passes through. To recover the salt, the water is evaporated. In summary:

1. Add water to dissolve salt. The sand is unaffected.
2. Filter the resulting salt water solution from the sand.
3. Evaporate water to recover the salt.

Exercise
How can a mixture of motor oil and water be separated? (Pour off, decant, the liquid that makes up the top layer, or draw off this layer using suction.)

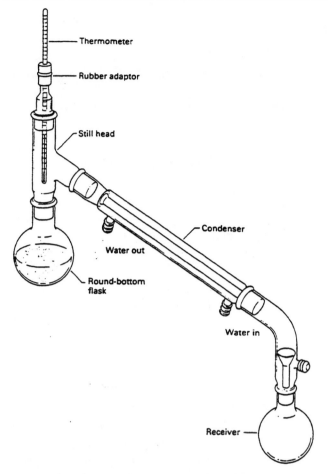

Figure 4.9 Some mixtures can be separated by distillation. A mixture is placed in a round-bottom flask and is then carefully heated to vaporize the component with the lowest boiling point. The vapors are condensed in a water-cooled condenser and the liquid drips into a receiving flask.

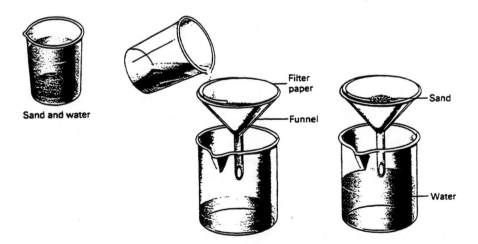

Figure 4.10 A sand-and-water mixture may be separated by gravity filtration. The mixture is poured into a funnel containing a filter paper cone. Water passes through the pores in the filter paper, and the sand particles are trapped in the filter paper.

REVIEW EXERCISE

4.14 (a) What criteria are used to classify mixtures?

(b) How do these criteria differ from the criteria used to classify pure substances?

4.15 (a) Distinguish between heterogeneous and homogeneous mixtures.

(b) Give an example of each.

4.16 Give two examples of solutions commonly used around the house.

4.17 How are the following mixtures separated?

(a) olive oil and vinegar
(b) carbonated water (carbon dioxide, a gas, dissolved in water),
(c) crushed rock and salt?

4.17 (a) Pour off the olive oil, (b) heat to remove the carbon dioxide, (c) dissolve salt in water, and filter.

4.4 ENERGY

Energy is the capacity to do work. What does this mean? **Work** is done when matter is moved by applying a force—a push or pull. Lifting a book off a table or pushing a stalled car requires work. In science, something must be moved in order for us to say that work has been done. Energy, therefore, is the capacity to move matter. More simply, energy is the capacity to effect changes in matter.

> Work can be done in many different ways; e.g., mechanical, expansion, electrical, and gravitational work

Two general classes of energy exist, potential and kinetic energy. **Potential energy** is stored energy. This potential or stored energy results from the *position*, *condition*, or *composition* of a body. A boulder moved from the ground to the top of a cliff has potential energy of position with respect to the ground. The boulder can fall off the cliff and crush objects below. A compressed spring has potential energy of condition; spontaneously, the spring can expand and do work by pushing something. A vial of nitroglycerine possesses potential energy of composition, or chemical potential energy. You do not want to drop a bottle of nitroglycerine and release this stored energy!

> Potential energy of position depends on mass, height, and acceleration due to gravity.

Kinetic energy is the energy associated with matter in motion. Whenever an object is moving, it possesses kinetic energy. Equation 1 is used to calculate the kinetic energy of a body:

$$E_{kinetic} = \frac{1}{2}mv^2 \tag{1}$$

in which $E_{kinetic}$ is the kinetic energy of an object, m is its mass, and v is its velocity or speed. This equation shows that the kinetic energy of a body is proportional to its mass and to the square of its velocity. The more massive an object and the faster the object is moving, the greater the kinetic energy it possesses.

Potential energy may be converted to kinetic energy. For example, a boulder on top of a cliff has potential energy only (Fig. 4.11). But as soon as the boulder falls from the cliff, its potential energy is changed to energy of motion, or kinetic energy. When the boulder hits the ground, it stops moving and thus no longer possesses kinetic energy.

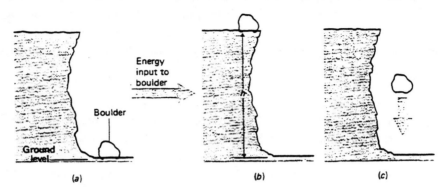

Figure 4.11 (a) A boulder on the ground has no kinetic energy because it is not moving and has no potential energy with respect to the ground. (b) Energy is required to move the boulder from the ground to the top of the cliff. On top of the cliff the boulder has no kinetic energy but it has potential energy with respect to the ground level. The greater the distance above the ground (h), the greater its potential energy. (c) If the boulder falls off the cliff, it possesses both kinetic energy and potential energy until it reaches the ground.

Energy is encountered in a variety of forms: (1) mechanical energy, (2) electric energy, (3) nuclear energy, (4) light, (5) heat, and (6) sound. These are energy forms because each has the capacity to produce changes in matter. Energy can be converted from one form to another. For example, the energy released when gasoline is burned in the engine of an automobile is transformed into mechanical energy. The chemical potential energy of the gasoline is released, causing a piston to move, which is mechanically linked to the wheels of the automobile. Along with the mechanical energy, heat is also released, an unavoidable transformation. Electric potential energy stored in a battery is transformed into light (radiant) energy inside a flashlight or into sound inside a radio.

Most power plants burn fuels to release heat. This heat is transferred to water, which is converted to high-pressure steam, which turns a turbine. A turbine is connected to an electric generator that changes the mechanical energy of the turbine into electricity. Finally, the electricity is sent to consumers who use the electricity to do innumerable tasks. In this example, chemical potential energy is converted to heat, mechanical energy, and finally electric energy. In nuclear power plants, the heat is generated by nuclear reactions.

REVIEW EXERCISES

4.18 What is the effect of work on an object? Give an example.

4.19 Distinguish between kinetic and potential energy. Give examples of each.

4.20 List four forms of energy.

4.21 What energy transformations take place within a television set?

4.21 Electric to heat, light, and sound.

Heat

Heat, or thermal energy, is especially important to chemists. Why? All other forms of energy can be transformed into heat, and chemical reactions either release or absorb heat. **Heat** is a form of kinetic energy; it can never be classified as potential energy. As we have previously discussed, heat brings about both chemical and physical changes. Solids melt, liquids evaporate, and some substances decompose or undergo chemical changes when heated.

When heat is transferred to matter, the heat increases the matter's potential energy, or its kinetic energy, or both. What happens when a substance is heated? It becomes hotter, you may say. In some cases you are correct. Substances become hotter because the heat transferred increases the average motion of the molecules—an average kinetic energy increase. We observe this increase in kinetic energy by measuring the temperature of the substance. **Temperature** is a measure of the average velocity of atoms and molecules. Higher temperatures of pure substances indicate faster-moving molecules, on average.

But heat transferred to ice at 0°C gives a different result. As long as ice is present, added heat does not increase its temperature. State changes of pure substances occur at a constant temperature. Added heat increases the potential energy of the solid ice molecules to the point where they become a liquid. Only after all the ice has melted does the temperature increase; this temperature change indicates an increase in the average kinetic energy of the molecules.

> A range of velocities is found for the particles in any sample of matter

Heat is detected only when it moves from one body to another. In our world, heat travels down a one-way street. Heat is always transferred from a hotter object to a colder object; the reverse never occurs spontaneously (Fig. 4.12).

When two objects at different temperatures contact each other, heat is transferred from the hotter object to the colder object. Faster-moving molecules in the hotter object collide with the slower-moving molecules in the colder object. During the molecular collisions energy is transferred, decreasing the average kinetic energy of the faster-moving molecules and increasing that of the slower-moving molecules. When the average energies of the molecules in both objects are equal, the heat transfer stops.

Consider what happens when a hot cup of coffee is allowed to sit for a period of time in a room. As time passes, the temperature of the coffee decreases. If the coffee is not

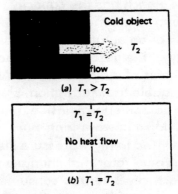

Figure 4.12 (a) If two objects at different temperatures ($T_1 > T_2$) contact each other, heat transfers spontaneously from the hot object at T_1 to the colder object at T_2. Initially T_1 decreases and T_2 increases until T_1 equals T_2; at that time, heat transfer ceases. (b) if two objects at the same temperature ($T_1 = T_2$) contact each other, no heat is transferred between the objects.

consumed, its temperature continues to drop until it equals the temperature of the room. What happens to the heat? Heat transfers from the coffee to the room. But, compared with the total amount of heat in the room, the small quantity of heat released by the coffee is insignificant.

> Heat can only be detected when it is in transit. Bodies cannot possess heat

To summarize, heat is a form of energy that always transfers spontaneously from warmer to colder objects. Temperature is a measure of how fast the particles that compose matter are moving. In other words, temperature is a measure of the average kinetic energy of atoms and molecules. Knowing the temperature of two objects in contact with each other allows us to predict the direction of heat transfer. ❖

REVIEW EXERCISES

4.22 Describe the difference between heat and temperature.

4.23 (a) Explain what happens to the particles within a hot object when it contacts a colder object.

(b) How is the motion of the particles in a body related to its temperature?

4.24 Describe the heat flow and temperature changes when a hot metal at 200°C is placed in a container of water at 25°C.

4.24 The metal temperature decreases and the water temperature increases until thermal equilibrium is reached.

4.5 MEASUREMENT OF ENERGY

Joules and Calories

The joule, J, is the SI unit of energy. It was named after James P. Joule (1818-1889), an English scientist who performed significant early experiments that related energy forms. Before the adoption of the SI, the joule was used exclusively to express mechanical equivalents of energy. A second unit, the calorie, was employed to express the amount of heat transferred. Today, the joule is the principal unit of energy used in chemistry, but in many other areas of science the calorie, a non-SI unit, is still

> Joule, self-educated, constructed his laboratory in his house. Joule was so dedicated to his work that he took a thermometer with him to make measurements during his honeymoon.

used. In the past, a calorie was defined as the amount of heat necessary to raise the temperature of exactly one gram of pure water from 14.5°C to 15.5°C. Because the calorie is a rather small unit of heat, the kilocalorie is the unit most commonly encountered. A kilocalorie equals 1000 calories. If 1 kcal of heat is transferred to 1 kg of water at 14.5°C, the added heat increases the temperature to 15.5°C.

How does the size of the calorie compare with that of the joule? The calorie is more than four times larger than the joule. By definition, one calorie is exactly equal to 4.184 joules.

$$1 \text{ cal} = 4.184 \text{ J}$$

As you can see, the joule is a relatively small unit of energy. Because the joule is small, it is the kilojoule that is most frequently encountered in chemistry. One kilocalorie is exactly equivalent to 4.184 kilojoules.

$$1 \text{ kcal} = 4.184 \text{ kJ}$$

Example Problem 4.4 shows how kilocalories are converted to joules.

Example Problem 4.4
Convert 34.5 kcal to joules and kilojoules.

Solution

1. What is unknown?   J and kJ
2. What is known? 34.5 kcal; 1000 cal/kcal; I cal/4. 184 J; 1 kJ/1000 J
3. Apply the factor-label method.

$$34.5 \text{ kcal} \times \frac{1000 \text{ cal}}{1 \text{ kcal}} \times \frac{4.184 \text{ J}}{1 \text{ cal}} = ? \text{ J}$$

$$34.5 \text{ kcal} \times \frac{1000 \text{ cal}}{1 \text{ kcal}} \times \frac{4.184 \text{ J}}{1 \text{ cal}} \times \frac{1 \text{ kJ}}{1000 \text{ J}} = ? \text{ kJ}$$

4. Perform the indicated math operations.

$$34.5 \text{ kcal} \times \frac{1000 \text{ cal}}{1 \text{ kcal}} \times \frac{4.184 \text{ J}}{1 \text{ cal}} = \mathbf{1.44 \times 10^5 \text{ J}}$$

$$34.5 \text{ kcal} \times \frac{1000 \text{ cal}}{1 \text{ kcal}} \times \frac{4.184 \text{ J}}{1 \text{ cal}} \times \frac{1 \text{ kJ}}{1000 \text{ J}} = \mathbf{1.44 \times 10^2 \text{ kJ}}$$

Exercise
Convert 575 kJ to calories. $(1.37 \times 10^5 \text{ cal})$

Specific Heat
When substances that are not undergoing state changes are heated, they increase in temperature. The **specific heat**, **c**, of a substance is the amount of heat required to increase the temperature of one gram of the substance by one degree Celsius (which is equal to one kelvin, 1 K). Each substance has its own characteristic specific heat. For example, the specific heat of water is 4.184 J/(g °C) or 1.00 cal/(g °C), which means that 4.184 J or 1.00 cal is required to increase the temperature of 1 g of water by 1.00°C. In comparison, the specific heat of copper is 0.38 J/(g °C), or 0.092 cal/(g °C). Only 0.38 J or 0.092 cal is required to increase 1 g Cu by 1°C.

> The high specific heat of water is one factor why it is an excellent coolant.

Less heat is needed to raise the temperature of a quantity of Cu by 1°C than is needed to raise the temperature of an equal quantity of water by the same amount. Substances with higher specific heats require more heat to increase the temperature of equal-mass samples by a fixed amount than do substances with lower specific heats.

The specific heat of a substance is calculated using Equation 2:

$$c = \frac{q}{m \, \Delta T} \tag{2}$$

in which c is specific heat in joules or calories per gram degree Celsius, q is the heat in joules or calories, m is mass of the substance in grams, and ΔT is the change in temperature $(T_2 - T_1)$, where T_2 is the final temperature and T_1 is the initial temperature.

You should add specific heat to your ever-growing list of conversion factors. Think of specific heat as the conversion factor that equates the quantity of heat transferred to raise 1 g of substance by 1°C.

Table 4.8 lists the specific heats of some common substances. They are determined by applying a known quantity of heat to a known mass, and then measuring the increase in temperature. Example Problem 4.5 illustrates the calculations required to find the specific heat of a solid.

TABLE 4.8 SPECIFIC HEAT OF SELECTED SUBSTANCES

Substance	Specific Heat	
	J/(g °C)	cal/(g °C)
Aluminum, Al(s)	0.902	0.216
Boron, B(s)	1.29	0.309
Copper, Cu(s)	0.38	0.092
Freon, $CCl_2F_2(g)$	0.598	0.143
Gold, Au(s)	0.128	0.306
Helium, He(g)	5.23	1.25
Hydrogen, $H_2(g)$	14.4	3.45
Iron, Fe(s)	0.451	0.108
Mercury, Hg(l)	0.138	0.331
Sand, $SiO_2(s)$	0.80	0.19
Silver, Ag(s)	0.23	0.056
Sugar, $C_{12}H_{22}O_{11}(s)$	1.3	0.30
Water, $H_2O(l)$	4.184	1.000
Wood(s)	1.76	0.421

Example Problem 4.5

If 1.448 kJ of heat is required to raise the temperature of a 215-g sample of an unknown solid from 25.3°C to 44.9°C, what is the specific heat of the solid in J/(g °C)?

Solution

1. What is unknown? c, the specific heat in J/(g °C)
2. What is known? $q = 1.448$ kJ; $m = 215$ g; $T_1 = 25.3$°C; $T_2 = 44.9$°C
3. To use Equation 2, the heat in kJ must be converted to J and the change in temperature calculated.

$$c = \frac{q}{m\,\Delta T}$$

$$q = 1.448 \text{ kJ} \times 1000 \text{ J/kJ} = 1448 \text{ J}$$

$$\Delta T = T_2 - T_1 = 44.9°C - 25.3°C = 19.6°C$$

4. Perform the indicated math operations.

$$c = 1448 \text{ J}/(215 \text{ g} \times 19.6°C) = \textbf{0.344 J/(g °C)}$$

The specific heat of the unknown solid is 0.344J/(g °C).

Exercise
If 0.595 kJ of heat is added to a 45.9-g object at 30.0°C, the temperature rises to 97.5°C. What is the specific heat of the object? (0.192 J/(g °C))

The amount of heat released, –q, or absorbed, +q, by a substance may be calculated from the specific heat, mass, and change in temperature of the substance. To find the value of q, the specific heat equation is rearranged a follows:

$$c = \frac{q}{m\,\Delta T}$$

Multiply both sides of the equation by $m\,\Delta T$ to obtain Equation 3.

$$q = m\,\Delta T\, c \tag{3}$$

Thus, to find the amount of heat transferred, the mass of substance is multiplied by its change in temperature and its specific heat. Example Problems 4.6 and 4.7 show how to apply this equation. You do not need to memorize this equation, if you just keep track of your units. Mass is in grams, change of temperature is in °C, and specific heat is J/(g °C). When these three quantities are multiplied the g and °C cancel, leaving J.

$$g \times °C \times J/(g °C) = J$$

Example Problem 4.6
How many joules of heat are required to increase the temperature of 1.0 kg of silver, Ag, from 22.1°C to 71.9°C?

Solution
1. What is unknown?   J
2. What is known? m = 1.0 kg Ag; 1000 g/kg; ΔT = 71.9°C – 22.1°C = 49.8°C; c_{Ag} = 0.23 J/(g °C) (from Table 4.8)
3. Apply the factor label method

$$q = m \times \Delta T \times c = 1.0 \text{ kg Ag} \times 1000 \text{ g Ag}/1 \text{ kg} \times 49.8°C \times 0.23 \text{ J/(g °C)}$$

The mass of Ag in kg is converted to g so the units will cancel when dividing by g in the specific heat.
4. Perform the indicated math operations.

$$q = 1.0 \text{ kg} \times 1000 \text{ g/kg} \times 49.8°C \times 0.23 \text{ J/(g °C)} = +11,454 \text{ J rounded to } \mathbf{+1.1 \times 10^4 J}$$

The answer, $+1.1 \times 10^4$ J, is expressed to two significant figures because the specific heat and mass of Ag are only known to two significant figures. When multiplying measurements, the answer can have no more significant figures than the measured quantity with the smallest number of significant figures. Also note that the sign for q is positive which means that heat is absorbed. A negative value for q means that heat is released.
Exercise
How much heat in kJ is released when 115 g H_2O cools from 95.5°C to 25.0°C? (–33.9 kJ)

Example Problem 4.7
When 3.55 kJ is added to 375 g sand initially at 29.4°C, what is the final temperature of the sand?

Solution
1. What is unknown?   Final temperature T_2
2. What is known? q = +3.55 kJ; 1000 J/kJ; m = 375 g; T_1 = 29.4°C; c_{sand} = 0.80 J/(g °C) (from Table 4.8)
3. Apply the equation.

$$q = m \times (T_2 - T_1) \times c_{sand}$$

$$3.55 \text{ kJ} \times 1000 \text{ J/kJ} = 375 \text{ g} \times (T_2 - 29.4°C) \times 0.80 \text{ J/(g °C)}$$

4. Perform the indicated math operations.

First divide both sides of the equation by 375 g $\times$ 0.80 J/(g °C), and then add 29.4°C to both sides to obtain the final answer.

$$12°C = T_2 - 29.4°C$$

$$T_2 = 41°C$$

The sand reaches a final temperature of 41°C.

Exercise

Consider a 275-g sample of He at 10.0°C. What is the final temperature of this He after the addition of 2.55 kJ of heat? (11.8°C)

REVIEW EXERCISES

4.25 (a) What is the SI unit of energy?

(b) What other energy units are commonly used in chemistry?

4.26 Perform the following conversions:

(a) 5.09×10^3 J to cal
(b) 8.9 cal to J
(c) 3.087×10^5 J to kcal

4.27 What does the specific heat tell you about a substance?

4.28 (a) Calculate the specific heat of a substance that requires 659 J to raise 93.4 g from 15.9°C to 34.6°C.

(b) What is the specific heat of the substance expressed in cal/(g °C)?

4.29 Calculate the amount of heat in joules required to raise 0.984 kg of water from 19.3°C to 84.5°C.

4.30 If 0.312 kJ of heat is added to 543 g of mercury at 11.0°C, what is the final temperature of the mercury? (Table 4.8 gives the specific heat of mercury.)

4.26   (a) 1.22×10^3 cal, (b) 37 J, (c) 73.78 kcal; 4.28 (a) 0.377 J/(g °C), (b) 0.0902 cal/(g °C); 4.29 2.68×10^5 J; 4.30 15.2°C.

4.6 CALORIMETRY

Calorimeters

In the last section, you learned the importance of measuring the amount of heat that transfers into or out of a system. The laboratory device used to make such energy measurements is a calorimeter. Figure 4.13 shows a schematic diagram of the main components of a calorimeter. Most calorimeters are constructed so that the system, sys, to be measured is surrounded by water. If the system releases heat $(-q_{sys})$, the water temperature increases from the addition of heat, and if the system absorbs heat ($+q_{sys}$), the water temperature decreases from the loss of heat. To maintain a constant temperature throughout the water, it must be constantly stirred. A thermometer is used to measure the temperature change of the water, ΔT_{water}.

     In the theoretical calorimeter that was just described, an assumption is made that all of the heat transferred to or from the system either is lost or gained by the water, respectively.

$$q_{sys} = -q_{water} \qquad (4)$$

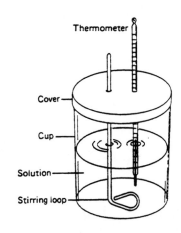

In actual calorimeters, heat lost by the system is absorbed by the stirrer, thermometer, calorimeter, and air above the sample, besides the water. Nonetheless, in a well-constructed calorimeter, the heat transfer to these objects can be held to a minimum. Collectively, ignoring this heat loss introduces greater uncertainty into the results. In other words, it decreases the number of significant figures that can be reported.

Figure 4.13 A "coffee cup" calorimeter is composed of a styrofoam cup and lid. Water inside the cup absorbs most of the heat that is transferred by whatever is placed into the cup. The thermometer measures the change in temperature, and a stirrer is used to equally disperse the heat throughout the water.

Calorimetry and Specific Heat

In chemistry, one use for a calorimeter is to measure the specific heat of a substance. The specific heat of a substance, c, is the amount of heat, J, that must be transferred to one gram, 1 g, to raise its temperature by 1°C (which is equivalent to 1 K).

$$c = J/(g\ °C)$$

     One way to accomplish this is to heat the substance above room temperature and then add it to water in a calorimeter. The heat lost by the substance is gained by the water, if it is assumed that none is lost to the calorimeter and air.

$$-q_{substance} = q_{water} \qquad (5)$$

The heat lost by the substance can be calculated as follows.

$$q_{substance} = m_{substance} \times \Delta T_{substance} \times c_{substance} \qquad (6)$$

Heat transferred to the water can be calculated as follows.

$$q_{water} = m_{water} \times \Delta T_{water} \times c_{water} \qquad (7)$$

Substituting Equations 6 and 7 into Equation 5 gives the following.

$$-(m_{substance} \times \Delta T_{substance} \times c_{substance}) = m_{water} \times \Delta T_{water} \times c_{water} \qquad (8)$$

To solve for the specific heat of the substance, Equation 8 is divided by the negative value of the product of the mass and change in temperature of the substance.

$$\frac{-(m_{substance} \times \Delta T_{substance} \times c_{substance})}{-(m_{substance} \times \Delta T_{substance})} = \frac{m_{water} \times \Delta T_{water} \times c_{water}}{-(m_{substance} \times \Delta T_{substance})}$$

Thus, Equation 9 can be used to calculate the specific heat of substance.

$$c_{substance} = -\frac{m_{water} \times \Delta T_{water} \times c_{water}}{m_{substance} \times \Delta T_{substance}} = -\frac{q_{water}}{m_{substance} \times \Delta T_{substance}} \qquad (9)$$

If you consider Equation 9 carefully, you will see that in the numerator that the product of the mass, change in temperature, and specific heat of water gives the units of J.

$$g_{water} \times {}^{\circ}C_{water} \times J/(g\ {}^{\circ}C)_{water} = J$$

In the denominator, the units for mass, m, time change in temperature, ΔT, are g × °C; thus, the units that result from applying Equation 9 are J/(g °C) or those of specific heat, c.

Let's us now apply Equation 9 and calculate the specific heat of an unknown hot metal placed into a calorimeter that contains water. Consider the following data.

	Unknown metal	Water
Mass, g	87.554	123.204
Initial temperature, T_1, °C	99.6	24.9
Final temperature, T_2, °C	30.1	30.1
Specific heat, J/(g °C)	?	4.184

To simplify the calculations first determine the change in temperatures for the water and metal.

$$\Delta T_{water} = 30.1°C - 24.9°C = 5.2°C$$

$$\Delta T_{metal} = 30.1°C - 99.6°C = -69.5°C$$

To find the heat transferred to the water use Equation 7.

$$q_{water} = m_{water} \times \Delta T_{water} \times c_{water}$$
$$q_{water} = 123.204\ g \times 5.2°C \times 4.184\ J/(g\ °C) = 2.7 \times 10^3\ J$$

Then substitute the remaining data into Equation 9.

$$c_{metal} = -q_{water}/(m_{metal} \times \Delta T_{metal})$$
$$c_{metal} = -2.7 \times 10^3\ J/(87.554\ g \times -69.5°C) = 0.44\ J/(g\ °C)$$

Our calculation shows that the specific heat of the metal is 0.44 J/(g °C). Example Problem 4.8 shows another example of how to calculate the specific heat of a metal using calorimetry.

Example Problem 4.8

The following data were collected when a student did an experiment to measure the specific heat of an unknown substance.

	Unknown substance	Water
Mass, g	44.333	155.041
Initial temperature, T_1, °C	95.8	20.1
Final temperature, T_2, °C	26.3	26.3
Specific heat, J/(g °C)	?	4.184

Calculate the specific heat of the substance.

Solution

1. What is unknown?   J/(g °C)
2. What is known? Summarized in the above table.
3. Determine the change in temperatures for the water and substance.

$$\Delta T_{water} = 26.3°C - 20.1°C = 6.2°C$$
$$\Delta T_{metal} = 26.3°C - 95.8°C = -69.3°C$$

4. Find the heat transferred to the water by using Equation 7.

$$q_{water} = m_{water} \times \Delta T_{water} \times c_{water}$$
$$q_{water} = 155.041 \text{ g} \times 6.2°C \times 4.184 \text{ J/(g °C)} = 4.0 \times 10^3 \text{ J}$$

5. Substitute the remaining data into Equation 9.

$$c_{metal} = -q_{water}/(m_{metal} \times \Delta T_{metal})$$
$$c_{metal} = -4.0 \times 10^3 \text{ J}/(44.333 \text{ g} \times -69.3°C) = \textbf{1.3 J/(g °C)}$$

The specific heat of this substance is 1.3 J/(g °C).

Exercise
A 75.88-g sample of metal at 100.0°C is placed into a calorimeter containing 275.6 g water at 25.0°C. a. If the final temperature of the water rises to 28.3°C, what is the specific heat of the metal? b. How much heat in kJ was transferred from the metal to the water? (a. 0.70 J/(g °C), b.3.8 kJ)

4.7 CONSERVATION OF MATTER AND ENERGY

One of the most fundamental laws of nature is applied when dealing with matter and energy. This is called the **law of conservation of mass/energy.**

At one time this law was stated separately as two different laws: the **law of conservation of mass** and the **law of conservation of energy**. However, these laws were merged by Albert Einstein, who proposed that matter and energy are equivalent. He showed that this relationship may be expressed by the following equation:

$$\Delta E = \Delta m \, c^2 \tag{10}$$

in which ΔE is the change in energy in joules, Δm is the change in mass in kilograms, and c is the velocity of light, 3.00×10^8 m/s.

Equation 10, the Einstein equation, tells us that matter and energy are interconvertible. An infinitesimal amount of matter is converted into a huge quantity of energy in nuclear bombs or nuclear power plants. For example, 1 g of uranium, U, is equivalent to about 9×10^{13} J or 2×10^{13} cal. Looking at this from a different point of view, 1 g U is equivalent to the energy needed to heat 2×10^5 tons of water from 0°C to 100°C.

> In 1905, while working in a patent office in Switzerland, Albert Einstein published three papers. Each paper was worthy of a Nobel prize in physics. Later, in 1921, he was awarded the Nobel prize for one of these works.

Example Problem 4.9

In a nuclear change, 1.00 μg of matter is converted totally to energy. Calculate the amount of energy released in kJ.

Solution

1. What is unknown?   kJ
2. What is known? $\Delta E = \Delta m \, c^2$, 1.00 μg, 1 g/10^6 g, 1 kg/10^3 g, $c = 3.00 \times 10^8$ m/s, 1 kJ/10^3 J
3. To use Equation 10, the change in mass, Δm, must have the unit kg. Thus, first convert the mass to kilograms

$$\Delta m = 1.00 \ \mu g \times 1 \ g/10^6 \ \mu g \times 1 \ kg/10^3 \ g = 1.00 \times 10^{-9} \ kg$$

4. Substitute the known information into Equation 10 to obtain the number of joules released.

$$\Delta E = \Delta m \, c^2 = 1.00 \times 10^{-9} \ kg \times (3.00 \times 10^8 \ m/s)^2 = 9.00 \times 10^7 \ J$$

5. Convert J to kJ.

$$9.00 \times 10^7 \ \cancel{J} \times 1 \ kJ/10^3 \ \cancel{J} = \mathbf{9.00 \times 10^4 \ kJ}$$

The loss of 1.00 μg of matter in a nuclear change produces 9.00×10^4 kJ of energy.

Exercise
What loss of mass in μg results in the production of 1.0 kJ of energy? (1.1 × 10⁻⁵ μg)

For most chemical reactions, which are nonnuclear changes, the amount of matter converted to energy is too small to measure on a balance, and it is safe to say that both matter and energy are conserved. Chemists are concerned with matter-energy conversions principally in nuclear reactions.

The **law of conservation of mass** states that there is no detectable change in mass in a chemical reaction. Stated differently: The total mass of the reactants equals the total mass of the products. Let's illustrate this fact by considering what happens when a log is burned in a fireplace. The mass of all gaseous products, soot, dust particles, and ash equals the initial mass of the log burned plus the mass of oxygen required for combustion. If for some reason we find that the masses are not equal, we can be perfectly sure we overlooked something. Matter cannot vanish. If matter is "lost" in one part of the universe, then it is residing somewhere else; it is not really lost.

The **law of conservation of energy**, also known as the First Law of thermodynamics, states that energy cannot be created or destroyed in chemical reactions. As we have previously discussed, energy may be converted from one form to another. During these conversions no energy is lost. If there is an apparent energy loss, we have not looked hard enough; the energy is somewhere else in the universe. Generally, energy that cannot be accounted for has escaped as heat.

Heat is unavoidably released in energy transformations. For example, only a small quantity of the electricity pumped into the filament of a light bulb is changed into light; most is released as heat. An efficient engine only converts 10 to 20 percent of the energy stored in the fuel into mechanical energy. Most of the energy released heats the engine and surrounding areas.❖

REVIEW EXERCISES

4.31 How many joules of energy is equivalent to 0.003 mg of matter?

4.32 (a) State the law of conservation of matter.

(b) State the law of conservation of energy.

4.31 3 × 10⁸ J

WorldWideWolfe CHEMISTRY LINKS

Connect to WorldWideWolfe at

http://www.mindspring.com/~drwolfe/WWWolfe_hcc_1025_links.htm

and link to the following sites.

Matter and Energy

1. **Composition of Matter**

This looks at the big picture of matter. You have the following selections: 1. Two Views Of Our World Around Us, 2. The Scientific Method-Inquiry In Action, 3. The Composition Of Matter, 4. The Classifications Of Matter, 5. Changes That Matter Undergo.

2. **Matter**

An excellent place to learn about the nature of matter. It has Learning Objectives, Lecture Slides (PowerPoint 4.0 Format), Lecture Notes, and References and Resources.

3. **Matter and Measurement**

Short discussion of physical properties, atoms, and units of measurement. It has links throughout the discussion.

SUMMARY

Our universe is composed entirely of matter and energy. **Matter** is anything that has mass and occupies space. **Energy** is the capacity to do work.

Physical properties are characteristics of individual substances that can be measured without changing the composition of the substance. Examples of physical properties are melting point, tensile strength, color, and shape. **Chemical properties** describe how the composition of a substance changes when it interacts with other substances or energy forms. Inertness, reactivity, and combustibility are terms employed to describe chemical properties.

The solid, liquid, and gaseous states are the three physical states. **Solids** are the most dense and most viscous. In contrast, **gases** are least dense and least viscous. Solids have a fixed shape and volume; gases expand and take the shape of their containers, and they have a variable volume. The structure of **liquids** more closely resembles that of solids than that of gases. Liquids have a relatively high average density and are incompressible.

Matter is subdivided into two general classes, pure substances and mixtures. **Pure substances** have a constant composition, cannot be separated by physical means, and undergo state changes at a constant temperature. **Mixtures** have a variable composition, can be separated using physical means, and undergo state changes over a wide temperature range.

Pure substances are subdivided into elements and compounds. **Elements** are the most fundamental units of matter. About 110 elements are known. **Compounds** are produced when elements are chemically combined. Elements are composed of small particles called atoms, and compounds are made up of molecules, which are chemical combinations of atoms.

Mixtures can be either homogeneous or heterogeneous. A **homogeneous mixture** is a combination of pure substances that can be separated by physical means, has a variable composition, undergoes state changes over a temperature range, and exhibits only one phase. Homogeneous mixtures are called **solutions. Heterogeneous mixtures** differ from homogeneous mixtures in that they exhibit two or more phases.

Potential energy is stored energy, and results from the position, condition, or chemical composition of an object. **Kinetic energy** is the energy of motion. All things that move possess kinetic energy. The kinetic energy of an object is proportional to its mass and to the square of its velocity.

Energy can be interconverted from one form to another. Whenever energy is interconverted, some of the energy is usually lost as heat. The SI unit of energy is the **joule,** and the non-SI unit is the **calorie.** One calorie is equivalent to 4.184 joules. The quantity of heat transferred depends on the difference in temperature of two objects that contact each other. Heat always transfers from a hotter object to a cooler one. Heat transfers are measured in a calorimeter.

Matter and energy are interconvertible—matter can be changed to energy or vice versa. However, in normal chemical changes, both matter and energy are conserved. The same quantity of matter is present after a chemical reaction as was originally present. Matter cannot be created or destroyed. Likewise, energy cannot be created or destroyed.

KEY TERMS

alloy	matter
boiling point	melting point
calorie	mixture
calorimeter	physical state
change of state	physical property
chemical formula	physical change
chemical symbol	potential energy
chemical change	product
chemical proper	property of matter
compound	pure substance
decomposition	reactant
element	solution
energy	specific heat
freezing point	subliming point
heterogeneous	viscosity
homogeneous	work
joule	
kinetic energy	

STUDY GUIDELINES

After completing Chapter 4, you should be able to

1. Distinguish between the composition and structure of matter

2. Define and give examples of physical and chemical properties, and physical and chemical

changes

3. List the fundamental properties of solids, liquids, and gases

4. Describe what changes of state occur during melting, freezing, boiling, and subliming

5. List and explain the criteria used to classify pure substances and mixtures

6. Distinguish between elements and compounds

7. Write symbols and names for the elements

8. State the number of atoms of each type indicated by chemical formula

9. Give examples of homogeneous and heterogeneous mixtures and explain how they can be separated Into their components

10. Define energy in terms of work

11. Describe different forms of potential and kinetic energy

12. Explain the heat transfers in terms of the temperature of objects in contact with each other

13. Explain the difference between heat and temperature

14. Identify and define the two units most commonly used to measure heat energy

15. Convert joules to calories and vice versa

16. Define specific heat and calculate the specific heat of a substance

17. Calculate the heat gain or loss by a substance given the specific heat, mass, and temperature change

18. Calculate the specific heat of a substance given calorimetry data

19. State the laws of conservation of matter and energy and describe their importance to chemistry

---

EXERCISES

4.33 Define each of the following terms: matter, energy, property of matter, physical property, chemical property, reactant, product, physical change, chemical change, decomposition, physical states, viscosity, change of state, melting point, boiling point, freezing point, subliming point, pure substance, mixture, element, compound, chemical symbol, chemical formula, homogeneous, heterogeneous, solution, work, kinetic energy, potential energy, calorie, joule, specific heat.

Physical and Chemical Properties

4.34 Classify each as either a physical or chemical property: (a) existence in the solid state, (b) magnetic properties, (c) explosiveness, (d) combustibility, (e) flammability, (f) boiling point, (g) rusting, (h) density, (i) specific heat, (j) undergoes decay, (k) viscosity, (l) hardness, (m) tensile strength, (n) reactivity, (o) inertness.

4.35 Classify each as a physical or chemical change: (a) formation of an ice cube from liquid water, (b) frying of an egg, (c) fizzing of an Alka Seltzer® tablet, (d) gasoline evaporating, (e) distillation of alcohol, (f) cutting a piece of paper, (g) digestion of food, (h) corrosion of a metal, (i) shaping of steel, (j) explosion of a bomb, (k) heating of a metal until it is red-hot.

4.36 Consider the following properties of diamond (a pure form of C): (a) Good conductor of heat; (b) electric insulator; (c) density = 3.51 g/cm^3; (d) chemically inert; (e) extremely hard; (f) burns in oxygen to produce carbon dioxide. Classify each of the listed properties of diamond as physical or chemical.

4.37 Sulfur is a yellow solid that burns in air to yield poisonous sulfur oxides. On heating, sulfur discolors and turns dark brown at 180°C. Sulfur melts at 115°C and boils at 445°C. Identify all stated properties of sulfur as physical or chemical.

4.38 Cesium, Cs, is a reactive metal that melts at 28°C and has a density of 1.87 g/cm^3. It reacts violently with cold water to produce cesium hydroxide, which is one of the strongest bases known. Cs is a soft, silvery-white solid that is a good conductor of electricity. It combines with chlorine to produce cesium chloride, and combines with oxygen to produce cesium oxide. Classify all of the stated properties of cesium as either physical or chemical.

Explain your reasoning in each case.

Physical States

4.39 List four general properties for each of the following: (a) solids, (b) liquids, (c) gases.

4.40 For each of the following pairs, determine which substance has the higher viscosity: (a) water or vegetable oil; (b) motor oil or antifreeze; (c) pudding or soft drink; (d) shaving cream or molasses.

4.41 Identify one or more of the states of matter with each of the following properties: (a) highest average density, (b) lowest viscosity, (c) intermediate densities, (d) constant volume, (e) takes the shape of the bottom of its container, (f) most orderly structure of particles, (g) strongest forces among particles, (h) highest viscosity, (i) random structure of particles, (j) highest average specific heat.

4.42 What accounts for the fact that some substances cannot exist in all three states?

4.43 What physical state is most commonly found under each of the following conditions: (a) very high temperatures and low pressures, (b) very low temperatures and high pressures?

4.44 What type(s) of matter possess the following properties: (a) has a variable composition with one phase; (b) is inseparable by chemical means; (c) exhibits two or more phases; (d) changes state at constant temperature, and its components can be separated chemically; (e) is composed of uncombined atoms?

Classification of Matter

4.45 Classify each of the following as a pure substance or a mixture: (a) wine, (b) beef, (c) gold bars at Fort Knox, (d) tap water, (e) charcoal, (f) baking soda, (g) sugar cube, (h) paint, (i) water vapor, (j) air, (k) cola drink.

4.46 Write the name for each of the following elements: (a) He, (b) Fe, (c) Li, (d) Se, (e) Ne, (f) Zr, (g) Mg, (h) Be, (i) F. (j) Ce, (k) C, (l) Ca.

4.47 Write the name for each of the following elements: (a) Hg, (b) Zn, (c) W, (d) Xe, (e) Sr, (f) Al, (g) Ge, (h) Kr, (i) Lu, (j) Hf.

4.48 Give the symbols for each of the following elements: (a) nickel, (b) nitrogen, (c) neodymium, (d) neon, (e) niobium, (f) nobelium, (g) neptunium.

4.49 Give the symbols for each of the following elements: (a) indium, (b) silicon, (c) chlorine, (d) potassium, (e) manganese, (f) beryllium, (g) platinum, (h) rubidium.

4.50 Write the names and symbols for all seven elements whose names begin with A.

4.51 Write the names and symbols for all eight elements in the second period of the periodic table.

4.52 (a) What are the four most abundant elements in the earth's crust? What percent of the earth's crust do they compose? (b) What are the four most abundant elements in the whole earth? What percent of the whole earth do they compose?

4.53 Write the names and symbols for all elements in the second chemical group (IIA) of the periodic table.

4.54 What is the difference between a chemical formula and a chemical symbol? Give an example of each.

4.55 State the name and number of each atom in the following formulas: (a) Na_2O, (b) SO_3, (c) N_2O_5, (d) Li_2CO_3, (e) $NaNO_3$, (f) RbH_2PO_4, (g) $Al(OH)_3$, (h) $(NH_4)_2C_2O_4$, (i) $XePtCl_6$, (j) CCl_2Br_2.

4.56 Classify each of the following as an element or a compound from the given information: (a) a substance that melts at 120°C, boils at 228°C, and decomposes to silicon and iodine; (b) a white solid that melts at 44°C and combines with oxygen to form P_2O_5; (c) a soft, silvery metal that reacts violently with water.

4.57 Explain the following statement: "Mixtures have variable compositions."

4.58 Classify the following as homogeneous or heterogeneous mixtures: (a) brass, (b) coffee, (c) cement, (d) motor oil, (e) cotton, (f) paper, (g) oil and vinegar, (h) smog.

4.59 Explain each step that is required to separate the following mixtures: (a) sand and salt; (b) alcohol and water; (c) sand and sugar; (d) oil and water.

4.60 How many phases are observed in each of the following (not including the container and air): (a) glass of iced tea; (b) bottle of seawater and oil residue; (c) aquarium with four different colors of sand; (d) glass of soda water with ice cubes?

Energy

4.61 What are the three ways that potential energy is stored? Give an example for each.

4.62 (a) What two factors are directly related to an object's kinetic energy? (b) How is the kinetic energy of an object calculated?

4.63 Kinetic energy in joules is calculated from the mass of a body in kilograms and its velocity in meters per second. (a) If a body has a mass of 5.23 kg and a velocity of 2.25 m/s, what is the kinetic energy of the body? (b) What is the kinetic energy of the body if its velocity decreases to 1.13 m/s? (c) What is the kinetic energy of the body if its velocity is 5.00 m/s?

4.64 Calculate the velocity of a body that has a mass of 8.23×10^3 g and a kinetic energy of 9.97 kJ.

4.65 What type(s) of potential energy are possessed by each of the following: (a) TNT, (b) apple on a tree, (c) mainspring of a watch that has just been wound, (d) stretched rubber band, (e) water at the top of a dam, (f) hamburger?

4.66 For each of the following pairs, determine which can transfer the largest quantity of heat: (a) match flame or bunsen burner flame; (b) cup of water at 90°C or bathtub filled with 90°C water; (c) ice cube at 0°C or a large block of ice at 0°C; (d) teaspoon of boiling water or gallon of water at 50°C; (e) two identical wooden blocks in contact with each other.

4.67 Perform the indicated energy conversions:
(a) 9.21 cal = ? J
(b) 7.09 J = ? cal

(c) 2.168×10^4 J = ? kcal
(d) 8.1×10^7 cal = ? kJ
(e) 0.00535 cal = ? kJ

Specific Heat

4.68 Calculate the specific heat of a substance if 812 J is required to raise the temperature of a 45.8-g sample by 2.11°C.

4.69 Calculate the specific heat of a substance if the addition of 521 J increases the temperature of a 217-g sample from 8.32°C to 15.9°C.

4.70 How much heat in joules is required to raise the temperature of 8.43 kg of water from 29.8°C to 54.1 °C ?

4.71 How many calories of heat are released when 8.19 kg of water at 75.0°C cools to 22.7°C?

4.72 (a) How many joules and how many calories are required to increase a 9.23-kg sample of hydrogen gas from −52.9°C to 25.0°C? (b) How many joules and how many calories are required to raise the temperature of a 9.23-kg sample of helium gas from −52.9°C to 25.0°C?

4.73 Calculate and compare the amount of heat released in joules when 1.00 kg of water and when 1.00 g of water, both at 100.0°C, cool to 25.0°C.

4.74 The specific heat of gold, Au, is 0.13 J/(g °C). (a) How much heat is required to increase 175 g Au from 15.0°C to 40.0°C? (b) Compare this quantity of heat with the amount of heat that would be required to increase the temperature of an equal mass of water through the same temperature range.

4.75 The initial temperature of a 29.3-g sample of copper is 15.4°C. What is the final temperature after 9.21×10^3 J of heat is transferred to it?

4.76 What is the final temperature of a 1.25-kg sample of helium initially at 0.0°C, if 3.34 kJ is transferred to it?

Conservation Laws

4.77 (a) If 12 g of carbon is exactly combined with 32 g of oxygen, how many grams of carbon dioxide form? (b) What law does this illustrate?

4.78 What energy transformations occur when electricity is produced through hydroelectric generation?

4.79 What mass in milligrams is equivalent to each of the following energies: (a) 6.0×10^9 J, (b) 5.5×10^{35} J, (c) 1.0 J?

4.80 What energy in joules is equivalent to each of the following masses: (a) 0.0015 g, (b) 12.9 mg, (c) 1.50 g?

Additional Exercises

4.81 An object has a kinetic energy of 5.78×10^4 J and a mass of 0.985 kg. What is the velocity of the object?

4.82 How many atoms of each type are indicated by each of the following formulas: (a) $Ca_3(PO_4)_2$, (b) $Al(C_2H_3O_2)_3$, (c) $(NH_4)_2Cr_2O_7$?

4.83 Write the names and symbols for elements 57 to 81.

4.84 (a) if all of the energy from the food that we consume in a day could be transferred to water and if a person eats a total of 3000 kcal per day, what mass of cold water at 0.0°C would be heated to 50.0°C by one day's food? (b) How many liters of water would this be? (Assume the density of water is 1.0 g/cm^3.)

4.85 Describe the temperature change and heat flow when liquid oxygen, $O_2(l)$, at −183°C comes in contact with an equal mass of liquid nitrogen, $N_2(l)$ at −196°C.

4.86 A 30.0-g sample of an alloy was heated to 100.0°C and then placed in a beaker that contained 123.8 g of water. The temperature of the water increased from 23.19°C to 26.88°C. If all of the heat from the metal was transferred to the water, what is the specific heat of the alloy?

4.87 Freon is a gas used as a heat transfer agent in cooling systems. The specific heat of freon is 0.543 J/(g °C). What mass of freon would absorb 34.5 kJ while increasing in temperature from −10.0°C to 30.0°C?

4.88 Closely related to specific heat is the heat capacity of a substance. Heat capacity is defined as the amount of heat required to raise the temperature of a given mass of a substance by one degree Celsius. What is the heat capacity in joules per

degree Celsius of each of the following:
(a) 449 g of water, (b) 9.22 kg of
mercury, (c) 1.99 g of boron?

4.89 How much heat is required to increase
the temperature of a cube of Pt that has
an edge length of 3.28 cm from 11.7°C
to 65.8°C? [The density of Pt is 21.45
g/cm^3, and its specific heat is 0.133 J/(g-
°C.)]

4.90 A swimming pool is 3.25 m wide, 6.50 m
long, and has an average depth of 2.50
m. Calculate the number of joules of
heat required to increase the
temperature of the water from 18.5°C to
30.4°C, assuming that the pool is
completely filled and the density of the
water is 1.00 g/cm^3.

4.91 Sterling silver is 92.5% Ag and 7.5% Cu.
Calculate the amount of heat in joules
required to increase the temperature of
0.438 kg of sterling silver from 24.9°C to
100.0°C.

4.92 A 92.777-g sample of metal at 121.4°C
is placed into a calorimeter containing
188.6 g water at 24.3°C. a. If the final
temperature of the water rises to 29.1°C,
what is the specific heat of the metal? b.
How much heat in kJ was transferred
from the metal to the water?

4.93 A 55.00-g sample of metal at 97.2°C is
placed into a calorimeter containing
115.0 g water at 23.6°C. a. If the final
temperature of the water rises to 26.6°C,
what is the specific heat of the metal? b.
How much heat in kJ was transferred
from the metal to the water?

Chapter 4 Pretest Assignment

1. Complete each of the following statements with the correct word, number, or phase.

    a. _____ a homogeneous mixture of pure substances.
    b. _____ is the ability to do work.
    c. A(n) _____ occurs when the substance changes its composition.
    d. _____ occurs when a liquid changes to a solid.
    e. _____ is the amount of heat needed to change one gram of substance by one degree Celsius.
    f. _____ is stored energy.

2. List three physical properties of matter.

    _____
    _____
    _____

3. List three properties of substances in the solid state.

    _____
    _____
    _____

4. List the three criteria needed to classify a pure substance.

    _____
    _____
    _____

5. Write the symbols for the following elements.

    a. beryllium   _____
    b. magnesium   _____
    c. vanadium   _____
    d. tin   _____

6. Write the names of the following elements.

    a. Mn   _____
    b. Pb   _____
    c. K   _____
    d. Hg   _____

7. Explain how a mixture of alcohol and water can be separated.

8. Convert 45.6 kJ to kcal.

9. How much heat is needed to increase the temperature of 197.44 g water from 15.4°C to 81.9°C?

10. Calculate the amount of energy produced in kJ can be liberated when 1.0 ng of matter is converted to energy.

CHAPTER 5

Atoms

5.1 DEVELOPMENT OF THE MODERN ATOMIC THEORY

Our contemporary theory regarding atoms has evolved over the last 200 years. Theory development is a dynamic process. Whenever new, solid evidence is uncovered that contradicts a theory, the theory must be flexible enough to incorporate the new data. Theories are not fact; they are the best explanation we can offer in light of known information.

The historical development of the modern atomic theory is an unusually interesting story that begins with **John Dalton** (1766-1844), an English chemist. He is credited with developing the first scientific theory of atoms. Dalton, unlike the Greek philosophers (Sec. 1.2), based his theory on approximately 150 years of investigations by scientists. Dalton's atomic theory stated that

1. Matter is composed of small, solid, spherical particles called atoms.
2. Atoms of one element have the same properties, but differ from atoms of all other elements.
3. Atoms cannot be subdivided or changed to other atoms.
4. Atoms combine chemically in simple, whole-number ratios.
5. Chemical changes involve the linkage and separation of atoms.

WWWolfe 1
(See WWWolfe section at the end of the chapter.)

Dalton's model of the atom was accepted for 100 years without a serious challenge. The longevity of Dalton's atomic theory is attributed to its ability to support two fundamental laws of nature; the law of conservation of matter—matter cannot be

Dalton was also a meteorologist, and he wrote a book entitled *Meteorological Observations and Essays*. Dalton also discovered color blindness, an affliction he had.

created or destroyed—and the law of constant composition, which states that all compounds are composed of elements in a fixed proportion by mass. In spite of this, scientific research during the late nineteenth and early twentieth centuries significantly changed our ideas about the structure of atoms.

Research into the nature of electricity showed that the atom was not just a solid sphere but was composed of even smaller particles. The first particles to be discovered were the proton and the electron. As we will soon discuss in detail, the proton is a positively charged body and the electron is a negatively charged body. Studies concerning the properties of these particles were conducted in discharge tubes. Figure 5.1 shows a diagram of a discharge tube. Scientists found that if they first pumped out much of the air in the tube, the tube glowed when a voltage was applied. Later it was found that negative particles, which were called cathode rays (electrons), passed from the negative electrode, the cathode, to the positive electrode, the anode. This and

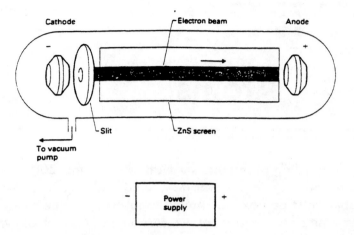

Cathode ⌐Electron beam Anode
−   +

−
To vacuum
pump
Slit   ZnS screen

Power
supply
−   +

Figure 5.1 Discharge tube is composed of an evacuated glass container that has two electrodes. The negative electrode is called the cathode and the positive electrode is called the anode. Electrons travel from the cathode to the anode. The electron beam can be seen when it strikes the zinc sulfide screen (ZnS), causing it to glow.

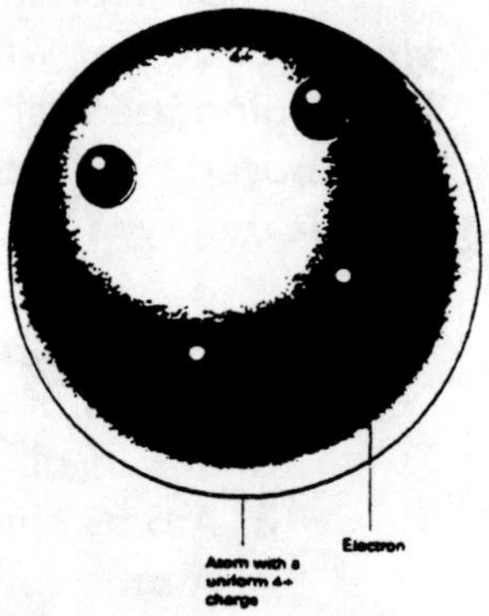

similar studies led English physicist **J. J. Thomson** (1856-1940) to propose in 1898 what is now known as the **"plum pudding"** model of the atom. Thomson envisioned a structure in which negatively charged electrons were embedded in an atom that had a uniform positive charge from the protons (Fig. 5.2).

By 1911 evidence was collected that allowed scientists to modify the Thomson model of the atom. **Ernest Rutherford** (1871-1937) conducted one of the most classic experiments of scientific history. He bombarded different types of matter with high-energy, positively charged alpha particles. We will discuss the properties of these particles in the next section. Based on the Thomson model of the atom, Rutherford hypothesized that the alpha particles should go through very thin metal foils undeflected. However, after performing an experiment on gold leaf, which is very thin gold foil, he found that a small but significant number of the alpha particles were deflected through large angles by the gold atoms (Fig. 5.3a). These results showed Rutherford that the Thomson model of the atom was not valid. A uniform positive charge with embedded negatively charged electrons would not interact with the alpha particles in such a manner. Rutherford proposed that the atom has a small, positively charged nucleus that repels the alpha particles and produces the large deflected angles (Fig. 5.3b). In other words, Rutherford gave us the **nuclear model** of the atom.

While Rutherford showed us that the atom has a nucleus, he did not know how the

Atom with a
uniform 4+
charge   Electron

Figure 5.2 Thomson proposed a model of the atom in which electrons were embedded in a matrix of positive charge. This figure shows a Be atom that has four protons and four electrons.

The famous experiment in which Ernest Rutherford, a New Zealander who lived in England, discovered the nucleus is called the gold leaf experiment. His assistant for this experiment, Hans Geiger, invented the radiation-detecting device that bears his name.

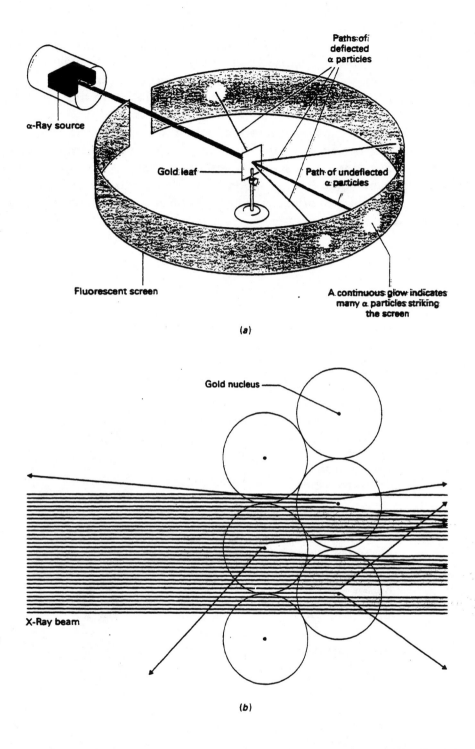

Figure 5.3 (a) Rutherford detected the alpha rays with a fluorescent screen that glowed when struck by radiation. Most of the alpha rays went through the gold leaf without being deflected, but a significant number were deflected through large angles. (b) Only the alpha particles that passed close to the gold nuclei were deflected through large angles.

electrons were arranged outside the nucleus. In 1913, the Danish physicist Neils Bohr (1885-1962) proposed an atomic model in which the electrons traveled around the nucleus in circular paths called *orbits*. His model was replaced with the current **quantum mechanical model** of the atom proposed by Erwin Schrödinger. We will discuss both models of the atom when we consider the electron configuration of atoms in Sec. 5.3. The discovery of a third particle in the atom did not occur until 1932. In that year, James Chadwick, an English scientist, discovered the neutral (uncharged) neutron.

Most work since 1930 has been directed toward elucidating the composition of the subatomic particles. Little has changed in the minds of scientists regarding overall atomic structure since the 1930s, a fact that suggests that our current atomic model is a valid one. Figure 5.4 shows the evolution of atomic models from Dalton to the present. In the next section, we will consider the properties of protons, neutrons, and electrons, as well as the composition of atoms.❖

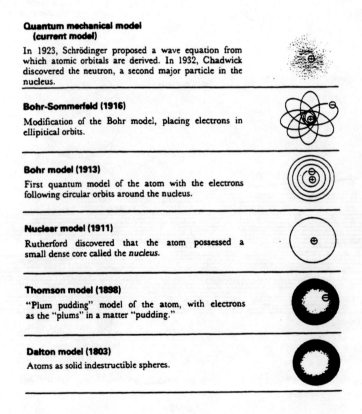

Quantum mechanical model (current model)

In 1923, Schrödinger proposed a wave equation from which atomic orbitals are derived. In 1932, Chadwick discovered the neutron, a second major particle in the nucleus.

Bohr-Sommerfeld (1916)

Modification of the Bohr model, placing electrons in ellipitical orbits.

Bohr model (1913)

First quantum model of the atom with the electrons following circular orbits around the nucleus.

Nuclear model (1911)

Rutherford discovered that the atom possessed a small dense core called the *nucleus*.

Thomson model (1898)

"Plum pudding" model of the atom, with electrons as the "plums" in a matter "pudding."

Dalton model (1803)

Atoms as solid indestructible spheres.

Figure 5.4 A summary of the development of the atomic theory.

REVIEW EXERCISES

5.1 Why is an atomic theory required to describe atoms?

5.2 List the most significant points of Dalton's atomic theory.

5.3 (a) Describe the Thomson model of the atom.

(b) Describe the Rutherford model of the atom.

(c) On what evidence did Rutherford base his model of the atom?

5.4 What are the names of the three particles that compose an atom?

5.4 protons, neutrons, and electrons

5.2 ATOMIC SUBSTRUCTURE

Protons, Neutrons, and Electrons

Atoms are composed of three fundamental particles—protons neutrons, and electrons. These particles are characterized by their mass and electric charge (Table 5.1). Protons and neutrons have approximately the same mass, about 1.67×10^{-24} g. The mass of an electron is only 9.11×10^{-28} g, about that of a proton (or neutron); in other words, 1837 electrons are needed to equal the mass of one proton.

TABLE 5.1 PROPERTIES of SUBATOMIC PARTICLES

Particle	Symbol	Mass, g	Mass, u	Relative charge
Proton	p^+	1.6726×10^{-24}	1.007276	1+
Neutron	n°	1.6749×10^{-24}	1.008666	0
Electron	e^-	9.1096×10^{-28}	0.0005486	1–

Masses of subatomic particles are frequently expressed using a relative unit, termed a **unified atomic mass unit,** u, or atomic mass unit, amu, for short. One atomic mass unit, 1 u, has a mass equivalent to 1.6606×10^{-24} g. Later, we will discuss how this unit is derived. For now, we can say that one unified atomic mass unit is approximately the mass of a proton (or neutron). The mass of an electron on this scale is only 0.000549 u.

Bodies can have a positive (+), negative (–), or no net charge (neutral). Electrons and protons have the smallest elementary unit of charge found in matter. Electrons are negatively charged (1–); protons possess the same magnitude of charge as electrons, but their charge is positive (1+). Neutrons, as the name implies, are electrically neutral particles. From physics, we find that particles with the same electric charge repel each other. Objects with unlike charges attract each other (Fig. 5.5). Two electrons or two protons in close proximity repel each other, or push each other apart. When unlike charged particles (+ and –) are brought close together, they attract each other. The force of electric attraction or repulsion is inversely related to the square of the distance that separates the particles. This

WWWolfe 2
(See WWWolfe section at the end of the chapter.)

relationship is known as **Coulomb's Law** and is expressed as follows:

$$F = k\frac{q_1 q_2}{r^2}$$

(1)

In this equation q_1 and q_2 are the magnitudes of the charges, k is Coulomb's constant, r is the distance that separates the particles, and F is the force either of attraction or repulsion. Neutral particles do not interact with charged particles.

| Electric charge is measured in coulombs. |

The Nucleus

Protons and neutrons are in a very small region of the atom called the nucleus (plural, *nuclei*). Most nuclei have diameters of roughly 10^{-6} nm (1 nm = 1×10^{-9} m). Diameters of whole atoms are many times (100,000 ×) larger than those of nuclei, ranging from 0.1 to 0.5 nm. The electrons are found in the relatively vast space outside the nucleus.

   Nuclear density is incredibly large; nearly all of the mass of an atom (protons and neutrons) is concentrated in the infinitesimal volume of the nucleus. Nuclear densities, roughly, are 100,000,000 tons/mL!

   To summarize atomic structure: The atom consists of a small, dense core, the nucleus, surrounded by minute particles, electrons, which occupy an immense, mainly empty, region of space. Atoms are not solid forms of matter; they are sparsely populated with matter.

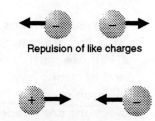

Repulsion of like charges

Attraction of unlike charges

Figure 5.5 Two particles with the same electric charge repel each other. Two particles with unlike electric charges attract each other.

Nuclear Properties of Atoms

Chemists are concerned with the number of protons and neutrons in the nucleus. Two values are needed to determine the composition of a nucleus. One is called the atomic number, and the other is the mass number. The **atomic number, Z,** of an atom equals the number of positive charges found in the nucleus of that atom, or stated another way, the number of protons in the nucleus.

| H. G. J. Moseley (1887-1915) a student of Rutherford, was the first to measure the charge on the nucleus—its atomic number. He accomplished this by reflecting x-rays off the surfaces of metals. |

Atomic number (Z) = number of protons in the nucleus of an atom

   Hydrogen, the simplest atom, has an atomic number of 1. Given its atomic number, we know that a hydrogen atom has one proton in its nucleus. The atomic number of helium is 2; thus, two protons are found in the nucleus of a helium atom. Lithium nuclei each possess three protons; accordingly, the atomic number of lithium atoms is 3. If you look at the periodic table located in the Appendix, you will find that the integer (whole number) next to the symbol of each element is the atomic number. Atoms are arranged in the periodic table in order of increasing atomic number.

Besides the atomic number, the **mass number, A,** of an atom is required to find the composition of the nucleus of an atom. The mass number of an atom equals the total number of protons and neutrons in the nucleus.

Mass number (A) = number of protons + number of neutrons

You should note that mass numbers are just numbers and are not masses. To express the atomic number and mass number of an atom, atomic symbols are written as follows:

$$_{Z}^{A}X$$

in which X is the symbol of the atom, A is the mass number, and Z is the atomic number.

To illustrate the writing of atomic symbols let's write the atomic symbol for a krypton atom that has 36 protons and 48 neutrons in its nucleus. The atomic number of Kr is 36 because it has 36 protons. Its mass number is 84 because the sum of the protons plus neutrons is 84 (36 p^+ + 48 $n°$). After writing the symbol of krypton (Kr), we write 36 as a subscript to the left of the symbol and 84 as a superscript, also to the left of the symbol.

$$_{36}^{84}Kr$$

To find the number of neutrons in a nucleus, given the mass number and atomic number, we subtract the atomic number (number of p^+) from the mass number (number of p^+ plus number of $n°$).

Number of $n°$ = mass number – atomic number
= (number of p^+ + number of $n°$) – number of p^+

Mass numbers are not found in the periodic table, so they will be given whenever they are needed.

Let's consider the hydrogen atom, and find the complete composition of its nucleus. Most hydrogen atoms have a mass number equal to 1 and an atomic number also equal to 1; they are written $_{1}^{1}H$.

Number of $n°$ = mass number – atomic number

Number of $n°$ in $_{1}^{1}H$ = 1 – 1 = 0

Consequently, $_{1}^{1}H$ atoms have one proton and zero neutrons in their nuclei. The $_{1}^{1}H$ atom is the only atom that does not have a neutron in the nucleus.

What is the nuclear composition of $_{26}^{56}Fe$ atoms? The symbol tells us that the atomic number is 26; hence, 26 protons are found in this atom. To find the number of neutrons, we subtract the atomic number, 26, from the mass number, 56, to obtain 30 neutrons.

Number of $n°$ in $_{26}^{56}Fe$ = mass number – atomic number = 56 – 26 = 30

$^{56}_{26}$Fe atoms have 26 protons and 30 neutrons in their nuclei. Example Problem 5.1 is another illustration of how to find the composition of a nucleus.

Example Problem 5.1

In 1911, Marie Curie first isolated radium, Ra. Radium causes severe biological effects if inhaled or ingested because of the intense radiation that it releases. Find the composition of the nucleus of the following Ra atom.

$$^{226}_{88}Ra$$

Solution

In our example, the mass number, A, is 226, and the atomic number, Z, is 88. The mass number is the number of protons and neutrons, and the atomic number is the number of protons. Therefore, **88 protons** are in the nucleus of $^{226}_{88}$Ra. The number of neutrons is calculated by subtracting the atomic number from the mass number.

$$\text{Number of } n° = \text{mass number} - \text{atomic number} = 226 - 88 = 138$$

$^{226}_{88}$Ra contains 88 protons and 138 neutrons in its nucleus.

Exercise

What is the composition of the nucleus of $^{52}_{24}$Cr? ($p^+ = 24$, $n° = 28$)

REVIEW EXERCISES

5.5 What happens when particles with (a) the same and (b) different charges interact with each other?

5.6 What can be determined about an atom given its (a) atomic number, (b) mass number, (c) atomic mass, (d) atomic number and mass number?

5.7 What are the atomic numbers of each of the following elements?

(a) Ca
(b) Ag
(c) U
(d) Lr

5.8 How many protons and neutrons are found in the nucleus of each of the following?

(a) ^{48}Ti
(b) ^{85}Rb
(c) ^{227}Ac
(d) ^{195}Pt

5.7 (a) 20, (b) 47, (c) 92, (d) 103; 5.8 (a) $p^+ = 22$, $n° = 26$; (b) $p^+ = 37$, $n° = 48$; (c) $p^+ = 89$, $n° = 138$; (d) $p^+ = 78$, $n° = 117$.

Isotopes

Whenever atoms have the same atomic number but different mass numbers, they are called

isotopes. Stated differently: Isotopes are atoms with the same number of protons but different numbers of neutrons in their nuclei.

A small percentage of naturally occurring hydrogen atoms are not $_1^1H$ atoms; they have a different nuclear composition. These hydrogen atoms have a mass number of 2 and an atomic number of 1.

$$\text{Number of neutrons in } _1^2H = 2 - 1 = 1 \ n°$$

Each of these atoms has one proton and one neutron in its nucleus. A third hydrogen isotope exists, with a mass number of 3, $_1^3H$. In these atoms two neutrons and a single proton are found in the nucleus. Consequently, $_1^1H$, $_1^2H$, and $_1^3H$ are all said to be isotopes of hydrogen. The three isotopes of hydrogen are expressed as follows:

$_1^1H$	$_1^2H$	$_1^3H$
Protium	Deuterium	Tritium

$_1^1H$ is regular hydrogen or protium and is the most abundant type of hydrogen. $_1^2H$ is deuterium or heavy hydrogen. Deuterium has a mass about twice that of regular hydrogen because it has both a proton and a neutron in its nucleus. Tritium, $_1^3H$, the heaviest form of hydrogen, cannot be detected in naturally occurring samples of hydrogen. Figure 5.6 shows the nuclear composition of the three hydrogen isotopes.

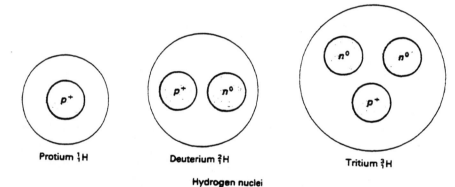

Protium $_1^1H$ Deuterium $_1^2H$ Tritium $_1^3H$

Hydrogen nuclei

Figure 5.6 Nuclei of regular hydrogen atoms (^1H) contain one proton and no neutrons. Nuclei of deuterium atoms (^2H) contain one proton and one neutron, and tritium atoms (^3H), the most massive isotope of hydrogen, contain nuclei with one proton and two neutrons.

A large percent of the elements are composed of mixtures of different isotopes. For example, three isotopes are found in naturally occurring samples of uranium: $_{92}^{234}U$, $_{92}^{235}U$, and $_{92}^{238}U$. Each of these uranium isotopes contains 92 protons in the nucleus. They differ with respect to the number of neutrons in the nucleus. $_{92}^{234}U$ nuclei contain 142 neutrons, $_{92}^{235}U$ nuclei contain 143 neutrons, and $_{92}^{238}U$ nuclei contain 146 neutrons. Of the three, $_{92}^{238}U$ is most abundant in natural samples, representing 99% of the total number of atoms. Consequently, the other two isotopes represent less than one percent of the atoms. $_{92}^{235}U$ is used as the fuel in nuclear power plants. Table 5.2 gives more examples of natural isotopic mixtures.

> All of the isotopes of uranium are radioactive. Each releases alpha radiation, and some undergo spontaneous fission—the nucleus splits.

TABLE 5.2 NATURAL ISOTOPIC COMPOSITION OF SELECTED ELEMENTS

Isotope	Protons	Neutrons	Natural abundance, %	Mass, u
$^{12}_{6}C$	6	6	98.89	12.000
$^{13}_{6}C$	6	7	1.11	13.003
$^{16}_{8}O$	8	8	99.76	15.9949
$^{17}_{8}O$	8	9	0.04	16.9991
$^{18}_{8}O$	8	10	0.20	17.9992
$^{63}_{29}Cu$	29	34	69.09	62.9298
$^{65}_{29}Cu$	29	36	30.91	64.9278
$^{70}_{32}Ge$	32	38	20.51	69.9243
$^{72}_{32}Ge$	32	40	27.43	71.9217
$^{73}_{32}Ge$	32	41	7.76	72.9234
$^{74}_{32}Ge$	32	42	36.54	73.9219
$^{76}_{32}Ge$	32	44	7.76	75.9214

Masses of Individual Atoms

An atom has a very small mass. A hydrogen atom, for example, has a mass of only 1.67 x 10^{-24} g. To avoid the inconvenience of working with such small numbers, chemists use a relative scale for the masses of individual atoms. On this scale, masses of all atoms are expressed relative to the mass of one $^{12}_{6}C$ atom.

By definition, the mass of one ^{12}C atom is equal to exactly 12 atomic mass units. Thus, **one atomic mass unit, 1 u,** is one-twelfth the mass of the ^{12}C atom. Because $^{12}_{6}C$ is composed of six protons and six neutrons, 1 u is about the average mass of a proton or a neutron.

The masses of other atoms are determined relative to the standard, C. For example, if an atom is found to have a mass three times that of ^{12}C, its relative mass is 36 u, 3 times 12 u. An atom with a mass one-fourth the mass of ^{12}C is assigned a mass of 3 u, one-fourth of 12 u. When the mass of an individual atom is given, it should be thought of relative to the mass of a ^{12}C atom.

Atomic Mass (Atomic Weight)

Atomic masses are the numbers listed in each block in the periodic table along with the symbol and atomic number of an element. Notice that the atomic masses of the elements are decimal numbers (e.g., Al, 26.9815; S. 32.06; V, 50.942); none are integers like the atomic number. Why is this? A large percent of the naturally occurring elements exist as a mixture of isotopes, each isotope with a different mass. Because chemists work with a large quantity of atoms that have different masses, they usually find it convenient to use the

WWWolfe 3
(see WWWolfe section at the end of the chapter.)

average mass of an element's isotopes, which is called the atomic mass. The **atomic mass** of an element is the average mass of its naturally occurring isotopes relative to the mass of ^{12}C.

Consider the atomic mass of carbon, which is 12.011 u. If you refer to Table 5.2, you will find that carbon is composed principally of two isotopes, ^{12}C, the one we just referred to as the standard for the atomic mass scale, and ^{13}C. In nature, approximately 9889 out of 10,000 carbon atoms are ^{12}C, and 111 are the heavier ^{13}C isotope. If we average 9889 particles with a mass of 12.00 u and 111 particles with a mass of 13.00 u, the average mass is 12.01 u. How is this number calculated? First we must consider how a *weighted average is* calculated.

Weighted averages are calculated in a similar way to any other average: We add each value and divide by the total number of values. For example, if a test is given to 100 students, and 60 students get a score of 80 points while the remaining 40 students score 95 points, the average

> In 1828, Berzelius produced one of the first accurate tables of atomic masses. Most of his values are in agreement with those we use today. He also proposed the modern symbols for the elements.

score is 86 points. The weighted average of scores is obtained in the following way. First, multiply 60, the number of students with 80 points, times their score, 80 points. Second, multiply 40, the number of students with 95 points, times their score, 95. Finally, add these two products and divide by the total number of students.

$$\text{Average} = \frac{(60 \text{ students} \times 80 \text{ pts}) + (40 \text{ students} \times 95 \text{ pts})}{100 \text{ students}} = 86 \text{ pts}$$

A similar calculation allows us to find the atomic mass of chlorine once we know the natural abundance of the two principal isotopes, ^{35}Cl and ^{37}Cl. In natural samples of the element chlorine, 75.53% is ^{35}Cl with a mass of 34.969 u. The remaining 24.47% is ^{37}Cl, which has a mass of 36.966 u. To obtain the atomic mass of chlorine, the

> Periodic tables differ with respect to the placement of the atomic number and atomic mass within each box. Remember that the atomic number is always an integer, and the atomic mass is a decimal.

weighted average of the masses of the two isotopes, assume that you have 100 atoms. Of these 100 total atoms, 75.53 have a mass of 34.969 u, and 24.47 have a mass of 36.966 u. Therefore, multiply 75.53 times 34.969 u, add that to the product of 24.47 times 36.966 u, and divide by the total number of atoms, 100.

$$\text{Atomic mass (Cl)} = \frac{(75.53 \times 34.969 \text{ u}) + (24.47 \times 36.966 \text{ u})}{100} = 35.46 \text{ u}$$

Thus the atomic mass of chlorine is 35.46 u.

Example Problem 5.2 is a second illustration of how to calculate the atomic mass of an element.

Example Problem 5.2
Calculate the atomic mass of boron, using the following data:

Isotope	Relative mass, u	Percent abundance, %
^{10}B	10.013	19.70
^{11}B	11.009	80.30

Solution

The atomic mass of B. is obtained by calculating the average mass of its naturally occurring isotopes:

$$\text{Atomic mass of B} = [(10.013 \text{ u} \times 19.70) + (11.009 \text{ u} \times 80.0)]/100 = \textbf{10.81 u}$$

Percents show the number of parts per 100 total parts. In this calculation, for every 100 B atoms, 19.70 have a mass of 10.013 u, and 80.3 have a mass of 11.009 u. Thus, 19.70 is multiplied by 10.013 u, and 80.3 is multiplied by 11.009 u. The two resultant quantities are added and the sum is divided by 100, giving the average, 10.81 u.

Exercise

Rubidium is composed of two isotopes, ^{85}Rb and ^{87}Rb. The mass of ^{85}Rb is 84.912 and it has a natural abundance of 72.15%. The mass of ^{87}Rb is 86.909 and it has a natural abundance of 27.85%. Calculate the atomic mass of Rb. (85.47)

REVIEW EXERCISES

5.9 (a) What are isotopes?

(b) List the naturally occurring isotopes of germanium, Ge (Table 5.2).

(c) Which isotopes of germanium are the most and least abundant in nature?

5.10 (a) Define atomic mass.

(b) How is the atomic mass of an element calculated?

5.11 Calculate the atomic mass of thallium using 202.97 as the mass of ^{203}Tl and 204.97 as the mass of ^{205}Tl given that the natural abundances of ^{203}Tl and ^{205}Tl are 29.50% and 70.50%, respectively.

5.11 204.4 u.

Radioactivity

Nuclei of certain atoms are unstable and undergo spontaneous changes that result in a particle or ray being emitted from the nucleus at high speed. Such nuclei are said to be **radioactive** because they emit radiation.

The three principal types of nuclear emissions are alpha (α) rays, beta (β) rays, and gamma (γ) rays.

Alpha rays are composed of the most massive particles of the three basic

Henri Becquerel accidentally discovered radioactivity in 1896 when he found that a uranium salt emitted rays that fogged his photographic plates.

forms of radiation. An alpha particle has a mass of 4 u and a charge of 2+. **Beta rays** are high-velocity electrons ejected from the nucleus. **Gamma rays** are one type of electromagnetic radiation. Other examples of electromagnetic radiations include x-rays, ultraviolet light, visible light, and infrared. These types of radiation exhibit properties of waves and have no measurable mass or charge.

Table 5.3 summarizes the properties of these three forms of radioactive emission.

TABLE 5.3 PROPERTIES OF THREE TYPES OF RADIATION

Name	Symbol	Mass, u (amu)	Charge	Penetration power
Alpha	α	4	2+	Low
Beta	β	1/1837	1−	Intermediate
Gamma	γ	none	none	High

Another distinguishing characteristic of the three types of radiation is their penetration power, their ability to penetrate and travel through matter. Gamma rays have the largest capacity to penetrate matter; in other words, they have the highest penetration power. Most gamma rays easily pass through wood and various thin metals. About 100 mm of lead or other dense type of matter is needed to provide

> Types of electromagnetic radiation include radio waves, microwaves, infrared, visible light, ultraviolet, x-rays, and gamma rays.

adequate shielding from gamma rays (Fig. 5.7). Beta rays are less penetrating than gamma rays. A 1-mm thick metal barrier will generally stop most beta rays. Alpha particles have the lowest penetration power. Most alpha rays are shielded by a 0.01 mm thickness of metal. Often a piece of paper, clothing, or your skin is an adequate shield against alpha rays.❖

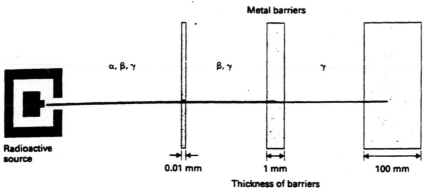

Figure 5.7 Alpha rays have the lowest penetration power of the three principal types of radiation. They are effectively locked by a 0.01 mm barrier of metal. Beta rays have higher penetration powers and can penetrate the barriers that block alpha rays. Most beta rays are stopped by a dense metal with a thickness of a few millimeters Gamma rays are the most penetrating rays. A barrier of about 100 mm of metal is required to provide adequate fielding from gamma rays.

REVIEW EXERCISES

5.12 (a) What are the three principal types of radioactivity?

(b) What is the mass and charge of each of these forms of radioactivity?

5.13 (a) What is meant by penetration power?

(b) Which form of radiation has the greatest capacity to penetrate matter?

5.3 ELECTRON CONFIGURATIONS OF ATOMS

Electrons

So far we have learned that electrons have a very small mass with respect to neutrons and protons, have a negative charge, and are found somewhere outside the nucleus. Because all atoms are electrically neutral, the number of electrons in an atom equals the number of protons (atomic number).

$$\text{Number of } e^- = \text{number of } p^+ = \text{atomic number (Z)}$$

It is only necessary to look at the periodic table to find the number of electrons in an atom: e.g., H. 1 e^-; C, 6 e^-; Ne, 10 e^-; and U, 92 e^-.

Bohr Model of the Atom

In 1913, Neils Bohr (1885-1962), a Danish physicist, proposed a model of the atom that was the forerunner of the current atomic model. He was principally concerned with the structure of the hydrogen atom, the simplest of all atoms, and how it related to the light released when the atom was heated to high temperatures. He visualized the H atom as having a nucleus with a series of circular orbits in which the electron traveled. Figure 5.8 shows a picture of the Bohr model of the atom. Bohr theorized that the electron in a H atom could only travel around the nucleus in these orbits and could never be found in the regions between the orbits.

The Bohr model of the atom was a very significant advance in the understanding of the structure of atoms. It incorporated the ideas of Max Planck (1858-1947), who proposed in 1900 that energy is not emitted in a continuous manner, but is released in discrete packets called *quanta*. Planck's proposal provided the foundation for one of the central theories of present-day

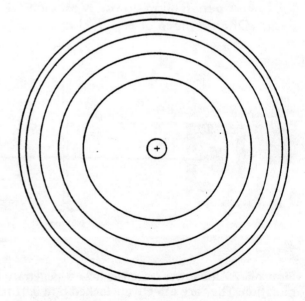

Figure 5.8 The Bohr model of the H atom has a positively charged nucleus surrounded by circular orbits where its one electron is found.

science—**quantum theory.** As an analogy to the quantum theory let us compare a person who walks up stairs to a person who walks up a ramp (Fig. 5.9). A person who walks up stairs can move only in fixed intervals as he climbs the stairs and can stop only at certain levels, corresponding to the steps, above the ground. In contrast a person who walks up the ramp can move up in any desired interval and can stop at any point above the ground.

The Bohr model could explain the spectrum of hydrogen. When samples of hydrogen gas or other gases are subjected to either high voltages or high temperatures, they release colored lights. For example, you have seen the characteristic intense red light released by a neon sign in a storefront. If the light released by gases is passed through a narrow slit and then through a prism, it is split into a series of bright lines (Fig. 5.10). Such an instrument for analyzing light is called a **spectroscope,** and the resulting colored lines at specific frequencies are called a **spectrum**. Figure 5.11 shows the spectrum produced by hydrogen. Each different element has its own characteristic spectrum.

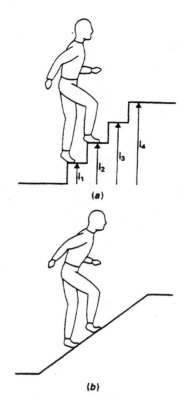

Figure 5.9 (a) A person who walks up stairs can only be at fixed distances from the ground (I_1, I_2, I_3, or I_4) because he must stop at one of the stairs. (b) A person who walks up a ramp can stop at many different heights above the ground.

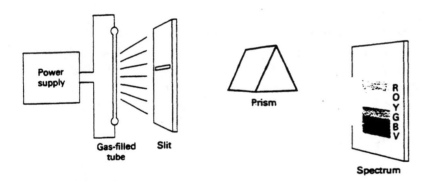

Figure 5.10 Light emitted from a gas excited by a high voltage is passed through a narrow silt and a prism. The prism diffracts (scatters) the light and separates it into its component frequencies.

Bohr used the quantum theory to explain the lines in the spectrum of hydrogen. He suggested that each orbit in the H atom corresponded to an energy level (Fig. 5.12). The first orbit, the one closest to the nucleus, was the lowest energy level; he called it the *ground-state* energy level. The second orbit was the second energy level, and each succeeding orbit was a higher energy level. He assigned a number, called the **principal**

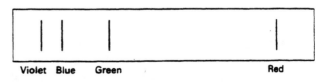

Violet Blue Green   Red

Figure 5.11 The visible spectrum of hydrogen shows red, green, blue, and violet lines. Bohr showed that the frequencies of these lines are related to differences in energies of the orbits in the H atom.

quantum number, n, to each energy level. The first energy level has the principal quantum number equal to 1 (n = 1). The second level has a principal quantum number equal to 2 (n = 2), and so forth. Most of the time the electron in hydrogen occupies the lowest energy state, the ground state (n = 1). When energy is transferred to the atom, the electron is moved, or excited, to a higher energy level (Fig. 5.13). Ultimately, the excited electron drops to lower energy levels and finally to the ground state. When electrons fall back, they release their energy in the form of quanta, discrete packets of energy with specific frequencies. Calculations by Bohr showed that his proposed energy levels could account for the frequencies of the lines in the H spectrum.

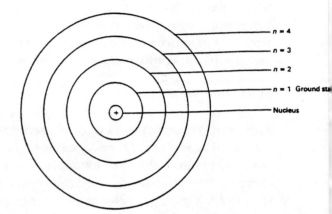

Figure 5.12 In the Bohr model of the atom, the lowest energy level or orbit is called the ground state (n = 1). The first excited state is the second energy level. Each orbit is at a fixed distance from the nucleus.

Bohr's theory showed that electrons are found in quantized energy levels. He used the model to explain the spectrum of H and calculated the velocity of the electron and the distance each energy level was from the nucleus. Nonetheless, the Bohr model had many limitations. The most serious limitation was that it could only explain the spectrum of H and hydrogenlike ions. It could not explain the structure of atoms that had two or more electrons.

The Bohr model of the atom was replaced with the **quantum mechanical** model of the atom in the mid-1920s, when men such as Louis de Broglie, Werner Heisenberg, and Erwin Schrödinger proposed new ideas concerning the nature and properties of electrons. The quantum mechanical model of the atom places electrons in regions of space called orbitals. While we no longer believe that electrons travel around the nucleus in circular orbits as suggested by Bohr, the idea of energy levels is carried over to the quantum mechanical model.

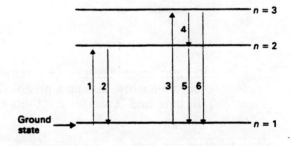

Figure 5.13 Energy is required to excite an electron from the first to the second energy level (1). When the electron falls back (2) to the first level, it releases that energy in the form a quantum, a packet of energy with a specific frequency. An electron excited from the first to the third energy level (3) can either release two quanta, falling from the third to the second (4) and then from the second to the first (5), or release one quantum if it falls directly from the third to the first level (6).

Orbital

An **orbital** is associated with a volume of space where there is a specific probability of finding electrons. An orbital can have no more than two electrons: orbital can be empty (no electrons), half-filled (one electron), or filled (two electrons). *It is important to note that orbitals are mathematical concepts and not "real" things, but are the product of the quantum mechanical theory* *of atoms. Thus, it is not technically correct to say that electrons occupy orbitals, but it is commonly done.*

Electrons are elusive particles, ones that cannot be directly observed. A German physicist, Werner Heisenberg (1901-1976), first proposed what is now called the **uncertainty principle**. This principle states that it is impossible to determine simultaneously the exact position and velocity of an electron. In simpler terms, the position of an electron in space cannot be pinpointed at a particular instant. Consequently, scientists no longer are concerned about identifying what path (the orbit) an electron takes as it travels around the nucleus. Instead, they identify the regions, or *orbital* where electrons are most likely to be found.

> In 1927, Werner Heisenberg (1901-1975), a student of Bohr, proposed the uncertainty principle. This radical idea and its implications were ultimately accepted by the scientific community, but it was never totally acceptable to Albert Einstein.

Chemists view orbitals as a geographer thinks of a population density map. A population density map shows an area such as the United States with regions shaded where a high probability of finding a person exists. Darkly shaded areas indicate regions where there is a good chance of finding a person (a high population density), and lightly shaded areas indicate regions where there is a lower probability (a low population density). Actually going to a darkly shaded region does not ensure that you will find a person; there is just a better chance of finding a person in this region.

Within the region of space defined by an orbital, electrons behave as if they are spinning on an axis. An electron can spin in either one direction or the other, in a manner similar to a spinning top. If there are two electrons in an orbital, one behaves as if it spins in one direction and the other behaves as if it spins in the opposite direction (Fig. 5.14). This idea that two electrons in an orbital have opposite spins was proposed by Wolfgang Pauli (1900-1958) and is referred to as the **Pauli exclusion principle**.

> In his teens, Wolfgang Pauli (1900 - 1958) published articles on relativity that were accepted by the scientific community. Pauli was an extremely productive theoretical physicist, but was clumsy in the laboratory.

Electron Energy Levels and Shells

A collection of orbitals at approximately the same average distance from the nucleus is referred to as an electron **shell.** Electrons closer to the nucleus are in lower energy shells, and electrons farther from the nucleus are in higher energy shells. On average, an electron in the first shell is closer to the nucleus than an electron that occupies the second shell because the first shell is at a lower energy level than the second shell. The average distance from the nucleus of an electron in the third shell is greater than that of one in the second shell (Fig. 5.15). Each shell is denoted by the **principal quantum number** *n*. The principal quantum number for the first shell is 1, the principal quantum number for the second shell is 2, etc.

Each shell has a maximum number of orbitals and

Figure 5.14 Electrons behave as if they were spinning on an axis. An electron can spin either in one direction or the opposite directing

electrons. Lower energy shells are closer to the nucleus, where less volume is available for the electrons to occupy. Mutual repulsion of electrons limits the number of electrons in a given region. Higher energy shells have greater volume for electrons to populate, diminishing the repulsion of the electrons. A shell, n, contains a maximum of n^2 orbitals and $2n^2$ electrons. Table 5.4 presents the theoretical maximum number of orbital and electrons for each shell.

TABLE 5.5 POPULATION OF ELECTRON ENERGY LEVELS

Shell, n	Orbitals, n^2	Electrons, $2n^2$
1	1	2
2	4	8
3	9	18
4	16	32
5	25	50

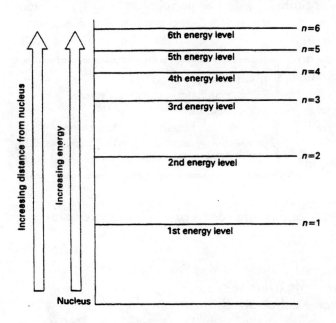

Figure 5.15 The first electron shell is the region closest to the nucleus. Higher energy shells are regions farther from the nucleus.

Subshells

All shells beyond the first are divided into two or more subshells. A **subshell** is composed of one or more orbitals that have similar characteristics. The number of subshells within a shell corresponds to the principal quantum number n of the shell. Thus, the first shell ($n = 1$) contains only one subshell. The second shell ($n = 2$) is composed of two subshells, the third shell ($n = 3$) has three subshells, and so on. We will consider the four lowest energy subshells. Subshells are denoted by a letter: *s* for the lowest-energy subshell; *p*, next higher energy subshell; *d*, higher still; and *f*, the highest-energy subshell of the four.

Each subshell contains a maximum number of orbitals and electrons that it can hold. Table 5.5 lists the maximum number of orbitals and electrons in each subshell. An *s* subshell can hold a maximum of two electrons because the *s* subshell is composed of only a single orbital. The 2*p* subshell is composed of three orbitals; thus, six electrons are the maximum number of electrons in a *p* subshell. Five and seven orbitals are found in the *d* and *f* subshells, which hold 10 and 14 electrons, respectively.

TABLE 5.5 ELECTRON SUBSHELL POPULATIONS

Subshell	Number of orbitals	Maximum number of electrons
s	1	2
p	3	6
d	5	10
f	7	14

Subshells are distinguished by the shapes of the orbitals of which they are composed. For example, the shape of the *s* subshell (or orbital) is shown in Fig. 5.16. Notice that the shading is darkest near the nucleus and becomes lighter farther from the nucleus, showing that the highest probability of finding an electron in an *s* orbital occurs closer to the nucleus rather than farther away. The overall shape of an *s* orbital is that of a sphere.

A more complex distribution is found for the *p* subshell. Each of the three *p* orbitals is shown in Fig. 5.17a. One of the *p* orbitals is aligned on the *x* axis, another along the *y* axis, and the third along the *z* axis. Note that the shape of a *p* orbital is different from that of the *s* orbital. The highest probability of finding electrons in a *p* orbital occurs along the axes. Figure 5.17b shows the three *p* orbitals superimposed on each other. Both *d* and *f* orbitals have even more complex distributions, and will not be considered in our discussion.

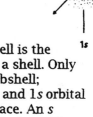

SUBLEVELS

s
p
d
f

1s

Figure 5.16 The 1s subshell is the lowest energy subshell in a shell. Only one orbital makes an *s* subshell; therefore, the 1s subshell and 1s orbital are the same region of space. An *s* orbital has the shape of a sphere. The highest probability for finding an electron in an 1s orbital is close to the nucleus.

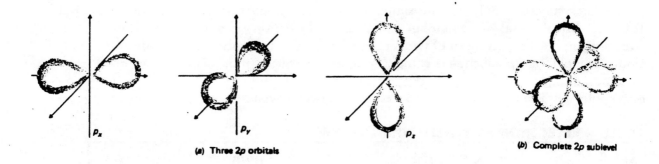

(a) Three 2p orbitals   (b) Complete 2p sublevel

Figure 5.17 The *2p* subshell is composed of three *2p* orbitals. Each *2p* orbital is located on a different axis and has a dumbbell shape. They are referred to as the p_x, p_y, and p_z orbitals.

REVIEW EXERCISES

5.14 How many total electrons are found in each of the following atoms?

(a) B
(b) K
(c) Mg
(d) Co
(e) Kr

5.15 Explain how the Bohr description of the placement of electrons in atoms is different from the quantum mechanical description.

5.16 (a) Where is the location of the fifth shell in relation to the fourth shell?

(b) Explain why electrons are identified according to the shell in which they reside.

5.17 What is the maximum number of electrons that can populate each of the following?

(a) second shell
(b) third shell
(c) an *s* subshell
(d) a *p* subshell
(e) an orbital?

5.17 (a) 8, (b) 18, (c) 2, (d) 6, (e) 2

Electron Arrangements

So far, we have found that each shell is divided into smaller regions called subshells, and each subshell is divided into orbitals. Each orbital contains a maximum of two electrons. Figure 5.18 shows the first through the sixth shells with their subshells and orbitals.

Electrons fill these orbitals starting from the lowest-energy orbital (first shell), and proceed, one electron at a time, filling each lower-energy orbital before filling a higher-energy orbital. The filling of lower-energy orbital before higher-energy orbital is known as the **aufbau principle**.

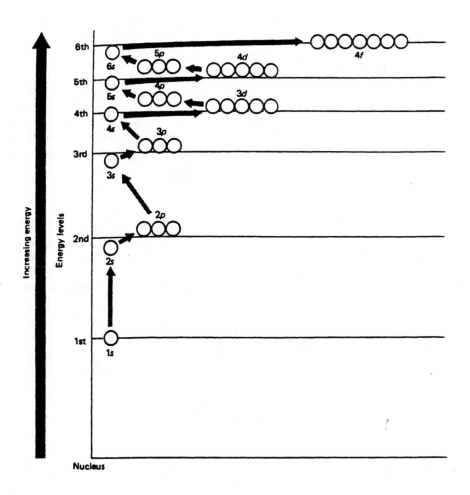

Figure 5.18 Each orbital is represented by a circle. Two electrons fill each orbital, starting with the lowest energy orbital and proceeding to the next higher energy orbital until all the electrons of an atom are accounted for.

We will now begin our study of the arrangement of electrons in atoms by considering where hydrogen's one electron is located. Then we will proceed to helium, which has two electrons. After He, we will add another electron to the two electrons of He to find the electron configuration of Li. In a similar manner, we will follow the order of the elements on the periodic table, adding one electron each time to the number found in the previous atom.

In all atoms, the lowest-energy orbital, the one closest to the nucleus, is the 1s orbital.

$$1s$$

Shell $\longrightarrow$ $\longleftarrow$ Subshell

The first number, 1 (the principal quantum number), refers to the shell where the electron is located, and the *s* identifies the subshell.

Hydrogen is the simplest atom with only one electron. We symbolize hydrogen's electron configuration (the representation of its occupied orbital) as follows:

Number of electrons in the subshell

$$1s^1$$

Hydrogen's electron is found in the *s* orbital of the lowest energy shell ($n = 1$).

Helium atoms contain two electrons ($Z = 2$). Because space is available for another electron in the $1s$ orbital, both electrons populate this orbital. The electron configuration of He is

$$He \quad 1s^2$$

A 2 is written as a superscript above the *s* to show that there are two electrons in the $1s$ orbital; the orbital is now filled. Because two is the maximum number of electrons that can occupy the first shell, the first shell is also filled.

Lithium ($Z = 3$) is the first atom to have an electron in the second shell. Three electrons are found in Li atoms; the first two electrons occupy the lower-energy shell, $1s$, and the remaining electron is found in the next higher energy $2s$ orbital. We write the electron configuration of Li as

> Lithium is a reactive metal with a very low density, 0.53g/cm^3. Because of its reactivity, it is not found uncombined in nature.

$$Li \quad 1s^2 2s^1$$

Although the second shell contains two subshells, *s* and *p*, the *s* subshell is lower in energy than that of the *p* (Fig. 5.19). Accordingly, the $2s$ subshell fills before an electron enters the $2p$ subshell.

The two lowest-energy electrons in beryllium ($Z = 4$) occupy the $1s$ orbital, the He configuration. The two outer electrons are in the $2s$ subshell, filling it. The configuration of Be is as follows.

$$Be \quad 1s^2 2s^2$$

In boron ($Z = 5$) the first four electrons occupy the same orbital as the four electrons in beryllium, $1s^2$ and $2s^2$. The fifth electron enters the higher-energy $2p$ subshell. Boron is the first element to possess an electron in the $2p$ subshell. The electron configuration of boron is

$$B \quad 1s^2 2s^2 2p^1$$

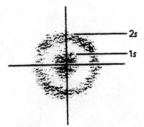

Figure 5.19 Electrons that occupy the $1s$ orbital are on an average closer to the nucleus than are electrons in the $2s$ orbital. The $2s$ orbital distribution is similar to the $1s$ except for being farther from the nucleus.

Because the p subshell has three orbitals and has the capacity to hold six electrons (Table 5.5), the next five atoms on the periodic table, C through Ne, fill the $2p$ subshell. Carbon (Z = 6) has one more electron than boron; therefore, the electron configuration of carbon is

$$C \quad 1s^2 2s^2 2p^2$$

In nitrogen (Z = 7), the next element on the periodic table, the $2p$ subshell becomes half-filled.

$$N \quad 1s^2 2s^2 2p^3$$

In the atoms O, F, and Ne, the $2p$ subshell fills as follows:

$$O \quad 1s^2 2s^2 2p^4$$
$$F \quad 1s^2 2s^2 2p^5$$
$$Ne \quad 1s^2 2s^2 2p^6$$

The $2p$ subshell of Ne (Z = 10) contains six electrons which is the maximum that the $2p$ can hold. Therefore, a Ne atom has a completely filled second shell. All atoms beyond Ne on the periodic table have more than 10 electrons, and thus have outer electrons in higher shells.

Sodium (Z = 11) has the same electron configuration as Ne for its inner level electrons ($1s^2 2s^2 2p^6$); the remaining electron occupies the lowest-energy subshell in the third shell: $3s^1$. The electron configuration for the Na atom is

$$Na \quad 1s^2 2s^2 2p^6 3s^1$$

You should note that the outer electron configuration of Na is the same as that of H and Li, except that the electron is in a higher-energy shell. Each of these atoms has one outer electron in an s subshell.

$$H \quad 1s^1$$
$$Li \quad 2s^1$$
$$Na \quad 3s^1$$

All group IA atoms have one outer-level s electron (s^1).

The **outer-level electron configuration** of an atom is also called the **valence electron configuration.** Both of these terms refer to the highest-energy occupied electron shell in an atom.

Magnesium (Z = 12), the next atom after Na on the periodic table, has the electron configuration

$$Mg \quad 1s^2 2s^2 2p^6 3s^2$$

All group IIA atoms have two electrons in their valence s subshell.

$$\begin{array}{ll} \text{Be} & 2s^2 \\ \text{Mg} & 3s^2 \\ \text{Ca} & 4s^2 \\ \text{Sr} & 5s^2 \\ \text{Ba} & 6s^2 \\ \text{Ra} & 7s^2 \end{array}$$

Always, atoms in the same group on the periodic table have the same number of valence electrons. Table 5.6 lists the valence electron configurations of the **representative elements**, those in groups IA (1) through VIIIA (18). From Table 5.6, we see that Al, an atom in group IIIA (13) with 13 electrons, has three valence electrons, two electrons in the $3s$ subshell and one in the $3p$ subshell. The complete electron configuration of Al is

$$\text{Al} \quad 1s^2 2s^2 2p^6 3s^2 3p^1$$

Each succeeding atom after aluminum has one more electron in the $3p$ subshell, ending with At with a completed $3p$ subshell.

$$\begin{array}{ll} \text{Si} & 1s^2 2s^2 2p^6 3s^2 3p^2 \\ \text{P} & 1s^2 2s^2 2p^6 3s^2 3p^3 \\ \text{S} & 1s^2 2s^2 2p^6 3s^2 3p^4 \\ \text{Cl} & 1s^2 2s^2 2p^6 3s^2 3p^5 \\ \text{Ar} & 1s^2 2s^2 2p^6 3s^2 3p^6 \end{array}$$

TABLE 5.6 OUTER ELECTRON CONFIGURATIONS of THE REPRESENTATIVE ELEMENTS

Group number in periodic table	Number of valence electrons	Valence electron configuration
IA (1)	1	s^1
IIA (2)	2	s^2
IIIA (13)	3	$s^2 p^1$
IVA (14)	4	$s^2 p^2$
VA (15)	5	$s^2 p^3$
VIA (16)	6	$s^2 p^4$
VIIA (17)	7	$s^2 p^5$
VIIIA (18)	8	$s^2 p^{6*}$

*Except He, which is s^2 only.

Up to this point, the electrons have filled the orbital in an orderly fashion. Despite the fact that the third shell has three subshells, s, p, and d, the $3d$ subshell is slightly higher in energy than the $4s$ subshell. Hence, the $4s$ subshell fills before the $3d$. Thus, the electron configurations for potassium, K, and calcium, Ca, are

$$K \qquad 1s^2 2s^2 2p^6 3s^2 3p^6 4s^1$$
$$Ca \qquad 1s^2 2s^2 2p^6 3s^2 3p^6 4s^2$$

Scandium, Sc, is the first atom to have an electron in the 3d orbital.

$$Sc \qquad 1s^2 2s^2 2p^6 3s^2 3p^6 3d^1 4s^2$$

The electron configuration of Sc is also written as follows to show the order in which the subshells fill.

$$Sc \quad 1s^2 2s^2 2p^6 3s^2 3p^6 4s^2 3d^1$$

> Scandium is a metal named for the Scandinavian countries where it is almost exclusively found on earth it 8 also found in rather Large amounts in the sun.

From Sc to Zn, the 3d subshell fills somewhat irregularly.
Zinc is the first atom to have a complete 3d subshell. Its electron configuration is

$$Zn \qquad 1s^2 2s^2 2p^6 3s^2 3p^6 3d^{10} 4s^2$$

After the 3d is full, the 4p fills. Gallium, Ga, is the first element with a 4p electron.

$$Ga \qquad 1s^2 2s^2 2p^6 3s^2 3p^6 3d^{10} 4s^2 4p^1$$

After Ga, the electrons fill the 4p in the atoms Ge to Kr.

$$Ge \qquad 1s^2 2s^2 2p^6 3s^2 3p^6 3d^{10} 4s^2 4p^2$$
$$As \qquad 1s^2 2s^2 2p^6 3s^2 3p^6 3d^{10} 4s^2 4p^3$$
$$Se \qquad 1s^2 2s^2 2p^6 3s^2 3p^6 3d^{10} 4s^2 4p^4$$
$$Br \qquad 1s^2 2s^2 2p^6 3s^2 3p^6 3d^{10} 4s^2 4p^5$$
$$Kr \qquad 1s^2 2s^2 2p^6 3s^2 3p^6 3d^{10} 4s^2 4p^6$$

bracket?

To save time, chemists have an abbreviated way to write electron configurations. They write the noble gas atom inside parentheses to represent the inner-core electrons. For example, the atoms Ge to Br have the inner-core configuration of Ar, $1s^2 2s^2 2p^6 3s^2 3p^6 3d^{10}$, which is represented by [Ar]. Therefore, the shorthand notation for the electron configurations of Ge to Br are as follows.

$$Ge \qquad [Ar]\ 3d^{10}\ 4s^2 4p^2$$
$$As \qquad [Ar]\ 3d^{10}\ 4s^2 4p^3$$
$$Se \qquad [Ar]\ 3d^{10}\ 4s^2 4p^4$$
$$Br \qquad [Ar]\ 3d^{10}\ 4s^2 4p^5$$

The next two atoms are rubidium, Rb, and strontium, Sr. With these atoms the 5s fills. After a p subshell fills, the next higher energy s subshell fills.

$$Rb \qquad 1s^2 2s^2 2p^6 3s^2 3p^6 3d^{10} 4s^2 4p^6 5s^1$$
$$Sr \qquad 1s^2 2s^2 2p^6 3s^2 3p^6 3d^{10} 4s^2 4p^6 5s^2$$

After the 5s fills, the 4d fills. The first atom with a 4d electron is yttrium, Y. The last atom in this series is cadmium, Cd, with a completely filled 4d and 5s.

$$Y \qquad 1s^2 2s^2 2p^6 3s^2 3p^6 3d^{10} 4s^2 4p^6 4d^1 5s^2$$
$$Cd \qquad 1s^2 2s^2 2p^6 3s^2 3p^6 3d^{10} 4s^2 4p^6 4d^{10} 5s^2$$

Again, after a d subshell fills then the next higher-energy p subshell fills. Thus, the 5p fills after the 4d.

$$In \qquad 1s^2 2s^2 2p^6 3s^2 3p^6 3d^{10} 4s^2 4p^6 4d^{10} 5s^2 5p^1$$
$$Sn \qquad 1s^2 2s^2 2p^6 3s^2 3p^6 3d^{10} 4s^2 4p^6 4d^{10} 5s^2 5p^2$$
$$Sb \qquad 1s^2 2s^2 2p^6 3s^2 3p^6 3d^{10} 4s^2 4p^6 4d^{10} 5s^2 5p^3$$
$$Te \qquad 1s^2 2s^2 2p^6 3s^2 3p^6 3d^{10} 4s^2 4p^6 4d^{10} 5s^2 5p^4$$
$$I \qquad 1s^2 2s^2 2p^6 3s^2 3p^6 3d^{10} 4s^2 4p^6 4d^{10} 5s^2 5p^5$$
$$Xe \qquad 1s^2 2s^2 2p^6 3s^2 3p^6 3d^{10} 4s^2 4p^6 4d^{10} 5s^2 5p^6$$

Method to Write Electron Configurations

It is not necessary to memorize the order of the filling of subshells. Instead recognize that the periodic table is organized according to the electron configurations of atoms. In Fig. 5.20, the periodic table is marked to indicate the order in which electrons fill subshells. All elements in groups IA (1) and IIA (2) have s electrons in their outer shell. Elements in groups IIIA (13) through VIIIA (18) have both s and p electrons in their outer levels. Elements in groups IIIB (3) through IIB (12), the transition elements, have electrons that fill the d and f subshells.

To write electron configurations, follow the periodic table in order of increasing atomic number. Numbers that denote periods, 1 to 7, correspond to electron shells, and the number at the top of each vertical column helps give the valence configuration. Example Problem 5.3 illustrates how the periodic table may be used to help you write electron configurations.

Example Problem 5.3

Using the periodic table, write the complete electron configuration for strontium, Sr.

> Strontium is a metal that was discovered by Sir Humphry Davy in 1808. Sr is found in nature as a mixture of four isotopes. It is a reactive metal that will spontaneously combust if finely divided.

Solution

1. Find Sr on the periodic table.
Sr has 38 electrons, is in the fifth period, and is a member of group IIA (2). All elements in group IIA (2) have an outer electron configuration of two electrons in the s orbital, s^2.

2. Follow the periodic table in order of increasing atomic number.
Considering the periodic table in Fig. 5.21, we see that the inner electron configuration of Sr is the same as that of Kr (Z = 36). The electron configuration of Kr is

$$Kr \qquad 1s^2 2s^2 2p^6 3s^2 3p^6 3d^{10} 4s^2 4p^6$$

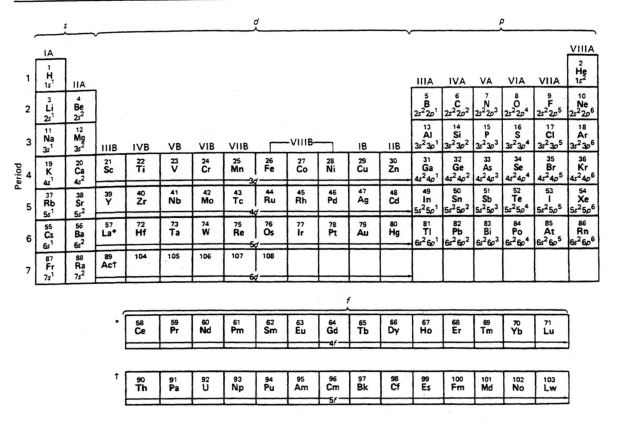

Figure 5.20 Elements are listed on the periodic table according to the electron configurations of their atoms. Atoms in the same group have the same valence subshell configurations. Following the periodic table in order of increasing atomic number is an easy way to write the electron configuration of an atom.

To this we add the two valence electrons, $5s^2$, producing the complete configuration for Sr:

$$\text{Sr} \quad 1s^2 2s^2 2p^6 3s^2 3p^6 3d^{10} 4s^2 4p^6 5s^2$$

The shorthand notation for Sr is [Kr] $5s^2$. Always check to see that the total number of electrons in the electron configuration equals the atomic number. For this example, the sum of the superscripts equals 38, which is the atomic number of Sr.

Exercise

Write the complete electron configuration for Ba. ($1s^2 2s^2 2p^6 3s^2 3p^6 3d^{10} 4s^2 4p^6 4d^{10} 5s^2 5p^6 6s^2$)

Group

Period	IA	IIA						Transition metals					IIIA	IVA	VA	VIA	VIIA	VIIIA
1	1 H $1s$																	2 He $1s$
2	3 Li	4 Be $2s$											5 B	6 C	7 N $2p$	8 O	9 F	10 Ne
3	11 Na	12 Mg $3s$											13 Al	14 Si	15 P $3p$	16 S	17 Cl	18 Ar
4	19 K $4s$	20 Ca	21 Sc	22 Ti	23 V	24 Cr	25 Mn $3d$	26 Fe	27 Co	28 Ni	29 Cu	30 Zn	31 Ga	32 Ge	33 As $4p$	34 Se	35 Br	36 Kr
5	37 Rb	38 Sr $5s^2$	39 Y	40 Zr	41 Nb	42 Mo	43 Tc	44 Ru	45 Rh	46 Pd	47 Ag	48 Cd	49 In	50 Sn	51 Sb	52 Te	53 I	54 Xe
6	55 Cs	56 Ba	57 La	72 Hf	73 Ta	74 W	75 Re	76 Os	77 Ir	78 Pt	79 Au	80 Hg	81 Tl	82 Pb	83 Bi	84 Po	85 At	86 Rn
7	87 Fr	88 Ra	89 Ac	104	105	106	107	108										

Figure 5.21 Start with H and follow along the periodic table until you reach Sr. As you proceed toward Sr write the electrons that fill each subshell: $1s^2 2s^2 2p^6 3s^2 3p^6 3d^{10} 4s^2 4p^6 5s^2$.

REVIEW EXERCISE

5.18 Write the complete electron configuration for each of the following atoms.

(a) Li
(b) N
(c) K
(d) Ga
(e) Br

5.18 (a) $1s^2 2s^1$, (b) $1s^2 2s^2 2p^3$, (c) $1s^2 2s^2 2p^6 3s^2 3p^6 4s^1$, (d) $1s^2 2s^2 2p^6 3s^2 3p^6 3d^{10} 4s^2 4p^1$, (e) $1s^2 2s^2 2p^6 3s^2 3p^6 3d^{10} 4s^2 4p^5$

Lewis Symbols

The valence configurations of atoms for the most part determine the properties of elements, especially their chemical properties. Chemists frequently draw Lewis symbols (also called dot formulas) as a means of conveniently expressing the valence electron configurations of atoms. Use the following two rules to write the Lewis symbol for an atom:

1. Write the symbol of the atom.
2. Place one dot around the symbol for each electron in the **outermost** shell of the atom.

Always remember that inner-level electrons are never shown in Lewis symbols. Because a H atom only has one electron ($1s^1$), its Lewis symbol has only one dot next to its atomic symbol.

$$H \cdot$$

Helium has two electrons ($1s^2$), so its Lewis symbol shows two dots next to its symbol.

$$He :$$

You should note that the two dots in the Lewis symbol for He are written together to show that the electrons are in the same orbital.

Lithium has an electron configuration of $1s^2 2s^1$. Only the $2s^1$ is in the valence shell, so only one dot is placed next to the symbol of Li (don't count the dot in the i of Li).

> G. N. Lewis (1875-1946) was an American chemist who obtained his Ph.D. from Harvard University. In 1933, he prepared a sample of heavy water, D_2O. Heavy water has two deuterium atoms, ^2H, in place of regular hydrogen atoms, ^1H.

$$Li \cdot$$

The valence electron configuration of Be is $2s^2$; therefore, two dots are placed next to Be in the Lewis symbol.

$$Be :$$

If the atom has p electrons in the outer shell, a number of different arrangements of dots around the symbol can be written. For example, the Lewis symbol for carbon ($1s^2 2s^2 2p^2$) can be written as follows:

$$\cdot \overset{\cdot}{\underset{\cdot}{C}} \cdot \qquad \overset{\cdot \cdot}{\underset{\cdot}{C}} \cdot$$

In the first Lewis symbol, the dots representing electrons are written symmetrically around the symbol. However, some chemists prefer to write the dots in a way corresponding to the way the electrons are paired in orbitals. In carbon, two electrons are paired in the $2s$; but each of the two electrons in the $2p$ occupies a different p orbital.

All atoms in a chemical group have the same number of dots around their Lewis symbols because all have the same number of outer electrons. For example, atoms in group VIIA (17) all possess seven outer-level electrons. Thus, the general Lewis symbol for these atoms is

$$\overset{\cdot \cdot}{\underset{\cdot \cdot}{:X}} \cdot$$

in which X is either F, Cl, Br, I, or At.

Figure 5.25 illustrates the Lewis symbols for all atoms in groups IA through VIIIA on the periodic table, and Example Problem 5.4 shows how the Lewis symbols are written for three different atoms. ❖

```
                              Group
                               IA                                                VIIIA
                        ┌──────┐                                              ┌──────┐
                      1 │  H•  │                                              │ He:  │
                        ├──────┼──────┬──────┬──────┬──────┬──────┬──────┐   ├──────┤
                        │      │ IIA  │ IIIA │ IVA  │  VA  │ VIA  │ VIIA │   │      │
                      2 │ Li•  │ Be:  │  B:  │ •C:  │ •N:  │ •O:  │ :F:  │   │ :Ne: │
                        ├──────┼──────┼──────┼──────┼──────┼──────┼──────┤   ├──────┤
                      3 │ Na•  │ Mg:  │ Al:  │ •Si: │ •P:  │ •S:  │ :Cl: │   │ :Ar: │
                  Period ├──────┼──────┼──────┼──────┼──────┼──────┼──────┤   ├──────┤
                      4 │  K•  │ Ca:  │ Ga:  │ •Ge: │ •As: │ •Se: │ :Br: │   │ :Kr: │
                        ├──────┼──────┼──────┼──────┼──────┼──────┼──────┤   ├──────┤
                      5 │ Rb•  │ Sr:  │ In:  │ •Sn: │ •Sb: │ •Te: │ :I:  │   │ :Xe: │
                        ├──────┼──────┼──────┼──────┼──────┼──────┼──────┤   ├──────┤
                      6 │ Cs•  │ Ba:  │ Tl:  │ •Pb: │ •Bi: │ •Po: │ :At: │   │ :Rn: │
                        ├──────┼──────┼──────┴──────┴──────┴──────┴──────┘   └──────┘
                      7 │ Fr•  │ Ra:  │
                        └──────┴──────┘
```

Figure 5.22 Lewis symbols of the representative elements.

Example Problem 5.4
Draw the Lewis symbols for (a) Si, (b) Rb, and (c) Te.

Solution
(a) Silicon belongs to group IVA (14) and has an outer electron configuration of $3s^2 3p^2$. Each member of group IVA has four outer electrons ($s^2 p^2$); therefore, the Lewis symbol for Si is

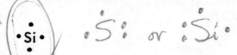

(b) Rubidium belongs to group IA (1) and has an outer electron configuration of $5s^1$, one outer electron. Consequently, the Lewis symbol for Rb is

Rb •

(c) Tellurium belongs to group VIA and has an outer electron configuration of $5s^2 5p^4$; thus, six dots are placed around its symbol.

:Te•

Exercise
Draw the Lewis structure for radium and lead. (Ra:, :Pb:)

REVIEW EXERCISES
5.19 Draw the Lewis symbols for each of the following atoms.

(a) S
(b) Kr

5.20 Draw Lewis symbols for each of the following atoms.

(a) Fr
(b) As.

5.19 (a) S has 6 valence electrons, (b) Kr has eight valence electrons; 5.20 (a) Fr has one valence electron, (b) As has five valence electrons.

WorldWideWolfe CHEMISTRY LINKS

Connect to WorldWideWolfe at

http://www.mindspring.com/~drwolfe/WWWolfe_hcc_1025_links.htm

and link to the following sites.

Atoms

1. Atomic Structure This includes a discussion of the history of the development of the modern concept of the atom. This is not that important in CHM1025. It also has a basic discussion of quantum theory. The most important information on this page is the discussion of electronic notations.

2. Atoms and Ions A good discussion of atoms and the history of the development of the atomic theory. It has Learning Objectives, Lecture Notes, References and Resources, and Glossary.

3. Atoms and Elements A short discussion of atoms, elements, isotopes, and the periodic table. It includes many links with the discussions.

SUMMARY

John Dalton proposed the first true scientific theory of atoms in the beginning of the nineteenth century. He thought that atoms were very small solid spheres. After the discovery of protons and electrons, a new model of the atom was proposed by **J. J. Thomson.** The Thomson model of the atom is called the "plum pudding" model because he pictured a structure that had electrons embedded in an atom that had a uniform positive charge from the protons. **Rutherford** changed our thoughts about atoms when he discovered that the atom has a nucleus.

According to modern atomic theory, the atom is a small particle composed of a very dense nucleus that contains protons and neutrons, with outer regions sparsely populated by electrons. **Protons** and **neutrons** have approximately the same mass, 1 u (unified atomic mass unit). Electrons have an extremely tiny mass, only 1/1837 u. However, electrons possess a full negative charge, equal in magnitude but opposite in sign to that of the proton. **Neutrons** have no electric charge.

The **atomic number, Z,** of an atom equals the number of protons in the nucleus of the atom, and the **mass number, A,** equals the total number of protons and neutrons in the nucleus. If atoms have the same atomic number but different mass members, they are called **isotopes.** When dealing with elements composed of a mixture of isotopes, chemists use **atomic mass** (atomic weight), which is the average mass of the isotopes of an element compared with the mass of the ^{12}C isotope.

Orbitals are regions around the nucleus where there is a high probability of finding electrons. An orbital holds a maximum of two electrons. A set of orbitals with similar characteristics and nearly the same energy is called a **subshell.** Electrons in their lowest energy states are found in four different subshells: s, p, d, and f. Subshells with similar energies are grouped into **shells.**

Electrons fill orbitals in atoms, starting with the lowest-energy orbital, and proceeding to higher-energy orbital Each different atom has its own specific **electron configuration.** Electron configurations are represented by writing the number that corresponds to the shell next to the letter that designates the subshell, then writing the number of electrons that occupy the subshell as a superscript above the letter. For example, the electron configuration of a hydrogen atom is $1s^1$.

Atoms in a chemical group the same number of valence electrons in the same configuration only differing in their energy. The number at the top of each group corresponds to the total number of electrons in the outermost shell. For example, each element in group IA has one valence electron. Outer electron configurations are often represented by writing **Lewis symbols.**

KEY TERMS

atomic number	orbit
atomic mass	orbital
electric charge	radiation
electron configuration	radioactivity
electron	shell
shell	spectroscopy
isotope	spectrum
Lewis symbol	subshell
mass number	subshell
nucleus	unified atomic mass unit

STUDY GUIDELINES

After completing Chapter 5, you should be able to:

1. List the main principles of Dalton's atomic theory, and explain how the Dalton model of the atom differs from the quantum mechanical model

2. Discuss how J. J. Thomson and Ernest Rutherford changed the model of the atom

3. List the properties of the fundamental components of an atom

4. Determine the composition of an atom given the atomic and mass numbers

5. Write the complete symbol of an atom given the number of protons and neutrons

6. Identify isotopes of an element

7. Calculate the atomic mass of an element given the masses of its isotopes and their natural abundances

8. Explain the importance of the atomic mass scale

9. Describe the Bohr model of the H atom

10. Discuss the quantum mechanical model of the atom

11. Describe what is meant by an electron orbital

12. Distinguish among electron shells, subshells, and orbitals

13. List the maximum number of electrons found in shells, subshells, and orbitals

14. Write the electron configuration and Lewis symbol for a given atom

15. Write the valence electron configuration for an atom

EXERCISES

5.21 Define the following terms: unified atomic mass unit, electric charge, nucleus, radioactivity, atomic number, mass number, isotope, atomic mass, orbit, orbital, electron shell, subshell, Lewis symbol, spectrum.

Development of the Modern Atomic Theory

5.22 Why is Dalton credited with the discovery of the first scientific atomic model when Democritus proposed an atomic theory many years before?

5.23 (a) What parts of Dalton's atomic theory are accepted today? (b) What parts of Dalton's atomic theory are no longer accepted?

5.24 Explain how J. J. Thomson changed the model of the atom.

5.25 (a) How did Rutherford change the model of the atom? (b) Describe the experiment he performed.

5.26 (a) What type of radiation did Rutherford use in the experiment in which he discovered the nucleus? (b) Why did Rutherford hypothesize that the radiation would go through the gold leaf undeflected? (c) Why was only a small percent of the radiation deflected through large angles?

5.27 (a) Describe the Bohr model of the atom.

(b) How was the Bohr model different from the Rutherford model of the atom? (c) How does the Bohr model of the atom differ from our modern concept of the atom?

5.28 How does the Bohr model of the atom explain the spectrum of hydrogen? Use a diagram in your explanation.

5.29 Propose a reason why the neutron was not discovered until 1932, approximately 50 years after the discovery of the proton and electron.

5.30 What is the mass in unified atomic mass units and the charge of (a) a proton, (b) an electron, (c) a neutron?

5.31 (a) Derive a conversion factor that equates unified atomic mass units and grams. (b) Calculate the mass in grams of a proton from its mass in atomic mass units.

5.32 Describe what happens when the following charged particles are brought close to each other: (a) two protons, (b) proton and electron, and (c) neutron and electron.

5.33 Complete the following table by providing all missing information:

Structure of Atoms

Symbol	Atomic number	Mass number	Number of protons	Number of neutrons	Number of electrons
(a) $^3_1$H					
(b) $^{18}_8$O					
(c) $^{23}_{11}$Na					
(d)	15	31			
(e)	18	40			
(f)	23	51			
(g)			27	32	
(h)			35	46	
(i)				62	46
(j)		195			78

5.34 How many protons, neutrons, and electrons are there in each of the following atoms: (a) ^{108}Pd, (b) ^{70}Ge, (c) ^{48}Ti, (d) ^{210}At?

5.35 Write the symbols for the atoms that have the following number of protons and neutrons: (a) $p^+ = 65$; $n° = 94$, (b) $p^+ = 53$; $n° = 74$, (c) $p^+ = 44$; $n° = 58$

5.36 What types of radiation have the following properties: (a) Penetrates relatively dense matter; (b) is an electron that moves at high speed; (c) resembles a form of energy more than matter; (d) most massive and has a low penetration power?

Isotopes and Atomic Mass

5.37 (a) What are the three principal isotopes found in a natural sample of uranium? (b) How do the isotopes differ?

5.38 (a) What atom is used as the standard for the atomic mass scale? (b) Could another atom be used as the standard? If so, how would this be accomplished?

5.39 How does atomic mass differ from mass number? Give an example.

5.40 Europium, Eu, is composed of two isotopes: ^{151}Eu (mass = 150.92 u) and ^{153}Eu (mass = 152.92 u). If ^{151}Eu and ^{153}Eu natural abundances are 47.82% and 52.18%, respectively, calculate the atomic mass of Eu.

5.41   Rubidium is composed of two isotopes: ^{85}Rb and ^{87}Rb. The mass of ^{85}Rb is 84.9117 u, and its natural abundance is 72.15%; the mass of ^{87}Rb is 86.909 u, and its natural abundance is 27.85%. What is the atomic mass of rubidium?

5.42   Use the following mass and natural abundance data to calculate the atomic mass of thallium, Tl.

Isotope	Mass, u	Percent abundance, %
^{203}Tl	202.97	29.50
^{205}Tl	204.97	70.50

5.43   (a) Calculate the atomic mass of copper, Cu. from the information given in Table 5.2. (b) Calculate the atomic mass of germanium, Ge, from the data in Table 5.2.

Electron configurations

5.44   (a) Draw a figure that shows the Bohr model of the hydrogen atom. (b) Label the first four shells. (c) What is the ground state orbit in the Bohr atom?

5.45   (a) Who first proposed the quantum theory? (b) What is the main premise of quantum theory?

5.46   Explain how Bohr incorporated quantum theory into his model of the atom.

5.47   (a) How is the spectrum of an element obtained? (b) What is the name of the instrument used to obtain the spectrum of an element?

5.48   How does the Bohr model of the atom explain the existence of the lines in the spectrum of H?

5.49   (a) What is the importance of the principal quantum number? (b) What is the principal quantum number for the ground state electron in a H atom?

5.50   What were the main limitations of the Bohr model of the atom?

5.51   (a) What is an orbital? (b) How are orbitals designated?

5.52   Write the maximum number of electrons that can be located in the ground state of each of the following: (a) an orbital, (b) the d subshell, (c) a Be atom, (d) third shell, (e) the f subshell, (f) a Ca atom, (g) 4p subshell of As, (h) 3d subshell of Cr, (i) 5s subshell of Sr, (j) fifth shell of Br, (k) 4d subshell of Cd.

5.53   How does the quantum mechanical model describe the location of electrons in atoms?

5.54   For each of the following, identify the region closest to the nucleus: fourth, fifth, sixth, or seventh shell, (b) 4s, 4p, or 4d subshell, (c) 3s, 4s, or 5s subshell.

5.55   Write the complete electron configuration for each of the following atoms: (a) Li, (b) C, (c) Na, (d) Al, (e) K, (f) Zn, (g) Kr, (h) Sc, (i) Ge, (l) Se.

5.56   Write the complete electron configuration for each of the following atoms: (a) Ba, (b) Fr, (c) Te, (d) Pb, (e) Rn.

5.57   Write the valence electron configuration for each of the following atoms: (a) Rb, (b) Ca, (c) Ga, (d) Se, (e) Br, (f) Sn, (g) Sb, (h) Ra, (i) At, (j) Fr.

5.58   Write the symbols for the elements with the following electron configurations:
(a) $1s^2 2s^2 2p^3$
(b) $1s^2 2s^2 2p^6 3s^2$
(c) $1s^2 2s^2 2p^6 3s^2 3p^3$
(d) $1s^2 2s^2 2p^6 3s^2 3p^6 3d^{10} 4s^2 4p^2$
(e) $1s^2 2s^2 2p^6 3s^2 3p^4$
(f) $1s^2 2s^2 2p^6 3s^2 3p^6 3d^{10} 4s^2 4p^5$
(g) $1s^2 2s^2 2p^6 3s^2 3p^6 3d^{10} 4s^2 4p^6 5s^1$
(h) $1s^2 2s^2 2p^6 3s^2 3p^6 3d^{10} 4s^2 4p^6 4d^{10} 5s^2 5p^6$

5.59   Draw the Lewis symbols for each of the following: (a) N, (b) Rb, (c) Sb, (d) Br, (e) Rn, (f) P, (g) Ge, (h) Se, (i) Si, (j) Ba.

5.60   Draw the Lewis symbols for each of the following atoms: (a) Al, (b) O. (c) Mg, (d) Pb, (e) Xe, (f) K, (g) s, (h) Ra, (i) Cs, (j) As.

5.61   Identify the atom or atoms with the following characteristics: (a) first group IIA (2) atom to have a 3s outer electron; (b) group VIA atom(s) with 4p electrons; (e) atom(s) with atomic number less than 43 that have electrons in the 4d subshell; (d) group IIA (2) atom(s) without occupied orbital; (e) period 4 atoms with more than five outer electrons; (f) atom(s) that only have s electrons.

5.62 What electron configuration would each of the following achieve if they lost or gained the stated number of electrons: (a) Mg, loses 2 electrons; (b) N, gains 3 electrons; (c) F, gains 1 electron; (d) I, gains one electron?

5.63 (a) Write the shorthand electron configuration for the element lead. (b) What is the inner-shell noble gas configuration?

5.64 (a) What is the valence electron configuration for antimony, Sb? (b) How many electrons would antimony need to gain to reach a noble gas configuration?

5.65 Consider the elements zinc, cadmium, and mercury. What common characteristic is shared in terms of their electron configurations?

Additional Exercises

5.66 How did the Dalton model of the atom differ from the model proposed by Democritus?

5.67 Which scientist gave us each of the following models of the atom: (a) quantum mechanical model, (b) nuclear model, (c) electrons orbiting a central nucleus, (d) "plum pudding" model?

5.68 How many protons, neutrons, and electrons are found in each of the following atoms: (a) ^{208}Po, (b) ^{235}U, (c) ^{180}Hf, (d) ^{205}Tl?

5.69 Write the symbols for at least two isotopes of each of the following atoms: (a) ^{131}Xe, (b) ^{16}O, (c) ^{24}Mg, (d) ^{139}La.

5.70 Write the electron configurations for the lowest-energy excited states for the following atoms: (a) Na, (b) Ne, (c) Xe.

5.71 (a) What is the electron configuration for Mg if it loses two electrons? (b) What atom has the same electron configuration as Mg has after it loses two electrons? (c) What would you have to do in order to remove two electrons from Mg?

5.72 (a) State the Pauli exclusion principle. (b) Why must we talk of the apparent spin of electrons instead of being more definite with regard to their spin

properties?

5.73 If the diameter of the nucleus of an atom could be increased in size to 1 cm, what would be the approximate diameter of the atom? *Hint*: Find the necessary data in the chapter.

5.74 By what degree would the attractive force between a proton and an electron decrease if the distance between the two was tripled?

5.75 Use the information in the following table to calculate the atomic mass of lead, Pb.

Isotope	Mass, u	Percent abundance, %
^{204}Pb	203.9731	1.50
^{206}Pb	205.9745	23.6
^{207}Pb	206.9759	22.6
^{208}Pb	207.9766	52.3

5.76 The atomic mass of silicon, Si, is 28.086. ^{28}Si, ^{29}Si, and ^{30}Si are the three isotopes that compose Si. ^{28}Si has a mass of 27.9769 u and natural abundance of 92.21%. ^{29}Si has a mass of 28.9765 u and a natural abundance of 4.70%. If the percent abundance is 3.09%, calculate the mass of ^{30}Si.

5.77 Manganese is composed of only one isotope. What is the mass number of this isotope?

5.78 How did Heisenberg's uncertainty principle change our thoughts about the nature of the atom?

5.79 (a) Write the electron configuration for Cr. (b) Compare the electron configuration you wrote to the actual configuration: $1s^2 2s^2 2p^6 3s^2 3p^6 3d^5 4s^1$. (c) Use the aufbau principle to propose a reason why the expected and actual configurations are different.

5.80 Bohr proposed the following equation to calculate the energies of the orbits in the H atom:

$$E_n = \frac{-2.18 \times 10^{-18} \, \text{J}}{n^2}$$

in which E_n is the energy of the nth orbit and n is the principal quantum number. Calculate the energies associated with the first four orbits of the H atom.

5.81 Describe how the shapes of each of the following pairs of orbitals differ: (a) $1s$ and $2s$, (b) $1s$ and $2p$, (c) $2p$ and $3p$.

5.82 Draw the orbital diagram for the outermost shell of each of the following: (a) In, (b) Sb, (c) Po, (d) Ba.

5.83 Write the electron configurations for the two elements that have completely filled outer shells.

5.84 Write the electron configuration for element 103, Lr.

5.85 ^{6}Li and ^{3}Li are the two isotopes of Li that exist in nature. $^6_3$Li has a mass of 6.015 u, and $^7_3$Li has a mass of 7.016 u. If the atomic mass of Li is 6.941, calculate the percent abundance of each isotope.

5.86 The approximate diameter of the nucleus of an Al atom is 286 pm. Calculate the volume of the nucleus of Al in cubic centimeters, using the formula $V = 4/3\pi r^3$, in which V is the volume, π is 3.14, and r is the radius of the nucleus.

Notes and Calculations:

Chapter 5 Pretest Assignment

1.   Complete each of the following statements with the correct word, number, or phase.

   a. _____ is a region of space where there is a high probability
   of finding an electron.
   b. _____ is the complete electron configuration for silicon.
   c. _____ is the type of radiation with the least penetration
   power.
   d. _____ are the four different types of subshells.
   e. _____ subshells make up the fourth shell.
   f. _____ equals the number of protons in the nucleus of an
   atom.
   g. _____ is the Lewis symbol for polonium, Po.
   h. _____ is the subshell that fills after the 4f.
   i. An isotope is an atom with the same _____ but has a
   different _____ .

2. Write the complete electron configurations for the following atoms.

   a. aluminum   _____

   b. strontium   _____

   c. thallium   _____

3.   Answer the questions about the following isotope.

$$^{197}Au$$

   a. number of protons   _____

   b. number of neutrons   _____

   c. number of electrons   _____

   d. atomic mass   _____

4.   List three components of the Dalton model of the atom.

   _____

   _____

   _____

5.   Copper is composed of two isotopes: ^{63}Cu and ^{65}Cu. The mass of the ^{63}Cu isotope is 62.9298 and its natural abundance is 69.09%. The mass of the ^{65}Cu isotope is 64.9278 and its natural abundance is 30.91%. Calculate the atomic mass of copper.

6.   a. Write the complete electron configuration for arsenic.

        _____

        b. Draw the Lewis symbol for arsenic.

        _____

        c. How many protons are in the nucleus of an arsenic atom?

        _____

CHAPTER 6

Periodic Properties of Elements and Atoms

6.1 INTRODUCTION

Development of the Modern Periodic Table

Chemists arrange the elements on the periodic table according to the electron configurations of their atoms. However, note that scientists developed the periodic table in the nineteenth century before the contemporary theory of atoms had been developed. To gain a better insight into the nature of our modern periodic table, let us begin this chapter by taking a brief look at the history of its development.

J. W. Dobereiner (1780-1849) was one of the first scientists to investigate elements that had similar properties. In 1819, he discovered that groups of three elements such as Fe, Co, and Ni or Cl, Br, and I had similar chemical properties. Dobereiner also noticed that the atomic mass of the middle element in these groups was almost the average of the atomic masses of the other two. He called these related elements **triads**. Dobereiner's idea of chemical triads was the first attempt to classify elements systematically according to their properties. However, his system could not be generalized to other groups of elements.

WWWolfe 1
(See W.W.Wolfe section at the end of the chapter.)

Following the lead of Dobereiner, many scientists proposed classification schemes for the elements. In 1864, John Newlands (1837-1899) made a notable attempt when he placed the elements in order of their atomic masses and discovered that similar chemical and physical properties recurred after intervals of seven elements. Newlands called his discovery the **law of octaves** because he saw a parallel with musical notes. While he could group some elements, Newlands was unsuccessful when he tried to group all of the elements known at that time.

In 1869, independent of each other, the German scientist Lothar Meyer (1830-1895) and the Russian scientist Dimitri Mendeleev (1834-1907) proposed periodic tables from which our modern tables have evolved. Meyer developed his periodic table mainly using physical properties while Mendeleev principally developed his table from the chemical properties of elements. Each scientist arranged the elements in order of increasing atomic masses. Both periodic

> In 1869, Mendeleev (1834-1907) published his first periodic table. In Russia, scientific papers were rarely translated into western languages, so the scientists of the western world usually had to rediscover such findings. Because of his fame as a renowned scientist, his table and explanations were translated immediately into German.

tables had groups of elements with similar properties in the same column—such as modern periodic tables.

Dimitri Mendeleev

Mendeleev became famous after using his periodic table to predict the properties of elements that had not yet been discovered. For example, Mendeleev found a gap in his table directly under silicon, a member of group IVA (14). He used group IVA (14) data to predict the properties of ekasilicon, the name he gave to that element. Mendeleev used the prefix "eka" which comes from a Sanskrit word that means "first"; thus, ekasilicon was the first element under silicon. Table 6.1 displays the properties proposed by Mendeleev in 1871 and the actual properties of ekasilicon (germanium) discovered 15 years later. In most cases Mendeleev's predictions were in fairly close agreement with the measured values. He also used his periodic table to show scientists that some accepted atomic masses of that day were incorrect because their values placed them in a chemical group with dissimilar properties.

TABLE 6.1 MENDELEEV'S PREDICTIONS FOR EKASILICON (GERMANIUM)

Property	Modern values	Predicted values (1871)[*]
Atomic mass	72.6	72
Color	Grayish white	Dark gray
Density	5.4 g/cm^3	5.5 g/cm^3
Specific heat	0.074 cal/(g °C)	0.073 cal/(g °C)
Formula of oxide	GeO_2	ESO_2

*Mendeleev's predictions were made 15 years before the discovery of Ge.

A new era in chemistry began when chemists accepted the arrangement of elements on the periodic table proposed by Mendeleev. His grouping of the elements united them in a logical manner.

The Modern Periodic Table

The periodic table used today (see the Appendix) has the same general form as Mendeleev's table, but incorporates many findings of the twentieth century. Discovery of the nucleus and its electric charge showed that the elements should be arranged according to their atomic numbers and not their atomic masses. Discovery of the electron configurations of atoms showed that the properties of elements in a chemical group were the result of having the same number of valence electrons.

Chemists place the elements into **chemical groups** (vertical columns) and **periods** (horizontal rows). Either an Arabic number from 1 to 18 or a Roman numeral from I to VIII and a letter A or B are assigned to each group. The periods are numbered consecutively from 1 to 7. Many chemists prefer to classify the elements in terms of their outer subshells (Fig. 6.1).

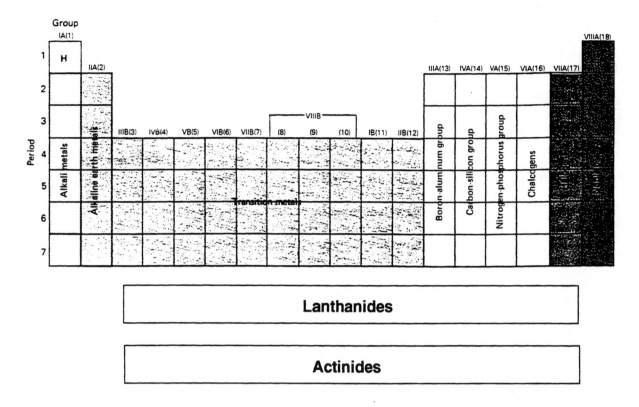

Figure 6.1 Periodic table with the names of the chemical groups.

Representative elements (also called the **main-group elements**) belong to chemical groups assigned the letter A and have outer electrons that fill the *s* or *p* subshells. **Transition elements** belong to chemical groups IIIB (3) to IIB (12) and have outer electrons that fill the *d* subshell. **Inner transition elements** are a third group of elements and have outer-shell electrons that fill the *f* subshell. The inner transition elements with an outer 4f subshell are called the **lanthanide series**. Those with an outer 5f subshell are termed the **actinide series**. The lanthanides and actinides derive their names from the two elements that come directly before the series: lanthanum, La, and actinium, Ac.

Elements in group IA (1), except H, are called alkali metals, while elements in group IIA (2) are called **alkaline earth metals** (the name used by the alchemists). The next 10 columns on the periodic table (group B. elements, 3 to 12) are the **transition elements or transition metals.** This group contains the most common metallic elements. Group IIIA (13) has no unique name; it is often called the **aluminum or boron-aluminum group.** Similarly, groups IVA (14) and VA (15) are designated the **carbon and nitrogen groups, respectively.** An old name for group VIA (16), the **chalcogens,** is presently being used. Finally, group VIIA (17) are the **halogens,** and VIIIA (18) are the **noble gases.**

Hydrogen, the least massive element, is the one most difficult to place on the periodic table. Hydrogen is usually placed at the top of group IA (1) only because it shares the common property of having a s^1 outer electron configuration. Nevertheless, the properties of hydrogen do not resemble those of the alkali metals. Hydrogen is a gas with low melting and boiling points, low density, and is an insulator of heat and electricity. In contrast, group IA (1) elements are reactive metallic solids. It should be noted that some properties of hydrogen are similar to those of the group VIIA (17) elements—the halogens. This may be attributed to the fact that both hydrogen and the halogens require one electron to obtain a noble gas configuration. Nonetheless, many properties of hydrogen are quite different from those of the halogens. ❖

REVIEW EXERCISES

6.1 How did Mendeleev show that his periodic table was a valid grouping of elements?

6.2 Write the names of the groups on the periodic table with the following Roman numeral and letter designations.

(a) IA (1)
(b) IIA (2)
(c) IVA (14)
(d) VIA (16)
(e) VIIA (17)
(f) VIIIA (18)
(g) all group B elements

6.2 (a) alkali metals, (b) alkaline earth metals, (c) carbon-silicon group, (d) chalcogens, (e) halogens, (f) noble gases, (g) transition elements

6.2 PERIODIC LAW

Let's turn our attention to what is now called the periodic law. The **periodic law** states that the properties of the elements are periodic functions of their atomic number. In other words, if the elements are listed in order of their atomic numbers, a regular pattern of chemical and physical properties is found. To illustrate the periodic law, we will consider the two main classes of elements—metals and nonmetals.

Metals and Nonmetals

Metals are usually solid elements with a silvery, gray color; their melting and boiling points are usually quite high. Metals share a set of common properties: (1) They have a high average density; (2) they are excellent conductors of heat and electricity; and (3) they are malleable—i.e., they can be hammered into various shapes and foils. Common examples of metals include iron, copper, gold, silver, lead, and platinum.

Nonmetals possess properties that, often, are opposite to those of metals. A large percent of the nonmetals are liquids and gases, not solids. On average, the melting points, boiling points, densities, and electric and heat conductivities of nonmetals are lower

> The largest percent of elements, over 80, are metals.

than those of metals. Common examples of nonmetals include carbon, oxygen, nitrogen, and chlorine.

As an example, let us consider the second period elements. Li and Be are metals, and C, N, O, F, and Ne are nonmetals. B has intermediate properties, not exactly metallic or nonmetallic, and is classified as a **metalloid** (or semimetal). Elements on the right side of the periodic table have a greater degree of nonmetallic character than those on the left side.

If we look beyond Ne to the third period of the periodic table, a similar trend in metallic and nonmetallic properties is found: Na, Mg, and Al possess metallic properties; Si is a metalloid; and P, S, Cl, and Ar are nonmetals. Table 6.2 presents selected physical properties of the elements in the third period of the periodic table.

6.2 SELECTED PROPERTIES OF THIRD-ROW ELEMENTS

Element	Atomic number	Physical state (25°C)	Melting point, °C	Density, g/cm³	Type
Na	11	Silvery solid	97.8	0.97	Metal
Mg	12	Gray solid	650	1.74	Metal
Al	13	Light-gray solid	660	2.70	Metal
Si	14	Bluish solid	1414	2.33	Metalloid
P	15	White, red, or black solid	44	1.83	Nonmetal
S	16	Pale-yellow solid	112	2.07	Nonmetal
Cl	17	Pale-green gas	−101	0.00321	Nonmetal
Ar	18	Colorless gas	−189	0.00178	Nonmetal

Figure 6.2 shows a periodic table that classifies elements as metals, nonmetals, and metalloids. You should note that the eight metalloids border a zigzag line that begins to the left of B and ends between Po and At. This line separates metals from nonmetals.

Specifically, if a physical property such as melting point is plotted on a graph, a better view of the periodic nature of properties of metals and nonmetals is obtained. Figure 6.3 presents a graph of melting point versus atomic number for the first 36 elements.

> The melting point of a substance is the temperature at which the solid and liquid states coexist in equilibrium. Higher melting points indicate stronger forces of attraction among atoms in the solid state.

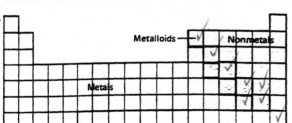

Figure 6.2 Metals are the elements on the left side of the periodic table. Nonmetals are listed on the right side of the periodic table. Metalloids are along a zigzag line separating the metals from the nonmetals.

Note the somewhat regular pattern of increasing and decreasing melting points. Except carbon, metals and metalloids are found at the maximum values, the peaks, while the nonmetals occupy the valleys, the minimum values. This repeating pattern of peaks and valleys as atomic number increases is an illustration of the periodic law.

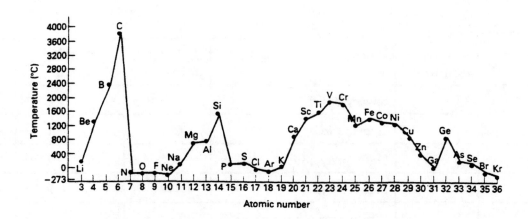

Figure 6.3 Graph of melting points versus atomic numbers.

CHEM TOPIC: Metals from Ores

Only a few metals exist free in nature—e.g., gold, silver, copper, platinum, and palladium. Most metals are found in **ores,** which are complex mixtures of different minerals. For example, Al is found as aluminum oxide, Al_2O_3, in a mineral called bauxite. Along with aluminum oxide in bauxite is silica, SiO_2, and hematite, Fe_2O_3.

Three major steps are required to extract metals from their ores. After the ore is mined, either it is treated to concentrate the desired mineral or it is converted to a form that is more easily extracted. Then the metallic compound is converted to the metal. This process is known as reduction. Reduction is accomplished by heating the compound to a high temperature (smelting) or through the use of electricity (electrolysis). Finally, the free metal is refined to remove impurities; in many cases, these are recovered and sold.

The chemical properties of metals differ from those of nonmetals. Metals have a small number of valence electrons, and they tend to lose these electrons during chemical changes. In contrast, nonmetals have more complete outer-energy shells and tend to gain electrons (except the noble gases). When atoms either lose or gain electrons, they form ions (Fig. 6.3). An ion is a charged atom, or as we will see in a later chapter, a charged group of atoms. Two different types of ions exist: positive ions, called **cations**, and negative ions, called **anions**. Cations are produced when metals release one or more electrons. For example, if a metal (M) loses one electron, it becomes an ion with a charge of 1+:

An easy way to remember that anions are negative ions is to break the word anion into **a n (negative) ion**. Mnemonics (memory aids) such as this can simplify the task of learning chemistry.

$$M \rightarrow M^+ + e^-$$

However, if it loses two electrons it becomes an ion with a charge of 2+:

$$M \rightarrow M^{2+} + 2e^-$$

Anions form when nonmetals (X) accept electrons. A 1− ion results if one electron is accepted and a 2− ion results if two electrons are taken in.

$$X + e^- \rightarrow X^-$$

$$X + 2e^- \rightarrow X^{2-}$$

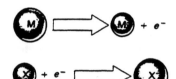

Metals give up their valence electrons and form cations that have noble gas electronic configurations. Nonmetals often take in enough electrons to complete their valence shell, also producing a noble gas configuration. As we will discuss in Chap. 8, the most stable electronic configuration is that of the noble gases. Ions that have the same electronic configurations as noble gases are said to be **isoelectronic** to noble gases.

Metals in group IA, the alkali metals, tend to lose one electron when they combine with other substances, producing 1 + cations. For example, Na and K each loses one electron to form 1+ cations.

$$Na \rightarrow Na^+ + e^-$$

$$K \rightarrow K^+ + e^-$$

Figure 6.3 Metal atoms lose one or more electrons forming cations. The resulting cation is smaller than the metal atom because the valence electrons are removed. Nonmetal atoms gain one or more electrons forming anions. The resulting anion is larger than the nonmetal atom because there are more electrons than protons.

A sodium ion, Na$^+$, becomes isoelectronic to Ne, and a potassium ion, K$^+$, becomes isoelectronic to Ar. Metals in group IIA, alkaline earth metals, tend to lose two electrons when they combine with other elements, yielding 2+ cations. Ca and Ba each lose two electrons to form 2+ cations.

Charges on ions are written as superscripts to the right of symbols, with the magnitude preceding the + or the −.

$$Ca \rightarrow Ca^{2+} + 2e^-$$

$$Ba \rightarrow Ba^{2+} + 2e^-$$

Calcium ions, Ca^{2+}, are isoelectronic to Ar, and barium ions, Ba^{2+}, become isoelectronic to Xe.

Nonmetals, except noble gases, accept electrons and produce anions that are isoelectronic to a noble gas. The elements in group VIIA (17), the halogens, most frequently gain one electron and produce 1– anions. For example, Cl and Br atoms each accept one electron and produce halide ions.

$$Cl + e^- \rightarrow Cl^-$$

$$Br + e^- \rightarrow Br^-$$

The chloride ion, Cl^-, is isoelectronic to Ar, and the bromide ion, Br^-, is isoelectronic to Kr. Similarly, group VIA elements, chalcogens, accept two electrons and form 2– anions. O and S each take in two electrons to form 2 ions.

$$O + 2e^- \rightarrow O^{2-}$$

$$S + 2e^- \rightarrow S^{2-}$$

The oxide ion, O^{2-}, is isoelectronic to Ne, and the sulfide ion, S^{2-}, is isoelectronic to Ar. A periodic table with selected ions is presented in Fig. 6.4.❖

Group IA	IIA	IIIA	IVA	VA	VIA	VIIA
1 H^+						
2 Li^+	Be^{2+}			N^{3-}	O^{2-}	F^-
3 Na^+	Mg^{2+}	Al^{3+}		P^{3-}	S^{2-}	Cl^-
4 K^+	Ca^{2+}	Ga^{3+}				Br^-
5 Rb^+	Sr^{2+}					I^-
6 Cs^+	Ba^{2+}					At^-
7 Fr^+	Ra^{2+}					

Figure 6.4 A periodic table is shown with selected ions. Many blank spaces are found in the table because some atoms do not readily form ions and some can form two or more ions with different charges.

REVIEW EXERCISES

6.3 State the periodic law and give an example that demonstrates it.

6.4 List three properties that distinguish metals from nonmetals.

6.5 What periodic trend is found for densities within the second period of the periodic table?

6.6 (a) How does a cation differ from an anion? (b) Describe how cations and anions are formed.

6.6 (a) A cation is a positive ion, and an anion is a negative ion. (b) Metals lose electrons to form cations, and nonmetals gain electrons to form anions.

6.3 PERIODIC PROPERTIES OF ATOMS

Trends in Ionization Energy

Periodic trends are found when the properties of individual atoms are studied. An important property of atoms that helps explain ion formation is called ionization energy. **Ionization energy, IE,** is the minimum amount of energy required to remove the most loosely held electron from a neutral gaseous atom.

$$A(g) + IE \rightarrow A^+(g) + e^-$$

The ionization energy of an atom is a measure of the degree to which the nucleus attracts the most loosely held valence electron, which is the one most distant from the nucleus. A *low ionization* energy indicates a smaller attractive force, and a *high ionization* energy indicates a larger attractive force between the nucleus and the most loosely held electron.

Our definition of ionization energy is for the first ionization energy. The second ionization energy is that minimum amount of energy required to remove the most loosely held electron in a monopositive cation, M^+.

A graph of ionization energy versus atomic number for the atoms in the first three periods is presented in Fig. 6.5, and Fig. 6.6 lists the ionization energies of most of the atoms in megajoules per mole, MJ/mol. Two distinct trends are evident. First, as we proceed from left to right across a period (increasing atomic number within a period), the ionization energy generally increases. More energy is required, on average, to remove the most loosely held electron from nonmetals than metals. Alkali metals, group IA elements, have the lowest ionization energies, and noble gases, group VIIIA elements, have the highest ionization energies within a period.

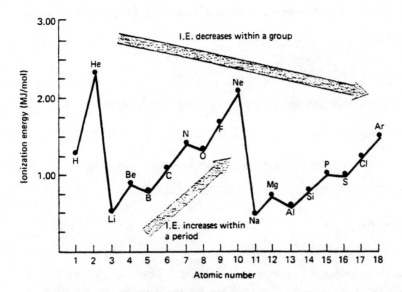

Figure 6.5 A graph of the ionization energies of atoms reveals two trends. Within a period the ionization energy increases with increasing atomic number. Within a group the ionization energy decreases with increasing atomic number.

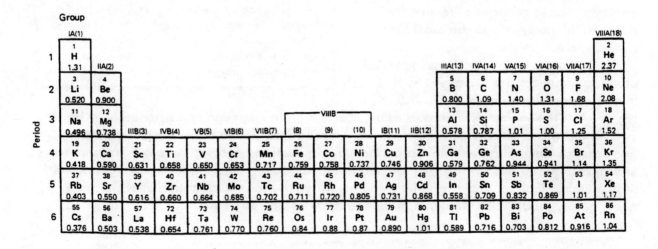

Group	IA(1)	IIA(2)	IIIB(3)	IVB(4)	VB(5)	VIB(6)	VIIB(7)	(8)	(9)	(10)	IB(11)	IIB(12)	IIIA(13)	IVA(14)	VA(15)	VIA(16)	VIIA(17)	VIIIA(18)
1	1 H 1.31																	2 He 2.37
2	3 Li 0.520	4 Be 0.900											5 B 0.800	6 C 1.09	7 N 1.40	8 O 1.31	9 F 1.68	10 Ne 2.08
3	11 Na 0.496	12 Mg 0.738						VIIIB					13 Al 0.578	14 Si 0.787	15 P 1.01	16 S 1.00	17 Cl 1.25	18 Ar 1.52
4	19 K 0.418	20 Ca 0.590	21 Sc 0.631	22 Ti 0.658	23 V 0.650	24 Cr 0.653	25 Mn 0.717	26 Fe 0.759	27 Co 0.758	28 Ni 0.737	29 Cu 0.746	30 Zn 0.906	31 Ga 0.579	32 Ge 0.762	33 As 0.944	34 Se 0.941	35 Br 1.14	36 Kr 1.35
5	37 Rb 0.403	38 Sr 0.550	39 Y 0.616	40 Zr 0.660	41 Nb 0.664	42 Mo 0.685	43 Tc 0.702	44 Ru 0.711	45 Rh 0.720	46 Pd 0.805	47 Ag 0.731	48 Cd 0.868	49 In 0.558	50 Sn 0.709	51 Sb 0.832	52 Te 0.869	53 I 1.01	54 Xe 1.17
6	55 Cs 0.376	56 Ba 0.503	57 La 0.538	72 Hf 0.654	73 Ta 0.761	74 W 0.770	75 Re 0.760	76 Os 0.84	77 Ir 0.88	78 Pt 0.87	79 Au 0.890	80 Hg 1.01	81 Tl 0.589	82 Pb 0.716	83 Bi 0.703	84 Po 0.812	85 At 0.916	86 Rn 1.04

Figure 6.6 Periodic table that lists the ionization energies, *IE*, of atoms in MJ/mol.

Second, within a group like the noble gases (VIIIA), ionization energies decrease with increasing atomic number. Helium has the highest ionization energy (2.37 MJ/mol) of the noble gases, and Rn has the lowest (1.04 MJ/mol). Similar trends are found in all chemical groups.

Overall, elements in the lower left corner of the periodic table have the lowest ionization energies; francium, Fr, is the element with the lowest ionization energy. As we move up and to the right on the periodic table, the ionization energies generally increase; He has the highest ionization energy of all atoms (Fig. 6.7).

Two factors account for the trends in ionization energy: (1) attractive forces between the nucleus and the electrons, and (2) the shielding effect of the inner-shell

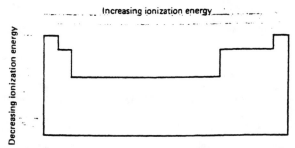

Figure 6.7 Periodic table that shows the trends in ionization energies.

electrons. Greater attraction of the electrons by the nucleus results in higher ionization energies. **Shielding** refers to the blocking effect that inner-shell electrons have on the nuclear attraction of the outer electrons. Greater shielding of the nucleus by inner electrons results in lower ionization energies.

The overall increasing trend in ionization energy across a period is explained as follows. The shielding effect of the inner electrons remains constant across a period, while the charge on the nucleus increases. Increasing nuclear charge produces a greater attractive force on the outer electrons, resulting in a higher ionization energy.

Decreasing trends in ionization energy within a chemical group are explained in terms of the location of the outer electrons. With each new energy level, the valence electrons are farther from the nucleus with more levels of inner electrons shielding the nuclear charge (Fig. 6.8). Greater distance from the nucleus and the greater shielding effects result in a smaller attractive force on the outer electrons; hence, they are easier to remove.

Consider Example Problem 6.1 that shows how to use the trends in ionization energy to make predictions about the ionization energies of atoms.

EXAMPLE PROBLEM 6.1
Using only a periodic table, determine which of the following elements has the highest and lowest ionization energies: S, Cl, Se, Br?

Solution
To predict a periodic property of an atom always begin by locating the atoms on the periodic table. Both S and Se are group VIA (16) members and Cl and Br are group VIIA (17) members. S and Cl belong to period 3 and Se and Br belong to period 4. After identifying the location of the atoms, state the general periodic trends. Ionization energies generally increase across a period and decrease within a chemical group. Thus, Cl has the highest ionization energy (1.2 MJ/mol) because it farther to the right in the period and a lower-molecular mass member of group VIIA (17). Selenium, Se, has the lowest first ionization energy (0.94 MJ/mol) of this group because it is closest to the left

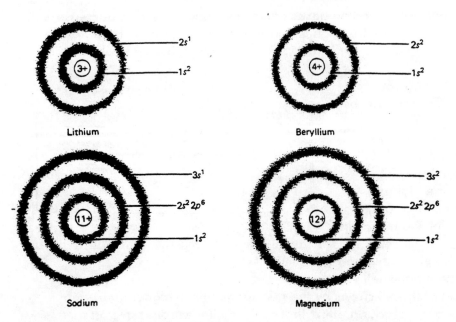

Figure 6.8 In Li, two of the three nuclear charges are shielded by the inner 1s orbital, leaving only one nuclear charge to hold the outer electron. In Be, two of the four nuclear charges are shielded, leaving two nuclear charges to hold the outer electrons. Because of having a greater nuclear change after shielding, Be has a higher ionization energy than Li. A similar argument can be used for Na and Mg.

side of the periodic table and is the higher-molecular mass member of group VIA (16).

Exercise

Which of the following has the highest and lowest first ionization energies: C, N, Si, P? (highest = N, lowest = Si)

Trends in Atomic Size (Atomic radius)

The **atomic size**, also known as **atomic radius**, is an estimate of the distance from the nucleus to a point that corresponds to the outermost region of a neutral atom. Atomic sizes for the elements in the second and third periods are plotted in Fig. 6.9, and the relative sizes of the atoms are illustrated as circles in Fig. 6.10.

Again, two trends can be identified. Moving across a period from left to right, the atomic size decreases, and within a group the atomic size increases. Thus, the largest atoms are in the bottom left corner of the periodic table, and the smallest atoms are in the upper right corner (Fig. 6.11).

Sizes of atoms are difficult to measure. In most cases estimates are obtained from measurements of atoms that are components of molecules.

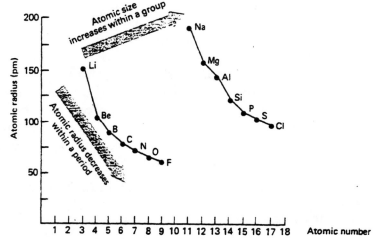

Figure 6.9 The atomic sizes in pm are plotted versus atomic number for the first 18 atoms. Noble gases are not included because a different means is used to measure their size.

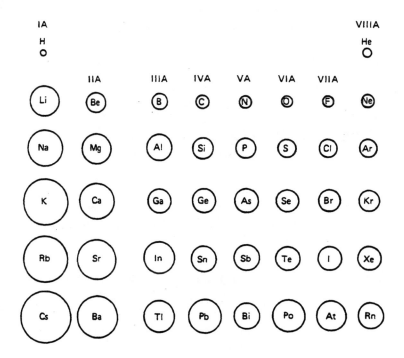

Figure 6.10 Periodic table that shows the relative sizes of atoms.

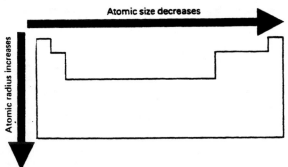

Figure 6.11 Periodic table that shows the major trends in atomic sizes.

Is this consistent with the trends in ionization energy? Yes. Across a period, the shielding effects of inner electrons are constant, and the nuclear charge increases with the addition of protons to the nucleus. Consequently, the attractive force of the nucleus for the electrons increases, and the size of the atom decreases as the electrons are attracted closer to the nucleus. Within a group, the attractive forces exerted on the valence electrons decrease because the outer electrons in each succeeding group member are farther from the nucleus and are more shielded by the inner electrons. Thus, the atomic size increases.

Example Problems 6.2 and 6.3 show additional examples of how to predict the properties of elements and atoms from the general trends. ❖

Example Problem 6.2
Which of the following is the largest atom: Rb, Sr, Cs, Ba?

Solution
Rb and Cs are members of group IA (1), and Sr and Ba are members of group IIA (2). Larger atoms are farther to the left within a period and have higher energy outer-shell electrons in a group. Thus, Cs is the largest of this group.

Exercise
Predict the smallest and largest atoms from the following group: P, Cl, Na, Sr. (smallest = Cl, largest = Sr)

Example Problem 6.3
Of the four atoms, Si, P, S, and Cl, which (a) is the most nonmetallic, (b) has the highest ionization energy, and (c) is the largest atom?

Solution
Si, P, S, and Cl belong to the third period of the periodic table. Thus, to answer this question, it is only necessary to know the periodic trends as the atomic number increases across the periodic table.

(a) Metallic character decreases or nonmetallic character increases as we go from left to right across the periodic table. Accordingly, Cl, a halogen, is the most nonmetallic atom of this group.
(b) Ionization energies increase from left to right across a period; consequently, Cl has the highest ionization energy of the four atoms.
(c) Atomic sizes decrease across a period; hence, Si is the largest atom.
Exercise
(a) Which is the largest halogen atom? (b) Which is the smallest chalcogen? ((a) At, (b) O)

Example Problem 6.4
Predict the (a) atomic size and (b) boiling point of krypton given the following data.

Noble gas	Atomic size, nm	Boiling point, °C
Neon, Ne	0.065	–246
Argon, Ar	0.095	–186
Xenon, Xe	0.130	–108

Solution
Kr is a member of the noble gases (group VIIIA). Its atomic mass is greater than that of Ar and less than that of Xe; thus, its atomic size and boiling point should be intermediate between the values for Ar and Xe. To make good predictions, it is necessary to follow the trends within the group.

(a) Atomic size increases within a group, which means that the atomic size of Kr is larger than that of Ar but smaller than that of Xe. We see an increase of 0.030 nm from Ne to Ar; however, we would not expect the same increase from Ar to Kr because such an increase gives a value (0.125 nm) almost identical to that for Xe. A better estimate might be the average value of Ar and Xe, (0.095 + 0.130)/2, which gives **0.113 nm.** The actual value for Kr is 0.110 nm.

(b) Considering the trend in boiling points of the noble gases, we find an increasing trend. Therefore, the boiling point of Kr is larger than that of Ar but smaller than that of Xe. If we again take the average value of the boiling points of Ar and Xe, we get a reasonable prediction. The value obtained when we average –186°C and –108°C is –147°C, which is fairly close to the actual value, –153°C.

Exercise
The atomic sizes of P, S, and Cl are 110 pm, 104 pm, and 99 pm. Predict the atomic size of Ar. (94 pm)

REVIEW EXERCISES
6.7 (a) Define ionization energy.

(b) What general trends in ionization energies are found?

6.8 From the set of elements that follows each description, select the element that best fits that description.

(a) Highest ionization energy: P, S, Cl, Ar
(b) Lowest ionization energy: Li, Be, Na, Mg
(c) Largest atomic size: Ga, Ge, As, Se
(d) Smallest atomic size: Br, Se, I, Te
(e) Most metallic: Be, B, C, N

6.8 (a) Ar, (b) Na, (c) Ga, (d) Br, (e) Be.

6.4 PREDICTION OF PROPERTIES

Knowledge of the periodic properties of the elements allows us to predict the properties of elements that have not been measured experimentally or that have not yet been discovered. The key to predicting properties of elements is to identify the location of the element on the periodic table. Once the location is known, determine its electron configuration, its period, its group, and if it is a metal, nonmetal, or metalloid.

Predicting the Properties of Strontium

To illustrate the prediction of properties from the position of an element on the periodic table, let's predict some of the properties of element 38, strontium (Sr). First determine that Sr belongs to the alkaline earth metals, group IIA (2), and is a member of period 5. All members of group IIA (2) have an outer electron configuration of s^2, specifically, Sr has an outer configuration of $5s^2$. Because all of the other members of group 2 (IIA) are metals, we should expect that Sr exhibits metallic properties such as existing in the solid state at room temperature and being a good conductor of heat and electricity. We might speculate that Sr atoms have a low ionization energy and a large atomic size because the effective nuclear charge is rather small in group IIA (2) elements. When Sr forms an ion, we predict that it loses two electrons to obtain the stable noble gas configuration of Kr.

$$Sr \rightarrow Sr^{2+} + 2e^-$$

Specific predictions can be made about the properties of Sr, if the properties of Ca, the group 2 (IIA) metal that precedes it, and Ba, the element that follows it, is known. For example, we can predict its melting point from the those of Ca (845°C) and Ba (725°C). The average value for the melting points of Ca and Ba, 785°C, is not far from the actual value of 770°C. Taking the average value for the ionization energies of Ca (0.590 MJ/mol) and Ba (0.503 MJ/mol) gives 0.546 MJ/mol for the predicted ionization energy of Sr. The actual value is 0.550 MJ/mol.

Predicting the Properties of Element-118

Like Mendeleev, who predicted the properties of elements years before their discovery, we can also predict the properties of elements that have not yet been discovered. Let us predict some of the properties of element-118.

To begin, identify the chemical group and period to which it belongs. Element-118 belongs to the noble gases in period 7. All of the other group VIIIA (18) elements are gases at 25°C. Hence, we would expect that element-118 is a gas. More massive noble gases, Xe and Rn, have boiling points of –107°C and –62°C, respectively. Therefore, an increase of 50 to 60°C above the boiling point of Rn gives a boiling point below 0.0°C for element-118. Hence this means that it should be a gas at 25°C. Recognizing that element-118 is a noble gas, we predict that element-118 should be the least reactive element in period 7 and the most reactive noble gas.

Element-118 is expected to have a valence configuration of $7s^27p^6$. Because the ionization energy decreases within a group and increases in a period, element-118 should have the lowest first ionization energy of the noble gases and the highest ionization energy in period 7. What is a good estimate of the first ionization energy of element-118? Because the data is incomplete on the ionization energies of period 7 members, the ionization energies of the noble gases can be used. The average difference in the decrease in ionization energies going from Kr to Rn is 0.16 MJ/mol. Thus, if the first ionization energy of element-118 is 0.16 MJ/mol lower than Rn, then its value should be close to 0.88 MJ/mol. Considering the size of element-118 atoms, we predict that they should be largest in group VIIIA (18) and the smallest in period 7.

One of the most important properties of element-118 is that it should be composed of intensely radioactive short-lived atoms. All elements beyond the actinide series are highly radioactive.

Study Example Problem 6.5 which gives you another illustration of how to predict the properties of an element. ❖

Example Problem 6.5
For each of the following properties, compare element-81, thallium (Tl) to element-34, selenium (Se): (a) boiling and melting points, (b) electrical conductivity, (c) malleability, (d) ionization energy.

Solution
Before attempting to answer this question find both Tl and Se on the periodic table. Thallium is the heaviest member of group III A (13); therefore, Tl is a heavy metal. Selenium is the third member of the chalcogens, group VIA (16); hence, it has the properties of a nonmetal.

(a) Generally the boiling and melting points of metals are higher than those of nonmetals. Therefore, we should predict that the boiling and melting points of Tl (mp = 304°C and bp = 1460°C) are higher than those of Se (mp = 217°C and bp = 685°C).
(b) The electrical conductivity of metals is greater than that of nonmetals; thus, we would expect that the conductivity of Tl is greater than that of Se. Experimentally, Tl is a much better conductor than Se.
(c) Malleability is the property of substances to be hammered or pounded into different shapes without breaking. Most metals are malleable. Nonmetals do not exhibit malleability. Because Tl is a metal, it is malleable. Se is a nonmetal and thus not malleable.
(d) The general trend in ionization energy is that nonmetals tend to have higher ionization energies than nonmetals. Also smaller atoms have higher one than larger atoms. From its placement on the periodic table, Tl is a large metal atom and Se is a much smaller nonmetal atom. Hence, the ionization energy of Se (*IE* = 0.94 MJ/mol) is higher than that of Tl (*IE* = 0.59 MJ/mol).

Exercise
For each of the following properties, compare element 31, gallium (Ga) to element 16, sulfur (S): (a) boiling and melting points, (b) thermal conductivity, (c) first ionization energy, (d) atomic size.
((a) Ga has higher melting and boiling points than S., (b) Ga is a better thermal conductor than S. (c) Ga has a lower first ionization energy than S. (d) Ga is composed of larger atoms than S.)

WorldWideWolfe CHEMISTRY LINKS

Connect to WorldWideWolfe at

http://www.mindspring.com/~drwolfe/WWWolfe_hcc_1025_links.htm

and link to the following sites.

Periodic Properties of Elements and Atoms

Many Web Periodic Tables This takes you to the area of WorldWideWolfe with lots of different styles of periodic tables.

Periodic Trends of the Elements This page covers the contribution of Mendeleev and Moseley to the development of the modern periodic table. It also has a brief discussion of the fundamental trends in element and atom properties.

Periodic Properties Tutorial A series of slides that cover all aspects of periodic trends. The figures load rather slowly.

Periodic Trends A very succinct look at various periodic trends as a function of atomic number.

SUMMARY

The **periodic law** states that the properties of the elements are periodic functions of their atomic numbers. When atoms are arranged in order of increasing atomic number, recurring chemical and physical properties are found. Elements with the same valence electron configuration are in the same group (vertical column). Group members have many common properties, and within most groups regular trends in properties are found. Periods (horizontal rows) contain elements that have outer-shell electrons in the same energy level. Likewise, somewhat regular trends in properties are observed when progressing from one side of the table to the other.

Elements are classified as metals, nonmetals, or metalloids (semi-metals), depending on their properties. **Metals** occupy the left side of the periodic table, and are usually solids with high densities and high melting and boiling points. They are also good conductors of heat and electricity and tend to lose electrons in chemical changes. **Nonmetals,** on the right side of the periodic table, have lower average densities, melting points, boiling points, and conductivities than metals. In chemical reactions, nonmetals tend to gain electrons and form anions. Metalloids resemble metals but have some nonmetallic properties.

Ionization energy is energy required to remove the most loosely held electron from a neutral gaseous atom. From left to right across a period, ionization energy increases. Within a chemical group, the ionization energy decreases with increasing atomic number. Elements near the bottom left side of the periodic table have the lowest ionization energies, and those near the top right side have the highest ionization energies.

From left to right across a period, the **atomic size** decreases, and within a group the atomic size increases as atomic number increases. Elements at the bottom left side of the periodic table are the largest, and those near the top right are the smallest.

KEY TERMS

anion
atomic radius
atomic size
cation
electron shielding
ion

ionization energy
isoelectronic
metal
metalloid
nonmetal
periodic properties

STUDY GUIDELINES

After completing Chapter 6, you should be able to

1. State the periodic law and use it to predict the properties of elements

2. State the names of representative groups of elements on the periodic table

3. Distinguish between the properties of metals and nonmetals

4. Define and give examples or cations and anions

5. Predict the charge on ions from their location in the periodic table

6. Predict a property of an element given the properties of related elements

7. Predict trends in ionization energy and atomic size

EXERCISES

6.15 Define the following terms: periodic properties, metal, nonmetal, metalloid, ion, cation, anion, ionization energy, atomic size, electron shielding, isoelectronic.

Periodic Properties

6.16 Explain why the periodic table is called by that name.

6.17 Write the name of the group on the periodic table to which each of the following elements belongs: (a) Na, (b) Al, (c) C, (d) As, (e) Cu, (f) I, (g) Be, (h) Fe, (i) Sb, (j) V, (k) Ce.

6.18 (a) How is a representative element distinguished from a transition element, using the periodic table? (b) Give three examples each of representative and transition elements.

6.19 What is the valence configuration of each of the following: (a) alkali metals, (b) halogens, (c) chalcogens, (d) noble gases, (e) alkaline earth metals, (f) nitrogen-phosphorus group elements?

6.20 (a) How do the properties of nonmetals differ from those of metals? (b) Give two specific examples.

6.21 Classify each of the following as a metal, nonmetal, or metalloid: (a) Ge, (b) Ar, (c) Zr, (d) N, (e) H, (f) Tl, (g) Li, (h) Sr, (i) Pb, (j) Ga.

6.22 Consider the following properties of hypothetical elements A and B, and classify each as a metal, nonmetal, or metalloid. (a) Element A boils at −195.8°C, has a density of 1.3 g/dm^3, and is a colorless gas at room temperature. (b) Element B boils at 3200°C, has a density of 10 g/cm^3, is a solid at room temperature, and is a good conductor.

6.23 Select the element that is the most metallic in each of the following groups of elements: (a) Be, B, C, N; (b) C, Si, Ge, Sn; (c) As, Se, Sb, Te; (d) Mg, Al, Si, P.

6.24 (a) How many added electrons are required to complete the valence shell of (1) P, (2) Cl, (3) F, (4) Se, (5) N, and (6) I? (b) What charge does each of the atoms in part a have after the atom gains the indicated number of electrons?

6.25 (a) How many electrons must be removed from each of the following atoms to give it a noble gas electronic configuration: (1) Cs, (2) Be, (3) Al, (4) Sc, (5) Mg, and (6) Rb? (b) What charge does each of the atoms in part a have after the electrons are lost?

6.26 What charge would the most stable ions of the following atoms possess: (a) Sr, (b) P, (c) S, (d) O, (e) Mg, (f) Te, (g) N, (h) Rb, (i) F, and (j) Ra?

6.27 Write equations, using Lewis symbols, to illustrate what happens when the following atoms form ions: (a) N, (b) Cl, (c) Ba, (d) Cs, (e) P, (f) Ca.

6.28 What noble gases are isoelectronic to the following ions: (a) Mg^{2+}, (b) Al^{3+}, (c) N^{3-}, (d) I^-, (e) Rb^+, (f) Se^{2-}?

6.29 Predict the value for the ionization energy of antimony, Sb, given the values of the ionization energies for all other members of group VA. Their ionization energies in kilojoules per mole are: N, 1400; P, 1062; As, 966.5; Bi, 774.0.

6.30 For each of the following groups of atoms predict which atom will have the lowest ionization energy: (a) C, Si, Ge, Sn; (b) As, Se, Br, Kr; (c) K, Ca, Rb, Sr; (d) F, Ne, Cl, Ar.

6.31 For each set of elements in question 6.30, select the element with the smallest atomic size.

6.32 Write the symbol for the element or elements that best fit these descriptions: (a) noble gas with the lowest ionization energy, (b) group IIIA element with the least metallic character, (c) highest density in the chalcogens, (d) highest melting point of the alkali metals, (e) period 2 member that forms 3− ions, (f) a member of the lanthanide series, (g) elements whose atomic size is smaller than that of fluorine.

6.33 Element-118 has not been discovered. For each of the listed properties make a prediction about the properties of element-118, and explain your decision: (a) metal, nonmetal, or metalloid; (b) gas, liquid, or solid; (c) good or bad conductor of electricity; (d) colored or colorless; (e) large or small atomic size compared with its group; (f) high or low ionization energy compared with its group; (g) charge on its ions; (h) high or low boiling point.

6.34 Write the symbol for the element that best fits each description: (a) lowest ionization energy on the periodic table, (b) largest atomic size on the periodic table, (c) smallest chalcogen, (d) atom that forms a 2− ion that is isoelectronic to Kr, (e) metalloid that belongs to the chalcogens, (f) group VA element with the highest density, (g) largest alkaline earth metal, (h) member of the actinide series, (i) transition element that has a completely filled 3d sublevel, (j) metallic members of group IIIA.

Additional Exercises

6.35 The melting points of fluorine, chlorine, bromine, and iodine are −220°C, −101°C, −7°C, and 114°C, respectively. The boiling points of fluorine, chlorine, bromine, and iodine are −188°C, −34°C, 59°C, and 184°C, respectively. Predict the melting and boiling points of astatine, At.

6.36 Use data from Table 6.2 to plot a graph of the density of period 3 elements. Describe density trends in the third period.

6.37 (a) Prepare a full-page graph of the ionization energies of the period 4 representative elements versus their atomic numbers, using data from Fig. 6.6. (b)

Compare and contrast the trends in ionization energy of the third period elements (Fig. 6.6) with those of the fourth period.

6.38 The densities of Ne, Ar, and Kr at 0°C are 0.900, 1.78, and 3.75 g/dm^3, respectively. Predict the density of Xe at the same conditions.

6.39 Predict the atomic size and density of Rb from the following data.

Element	Atomic size, nm	Density, g/cm^3
Na	0.186	0.968
K	0.227	0.856
Cs	0.265	1.88

6.40 Provide a complete explanation for the fact that helium has the highest ionization energy of all atoms. Consider nuclear charge, shielding, and the size of a helium atom.

6.41 Predict as many properties as possible for the yet to be discovered element-120.

6.42 The second ionization energy of an atom is the amount of energy required to remove an electron from the 1+ cation of the atom. What group on the periodic table would be expected to have the highest second ionization energy? Fully explain.

6.43 Propose a reason why the ionization energy for S (1.00 MJ/mol) is slightly less than that for P (1.01 MJ/mol).

6.44 (a) Arrange the following in order of increasing atomic size: Cl, Cl⁻, Cl⁺, (b) Explain your reasoning completely.

6.45 (a) Write the complete electronic configuration for Ba. (b) Write the complete electronic configuration for Ba^{2+}. (c) What atom is Ba^{2+} isoelectronic to? (d) Compare the atomic size of Ba^{2+} to that of its isoelectronic species.

6.46 Answer the following questions for the period 2 elements. (a) Which elements are metallic? (b) Which element is composed of the largest atoms? (c) Which elements do not conduct an electric current? (d) Which has the highest ionization energy?

6.47 From what sublevel is an electron removed when the ionization energy is added to each of the following atoms: (a) Al, (b) Sr, (c) I, (d) Ar, (e) Ga?

6.48 Write Lewis symbols for each of the following: (a) Mg^{2+}, (b) F⁻, (c) S^{2-}, (d) K^+.

6.49 Use data in the chapter to calculate the melting point of silicon in kelvins and the density of silicon in kilograms per liter.

6.50 From its position on the periodic table predict as many properties as possible for the element technetium, Tc.

6.51 The atomic sizes of Pb, Bi, and Po atoms are 0.175, 0.155, and 0.118 nm, respectively. From this data predict the radius of an At atom.

6.52 The atomic sizes of Cl, Br, and I are 0.099, 0.114, and 0.133 nm, respectively. Use this data to predict the radius of an At atom.

6.53 Only using a periodic table, make general predictions (e.g., high or low, small or large, . . .) about the physical states, melting points, ionization energies, and atomic sizes of the elements with the following atomic numbers: (a) 16, (b) 34, (c) 45.

Notes and Calculations

Chapter 6 Pretest Assignment

1.   Complete each of the following statements with the correct word, number, or phase.

   a. _____ is considered the father of the modern periodic table.
   b. _____ is the minimum energy needed to remove an electron from a
   neutral gaseous atom.
   c. _____ is the atom with the highest ionization energy.
   d. _____ is the smallest alkaline earth metal.
   e. _____ is the group of elements on the right side of the periodic table.
   f. _____ is an example of a metalloid.
   g. _____ is the smallest period 2 element.
   h. _____ is isoelectronic to He.

2.   What are the names of the following chemical groups on the periodic table?

   a. group IIA (2)   _____

   b. group VIIA (17)   _____

   c. group VIIIA (18)   _____

   d. B group elements   _____

   e. group VIA (16)   _____

3.   Circle the atom that best fits the following descriptions.

a. smallest atom	Be	Mg	Li	Na
b. most metallic	S	Si	Te	Sr
c. lowest melting point	Pd	Si	Ni	F
d. lowest ionization energy	Al	Ga	B	In
e. insulator	Au	Co	O	Si
f. highest density	C	Xe	Ag	He
g. actinide	Ce	Hg	Ba	Th
h. highest specific heat	Cu	He	C	S
i. smallest atom	Cs	Ba	Fr	Ra

(Continued on the next page)

j. chalcogen	Si	Cd	Te	Sb
k. metalloid	Ga	Se	Sn	Sb
l. $5s^2 5p^5$ valence configuration	I	Te	Br	Xe

4.   Predict the following properties (i.e., high, low, good, bad, large, small, etc) of the element with an atomic number of 77.

a. physical state

_____

b. melting point

_____

c. ionization energy

_____

d. atomic size

_____

e. color

_____

f. electric conductivity

_____

g. density

_____

h. type of ions formed

_____

CHAPTER 7

Chemical Calculations:
The Mole Concept

7.1 THE MOLE: A COUNTING UNIT

Atoms and molecules are very small particles and cannot be handled on an individual basis. Minute samples of matter contain a staggering number of particles. In this chapter we will begin our study of how chemists deal with matter in such a way that macroscopic (large) samples reflect their microscopic (very small) composition.

WWWolfe 1
(See WWWolfe
section at the end of
the chapter.)

In Chap. 3 we discovered that the mole is the base SI unit for the amount of substance. What is a mole, and how is it applied in chemistry? The mole is a **counting unit**, a unit that allows us to keep track of the number and mass of atoms, molecules, and ions. While you may not have encountered moles in the past, you are familiar with a common counting unit called the "dozen."

Discrete (separate) objects, like oranges or eggs, often are not sold by weight, but by quantity. In such a case, the dozen can represent a mass of oranges or eggs. Counting units can be used to "weigh things by counting."

> A dozen is the counting unit for 12 objects.

Frequently, the dozen is too small, so other counting units are employed. Paper is bought by the ream (480 sheets or 20 quires). We say that a gross of pencils are purchased, rather than 144 pencils. Counting units are used whenever it is not easy to deal with objects because of their large number or small size.

Moles

Chemists use a counting unit that allows them to efficiently keep track of small particles such as atoms, ions, or molecules. This counting unit, the mole, is a fixed number of objects. The number of objects

> $1 \text{ mol} = 6.022045 \times 10^{23}$ entities

in a **mole** is 6.022×10^{23}, called **Avogadro's number.** Amedeo Avogadro (1776-1856) was an Italian scientist who conducted pioneering experiments on the properties of gases. The actual SI definition of the mole is as follows: One mole is the amount of pure substance that contains the same number of particles as there are atoms in exactly 12 grams of ^{12}C.

What is the importance of Avogadro's number, 6.022×10^{23}? If you multiply

Avogadro's number by the mass in grams of one atom, the product is the atomic mass in **grams**. For example, the mass of one H atom is approximately 1.67×10^{-24} g, and the atomic mass of H (obtained from the periodic table) is 1.01. What number, when multiplied times 1.66×10^{-24} g, gives 1.01 **grams?** You guessed it, the answer is Avogadro's number, 6.022×10^{23}

Amedeo Avogadro, Count of Quaregna (1776-1856), was the first person to distinguish between atoms and molecules (a word he coined). Most of his work was overlooked during his lifetime, and it was not until 50 years after his death that his discoveries were recognized

Stated another way, if 6.02×10^{23} atoms of an element are placed on a balance, their mass is the **atomic mass in grams**. Consider the following 1-mol samples of atoms:

Element	Number of Atoms	Mass
1.00 mol He	6.02×10^{23} atoms He	4.00 g
1.00 mol Li	6.02×10^{23} atoms Li	6.94 g
1.00 mol C	6.02×10^{23} atoms C	12.0 g
1.00 mol Ne	6.02×10^{23} atoms Ne	20.2 g
1.00 mol Fe	6.02×10^{23} atoms Fe	55.8 g
1.00 mol U	6.02×10^{23} atoms U	238 g

In all cases, one mole of atoms contains Avogadro's number of atoms, which has a mass equal to the atomic mass in grams.

How large is one mole? Well, one mole is much too large for any person to conceive. For example, it has been estimated that approximately one mole of grains of sand are found on all the beaches on earth. It is best to consider the fact that the magnitude of a mole is beyond comprehension when considering normal-size objects, but is a convenient number of particles when dealing with atoms, ions,

One mole of baseballs would cover the entire earth (land and water) to a depth of about 50 mi.

and molecules. Avogadro's, number of atoms can readily be measured on a balance in the laboratory. ❖

REVIEW EXERCISES

7.1 What similarities exist for the units dozen and mole?

7.2 State the accepted SI definition of a mole.

7.3 What is Avogadro's number, and why is it important?

7.4 Calculate how many billions (10^9) there are in exactly 1 mol.

7.4 6.022×10^{14} billion

7.2 MOLAR MASS OF ATOMS

Each element has a molar mass, the number of grams of that element that contains 6.022×10^{23} atoms (1.000 mol). In all cases, the molar mass is the atomic mass in grams
    The mass of 1.00 mol of hydrogen atoms is 1.00 g, while the mass of 1.00 mol of He atoms is 4.00 g. Figure 7.1 shows a periodic table with the molar masses of the elements. Note that the ratio of molar masses of He to H is 4 to 1, or

> Molar masses are sometimes called gram atomic masses.

the same ratio found when comparing one He atom to one H atom. As long as an equal number of particles are compared, the mass ratio remains fixed.

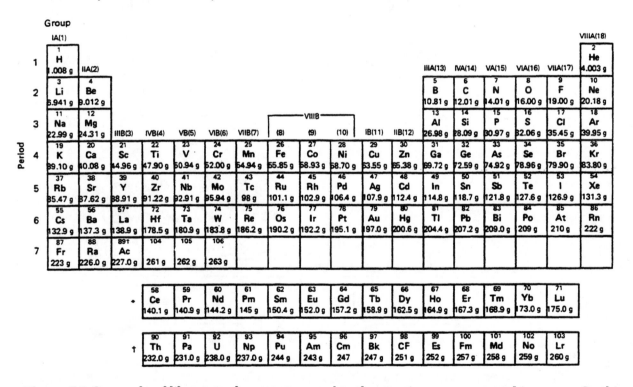

Figure 7.1 One mole of like atoms has a mass equal to the atomic mass expressed in grams. On this periodic table the molar masses of the atoms are given to four significant figures when possible.

Let us discuss normal-size objects to help develop a mental picture of what is unobservable. Consider two bags of potatoes, the first a 1-kg bag, and the other a 4-kg bag (Fig. 7.2). What is the mass ratio of the two potato bags? It is 1 to 4. If two 1-kg bags are compared to two 4-kg bags, the mass ratio is 2 kg to 8 kg, still a 1-to-4 ratio. Comparing a dozen 1-kg bags of potatoes to a dozen 4-kg bags, we find a mass ratio of 12 kg to 48 kg; a 1-to-4 ratio of

WWWolfe 2
(See WWWolfe section at the end of the chapter.)

masses still exists. If we compare a thousand 1-kg bags to a thousand 4-kg bags, the mass ratio is still 1 to 4. If 1 mol of each is compared, the ratio remains unchanged.

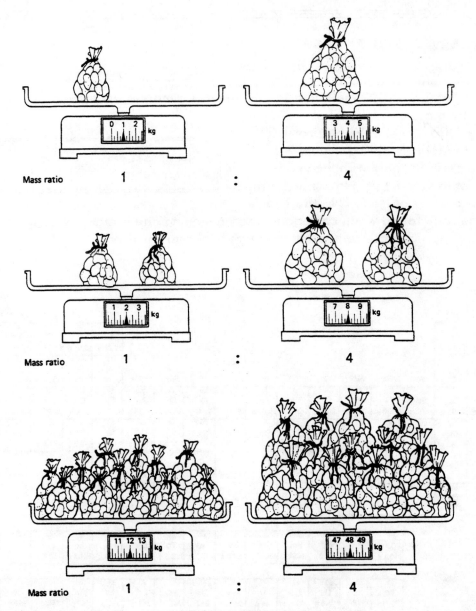

Figure 7.2 If the mass ratio of two different bags of potatoes is 1 to 4 (1 to 4 kg), then the mass ratio of equal quantities of these two different bags of potatoes is always 1 to 4.

We can use the same reasoning for atoms. For example, a He atom is four times as massive as a H atom. Therefore, 6.022×10^{23} atoms of He (1.000 mol He) have four times the mass of 6.022×10^{23} atoms of H (1.000 mol H).

The molar mass of an element is obtained by writing the numerical value for the atomic mass (from the periodic table), and placing the unit grams after the number (Table 7.1). For example, the atomic mass of Ne is 20; thus, its molar mass is 20 g. The atomic mass of Ar is 40, and its molar mass is 40 g. Both 20 g of Ne and 40 g of Ar contain

Avogadro's number of atoms. One mol of Ar is twice as massive as one mol of Ne, because one Ar atom is twice as massive as one Ne atom (Fig. 7.3).

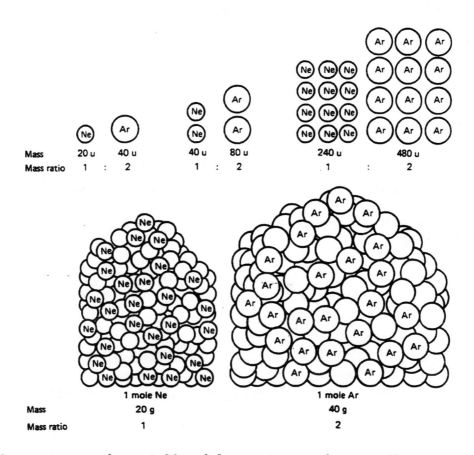

Figure 7.3 The atomic mass of neon is 20, and the atomic mass of argon is 40; an argon atom is therefore twice as massive as a neon atom. The mass of one dozen argon atoms (480 u) is twice as massive as one dozen neon atoms (240 u), and the mass of one mole of argon atoms (40 g) is twice as massive as one mole of neon atoms (20 g).

TABLE 7.1 MOLAR MASS OF ATOMS

Element	Atomic mass	Molar Mass	Number of atoms
C	12.01	12.01 g	6.022×10^{23}
Na	22.99	22.99 g	6.022×10^{23}
Cl	35.45	35.45 g	6.022×10^{23}
Au	196.9	196.9 g	6.022×10^{23}
Th	232.0	232.0 g	6.022×10^{23}

Mole Calculations: Elements
The beauty of using moles is that after making a simple mass measurement in a laboratory

the investigator can readily calculate the number of moles of atoms or the total number of atoms contained in the sample. When you solve mole problems, it is only necessary to apply the factor-label method, employing a procedure similar to the one used when converting one SI unit to another. Two conversion factors are used in mole calculations that involve elements:

$$\frac{g}{mol} \quad \text{or} \quad \frac{mol}{g}$$

and

$$\frac{6.022 \times 10^{23}}{1 \text{ mol atoms}} \quad \text{or} \quad \frac{1 \text{ mol atoms}}{6.022 \times 10^{23}}$$

For any quantity given—grams, atoms, or moles—the other two quantities can be calculated.

Figure 7.4 shows the pathway to follow when solving most mole problems. Atoms are converted to moles of atoms or moles of atoms are converted to atoms using 6.022×10^{23} atoms/mol. Moles of atoms are converted to grams or grams are converted to moles of atoms using the molar mass. Refer to this diagram when you attempt the problems and exercises.

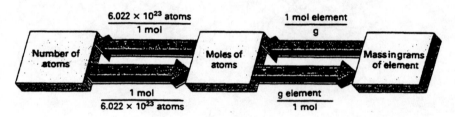

Figure 7.4 To change the number of atoms to moles of atoms, use the conversion factor 1 mol of atoms per 6.022×10^{23} atoms. To change the number of moles of atoms to its mass in grams, use the conversion factor grams of element per 1 mol. To go in the opposite direction, mass to moles, and then to atoms, use the reciprocals of these two conversion factors.

In the following series of example problems, we will consider different types of mole problems that involve atoms. Study each carefully before proceeding to the next one. Example Problem 7.1 illustrates the procedure for converting the mass of a sample to moles.

Example Problem 7.1
Chromium, Cr, is a hard, silvery-white solid used to plate iron and copper objects such as plumbing fixtures and automobile trim. How many moles of Cr atoms are there in a 1.00 g sample of Cr?

Solution
1. What is unknown?   mol Cr

2. What is known?   1.00 g Cr; l mol Cr = 52.0 g Cr, or 1 mol Cr/52.0 g Cr

Beside the mass, which is given in the problem, we also know the molar mass of Cr, 52.0 g Cr/mol Cr, from the periodic table. In all mole problems, the molar mass is found on the periodic table. Refer to Fig. 7.4, which illustrates the factor-label pathway taken.

3. Apply the factor-label method.

$$1.00 \text{ g Cr} \times \frac{1 \text{ mol Cr}}{52.0 \text{ g Cr}} = \text{? mol Cr}$$

Grams are the known units, and moles are the units we want; thus, the conversion factor is written with grams in the denominator and moles (the desired unit) in the numerator. After the grams cancel, we are left with moles.

4. Perform the indicated math operations.

$$1.00 \text{ g Cr} \times \frac{1 \text{ mol Cr}}{52.0 \text{ g Cr}} = \textbf{0.0192 mol Cr}$$

Dividing 52.0 g Cr into 1.00 g Cr, we obtain 0.0192 mol Cr. Note that in the statement of the problem the mass of Cr was 1.00 g, which represents three significant figures; therefore, the answer must also have three significant figures. Never allow the molar mass to determine the number of significant figures in the answer—always use the same or more significant figures to express the molar mass.

Exercise

How many moles of sulfur, S, are in a 55.5-g sample of sulfur? (1.73 mol S)

Example Problem 7.1 illustrates the general method for solving the majority of mole problems. As in many chemistry problems, careful attention to the units usually results in success in obtaining the correct answer.

If the number of moles of atoms is known, how is the mass of an element found? Study Example Problem 7.2, and see that it is similar to Example Problem 7.1 except for proceeding in the opposite direction with respect to the units.

Example Problem 7.2

Aluminum is the most abundant metal in the earth's crust. Al is one of the best reflectors of heat and light and is used to produce low-density alloys. What is the mass of 2.5 mol Al?

> Wohler discovered Al in 1827: it was named alumium by Davy. Its name was then changed to aluminium. Many countries still use this name, but in 1925 it was changed to aluminum in the United States.

Solution

1. What is unknown?   Mass of Al in g

2. What is known? 2.5 mol Al; 1 mol Al/27.0 g Al (from the periodic table) A glance at Fig. 7.4 shows us that to solve such a problem we need to know the mass of one mol Al.

3. Apply the factor-label method.

$$2.5 \text{ mol Al} \times \frac{27.0 \text{ g Al}}{1 \text{ mol Al}} = ? \text{ g Al}$$

Mol is canceled by g/mol, which leaves g, the desired unit.
4. Perform the indicated math operations.

$$2.5 \text{ mol Al} \times \frac{27.0 \text{ g Al}}{1 \text{ mol Al}} = \textbf{68 g Al}$$

Our answer is 68 g Al because the initial number of moles was only expressed to two significant figures.

Exercise
What is the mass of a 0.479-mol sample of titanium? (22.9 g Ti)

Given a specified quantity of moles of atoms, the number of atoms contained therein is easily found—somewhat in the same way that the number of eggs is found given how many dozen. Example Problems 7.3 and 7.4 are models for such conversions.

Example Problem 7.3

Calcium is a silvery-white metal. Calcium ions, Ca^{2+}, are a major component of the skeletal systems of animals. How many Ca atoms are in a 1.200-mol sample of Ca?

Solution

1. What is unknown?   Atoms of Ca
2. What is known? 1.200 mol Ca; 1 mol Ca/6.022×10^{23} atoms Ca
3. Apply the factor-label method.

$$1.200 \text{ mol Ca} \times \frac{6.022 \times 10^{23} \text{ atoms Ca}}{1 \text{ mol Ca}} = ? \text{ atoms Ca}$$

Moles of Ca are converted to atoms using the relationship between Avogadro's number and 1 mol.

4. Perform the indicated math operations.

$$1.200 \text{ mol Ca} \times \frac{6.022 \times 10^{23} \text{ atoms Ca}}{1 \text{ mol Ca}} = \textbf{7.226} \times \textbf{10}^{\textbf{23}} \textbf{ atoms Ca}$$

A 1.200-mol sample of calcium contains 7.226×10^{23} atoms Ca. The molar mass is not needed in this problem; no mass is specified, just the number of moles. It should be evident that any element could be substituted for Ca, and the answer would be the same: 1.200 mol of any element contains the same number of atoms (think about dozens, if this statement does not register).

Exercise
How many moles of Ni atoms are in a sample of 3.1×10^{23} atoms of Ni? (0.51 mol Ni)

Example Problem 7.4

Gold, silver, and copper are known as the coinage metals. They have been used for coins and jewelry for thousands of years. A sample of Au has 9.7×10^{23} atoms Au. How many moles of Au atoms are there in the sample?

> Two forms of gold are found in nature, native gold (1 to 50% silver alloy) and telluride ore ($AuTe_2$). Native gold is found as veins and dust in quartzite rock or in deposits that result after the rock weathers.

Solution

1. What is unknown?   Mol Au

2. What is known? 9.7×10^{23} atoms Au; 6.022×10^{23} atoms Au/mol Au

3. Apply the factor-label method.

$$9.7 \times 10^{23} \text{ atoms Au} \times \frac{1 \text{ mol Au}}{6.022 \times 10^{23} \text{ atoms Au}} = ? \text{ mol Au}$$

4. Perform the indicated math operations.

$$9.7 \times 10^{23} \text{ atoms Au} \times \frac{1 \text{ mol Au}}{6.022 \times 10^{23} \text{ atoms Au}} = \textbf{1.6 mol Au}$$

When you divide numbers expressed in scientific notation, remember to divide the coefficients and subtract the exponents. Our answer is expressed to two significant figures because two significant figures are given for the initial number of atoms of Au.

Exercise

How many moles of Li atoms are in a sample that contains 9.087×10^{24} atoms of Li? (15.09 mol Li)

In Example Problems 7.1 through 7.4 all conversions were accomplished using one conversion factor. To convert masses of elements to atoms, or find the masses of given numbers of atoms, more than one conversion factor is required. Given the mass of an element, no simple conversion to the number of atoms is known; hence, two conversion factors are used: molar mass (grams per mole) and Avogadro's number (atoms per mole) (refer to Fig. 7.4). Consider Example Problems 7.5 and 7.6 as illustrative models for such problems. ❖

Example Problem 7.5

Because lead, Pb, is easily extracted from its ore, it was known and used by the ancient Egyptians. Lead pipes were used to carry the water of the ancient Romans. How many Pb atoms are in a 100.0-g sample of pure Pb?

> The Latin name for lead is *plumbum*. From this old name the symbol Pb is derived. Lead is a soft, malleable, bluish-white metal with a density of 11.4 g/cm^3.

Solution
1. What is unknown?   Number of atoms of Pb
2. What is known? 100.0 g Pb; 1 mol Pb/207.2 g Pb; 6.022×10^{23} atoms Pb/mol Pb
3. Apply the factor-label method.

$$100.0 \ \text{g Pb} \times \frac{1 \ \text{mol Pb}}{207.2 \ \text{g Pb}} \times \frac{6.022 \times 10^{23} \ \text{atoms Pb}}{1 \ \text{mol Pb}} = ? \ \text{atoms Pb}$$

4. Perform the indicated math operations.

$$100.0 \ \text{g Pb} \times \frac{1 \ \text{mol Pb}}{207.2 \ \text{g Pb}} \times \frac{6.022 \times 10^{23} \ \text{atoms Pb}}{1 \ \text{mol Pb}} = \mathbf{2.906 \times 10^{23} \ atoms \ Pb}$$

Our answer is expressed to four significant figures because the initial mass of Pb is expressed to four significant figures.

A good habit to develop is to ask yourself if your answer is reasonable. In this problem, the mass, 100.0 g Pb, is slightly less than half the molar mass of Pb, which gives an answer smaller than 0.5 moles, or one-half of Avogadro's number.

Exercise
How many He atoms are in a 111-g sample of He? (1.67×10^{25} atoms He)

Example Problem 7.6

Uranium is a dense, radioactive metal that can burst into flames if finely divided. What is the mass of 5.64×10^{23} atoms of uranium?

> In 1789, Uranium was discovered by Klaproth. He found it in an ore called pitchblende. All the isotopes of U are radioactive.

Solution
1. What is unknown?   Mass of U in g
2. What is known? 5.64×10^{23} atoms U; 1 mol U/6.022×10^{23} atoms U; 238 g U/mol U
3. Apply the factor-label method.

$$5.64 \times 10^{23} \ \text{atoms U} \times \frac{1 \ \text{mol U}}{6.022 \times 10^{23} \ \text{atoms U}} \times \frac{238 \ \text{g U}}{1 \ \text{mol U}} = ? \ \text{g U}$$

4. Perform the indicated math operations.

$$5.64 \times 10^{23} \ \text{atoms U} \times \frac{1 \ \text{mol U}}{6.022 \times 10^{23} \ \text{atoms U}} \times \frac{238 \ \text{g U}}{1 \ \text{mol U}} = \mathbf{223 \ g \ U}$$

Is the answer reasonable? Yes, 5.64×10^{23} atoms U is smaller than Avogadro's number, which is the number of particles in 1 mol. Thus, the answer should be less than the molar mass of U, which is 238 g/mol.

Exercise
What is the mass of 8.2×10^{23} atoms of palladium, Pd? (1.4×10^2 g Pd)

REVIEW EXERCISES

7.5 How many moles of atoms are in the following samples?

(a) 5.5 g Ne
(b) 3.01 g Fe
(c) 0.087 kg Ar
(d) 22.5 mg Mn

7.6 Calculate the mass of each of the following samples?

(a) 8.19 mol V
(b) 0.0044 mol Ge
(c) 5.03×10^3 mol As
(d) 4.100 mmol Al

7.7 How many atoms are in each of the following noble gas samples?

(a) 5.00 g He
(b) 5.00 g Ne
(c) 5.00 g Ar
(d) 5.00 g Kr

7.8 Calculate the number of moles of atoms represented by each of the following.

(a) 8.211×10^{23} atoms B
(b) 4.7×10^{20} atoms Ag
(c) 9.904×10^{26} atoms Cu
(d) 6.29×10^{21} atoms Cs

7.5 (a) 0.27 mol Ne, (b) 0.0539 mol Fe, (c) 2.2 mol Ar, (d) 4.10×10^{-4} mol Mn; 7.6 (a) 417 g V, (b) 0.32 g Ge, (c) 3.77×10^5 g As, (d) 0.1106 g Al; 7.7 (a) 7.52×10^{23} He, (b) 1.49×10^{23} Ne, (c) 7.54×10^{22} Ar, (d) 3.59×10^{22} Kr; 7.8 (a) 1.364 mol B. (b) 7.8×10^{-4} mol Ag, (c) 1645 mol Cu, (d) 0.0104 mol Cs

7.3 MOLAR MASS OF COMPOUNDS

A compound is a chemical combination of atoms. Each compound has a fixed ratio of elements; or on a smaller scale, each molecule is composed of a fixed ratio of atoms. Accordingly, we can apply the mole concept to molecules, as we did to atoms.

Molecular Mass

Molecular mass (traditionally, molecular weight) is the sum of the atomic masses of the atoms within a molecule. Let us use water, H_2O, as an example. Each water molecule contains two H atoms and one O atom. The atomic masses of H and O are 1.0 and 16.0, respectively. To find the molecular mass of water, multiply 2 times 1.0 to obtain the total mass of H, and add that to 16.0; the result, 18, is the molecular mass.

$$
\begin{array}{lll}
\text{H} & 2 \text{ atoms} \times 1.0 = & 2.0 \\
\text{O} & 1 \text{ atom} \times 16.0 = & \underline{+16.0} \\
\text{H}_2\text{O} & & = \textbf{18.0}
\end{array}
$$

If the molecular mass of water is 18, then its molar mass is **18.0 g** and 18.0 g H_2O contains Avogadro's number of molecules, 6.02×10^{23} molecules of H_2O. Example Problem 7.7 shows how to calculate the molecular masses of three compounds.

Example Problem 7.7
Find the molecular masses of (a) CH_4, (b) HNO_3 (c) $B_{10}H_{16}$

Solution
(a) Molecular mass of CH_4:

$$
\begin{array}{lll}
\text{C} & 1 \text{ atom} \times 12.0 = & 12.0 \\
\text{H} & 4 \text{ atoms} \times 1.0 = & \underline{+\ 4.0} \\
\text{CH}_4 & & = \textbf{16.0}
\end{array}
$$

> CH_4 methane is the primary component of natural gas, an important fuel.

(b) Molecular mass of HNO_3:

$$
\begin{array}{lll}
\text{H} & 1 \text{ atom} \times 1.0 = & 1.0 \\
\text{N} & 1 \text{ atom} \times 14.0 = & 14.0 \\
\text{O} & 3 \text{ atoms} \times 16.0 = & \underline{+48.0} \\
\text{HNO}_3 & & = \textbf{63.0}
\end{array}
$$

> HNO_3 is nitric acid a strong mineral acid of great commercial importance.

(c) Molecular mass of $B_{10}H_{16}$:

$$
\begin{array}{lll}
\text{B} & 10 \text{ atoms} \times 10.81 = & 108.1 \\
\text{H} & 16 \text{ atoms} \times 1.01 = & \underline{+\ 16.1} \\
\text{B}_{10}\text{H}_{16} & & = \textbf{124.2}
\end{array}
$$

> Boron-hydrogen compounds belong to a group of compounds called boranes.

In these molecular mass calculations, the number of atoms of each type is multiplied by the element's atomic mass, and then the quantities are added to obtain the sum.

Exercise
What is the molecular mass of $Ca(OH)_2$? (74.1)

Mole Calculations: Compounds
Mole calculations with molecules are the same as those that with atoms, except that the fundamental particle is a molecule. Thus, the molar mass of a compound is the molecular mass in grams, and Avogadro's number of molecules are within the molar mass of a compound.

What is the molar mass of carbon dioxide, CO_2, and how many particles are contained in that mass? Calculate the molecular mass of CO_2; one C atom, 12, and two O atoms, each 16, give a molecular mass if of 44. Adding grams as

> 1 mol CO_2 = 44g
> 1 mol CO_2 = 6.022×10^{23} CO_2 molecules

the unit, we obtain 44 g as the molar mass of CO_2. In 44 g of CO_2, there are 6.0×10^{23} molecules of CO_2.

From Example Problem 7.7, we found that the molar masses of CH_4, HNO_3, and $B_{10}H_{16}$ are 16.0 g, 63.0 g, and 124.2 g, respectively. Avogadro's number of CH_4 molecules are found in 16.0 g CH_4. Also, 63.0 g HNO_3 and 124.2 g $B_{10}H_{16}$ each contain 6.02×10^{23} molecules.

As was the case with atoms, most mole calculations for compounds involve interconversions of units—moles, molecules, and grams. Figure 7.5 summarizes mole conversions for compounds.

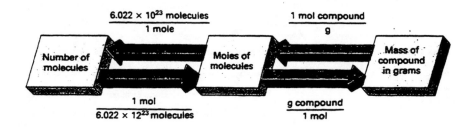

Figure 7.5 To change the number of molecules to moles of molecules, use the conversion factor 1 mol of molecules per 6.022×10^{23} molecules. To change the number of moles of molecules to grams, use the conversion factor grams per 1 mol. To go in the opposite direction, mass to moles, and then to molecules, use the reciprocals of these two conversion factors.

Carefully go through Example Problems 7.8 through 7.10, using Fig. 7.5 when necessary. Note that the calculations are similar to mole calculations with atoms except that molecular masses are used instead of atomic masses.

Example Problem 7.8
Nitrous oxide, N_2O, is a colorless gas with a pleasant odor. It is also called laughing gas. Nitrous oxide has been used as a general anesthetic for medical and dental operations for many years. What is the mass of a 4.05 mol sample of N_2O?

> The nickname "laughing gas" for nitrous oxide was coined by Sir Humphry Davy, after he discovered the anesthetic effects of the gas.

Solution
1. What is unknown?   Mass of N_2O in g
2. What is known? 4.05 mol N_2O; the molar mass of N_2O, which is calculated from the atomic masses as follows:

$$N \quad 2\ \cancel{mol\ N} \times \frac{14.0\ g\ N}{1\ \cancel{mol\ N}} \quad = \quad 28.0\ g\ N$$

$$O \quad 1\ \cancel{mol\ O} \times \frac{16.0\ g\ O}{1\ \cancel{mol\ O}} \quad = \underline{+\ 16.0\ g\ O}$$

$$N_2O = 44.0\ g/mol\ N_2O$$

3. Apply the factor-label method.

$$4.05 \; \cancel{mol \; N_2O} \times \frac{44.0 \; g \; N_2O}{1 \; \cancel{mol \; N_2O}} = ? \; g \; N_2O$$

4. Perform the indicated math operations.

$$4.05 \; \cancel{mol \; N_2O} \times \frac{44.0 \; g \; N_2O}{1 \; \cancel{mol \; N_2O}} = \textbf{178 g N}_2\textbf{O}$$

The mass of 4.05 mol N_2O is 178 g.

Exercise

What is the mass of 0.1010 mol CCl_4? (15.53 g CCl_4)

Example Problem 7.9

Sulfuric acid, H_2SO_4, is the industrial chemical produced in greatest amount in the United States. It has hundreds of uses in industry. How many sulfuric acid molecules are in a 0.100-g sample of H_2SO_4?

Sulfuric acid is used to make fertilizers, drugs, and dyes. It is an important compound in the refining of crude oil and is used by the steel industry to clean the surfaces of metals.

Solution

1. What is unknown?   Molecules of H_2SO_4
2. What is known? 0.100 g H_2SO_4; 1 mol H_2SO_4/6.022 $\times$ 10^{23} molecules H_2SO_4; the molar mass of H_2SO_4, calculated from its atomic masses:

$$H \quad 2 \; \cancel{mol \; H} \times \frac{1.0 \; g \; H}{1 \; \cancel{mol \; H}} \quad = 2.0 \; g \; H$$

$$S \quad 1 \; \cancel{mol \; S} \times \frac{32.1 \; g \; S}{1 \; \cancel{mol \; S}} \quad = 32.1 \; g \; S$$

$$O \; 4 \; \cancel{mol \; O} \times \frac{16.0 \; g \; O}{1 \; \cancel{mol \; O}} \quad = \underline{+64.0 \; g \; O}$$

$$H_2SO_4 \quad\quad\quad = 98.1 \; g/mol \; H_2SO_4$$

3. Apply the factor-label method.

$$0.100 \; \cancel{g \; H_2SO_4} \times \frac{1 \; \cancel{mol \; H_2SO_4}}{98.1 \; \cancel{g \; H_2SO_4}} \times \frac{6.022 \times 10^{23} \; molecules \; H_2SO_4}{1 \; \cancel{mol \; H_2SO_4}} = ? \; molecules$$

4. Perform the indicated math operations.

$$0.100 \; \cancel{g \; H_2SO_4} \times \frac{1 \; \cancel{mol \; H_2SO_4}}{98.1 \; \cancel{g \; H_2SO_4}} \times \frac{6.022 \times 10^{23} \; molecules \; H_2SO_4}{1 \; \cancel{mol \; H_2SO_4}} = \textbf{6.14} \times \textbf{10}^{\textbf{20}}$$

$$\textbf{molecules H}_2\textbf{SO}_4$$

A 0.100-g sample of H_2SO_4 contains 6.14×10^{20} molecules H_2SO_4.
Exercise
How many molecules are in a 525-g sample of CO_2? (7.18×10^{24} molecules of CO_2)

Example Problem 7.10
Glucose, $C_6H_{12}O_6$, is also known as blood sugar because it circulates in the blood. It is also in grapes, honey, and various fruits. What is the mass in grams of 3.39×10^{22} molecules of glucose?

Solution
1. What is unknown?   Mass in g $C_6H_{12}O_6$
2. What is known? 3.39×10^{22} molecules $C_6H_{12}O_6$; 1 mol $C_6H_{12}O_6$/6.02×10^{23} $C_6H_{12}O_6$ molecules; the molar mass of $C_6H_{12}O_6$, calculated as follows:

$$C \quad 6 \text{ mol C} \times \frac{12.02 \text{ g C}}{1 \text{ mol C}} \quad = 72.0 \text{ g C}$$

$$H \quad 12 \text{ mol H} \times \frac{1.0 \text{ g H}}{1 \text{ mol H}} \quad = 12.0 \text{ g H}$$

$$O \quad 6 \text{ mol O} \times \frac{16.0 \text{ g O}}{1 \text{ mol O}} \quad = \underline{+96.0 \text{ g O}}$$

$$C_6H_{12}O_6 \quad = 180.0 \text{ g/mol } C_6H_{12}O_6$$

3. Apply the factor-label method.

$$3.39 \times 10^{22} \text{ molecules } C_6H_{12}O_6 \times \frac{1 \text{ mol } C_6H_{12}O_6}{6.02 \times 10^{23} \text{ molecules}} \times \frac{180.0 \text{ g } C_6H_{12}O_6}{1 \text{ mol } C_6H_{12}O_6} = ? \text{ g } C_6H_{12}O_6$$

4. Perform the indicated math operations.

$$3.39 \times 10^{22} \text{ molecules } C_6H_{12}O_6 \times \frac{1 \text{ mol } C_6H_{12}O_6}{6.02 \times 10^{23} \text{ molecules } C_6H_{12}O_6} \times$$

$$\frac{180.0 \text{ g } C_6H_{12}O_6}{1 \text{ mol } C_6H_{12}O_6} = \mathbf{10.1 \text{ g } C_6H_{12}O_6}$$

The mass of 3.39×10^{22} molecules of glucose is 10.1 g.
Exercise
What is the mass of 1.77×10^{23} molecules of water? (5.29 g H_2O)

Moles of Elements in Compounds
In the future, it will sometimes be necessary to calculate the number of moles of atoms or the number of atoms in a specified quantity of a compound. For example, how many moles of H and O are there in 1 mol of water, H_2O? Water molecules have two atoms of H and one atom of O; consequently, 1 mol H_2O contains 2 mol H (2 g H) and 1 mol O (16 g O).

Using another large-scale analogy, let us consider the face of a person. Each person has one nose and two eyes. One dozen people, among them, possess one dozen noses and two dozen eyes (Fig. 7.6). It stands to reason that 1 mol of people have 1 mol of noses and 2 mol of eyes.

> One mole of H_2O has 2 moles of H and 1 mole of O.

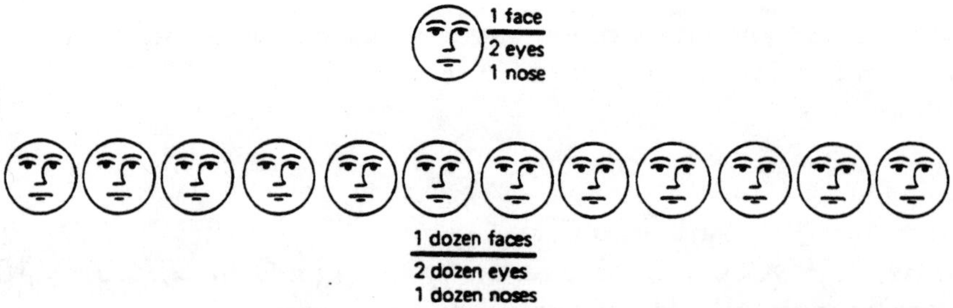

$$\frac{1 \text{ face}}{2 \text{ eyes}}$$
$$1 \text{ nose}$$

$$\frac{1 \text{ dozen faces}}{2 \text{ dozen eyes}}$$
$$1 \text{ dozen noses}$$

Figure 7.6 One person has two eyes and one nose. One dozen people have two dozen eyes and one dozen noses. One mole of people have 2 mol of eyes and 1 mol of noses.

When confronted with such problems, find the number of moles of the compound of interest, and then use the appropriate conversion factor that gives the number of atoms per molecule. Figure 7.7 maps the pathway to be taken, and Example Problems 7.11 and 7.12 show how such problems are solved.

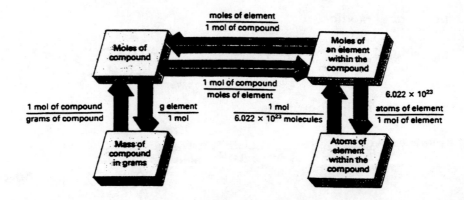

Figure 7.7 To find the number of atoms of a specific type in a given mass of compound, three conversion factors are required. The first is the mass of 1 mol of the compound (1 mol/g compound); the second factor is the number of moles of the desired element per 1 mol of compound (mol element/1 mol compound); and the third factor is the number of atoms per 1 mol of the element (6.022×10^{23} atoms/1 mol element).

Example Problem 7.11
How many moles of C and H atoms are in a 9.25-g sample of cyclopentane, C_5H_{10}?

Solution
1. What is unknown?   Mol C and mol H

2. What is known? 9.25 g C_5H_{10}; 5 mol C/mol C_5H_{10}; 10 mol H/mol C_5H_{10}; the molar mass of C_5H_{10}:

$$C \quad 5 \text{ mol C} \times \frac{12.0 \text{ g C}}{1 \text{ mol C}} \quad = \quad 60.0 \text{ g C}$$

$$H \quad 10 \text{ mol H} \times \frac{1.0 \text{ g H}}{1 \text{ mol H}} \quad = \quad \underline{+10.0 \text{ g H}}$$

$$C_5H_{10} \qquad\qquad = 70.0 \text{ g/mol } C_5H_{10}$$

3. Apply the factor-label method (refer to Fig. 7.7).

$$9.25 \text{ g } C_5H_{10} \times \frac{1 \text{ mol } C_5H_{10}}{70.0 \text{ g } C_5H_{10}} \times \frac{5 \text{ mol C}}{1 \text{ mol } C_5H_{10}} \quad = \text{ ? mol C}$$

It is not necessary to write the full setup to find the number of moles of H. The ratio of H to C in C_5H_{10} is 10 to 5, or 2 to 1: 2 mol H/1 mol C. After calculating the number of moles of C, we can use this conversion factor to find the moles of H.

$$\text{mol C} \times \frac{2 \text{ mol H}}{1 \text{ mol C}} = \text{mol H}$$

4. Perform the indicated math operations.

$$9.25 \text{ g } C_5H_{10} \times \frac{1 \text{ mol } C_5H_{10}}{70.0 \text{ g } C_5H_{10}} \times \frac{5 \text{ mol C}}{1 \text{ mol } C_5H_{10}} = \textbf{0.661 mol C}$$

$$0.661 \text{ mol C} \times \frac{2 \text{ mol H}}{1 \text{ mol C}} = \textbf{1.32 mol H}$$

After calculating the number of moles of C in 9.25 g C_5H_{10}, it is only necessary to double the value to obtain the number of moles of H atoms.

Exercise

How many Cl atoms are in a 5.99-g sample of $CaCl_2$? (6.49×10^{22} atoms Cl)

Example Problem 7.12

What mass of ammonia, NH_3, has the same number of H atoms as 40 g HNO_3?

Solution

1. What is unknown?   Mass in g of NH_3 that contains the same number of H atoms as 40 g HNO_3

2. What is known? The molar masses are as follows: 63 g HNO_3/1 mol HNO_3 and 17 g NH_3/1 mol NH_3. One mole of HNO_3 contains one mole H atoms, 1 mol HNO_3/1 mol H. One mole of NH_3 contains three moles of H atoms, 1 mol NH_3/3 mol H.

If both samples have the same number of H atoms, they also have the same number of moles of H atoms. Thus, first calculate the number of H atoms in 40 g HNO_3. This quantity of moles equals the number of moles in the NH_3 sample.

3. Apply the factor-label method.

$$40 \text{ g } HNO_3 \times \frac{1 \text{ mol } HNO_3}{63 \text{ g } HNO_3} \times \frac{1 \text{ mol } H}{1 \text{ mol } HNO_3} \times \frac{1 \text{ mol } NH_3}{3 \text{ mol } H} \times \frac{17 \text{ g } NH_3}{1 \text{ mol } NH_3} = ? \text{ g } NH_3$$

4. Perform the indicated math operations.

$$40 \text{ g } HNO_3 \times \frac{1 \text{ mol } HNO_3}{63 \text{ g } HNO_3} \times \frac{1 \text{ mol } H}{1 \text{ mol } HNO_3} \times \frac{1 \text{ mol } NH_3}{3 \text{ mol } H} \times \frac{17 \text{ g } NH_3}{1 \text{ mol } NH_3} = \textbf{3.60 g } NH_3$$

A 3.60-g sample of NH_3 contains the same number of H atoms as a 40-g sample of HNO_3.
Exercise
What mass of $MgCl_2$ has the same number of Cl atoms as a 75-g sample of $AlCl_3$? (80 g $MgCl_2$)

Compounds Not Composed of Molecules
When two nonmetals combine chemically, the resulting compound is usually composed of discrete molecules; examples of compounds such as these are CO, NO, CH_4, and H_2O. Compounds composed of metals and nonmetals or metals and polyatomic ions are not made up of discrete, or separate, molecules. Instead, their structures are networks of ions chemically bonded together. For these compounds,

Formula mass NaCl = 8.5 g NaCl = 6.022 × 10²³ formula units NaCl

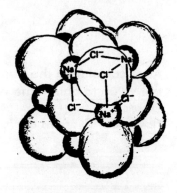

Figure 7.8 Sodium chloride, NaCl, is composed of a cubic network of sodium ions, Na⁺, surrounded by chloride ions, Cl⁻, (or chloride ions surrounded by sodium ions). Discrete molecules of sodium chloride do not exist.

the term molecular mass has no real meaning because no molecules are present. A more accurate term is applied to these compounds: formula mass. **Formula mass** is used for those substances not composed of discrete molecules in the same way that molecular mass is used for compounds composed of molecules.

WWWolfe 3
(See WWWolfe
section at the end of
the chapter.)

An example of a compound not composed of discrete molecules is sodium chloride, NaCl. Sodium chloride is composed of Na^+ and Cl^- anions in a three-dimensional pattern (Fig. 7.8). Each Na^+ cation is surrounded by Cl^- ions, and each Cl^- anion is surrounded by Na^+ ions. In NaCl, for every Na^+ there is one Cl^-: the two elements are found in a 1-to-1 ratio. We speak of this as the **formula unit** or the simplest ratio of atoms within the compound.

In Chap. 8, we will investigate the structure of these compounds; for now, we will simply say that most compounds that result from combinations of metals and nonmetals or metals and the charged groups of atoms called polyatomic ions do not exist as discrete molecules. Members of this group of substances are called ionic compounds. Examples include calcium fluoride, CaF_2; sodium nitrate, $NaNO_3$; copper sulfate, $CuSO_4$; and many others. Table 7.2 lists some commonly encountered ionic substances.

TABLE 7.2 EXAMPLES OF IONIC COMPOUNDS

Compound	Formula	Formula Mass
Ammonium nitrate	NH_4NO_3	80.0
Calcium chloride	$CaCl_2$	111.0
Iron(II) sulfide	FeS	87.9
Magnesium hydroxide	$Mg(OH)_2$	58.3
Titanium(IV) oxide	TiO_2	79.9

To calculate the formula mass of an ionic compound, you should follow the same procedure you used to find the molecular mass of a substance composed of molecules. In most cases, the formula mass is treated in the same way as molecular mass. For example, NaCl has a formula mass of 58.5 and a molar mass of 58.5 g composed of Avogadro's number of formula units. ❖

REVIEW EXERCISES

7.9 Calculate the molar mass of each of the following.

(a) Br_2
(b) SO_3
(c) HNO_3
(d) $Al_2(SO_4)_3$

7.10 What is the mass in grams of each of the following samples?

(a) 5.11 mol PF_3
(b) 8.012×10^{23} molecules $SiCl_4$

(c) 0.0809 mmol P_4O_{10}

7.11 How many molecules are there in each of the following samples?

(a) 10.00 g H_2S
(b) 10.00 g ClF_3
(c) 10.00 g C_5Br_{12}

7.12 Which of the following contains the largest number of moles of oxygen atoms: (a) 25 g CO_2, (b) 25 g $C_6H_{12}O_6$, or (c) 25 g H_3PO_4?

7.13 Explain why it is incorrect to refer to the "molecular mass" of NaCl.

7.9 (a) 159.81 g/mol Br_2, (b) 80.04 g/mol SO_3, (c) 63.00 g/mol HNO_3, (d) 342.07 g/mol $Al_2(SO_4)_3$; 7.10 (a) 450 g PF_3, (b) 226.0 g $SiCl_4$, (c) 0.0230 g P_4O_{10}; 7.11 (a) 1.766×10^{23} molecules H_2S, (b) 6.514×10^{22} molecules ClF_3, (c) 5.910×10^{21} molecules C_5Br_{12}; 7.12 (a) 25.0 g CO_2

7.4 MOLES AND CHEMICAL FORMULAS

Armed with the mole concept, chemists can obtain a tremendous amount of information about a compound, solution, or mixture by finding the mass of its components. Moles are used by chemists to calculate (1) formulas of compounds, (2) mass relationships in chemical reactions, and (3) concentrations of solutions and mixtures.

In this section, we will study formula calculations and determinations, and in the next section we will apply the mole concept to solutions.

Law of Constant Composition
Each compound is composed of elements in a fixed mass ratio. Any sample of H_2O contains 11% H and 89% O by mass. If a sample of a H and O compound is studied and different percents by mass are found, it must be concluded that the substance is not pure water. To generalize: *All samples of a given compound contain the same elements in a fixed mass ratio.* This is a statement of the **law of constant composition,** which is also called **the law of definite proportions.**

The law of constant composition was proposed by the French scientist Joseph-Louis Proust (1754-1826). At the time, it was thought that the composition of a substance could vary, depending on the sample. Proust's "radical" new hypothesis took about 10 years to catch on.

> Proust was the son of an apothecary (pharmacist) and was one of the first chemists to study sugars. Proust was an avid balloonist making of the first ascensions in 1784.

Percent Composition
A direct result of the law of constant composition is that each element in a compound can be expressed as a mass percent. Collectively, all mass percents of elements in a compound are called the **percent composition** of the substance. The percent composition of water is 11% H and 89% O, and the percent composition of table sugar (sucrose, $C_{12}H_{22}O_{11}$) is 42.1% C, 6.4% H, and 51.5% O. For all compounds, the sum of the mass percents equals 100%.

How is the percent composition of a compound determined? A specific mass of the compound is analyzed to find the masses of each element. Percent by mass of each element is then calculated by dividing the mass of each element by the total mass

> A percent is the number of parts per 100 total parts. Percent by mass is the ratio of the mass of a component to 100 g total mass.

of the compound, and then multiplying by 100. As with all percent calculations you take the part and divide it by the whole and multiply times 100.

It is most convenient to use the molar mass of a compound in percent composition calculations. When you calculate molar mass, the mass of each element is found. It is then only necessary to convert these masses to percents. Example Problem 7.13 shows how the percent composition of nitrogen(V) oxide, N_2O_5, is found.

Example Problem 7.13

Nitrogen(V) oxide, N_2O_5, is a gas that combines with water to produce nitric acid, HNO_3, which is one of the most important industrial acids. What is the percent composition of N_2O_5?

Solution

1. What is unknown?   %N and %O in N_2O_5, in which %N is (g N/g N_2O_5) × 100, and %O is (g O/g N_2O_5) × 100
2. What is known? Molecular formula of the compound, N_2O_5; atomic masses of N and O, 14.0 g N/mol N and 16.0 g O/mol O

From this information, the molar mass is determined:

$$N \quad 2 \text{ mol N} \times \frac{14.0 \text{ g N}}{1 \text{ mol N}} \quad = 28.0 \text{ g N}$$

$$O \quad 5 \text{ mol O} \times \frac{16.0 \text{ g O}}{1 \text{ mol O}} \quad = 80.0 \text{ g O}$$

$$N_2O_5 \quad = 108.0 \text{ g/mol } N_2O_5$$

3. Calculate the percent by mass of N and O in N_2O_5.

$$\%N = \frac{g \text{ N}}{g \text{ } N_2O_5} \times 100 = \frac{28.0 \text{ g N}}{108.0 \text{ g } N_2O_5} \times 100 = \textbf{25.9\% N}$$

$$\%O = \frac{g \text{ O}}{g \text{ } N_2O_5} \times 100 = \frac{80.0 \text{ g O}}{108.0 \text{ g } N_2O_5} \times 100 = \textbf{74.1\% O}$$

N_2O_5 has a percent composition of 25.9% N and 74.1% O. Note that the percents always add up to 100%. A common practice is to calculate the percent of one element and then subtract that value from 100 to obtain the percent for the second element. This philosophy is fine as long as the first value is correct. A better strategy is to compute both percents and check to see if they add up to 100%.

Exercise

What is the percent composition of PBr_3 expressed to four significant figures? (%P = 11.44%, %Br = 88.56%)

Example Problem 7.14 illustrates the calculation of the percent composition of a compound containing more than two elements: ethanol, C_2H_6O, which is also called grain or drinking alcohol.

> Ingestion of a large quantity of ethanol causes unconsciousness and a comalike state. Death can result if the blood ethanol concentration exceeds 5%.

Example Problem 7.14

Ethanol, C_2H_6O, is produced when grains or fruits are fermented by yeast. Find the percent composition of ethanol.

Solution

1. What is unknown? %C, %H, and %O in C_2H_6O
2. What is known? The molar mass of each element and the molecular formula

The molar mass of ethanol is calculated as follows:

$$C \quad 2 \text{ mol C} \times 12 \text{ g C/mol C} = 24.0 \text{ g C}$$
$$H \quad 6 \text{ mol H} \times 1.01 \text{ g H/mol H} = 6.06 \text{ g H}$$
$$O \quad 1 \text{ mol O} \times 16.0 \text{ g O/mol O} = \underline{+16.0 \text{ g}}$$
$$C_2H_6O = 46.1 \text{ g/mol } C_2H_6O$$

3. Calculate the percent by mass of C, H, and O in C_2H_6O.

$$\%C = \frac{g\ C}{g\ C_2H_6O} \times 100 = \frac{24.0\ g\ C}{46.1\ g\ C_2H_6O} \times 100 = \mathbf{52.1\%}$$

$$\%H = \frac{g\ H}{g\ C_2H_6O} \times 100 = \frac{6.06\ g\ H}{46.1\ g\ C_2H_6O} \times 100 = \mathbf{13.1\%}$$

$$\%O = \frac{g\ O}{g\ C_2H_6O} \times 100 = \frac{16.0\ g\ O}{46.1\ g\ C_2H_6O} \times 100 = \mathbf{34.7\%}$$

Our calculations show that the percent composition is 52.1% C, 13.1% H, and 34.7% O. The sum of these three percents is 99.9%. Sometimes, due to rounding errors, the percents will not add up to exactly 100%.

Exercise

What is the percent composition of $AuNO_3$? (%Au = 76.1%, %N = 5.41%, %O = 18.5%)

Empirical Formula

In the laboratory, chemists determine formulas of compounds as one way of characterizing compounds. All that is needed to calculate the empirical formula of a compound is the percent composition or other mass data on the elements in the compound. **Empirical formulas** express the smallest whole-number ratio of atoms within a molecule.

To calculate the empirical formula of a compound, we must know either the percent composition or the mass ratio of the elements. The mass of each element in the compound is converted to moles and the mole ratio is calculated. The empirical formula is obtained when the simplest mole ratio is calculated. In most cases, the empirical formula is a ratio of whole numbers, such as 3 to 1, or 5 to 2.

Let us consider hydrogen peroxide, which is an antiseptic and bleaching agent. Its molecular formula is H_2O_2. A molecular formula expresses the actual number of atoms in the molecule. One hydrogen peroxide molecule has two H atoms and two O atoms. Its empirical formula, HO (H_1O_1), is obtained by dividing the subscripts of the molecular formula by 2. Table 7.3 lists molecular and empirical formulas for selected molecules.

> A 3% solution of hydrogen peroxide is used as a germicide. In research and industry, 30% solutions are often used. Pure H_2O_2 is a pale-blue liquid that must be handled with extreme care because it decomposes violently or readily combines with substances that it contacts.

TABLE 7.3 SIMPLEST AND MOLECULAR FORMULAS

Compound	Molecular Formula	Empirical Formula
A borane	$B_{10}H_{12}$	B_5H_6
Benzene	C_6H_6	CH
Glucose	$C_6H_{12}O_6$	CH_2O
Mercury(I) chloride	Hg_2Cl_2	HgCl
Propane	C_3H_8	C_3H_8
Sodium oxalate	$Na_2C_2O_4$	$NaCO_2$
Tetraphosphorus decoxide	P_4O_{10}	P_2O_5

Many compounds have the same molecular and empirical formula—e.g., propane in Table 7.3. Whenever the subscripts of the molecular formula of a compound are not divisible by a common number, the empirical formula is the same as the molecular formula. Other examples of such compounds are potassium nitrate, KNO_3; sulfur trioxide, SO_3; and phosphorus pentachloride, PCl_5.

Example Problem 7.15 shows how the empirical formula of a compound is calculated, given the percent composition. Each step in the calculation is illustrated in Fig. 7.9.

Example Problem 7.15
The percent composition of a N—F compound is 26.9% N and 73.1% F. What is the empirical formula of the compound?

Solution
1. What is unknown?   Empirical formula, the mole ratio of N to F or vice versa, mol N/mol F or mol F/mol N
2. What is known? 26.9% N and 73.1% F; the molar masses of N nd F, 14.0 g N/mol N and 19.0 g F/mol F

3. Calculate the number of moles of each element.

The percents given are the mass ratios of each element per 100 g of compound; specifically,

$$29.6\% \, N = \frac{26.9 \, g \, N}{100 \, g \, compound}$$

$$73.1\% \, F = \frac{73.1 \, g \, F}{100 \, g \, compound}$$

Thus, it is convenient to calculate the number of moles of N and F that correspond to 26.9 g N and 73.1 g F.

$$26.9 \, \cancel{g \, N} \times \frac{1 \, mol \, N}{14.0 \, \cancel{g \, N}} = 1.92 \, mol \, N$$

$$73.1 \, g \, F \times \frac{1 \, mol \, F}{19.0 \, \cancel{g \, F}} = 3.85 \, mol \, F$$

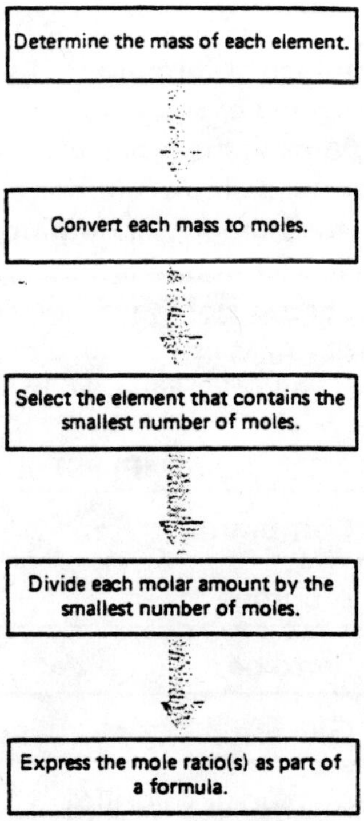

4. Calculate the smallest whole-number mole ratio.

Identify the element with the smallest number of moles and then divide this value into the number of moles of each element. In our problem, 1.92 mol N is the smallest quantity of moles; thus, it is divided into itself, giving exactly 1, and then divided into 3.85 mol F, giving 2.01.

$$\frac{1.92 \, mol \, N}{1.92 \, mol \, N} = 1.00$$

$$\frac{3.85 \, mol \, F}{1.92 \, mol \, F} = \frac{2.01 \, mol \, F}{1 \, mol \, N}$$

The simplest ratio is 2 mol F to 1 mol N, or, translated into an empirical formula, **NF₂**. If the simplest mole ratio is 1 to 2, this shows that the ratio of N to F atoms in the molecule is also 1 to 2. With no other information, the molecular formula cannot be calculated. All that we know is the empirical formula; the molecular formula could possibly be NF_2, N_2F_4, N_3F_6, or N_4F_8, all of which have a ratio of 1 N atom to 2 F atoms.

Exercise

A compound contains 54.4% I and 45.6% Cl. What is the empirical formula of the compound? (ICl_3)

Figure 7.9 Use this stepwise procedure to calculate the empirical formula of a compound.

It is not necessary to know the percent composition to calculate the empirical formula of a compound. All that is required is mass data on the elements in a sample of the compound (Fig. 7.9). The mass of each element is converted to moles, and the simplest mole ratio is calculated. Example Problem 7.16 shows such a computation.

Example Problem 7.16

Ascorbic acid is the chemical name for vitamin C. Vitamins are essential substances required in the human diet almost every day. Analysis of a 2.642 g sample of ascorbic acid reveals that there is 1.081 g C, 0.121 g H, and the remainder is oxygen. What is the empirical formula of ascorbic acid?

> An insufficient amount of ascorbic acid in a person's diet leads to the vitamin deficiency disease called scurvy. A minimum of 60 mg daily of ascorbic acid is required in the human diet to prevent scurvy.

Solution

1. What is unknown?   Empirical formula of ascorbic acid, the simplest mole ratio of C, H, and O

2. What is known? To perform this calculation, the masses of all substances must be identified. The problem gives the total mass of ascorbic acid and the masses of C and H. The mass of O can be found by subtracting the sum of the masses of C and H from the total mass.

$$\begin{aligned} \text{Mass of O} &= \text{total mass} - (\text{mass C} + \text{mass H}) \\ &= 2.642 \text{ g total } (1.081 \text{ g C} + 0.121 \text{ g H}) \\ &= 1.440 \text{ g O} \end{aligned}$$

The molar masses of C, H, and O are obtained from the periodic table. They are 12.01 g C/mol C, 1.01 g H/mol H, and 16.00 g O/mol O.

3. Calculate the number of moles of each element.

$$1.081 \text{ g C} \times \frac{1 \text{ mol C}}{12.01 \text{ g C}} = 0.09001 \text{ mol C}$$

$$0.121 \text{ g H} \times \frac{1 \text{ mol H}}{1.01 \text{ g H}} = 0.120 \text{ mol H}$$

$$1.440 \text{ g O} \times \frac{1 \text{ mol O}}{16.00 \text{ g O}} = 0.09000 \text{ mol O}$$

4. Find the simplest mole ratio. Because 0.09000 mol O is the smallest number of moles, divide 0.09000 mol O into each quantity to find the ratio of whole numbers.

$$\frac{0.09001 \text{ mol C}}{0.09000 \text{ mol O}} = \frac{1.000 \text{ mol C}}{1 \text{ mol O}}$$

$$\frac{0.120 \text{ mol H}}{0.09000 \text{ mol O}} = \frac{1.33 \text{ mol H}}{1 \text{ mol O}}$$

$$\frac{0.09000 \text{ mol O}}{0.09000 \text{ mol O}} = 1.000$$

To eliminate the fraction obtained in the mole ratio of H to O, we multiply the mole ratios by small integers to find the ratio of whole numbers. If we multiply by 2, we do not get a ratio of whole numbers, but if we multiply each quantity by 3 we get the following:

$$1.000 \text{ mol C} \times 3 = 3.000 \text{ mol C}$$
$$1.33 \text{ mol H} \times 3 = 3.99 \text{ mol H}$$
$$1.000 \text{ mol O} \times 3 = 3.000 \text{ mol O}$$

Thus, the empirical formula for ascorbic acid is $C_3H_4O_3$. You should always remember that the final calculated ratios will rarely be exact integers, but they should be fairly close, within ± 0.05 mol.

Exercise

A 3.10-g sample of a C, H, and F compound is found to contain 1.80 g C, 0.350 g H, and the remainder is F. Calculate the empirical formula of this compound. (C_3H_7F)

A word of caution: When calculating empirical formulas, it is imperative to observe all rules regarding significant figures. *Failure to observe these rules results in obtaining incorrect ratios.*

After calculating the final mole ratio, sometimes whole numbers are not obtained, as was the case in Example Problem 7.16. To eliminate the fraction, you should multiply by increasingly larger integers until a ratio of whole numbers is obtained. For example, if a mole ratio of 1 to 1.5 results, this indicates a 2-to-3 ratio; a ratio of 1 to 1.33 indicates a 3-to-4 ratio, and 1 to 1.667 is 3-to-5 ratio.

$$1 \times 2 = 2$$
$$1.5 \times 2 = 3$$

$$1 \times 3 = 3$$
$$1.33 \times 3 = 4$$

$$1 \times 3 = 3$$
$$1.667 \times 3 = 5$$

Molecular Formula Calculations

While knowledge of the empirical formula gives the simplest ratio of the various types of atoms in a molecule, the molecular formula expresses the actual ratio.

Once the empirical formula is known, only the molecular mass of a compound is needed to calculate its molecular formula. Because the molecular formula either is identical to the empirical formula or is a higher multiple of the empirical formula, if the mass of the empirical formula unit (empirical formula mass) is divided into the molecular mass, a whole number is obtained. This value gives the number of empirical formula units per molecular formula.

For example, if a substance has an empirical formula of CH and a molecular mass of 104, find the empirical formula mass of CH, and divide it into the molecular mass. The empirical formula mass of CH is $12 + 1 = 13$. Therefore,

$$\frac{\text{Molecular mass}}{\text{Empirical formula mass}} = \frac{104}{13} = 8$$

Eight empirical formula units comprise this molecule, so the molecular formula of the compound is $8 \times CH$, or C_8H_8. A complete molecular formula calculation is shown in Example Problem 7.17. ❖

Example Problem 7.17
A 10.000-g sample of a P–O contains 4.364 g P. If the molecular mass of this compound is 284, what is the molecular formula of the compound?

Solution
1. What is unknown?   Molecular formula of the P-O compound (the actual number of P and O atoms in a molecule)
2. What is known? Molecular mass = 284, total mass of sample = 10.000 g, mass of P in sample = 4.364 g P

The mass of O in the sample is obtained by subtraction:

$$\text{Mass of O} = \text{total mass} - \text{mass of P} = 10.000 \text{ g} - 4.364 \text{ g P} = 5.636 \text{ g O}$$

3. Find the mole ratio of P and O.

$$4.364 \text{ gP} \times \frac{1 \text{ mol P}}{30.97 \text{ gP}} = 0.1409 \text{ mol P}$$

$$5.636 \text{ gO} \times \frac{1 \text{ mol O}}{16.00 \text{ gO}} = 0.3523 \text{ mol O}$$

4. Find the simplest mole ratio.

$$\frac{0.1409 \text{ mol P}}{0.1409 \text{ mol P}} = 1.000$$

$$\frac{0.3523 \text{ mol O}}{0.1409 \text{ mol P}} = \frac{2.500 \text{ mol O}}{1 \text{ mol P}}$$

After multiplying 2 times $PO_{2.5}$, we obtain the correct empirical formula, P_2O_5.

5. Calculate the molecular formula by dividing the empirical formula mass into the molecular mass.

$$\text{Empirical formula mass} = (2 \times \text{atomic mass P}) + (5 \times \text{atomic mass O})$$
$$= (2 \times 31.0) + (5 \times 16.0) = 142$$

$$\frac{\text{Molecular mass}}{\text{Empirical formula mass}} = \frac{284}{142} = 2.00$$

Two formula units compose the total molecular mass; accordingly, the molecular formula is $2 \times P_2O_5$, or **P_4O_{10}**. This molecule is composed of four P atoms and ten O atoms. When P_4O_{10} is mixed with water, it produces phosphoric acid, H_3PO_4.

Exercise

A S-F compound contains 25.27% S and has a molecular mass of 254.1. What is the molecular formula of this compound? (S_2F_{10})

REVIEW EXERCISES

7.14 (a) State the law of constant composition.

(b) Use carbon dioxide, CO_2, as an example to illustrate the law of constant composition.

7.15 Find the percent composition of each of the following compounds:

(a) OF_2
(b) $ZnCl_2$
(c) HIO_2
(d) $Mg(NO_3)_2$
(e) $(NH_4)_2SO_4$

7.16 Find the empirical formula for compounds with the following percent compositions?

(a) 75.0% C and 25.0% H
(b) 50.0% S and 50.0%
(c) 46.7% N and 53.35% O
(d) 87.5% Si and 12.5% H
(e) 17.98% Li, 26.75% P, and 55.27% O

7.17 A 10.00-g sample contains 5.99 g Ti, and the remaining mass is oxygen. What is the empirical formula of the compound?

7.18 A compound has a molecular mass of 112 and an empirical formula of CH_2. What is the molecular formula of the compound?

7.19 A boron-hydrogen compound is composed of 78.1% B and 21.9% H and has a molecular mass of 27.7. Calculate the molecular formula of the compound.

7.15 (a) 29.6% O, 70.4% F; (b) 48.0% Zn, 52.0% Cl; (c) 0.630% H, 79.4% 1, 20.0% O; (d) 16.4% Mg, 18.9% N, 64.7% O; (e) 21.2% N, 6.10% H, 24.3% S, 48.4% O; 7.16 (a) CH_4, (b) SO_2, (c) NO, (d) SiH_4, (e) Li_3PO_4; 7.17 TiO_2; 7.18 C_8H_{16}; 7.19 B_2H_6.

7.5 SOLUTIONS AND MOLES

Solutions

Solutions are homogeneous mixtures of substances that have a uniform composition throughout their volume. When a solution is prepared, one substance is mixed with another substance in such a manner that, after mixing, only one physical state is observed.

In a solution, the substance in larger amount and the one whose physical state is observed is called the **solvent**. The substance in smaller amount, the one that becomes incorporated into the solvent, is the **solute**. When a solute mixes with a solvent to produce a solution, the process is called **dissolving** or **dissolution**. Solutes dissolve in solvents to yield solutions.

Solute particles (atoms, molecules, or ions) interact with solvent particles and become incorporated in the structure of the solvent during the dissolving process. For example, when a sugar such as glucose, $C_6H_{12}O_6$, dissolves in water (the solvent),

> Glucose is sometimes called blood sugar. It leaves the blood and enters cells when an energy demand exists.

the solid crystalline structure of glucose (the solute) is broken down by the water molecules. When totally dissolved, glucose molecules are evenly distributed throughout the water (Fig. 7.10).

$$\text{Glucose(s)} \xrightarrow{\text{water}} \text{Glucose(aq)}$$

V correction

If the conditions remain constant, glucose molecules remain in solution and do not settle out on standing. Any equal-volume portion of this solution contains the same number of glucose molecules. Anytime, the dissolved glucose could be recovered by evaporation of the water.

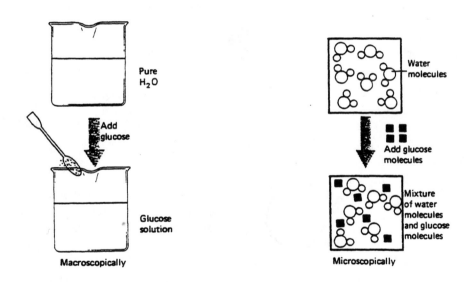

Figure 7.10 When glucose (solute) dissolves in water (solvent), the glucose molecules become a part of the structure of water. Glucose molecules are surrounded by and bond to many water molecules.

Types of solutions

Solutions are categorized according to the physical states of the solute and solvent. For example, at room conditions glucose is a solid and water is a liquid, and a glucose-water solution is therefore a solid-liquid solution. Solid-liquid solutions are commonly encountered because many solids dissolve in water. Oceans contain many dissolved substances, including sodium chloride, NaCl(aq); sodium bromide, NaBr(aq); magnesium chloride, $MgCl_2$(aq); and many others.

WWWolfe 4
(See WWWolfe section at the end of the chapter.)

Another commonly encountered type of solution is a liquid-liquid solution in which two liquids are dissolved in each other. For example, an alcohol, such as ethanol, C_2H_6O(*l*), dissolves in water to produce a solution of alcohol and water. It is difficult to differentiate the solute from the solvent in a liquid-liquid solution because the solution is in the same physical state as its two components. Which component is the solvent and which is the solute? If a small quantity of ethanol is added to a large quantity of water, then the ethanol is the solute and water is the solvent. Water is the solute and ethanol is the solvent if a small quantity of water is mixed with a larger quantity of ethanol.

When dealing with liquid-liquid solutions, we use two additional terms. They are "miscible" and "immiscible." Two liquids are categorized as **miscible** if they are mutually soluble in each other. Ethanol and water are miscible liquids. **Immiscible** liquids are not soluble in each other and do not mix. When mixed, immiscible liquids form two layers. For example, oil and water are immiscible liquids (Fig. 7.11). Many different degrees of miscibility lie between the two examples given; such combinations are classified as **partially miscible.**

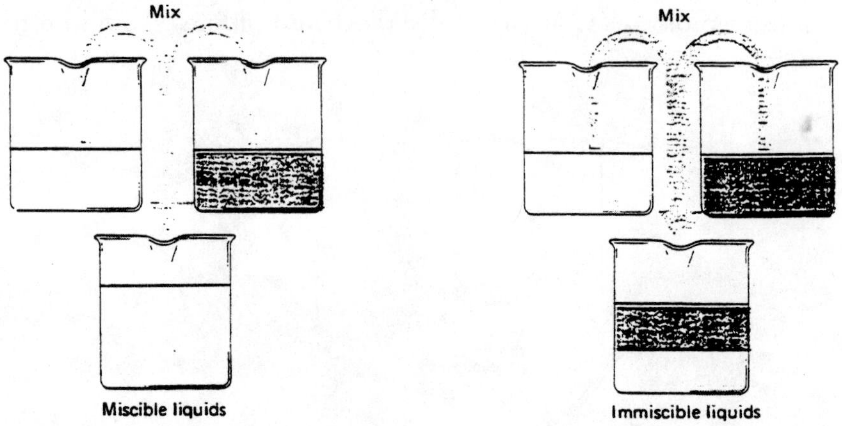

A third class of solutions is gas-liquid solutions. In these solutions, a gas is the solute and a liquid is the solvent. Carbonated beverages are aqueous solutions of gaseous carbon dioxide, $CO_2(aq)$. Nitrogen and oxygen gas, principal components of the atmosphere, are dissolved to a small degree in most water samples.

Besides liquids,

Miscible liquids

Immiscible liquids

Figure 7.11 If two miscible liquids are mixed they dissolve in each other; they are mutually soluble. If two immiscible liquids are combined, they do not mix; they form two separate layers with the most dense liquid on the bottom.

both gases and solids can be solvents. Gas-gas solutions are those that contain two or more nonreacting gases. Air is a gaseous solution composed of $N_2(g)$, $O_2(g)$, $Ar(g)$, $H_2O(g)$, $CO_2(g)$, and many other gases. All nonreacting gases are miscible with all other gases. Terms such as "solvent" and "solute" have no meaning when applied to gas-gas solutions.

Less frequently, solids are solvents. Alloys are solid-solid solutions that are most commonly composed of two or more different metals. Sterling silver is a solution of 7.5% Cu and 92.5% Ag. Eighteen carat gold is an alloy of 75% Au and variable amounts of Ag (10 to 20%) and Cu (5 to 14%). Solids can dissolve liquids and produce a solution. A good example of such solutions is a class of solids called amalgams. Amalgams contain different amounts of liquid mercury, $Hg(l)$, dissolved in metals.

Most other combinations of physical states are possible, but they are rather rare compared to those already discussed. Gases can be dissolved by solids—$H_2(g)$ forms a solution with the metal palladium, Pd. Table 7.4 lists examples of selected classes of solutions.

Table 7.4 TYPES OF SOLUTIONS

Solute	Solvent	Examples
Solid	Liquid	NaCl(aq); sugar water, $C_{12}H_{22}O_{11}$(aq)
Liquid	Liquid	Vinegar, CH_3COOH(aq); Antifreeze, $C_2H_6O_2$(aq)
Gas	Liquid	O_2(aq); CO_2(aq); N_2(aq)
Gas	Gas	Atmosphere, N_2(g), O_2(g), Ar(g), CO_2(g), H_2O(g), . . .
Solid	Solid	Solder, Sn and Pb; brass, Zn and Cu
Gas	Solid	H_2(Pd)

REVIEW EXERCISES

7.20 Describe the difference between homogeneous and heterogeneous mixtures. Give an example of each.

7.21 Give an example for each of the following types of solutions: (a) both solute and solvent are gases, (b) solute is a solid and solvent is a liquid, (c) solute is a liquid and solvent is a liquid

7.22 What is the meaning of "dissolution?" Give an example.

7.23 (a) Give two examples of miscible liquids.

(b) Give two examples of immiscible liquids.

Concentration of Solutions

Terms such as "concentrated" or "dilute" refer to the amount of solute in a solvent. Various solutions when saturated are quite dilute. A saturated solution of magnesium hydroxide, $Mg(OH)_2$, only contains 9×10^{-4} g $Mg(OH)_2$/100 mL H_2O at 25°C. On the other hand, a dilute solution of magnesium chloride hexahydrate, $MgCl_2 \cdot 6H_2O$, might contain from 1 to 10 g of magnesium chloride per 100 mL of solution, which has a solubility of 167 g/100 mL H_2O at 25°C. Therefore, a quantitative means is required to exactly express the amount of solute in a solution.

　　　Many units of concentration are used by scientists. Table 7.5 lists the most common units of concentration employed in science. In this section, we will discuss only **percent by mass and molarity.**

Percent by Mass

Percent by mass is the unit of concentration that expresses the mass of solute per 100 grams of solution (mass of solute + mass of solvent).

$$\% \, m/m = \frac{mass \ of \ solute}{mass \ of \ solution} \times 100$$

By definition, a 5% m/m sugar solution is one that has 5 g of sugar in every 100 g of solution. A 5% m/m sugar solution may be prepared by dissolving 5 g of sugar in 95 g of water. Example Problem 7.18 and Figure 7.12 show the calculations required to calculate the masses of solute and solvent when preparing a solution with a specific percent by mass of solute.

TABLE 7.5 SOLUTION CONCENTRATION UNITS

Unit	Symbol	Definition
Percent by mass	% m/m	$$\% \, m/m = \frac{\text{mass of solute}}{\text{mass of solution}} \times 100$$
Percent by mass to volume	% m/v	$$\% \, m/v = \frac{\text{mass of solute}}{\text{volume of solution}} \times 100$$
Percent by volume	% v/v	$$\% v/v = \frac{\text{volume of solute}}{\text{volume of solution}} \times 100$$
Parts per million	ppm	$$ppm = \frac{\text{mass of solute}}{\text{mass of solution}} \times 10^6$$
Parts per billion	ppb	$$ppb = \frac{\text{mass of solute}}{\text{mass of solution}} \times 10^9$$
Molarity	M	$$M = \frac{\text{moles of solute}}{\text{volume of solution (L)}}$$
Molality	m	$$m = \frac{\text{moles of solute}}{\text{kilograms of solvent}}$$
Mole fraction	X	$$X = \frac{\text{moles of solute}}{\text{total moles (solute+solvent)}}$$

Example Problem 7.18
How is 185.00 g of 1.39% m/m NaCl(aq) prepared?

Solution
1. What is unknown?   Masses of NaCl and H_2O in g
2. What is known? 185.00 g of solution; 1.39% m/m NaCl(aq)

From the given data, we know that the total mass of the solution is 185.00 g, which is the mass of the solute, NaCl, plus the solvent, H_2O. Also, a 1.39% m/m NaCl solution contains 1.39 g NaCl per 100 g of solution.

$$1.39\% \text{ NaCl} = \frac{1.39 \text{ g NaCl}}{100 \text{ g solution}}$$

(handwritten: 1.39 above crossed-out 139; "✓ Correction")

Percent by mass is a conversion factor that expresses the ratio of mass of solute to the mass of total solution; accordingly, we apply the factor-label method (Fig. 7.12).

3. Apply the factor-label method to find mass of NaCl.

$$185.00 \text{ g solution} \times \frac{1.39 \text{ g NaCl}}{100 \text{ g solution}} = \textbf{2.57 g NaCl}$$

4. Calculate the mass of water.

Knowing the mass of NaCl, 2.57 g, subtract it from the total mass of the solution to obtain the mass of water.

Mass of water = mass of solution (solute + solvent) – mass of solute

g H_2O = 185.00 g – 2.57 g NaCl = **182.43 g H_2O**

To prepare a 1.39% m/m NaCl solution, dissolve 2.57 g NaCl in 182.43 g H_2O.
Exercise
How is 50.00 g of 10.5% m/m KI(aq) prepared? (Dissolve 5.25 g KI in 44.75 g H_2O)

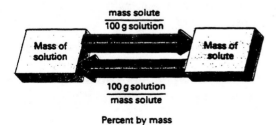

mass solute / 100 g solution

Mass of solution

Mass of solute

100 g solution / mass solute

Percent by mass

Figure 7.12 The percent by mass of a solution is a conversion factor that expresses the mass of solute per 100 g of solution. To calculate the mass of solute contained in a solution multiply the percent by mass times the mass of the solution. To calculate the mass of solution that contains a fixed mass of solute invert the percent by mass conversion factor and

Often in the laboratory a solution is available with a known concentration, and a specific mass of solute is needed. Example Problem 7.19 illustrates how the mass of solute is calculated from the concentration expressed in percent by mass.

Example Problem 7.19
Concentrated nitric acid, HNO_3, is usually sold as a 70% m/m aqueous solution. Calculate the mass of concentrated nitric acid that contains 23 g HNO_3.

> Alchemists of the eighth century called nitric acid *aqua fortis*, which means strong water. Today nitric acid is used to produce fertilizers, explosives, plastics, dyes, and drugs.

Solution
1. What is unknown?   Mass in g of concentrated HNO_3 solution
2. What is known? 23 g HNO_3; 70% m/m nitric acid solution
3. Apply the factor-label method (Fig. 7.13).

$$23 \text{ g HNO}_3 \times \frac{100 \text{ g HNO}_3 \text{ solution}}{70 \text{ g HNO}_3} = \textbf{33 g HNO}_3 \textbf{ solution}$$

Our answer, 32.9 g HNO_3, is rounded to 33 g to display the correct number of significant figures. A 33-g sample of 70% m/m HNO_3 solution contains 23 g pure HNO_3, and 10 g is water.

Exercise
Calculate the mass of 5.00% $NaNO_3$ solution that contains 100 g $NaNO_3$. (2.00×10^3 g solution)

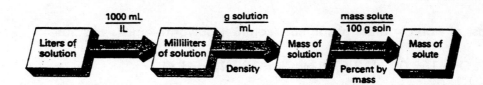

Figure 7.13 Three conversion factors are needed to calculate the mass of solute in a given number of liters of solution. These factors are the number of milliliters per liter, the density of the solution, and the percent by mass of the solution. First, convert the number of liters of solution to milliliters. Then calculate the mass of the solution using the density, and finally multiply by the percent by mass to obtain the mass of solute.

More often than not, when dealing with percent by mass, volumes of solutions must also be considered. Example Problem 7.20 illustrates this type of problem.

Example Problem 7.20
Hydroiodic acid, HI(aq), is commercially available as a 57% m/m aqueous solution that has a density of 1.70 g/cm^3. Calculate the mass of HI in 1.0 L of 57% m/m HI solution.

Solution
1. What is unknown?   Mass of HI in g
2. What is known? 1.0 L of 57% m/m HI, with a density of 1.70 g/cm^3

In this problem, the volume of the solution is given; thus, by using the density, the total mass of the solution is calculated (Fig. 7.12).
3. Apply the factor-label method.

1.0 ~~L solution~~ × $\dfrac{1000 \text{ ~~mL solution~~}}{1 \text{ ~~L solution~~}}$ × $\dfrac{1.70 \text{ ~~g solution~~}}{1 \text{ ~~mL solution~~}}$ × $\dfrac{57 \text{ g HI}}{100 \text{ ~~g solution~~}}$ =

$$969 \text{ g HI} = \mathbf{9.7 \times 10^2 \text{ g HI}}$$

A solution of 1.0 L of 57% m/m HI contains 9.7×10^2 g HI.

Exercise

Calculate the mass of NaOH in 5.50 L of 12.0% NaOH. The density of 12.0% NaOH is 1.13 g/cm³.
(746 g NaOH)

Other less commonly used percent concentration units in chemistry are percent by volume and percent by mass to volume. They are defined as follows.

$$\% \ v/v = \frac{\text{volume of solute}}{\text{volume of solution}} \times 100$$

$$\% \ m/v = \frac{\text{mass of solute}}{\text{volume of solution}} \times 100$$

Problems that involve these units are similar to those involving percent by mass except for the comparison to the total volume of solution.

REVIEW EXERCISES

7.24 Name the unit of concentration represented by each of the following:

(a) moles of solute per liter of solution
(b) mass of solute per 100 mL of solution
(c) moles of solute per kilogram of solvent
(d) mass of solute per 100 g of solution

7.25 Explain exactly how 486 g of a 12.1% m/m solution of aqueous acetone solution is prepared.

7.26 What is the mass of $CaCl_2$ in 233.5 g of a 6.19% m/m $CaCl_2$(aq) solution?

7.24 (a) molarity, (b) % m/w, (c) molality, (d) % m/m; 7.25 Add 58.8 g acetone to 427 g H_2O; 7.26 14.5 g $CaCl_2$

Molarity

Molarity is the concentration unit most frequently encountered in beginning chemistry courses. **Molarity** is the number of moles of solute per liter of solution. When using or calculating molarity, moles of solute particles are compared with the total volume of the solution, i.e., both the solute and solvent.

$$M = \frac{\text{moles of solute}}{\text{volume of solution (L)}}$$

One way to prepare a I M (we say, "one molar") aqueous solution is to add 1 mol of solute to a 1-L volumetric flask, and then add enough water so that the total volume is 1 L (Fig. 7.14).

    A one molar solution can be prepared in many other ways. If a 250-mL volumetric flask is available, 0.250 mol of solute is placed in the 250-mL flask, and then enough water is added to yield a total volume of 250 mL.

$$1.00\, M = \frac{0.250 \text{ mol solute}}{0.250 \text{ L solution}}$$

Example Problem 7.21 shows the calculation required before a specific volume of a solution of given molarity can be prepared.

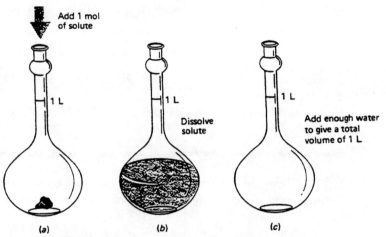

Figure 7.14 One way to prepare a 1-*M* aqueous solution is to (a) measure one mole of solute on a balance and transfer it to a 1-L volumetric flask, (b) add water and dissolve the solute, and (c) continue adding water until the total volume of the solution is 1 L and shake to produce a homogeneous mixture.

Example Problem 7.21
Explain how 175 mL of a 0.320 M KI(aq) solution is prepared.

Solution
1. What is unknown?   Mass of KI in g in 175 mL of 0.320 M KI(aq)
2. What is known? 175 mL; 0.320 M KI (0.320 mol KI/L); 166 g KI/mol KI

To calculate the mass of KI required to prepare this solution, we use conversion factors, changing the volume from mL to L and then using the molarity, the ratio of moles of solute to liters of solution, and the molar mass of KI (Fig. 7.15).

3. Apply the factor-label method.

$$175 \text{ mL} \times \frac{1 \text{ L}}{1000 \text{ mL}} \times \frac{0.320 \text{ mol KI}}{1 \text{ L}} \times \frac{166 \text{ g KI}}{1 \text{ mol KI}} = \textbf{9.30 g KI}$$

After calculating the volume in L, the number of moles of KI is calculated using the molarity. Finally, the mass is obtained by multiplying by the molar mass of KI.

4. Explain how the solution is prepared.

To prepare 175 mL of 0.320 M KI, add 9.30 g KI to a container with a graduation mark at 175 mL. Place water in the container and dissolve the KI, and continue adding water until the total volume is 175 mL. Mix the solution so that the KI is distributed throughout.
Exercise
Explain how 100 mL of 0.250M KBr is prepared? (Dissolve 3.00 g KBr in enough water to have a total volume of 100 mL)

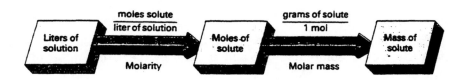

Figure 7.15 To calculate the mass of solute in a given volume of solution, multiply the volume of the solution in liters times the molarity of the solution (moles of solute per liter of solution) and then multiply by the molar mass (grams of solute per 1 mol).

Example Problem 7.22 presents the method that you should use to calculate the molarity of a solution given all necessary data.

Example Problem 7.22
What is the molarity of a solution prepared by adding 18.3 g of methanol, CH_3OH, to a container and then mixing it with enough water to give a total volume of 50.0 mL?

Solution
1. What is unknown?   M CH_3OH(aq), (mol CH_3OH/L solution)

2. What is known? 18.3 g CH_3OH; total volume = 50.0 mL; 32.0 g CH_3OH/mol CH_3OH
Because molarity is the ratio of moles of solute, CH_3OH, to liters of solution, find the number of moles of CH_3OH and then divide it by the number of liters of solution (Fig. 7.16).

3. Calculate the number of moles of solute and the volume of solution in L.

$$18.3 \text{ g } CH_3OH \times \frac{1 \text{ mol } CH_3OH}{32.0 \text{ g } CH_3OH} = 0.572 \text{ mol } CH_3OH$$

$$50.0 \text{ mL} \times \frac{1 \text{ L}}{1000 \text{ mL}} = 0.0500 \text{ L}$$

$$\text{Molarity} = \frac{\text{moles } CH_3OH}{\text{L solution}} = \frac{0.572 \text{ mol } CH_3OH}{0.0500 \text{ L}} = \textbf{11.4 M } CH_3OH$$

When 18.3 g CH_3OH is dissolved in enough water to give a total volume of 50.0 mL, the molarity of the solution is 11.4 M.
Exercise
Calculate the molarity of a solution in which 25.0 g CH_3OH is dissolved in enough water to have 700

mL of solution. (1.12M CH_3OH)

Figure 7.16 To find the molarity of a solution given the mass of solute and total volume of the solution, convert the mass of solute to moles and divide it by the total volume of the solution in liters.

At various times, the concentration of a laboratory stock solution may not be given in the units that you want. Therefore, these units must be converted to the desired concentration units. Example Problem 7.23 shows how percent by mass is converted to molarity.

Example Problem 7.23
What is the molarity of an 85.0% m/m phosphoric acid, H_3PO_4, solution? An 85.0% m/m H_3PO_4 solution has a density of 1.70 g/cm^3.

Solution
1. What is unknown?   M H_3PO_4 (mol H_3PO_4/L solution)

2. What is known? 85.0% m/m H_3PO_4; density of solution = 1.70 g/mL; molar mass = 98.0 g H_3PO_4/mol H_3PO_4
To solve this problem, first consider what we are starting with: % m/m, or the ratio of mass of solute to 100 g of solution.

$$85.0\% \text{ m/m } H_3PO_4 = \frac{85.0 \text{ g } H_3PO_4}{100 \text{ g solution}}$$

Thus, the mass of the solute should be converted to moles, and then the volume of the solution is calculated from its mass (Fig. 7.17).

3. Calculate the number of moles of H_3PO_4, and the volume of solution.

$$85.0 \text{ g } H_3PO_4 \times \frac{1 \text{ mol } H_3PO_4}{98.0 \text{ g } H_3PO_4} = 0.867 \text{ mol } H_3PO_4$$

$$100 \text{ g solution} \times \frac{1 \text{ mL}}{1.70 \text{ g solution}} \times \frac{1 \text{ L}}{1000 \text{ mL}} = 0.0588 \text{ L}$$

4. Calculate the molarity.

$$M\ H_3PO_4 = \frac{0.867\ M\ H_3PO_4}{0.0588\ L} = \textbf{14.7 M } \textbf{\textit{H}}_3\textbf{\textit{PO}}_4$$

An 85.0% m/m H_3PO_4 solution is 14.7 M, or 14.7 mol H_3PO_4 is dissolved per liter of solution.

Exercise

What is the molarity of a 4.00% $KMnO_4$ solution? The density of this solution is 1.025 g/cm^3.
(0.260M $KMnO_4$)

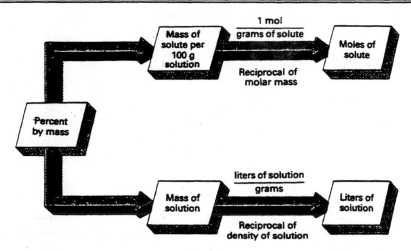

Figure 7.17 To change percent by mass of a solution to molarity, calculate the number of moles of solute per 100 g of solution. Then calculate the volume in liters of the 100 g of solution, using the density of the solution. The molarity is found by dividing the number of moles of solute by the volume of the solution.

REVIEW EXERCISES

7.27 How is 54.0 mL of 1.58 M NaOH(aq) prepared?

7.28 What mass of $Mg(NO_3)_2$ is required to prepare 121 L of 0.0752 M $Mg(NO_3)_2(aq)$?

7.29 Calculate the molarity of a solution that contains 5.991 g C_2H_6O in a total volume of 540.0 mL of solution.

7.30 (a) What is the molarity of a 90.0% m/m formic acid, CH_2O_2, solution? The solution has a density of 1.20 g/cm^3.

(b) What is the molarity of a 34.0% m/m lead(II) nitrate, $Pb(NO_3)_2$, solution? The solution has a density of 1.39 g/cm^3.

7.27 3.41 g NaOH; 7.28 1.35 × 10³ g $Mg(NO_3)_2$; 7.29 0.2408 M C_2H_6O; 7.30 (a) 23.5 M CH_2O_2, (b)
1.43 M $Pb(NO_3)_2$

Dilution of Solutions

Chemists must frequently dilute more-concentrated solutions to obtain less-concentrated ones, or deal with a situation in which two or more solutions have been mixed, diluting all of the dissolved species. Dilution frequently occurs when pure solvent is added to the solution. This increases the total volume of the solution, but does not change the number of moles of dissolved solute. To solve dilution problems, we must calculate the total number of moles of dissolved particles and then divide

> When two liquids or solutions are mixed, their total volume does not always equal the sum of the individual volumes.

by the new volume. For example: What is the final concentration of 50.0 mL of a 6.00 M NaOH solution, if its total volume is increased to 75.0 mL? We first calculate the number of moles of NaOH in solution, using the factor-label method as follows:

$$50.0 \text{ mL} \times \frac{1 \text{ L}}{1000 \text{ mL}} \times \frac{6.00 \text{ mol NaOH}}{\text{L}} = 0.300 \text{ mol NaOH}$$

To calculate the molarity of the diluted solution, we divide the number of moles of NaOH by the total volume in liters, which is 75.0 mL or 0.0750 L.

$$M = \frac{0.300 \text{ mol NaOH}}{0.0750 \text{ L}} = 4.00 \text{ M NaOH}$$

After diluting to 75.0 mL, the molar concentration of the NaOH solution is 4.00 M. If we increase the total volume of this solution to 100.0 mL, the concentration decreases to 3.00 M. Doubling the initial volume (50.0 mL) to 100.0 mL decreases the concentration to one-half of the initial concentration.

Example Problem 7.24

Calculate the molarity of an ethanol, C_2H_6O, solution that is prepared by diluting 125 mL of 4.23 M C_2H_6O to 845 mL.

Solution
1. What is unknown?   M C_2H_6O of diluted solution
2. What is known? 125 mL of 4.23 M C_2H_6O diluted to 845 mL; 1000 mL/L
3. Calculate the total number of moles of C_2H_6O.

$$125 \text{ mL} \times \frac{1 \text{ L}}{1000 \text{ mL}} \times \frac{4.23 \text{ mol } C_2H_6O}{\text{L}} = 0.529 \text{ mol } C_2H_6O$$

4. Calculate the molarity of the diluted solution.
Before calculating the molarity, we must convert the volume of the diluted solution to L.

$$845 \text{ mL} \times \frac{1 \text{ L}}{1000 \text{ mL}} = 0.845 \text{ L}$$

To find the molarity of the diluted solution, we divide the total number of moles by the total volume of solution.

$$M = \frac{mol\ C_2H_6O}{L} = \frac{0.529\ mol\ C_2H_6O}{0.845\ L} = \mathbf{0.626\ M\ C_2H_6O}$$

After dilution, we have a 0.626 M C_2H_6O solution.

Exercise
(a) If a solution of 85.0 mL of 0.777M $CaCl_2$ is diluted to 500 mL, what is the new molarity of the solution? (b) If this solution is further diluted to 1.00 L, what is the molarity of the solution? (0.132 M $CaCl_2$, (b) 0.0661M $CaCl_2$)

Often chemists must calculate the volume that a solution must be diluted to in order to have a specific concentration. To solve such a problem, we first calculate the total number of moles of solute, then the total volume of the diluted solution is calculated from its molarity. Example Problem 7.25 is an example of such a problem.

Example Problem 7.25

What total volume in mL must 235.0 mL of 12.00 M HCl be diluted to in order to produce a 1.000 M HCl solution?

> When diluting concentrated acids, never add water to the acid. The acid is likely to splatter when it contacts the water. Instead, **always cautiously add concentrated acids to water.**

Solution

1. What is unknown?   mL of 1.000 M HCl
2. What is known? 235.0 mL of 12.00 M HCl to be diluted to 1.000 M HCl
First, calculate the number of moles of HCl present in 235.0 mL of 12.00 M HCl. Once the number of moles of HCl is known, the total volume of the diluted solution can be found from its molarity, 1.000 M.
3. Calculate the total number of moles of HCl.

$$235.0\ \cancel{mL} \times \frac{1\ \cancel{L}}{1000\ \cancel{mL}} \times \frac{12.00\ mol\ \cancel{HCl}}{\cancel{L}} = 2.820\ mol\ HCl$$

4. Calculate the total volume of 1.000M HCl that contains 2.820 mol HCl.

$$2.820\ \cancel{mol\ HCl} \times \frac{1\ \cancel{L}}{1.000\ \cancel{mol\ HCl}} \times \frac{1000\ mL}{1\ \cancel{L}} = \mathbf{2.820 \times 10^3\ mL}$$

We find that the initial 235.0 mL of 12.00 M HCl should be diluted to 2.820×10^3 mL, 2.820 L, in order to decrease the concentration to 1.000 M.

Exercise
What volume in mL should 150 mL of 0.555M KOH be diluted to in order to produce a 0.125M KOH solution? (666 mL)

Mixing two solutions dilutes all of the dissolved chemical species. Example Problem 7.26 shows how to solve dilution problems in which two nonreacting solutions are mixed. ❖

Example Problem 7.26

What is the resulting molar concentration of acetone, C_3H_6O, when 40.0 mL of 0.100 M acetone solution is mixed with 20.0 mL of 0.0750 M acetone? Assume that the total volume of the resulting solution equals the sum the volumes of the two solutions. In other words, assume the volumes are additive.

Solution

1. What is unknown?   M (mol C_3H_6O/L) of the diluted solution
2. What is known? 40.0mL of 0.100 M C_3H_6O (initial concentration); 20.0 mL of 0.0750 M C_3H_6O (initial concentration); 1 L/1000 mL
3. Calculate the total number of moles of acetone from both solutions.

$$40.0 \text{ mL} \times \frac{1 \text{ L}}{1000 \text{ mL}} \times \frac{0.100 \text{ mol } C_3H_6O}{\text{L}} = 0.00400 \text{ mol } C_3H_6O$$

$$20.0 \text{ mL} \times \frac{1 \text{ L}}{1000 \text{ mL}} \times \frac{0.0750 \text{ mol } C_3H_6O}{\text{L}} = 0.00150 \text{ mol } C_3H_6O$$

Thus, the total number of moles of acetone in the two solutions is 0.00550 mol (0.00400 mol C_3H_6O + 0.00150 mol C_3H_6O).

4. Calculate the molarity of the combined solutions. Because the volumes are assumed to be additive, the total volume of the resulting solution is 60.0 mL (40.0 mL + 20.0 mL), or 0.0600 L. Hence, we divide the total number of moles by the total volume in L.

$$M = \frac{\text{mol } C_3H_6O}{\text{L soln}} = \frac{0.00550 \text{ mol } C_3H_6O}{0.0600 \text{ L}} = \textbf{0.0917 M } C_3H_6O$$

When 40.0 mL of 0.100 M C_3H_6O is mixed with 20.0 mL of 0.0750 M C_3H_6O, the resulting concentration is 0.0917 M C_3H_6O. We would expect the final concentration to be closer to 0.100 M than 0.07500 M because twice the volume of the more-concentrated solution is present initially.

Exercise

What is the final concentration of NaCl when 350 mL 0.666M NaCl is mixed with 650 mL 0.333M NaCl? (0.450M NaCl)

REVIEW EXERCISES

7.31 Glacial acetic acid, CH_3COOH, is 99.8% acetic acid, which is 17.4 M. Calculate the total volume to which 120.0 mL of glacial acetic acid must be diluted in order to produce a 6.00 M acetic solution.

7.32 What is the final concentration of hydrobromic acid, HBr(aq), when 155 mL of 0.925 M HBr solution is mixed with 245 mL of 0.831 M HBr solution? Assume the volumes are additive.

7.31 348 mL.; 7.32 0.867M HBr

WorldWideWolfe CHEMISTRY LINKS

Connect to WorldWideWolfe at

http://www.mindspring.com/~drwolfe/WWWolfe_hcc_1025_links.htm

and link to the following sites.

Chemical Calculations: The Mole Concept

1. The Mole And Its Uses This site reviews atomic mass, the mole, molecular mass and percent composition. A good place to begin your study of moles.

2. Mole Concept and Mole Conversions Defines and shows how moles are used in chemistry. Shows how to do mole conversion problems.

Moles Calculator You can use this calculator to moles to particles, particles to moles, molarity, molar mass, grams to moles, grams to particles, moles to grams, and particles to grams. It also has a periodic table that you click to get molar masses.

3. Types of Formulas Discussion of empirical, molecular, and structural formulas.

Determining Empirical and Molecular Formulas Shows you how to calculate formulas.

4. Solutions A set of 26 slides that covers solutions and solution concentrations.

Solutions and Solution Concentrations A set of 68 slides that covers all aspects of solutions and solution concentrations. It also discusses solution properties at a general chemistry level.

SUMMARY

A **mole** is a counting unit that allows chemists to calculate the number of atoms, molecules, or ions contained in a sample by weighing it. One mole contains 6.022×10^{23} particles. This number of particles is called **Avogadro's number.**

For each element, the mass of one mole of atoms is the atomic mass in grams. A mole of molecules has a mass equal to the molecular mass in grams; **molecular mass** is the sum of the atomic masses of all the elements in a compound. For those compounds whose structures do not contain identifiable molecules, the **formula mass** is used instead. The formula mass is the mass in grams of one mole of formula units of a compound.

Mole calculations involve the application of the factor-label method to change the given quantity to the desired quantity. Two conversion factors are employed: (1) ratio of moles to grams (either grams per mole or moles per gram) and (2) ratio of particles to moles or moles to particles. For elements, the first ratio (grams per mole) is obtained by finding the atomic mass of the element and adding the unit grams—this is the molar mass. For molecules, grams are the units attached to the molecular mass (molar mass of molecules). The second ratio, particles per mole is the same for all chemical species: it is

6.022×10^{23} particles/mol.

     Mole calculations are used to determine chemical formulas, both the empirical formulas and the molecular formulas. The **molecular formula** of a compound gives the actual number of each type of atom in the molecular or formula unit. The **empirical formula** is the simplest ratio of whole numbers of atoms in the molecule. Empirical formulas are calculated from mass data on the elements that compose a compound. This is accomplished by converting the mass of each element to moles and calculating the simplest ratio of whole numbers. Molecular formulas are calculated from the empirical formula and molecular mass.

     Formulas of compounds are determined as a direct result of a basic law of chemistry called the **law of constant composition (law of definite proportions).** This law states that all samples of a compound contain the same elements in a fixed mass ratio.

     Solutions are homogeneous mixtures. A solution is composed of a **solute, the** component in smaller amount, dissolved in a **solvent**, the component in larger amount. Solute molecules become incorporated into the structure of the solvent.

     Solutions are classified according to the physical states of the solute and solvent. Solid-liquid, liquid-liquid, gas-liquid, and gas-gas solutions are the classes of solutions most frequently encountered.

     Solution concentrations are measured in a number of different ways. The concentration units used most frequently in beginning chemistry courses are (1) **molarity,** moles of solute per liter of solution, and (2) **percent by mass,** mass of solute per 100 g of solution.

KEY TERMS

Avogadro's number	law of constant composition
concentrated	miscible
concentration unit	molar mass
counting unit	mole
dilute	molecular formula
dilution	molecular mass
dissolution	percent composition
dissolving	saturated solution
empirical formula	solubility
formula unit	solute
formula mass	solution
immiscible	solvent

STUDY GUIDELINES

After completing Chapter 7, you should be able to

1. Explain the meaning of a counting unit

2. Define mole, and state the number of particles in one mole

3. Calculate the molar mass of atoms, molecules, formula units, and ions

4. Calculate the mass of a substance given the number of moles

5. Calculate the number of moles of a substance given the mass

6. Calculate the number of atoms or molecules contained in a substance given either mass or number of moles

7. Calculate the number of moles or the mass of a substance given the number of atoms or molecules

8. Calculate the molecular mass or the formula mass of a compound

9. Calculate the number of moles of atoms in a compound given all necessary data

10. State the law of constant composition, and show how it is applied

11. Calculate the percent composition of a compound

12. Distinguish between the empirical and molecular formula of a compound

13. Calculate the empirical formula of a compound given mass data

14. Find the molecular formula of a compound given mass data and the molecular mass

15. Describe how a solution is prepared

16. Distinguish between a solute and a solvent

17. List and give examples of the principal classes of solutions

18. List and define the primary units of concentration

19. Calculate % m/m and molarity of a solution, given all necessary data

20. Explain how a specific solution concentration (% m/m or molarity) is prepared

EXERCISES

7.33 Define each of the following: counting unit, mole, Avogadro's number, molar mass, molecular mass, formula mass, formula unit, law of constant composition, percent composition, empirical formula, molecular formula, solution, solute, solvent, percent by mass, molarity, dilution.

Moles

7.34 (a) Why is the mole called a counting unit? (b) Give two other examples of counting units.

7.35 If Avogadro's number of like atoms is placed on a balance, what mass is observed?

7.36 What is the mass of 1.000 mol of each of the following atoms? (a) B, (b) Co, (c) Mo, (d) Ge, (e) Ra, (f) Ag, (g) Th?

7.37 Do a rough calculation to determine how many centuries it would take exactly 1 billion people working 24 hours per day, 365 days per year, to produce exactly 1 mol of doughnuts at a rate of 10 doughnuts per person each second. (*Hint: First use conversion factors to calculate how many doughnuts could be produced per year.*)

Moles and Atoms

7.38 Complete the following table by calculating the missing quantities for each element. For example, in part a calculate the number of atoms and the mass of 1.00 mol B.

Element	Number of moles	Number of atoms	Mass, g
(a) B	1.000		
(b) Al		1.99×10^{23}	
(c) Ni			5.87
(d) Zr			182.4
(e) Cs	0.500		
(f) Sn		6.02×10^{24}	
(g)	1.00		101.07
(h)		1.204×10^{24}	80.16
(i) Bi	3.115		
(j) Kr		8.94×10^{22}	

7.39 How many moles of potassium atoms are contained in each of the following? (a) 0.0145 g K, (b) 1.00 g K, (c) 87.2 kg K, (d) 500.00 mg K?

7.40 Calculate the number of moles of atoms in the following. (a) 3.99 g As, (b) 1.414 g Te, (c) 5.66 mg Ni, (d) 3.7 kg Ir

7.41 How many atoms are contained in each sample listed in 7.40?

7.42 Calculate the mass of each of the following samples of elements: (a) 7.11 mol Ar, (b) 0.0044 mol Li, (c) 9.311 M mol Na, (d) 2.30 mmol V.

7.43 How many atoms are contained in each of the following samples? (a) 9.97 g Pb, (b) 2.077 g U, (c) 4.62 kg Mo, (d) 23.189 mg Ra

7.44 How many moles of atoms are in each of the following samples?
(a) 5.03×10^{23} atoms Xe
(b) 4.1×10^{24} atoms Cu
(c) 5.320×10^{20} atoms Pd
(d) 8.0002×10^{19} atoms Hg

7.45 What is the mass of each of the following?
(a) 3.0×10^{23} atoms Kr (b) 2.5409×10^{25} atoms Mg, (c) 5.36×10^{20} atoms Ge, (d) 6.413×10^{28} atoms Cd

7.46 What is the mass of each of the following samples of iron atoms? (a) 3×10^{23} atoms Fe, (b) 5.40 billion atoms Fe, (c) 711 atoms Fe, (d) exactly 1 atom Fe?

7.47 Find the unknown quantity:
(a) 5.5 g Cr = ? mol Cr
(b) 7.221×10^{23} atoms Os = ? mol Os
(c) 0.000199 mol Ar = ? g Ar
(d) 4.8×10^{-6} g Mn = ? atoms Mn
(e) 9.374×10^{21} atoms Ce = ? g Ce

7.48 Find the unknown quantity:
(a) 67.5 mg Re = ? mol Re
(b) 2.000 kg Pd = ? atoms Pd
(c) 1 atom Hf = ? mol Hf
(d) 0.001160 mmol Bi = ? mg Bi
(e) 3.66×10^{26} atoms Nb = ? kg Nb

7.49 Arrange the following from highest to lowest mass: (a) 0.651 mol He, (b) 0.750 g He, (c) 0.375 mol Li, (d) 3.95×10^{23} atoms Li.

7.50 Arrange the following from largest to smallest number of atoms: (a) 25.9 mg Pt, (b) 1.51×10^{-2} g Pd, (c) 7.79 mg Ni, (d) 2.62×10^4 μg Au.

Moles and Molecules

7.51 Calculate the molecular mass to three significant figures for each of the following. (a) IBr, (b) NO, (c) Br_2, (d) Cl_4, (e) S_2F_2, (f) XeF_4, (g) $BrCl_5$, (h) $H_2S_2O_8$

7.52 Calculate the molecular mass to four significant figures for each of the following molecules. (a) P_4O_6, (b) NI_3, (c) OBr_2, (d)

XeOF$_4$, (e) N$_2$O$_5$, (f) H$_2$C$_2$O$_4$, (g) POCl$_3$, (h) C$_{12}$H$_{22}$O$_{11}$

7.53 Complete the following table by calculating the missing quantities for each compound. For example, in part a calculate the number of molecules and the mass of 1.000 mol of SO$_2$.

Compound	Number of moles	Number of molecules	Mass, g
(a) SO$_2$	1.000		
(b) BrF	0.34		
(c) NCl$_3$	0.175		
(d) H$_2$SO$_3$		6.02×10^{21}	
(e) N$_2$O$_5$		9.641×10^{23}	
(f) AlCl$_3$			34.9
(g) PBr$_5$			55.721
(h) OF$_2$	3.030		
(i) SO$_3$		8.21×10^{25}	
(j) C$_5$H$_{12}$		7.54×10^{24}	

7.54 What is the mass of each of the following samples? (a) 0.00344 mol ClO$_2$, (b) 5.67 mol HBr, (c) 3.4×10^{-4} mol SeO$_2$, (d) 3 mol H$_2$SO$_4$, (e) 1.110 mmol N$_2$O$_4$

7.55 How many molecules are contained in each of the following samples? (a) 6.2 g H$_2$O$_2$, (b) 0.04499 g ClF$_3$, (c) 12.5 g N$_2$H$_4$, (d) 7.8 g H$_3$PO$_4$, (e) 3.9010 kg ClF

7.56 How many moles of oxygen atoms are in each of the following? (a) 8.207 mol H$_2$O, (b) 4.5 mol CO$_2$, (c) 0.00349 g P$_2$O$_5$, (d) 8 $\times 10^{22}$ molecules H$_5$IO$_6$

7.57 What is the mass of hydrogen in each of the following?
(a) 0.37 mol H$_2$SO$_4$
(b) 5.92 mg SiH$_4$
(c) 5.912×10^{23} molecules C$_8$H$_{16}$
(d) 23.775 kg B$_{10}$H$_{14}$

7.58 What are the masses of the following quantities of molecules?
(a) 5.1×10^{22} molecules AsH$_3$
(b) 6.88×10^{21} molecules H$_2$Te
(c) 1.004×10^{25} molecules HClO$_4$
(d) 4.0×10^{12} molecules UF$_6$

7.59 Find the unknown quantity.
(a) 3.643 mg SF$_6$ = ? mol F

(b) 9.99×10^{23} molecules S$_2$O$_3$ = ? g S$_2$O$_3$
(c) 8.33 mmol C$_9$H$_{20}$ = ? mol H
(d) 5.00×10^{-6} g H$_3$PO$_4$ = ? molecules H$_3$PO$_4$

7.60 Arrange the following in order, largest to smallest, of total number of phosphorus atoms. (a) 159 mg PCl$_3$, (b) 2.96×10^{-5} kg P$_4$O$_{10}$, (c) 0.120 mol P$_4$O$_6$, (d) 0.120 mol H$_3$PO$_3$

Formula Unit Calculations

7.61 What is the formula mass (expressed to three significant figures) of each of the following? (a) CuCl, (b) CaI$_2$, (c) Zn(NO$_3$)$_2$, (d) Li$_2$SO$_4$, (e) Fe$_2$(SO$_4$)$_3$

7.62 Calculate the number of moles of compound in each of the following samples. (a) 47 g NaClO$_3$, (b) 700.0 mg Ca$_3$(PO$_4$)$_2$, (c) 9.33 kg RbBrO$_2$

7.63 What is the mass of each of the following? (a) 9.55 mol TiO$_2$, (b) 7.07 mol K$_2$SnCl$_6$, (c) 0.004529 mmol PbC$_2$O$_4$

7.64 How many formula units are in each of the following? (a) 9.34 g MgSiO$_3$, (b) 5.8 kg Hg$_2$(NO$_2$)$_2$, (c) 234.0 mmol NH$_4$C$_2$H$_3$O$_2$, (d) 8.7 mg Na$_2$HPO$_4$

Percent Composition

7.65 Find the percent composition to three significant figures for each of the following compounds. (a) HI, (b) MgS, (c) Hg_2I_2, (d) Si_3N_4, (e) OsO_5.

7.66 Find the percent composition to four significant figures for each of the following compounds. (a) $KMnO_4$, (b) $KHCO_3$, (c) $Ba(NO_2)_2$, (d) $Ni(CO)_4$, (e) $(NH_4)_2Cr_2O_7$

7.67 For each of the following compounds, calculate the percent by mass of Ag to three significant figures. (a) Ag_2S, (b) $AgIO_3$, (c) Ag_2CrO_4, (d) Ag_3AsS_3.

7.68 For each of the following compounds, calculate the percent by mass of K to three significant figures. (a) $K_2S_2O_6$, (b) K_3AsO_4, (c) K_2PtO_3, (d) $KC_7H_5O_3$.

7.69 Hydrated salts are ionic compounds that have a fixed number of water molecules bonded to them. Calculate the percent by mass of water (to four significant figures) in each of the following hydrated salts:
(a) $CuSO_4 \cdot 5H_2O$
(b) $BaCl_2 \cdot 2H_2O$
(c) $LiClO_4 \cdot 3H_2O$
(d) $Ni(IO_3)_2 \cdot 4H_2O$

7.70 Arrange the following from highest to lowest percent by mass of iron. (a) $FeCl_3$, (b) $Fe(OH)_2$, (c) Fe_3O_4, (d) $Fe_3(PO_4)_2$, (e) $FeCO_3$.

Empirical Formulas

7.71 Calculate the empirical formulas for each of the following compounds, given their percent compositions.
(a) 46.55% Fe and 53.45% S
(b) 46.67% N and 53.33% O
(c) 80.0% C and 20.0% H
(d) 5.24% Si and 94.76% I
(e) 11.63% N and 88.37% Cl
(f) 76.62% Ce and 23.38% S

7.72 Calculate the empirical formulas for each of the following compounds.
(a) 60.1% K, 18.4% C, and 21.5% N
(b) 70.2% Pb, 8.1% C, and 21.7% O
(c) 46.54% Cu, 11.72% S, and 41.75% F
(d) 6.90% C, 1.15% H, and 91.95% Br
(e) 18.79% Li, 16.24% C, and 64.97% O.

7.73 A 25.0-g sample of a chromium-oxygen compound contains 13.0 g of chromium, and the remainder is oxygen. What is the empirical formula of the compound?

7.74 A calcium-phosphorus compound is analyzed and is found to contain 0.66 g of Ca and 0.34 g of P. Calculate the empirical formula of the compound.

7.75 On analysis, a 40.0-g sample was found to contain 16.0 g C, 18.7 g N, and 5.3 g H. Calculate the empirical formula of the compound.

7.76 A 500.0-mg sample contains 64.1 mg C and 152.1 mg F, and the remainder is Cl. What is the empirical formula of this compound?

7.77 Calculate the empirical formula for the compound that contains 28.2% N, 20.8% P, 42.9% O, and 8.1% H.

7.78 Aspirin, acetyl salicylic acid, is the most widely used painkiller in the world. A 0.8164-g aspirin sample contains 0.4898 g C and 0.03657 g H, and the remainder is oxygen. Calculate the empirical formula of aspirin.

Molecular Formulas

7.79 The molecular mass of a compound is 168, and its percent composition is 85.7% C and 14.3% H. Calculate the molecular formula of the compound.

7.80 A 1.000-g sample of a compound contains 0.202 g Al and 0.798 g Cl. The compound's molecular mass is 267. What is its molecular formula?

7.81 Analysis of a compound reveals that it is composed of H, O, and Br. The sample contains 0.640 g H, 10.15 g O, and 50.71 g Br. If the compound's molecular mass is 96.9, calculate its molecular formula.

7.82 Boranes are boron and hydrogen compounds. A borane is analyzed and found to contain 11.843 g B and 0.885 g H, and its molecular mass is 232.4. What is the molecular formula of the compound?

7.83 A compound is composed of 50.00 g C, 66.75 g O, and 8.25 g H. If its molecular mass is 90.0, what is its molecular formula?

7.84 Lauric acid is one of the fatty acids in living things. A 3.824-g sample of lauric acid contains 2.750 g C and 0.463 g H, and the remainder is O. If the molecular mass of lauric acid is 200, what is its molecular formula?

Solutions

7.85 Define each of the following terms: solution, solute, solvent, dissolving, dissolution, miscible, immiscible, dilute, concentrated, concentration unit, dilution, molarity, percent by mass.

7.86 Identify the solute and solvent in each of the following solutions:
(a) 1 L water and l g NaCl
(b) 1 L alcohol and 50 mL water
(c) 1 L alcohol and 1 L water
(d) 1 L water and 1 mL $O_2(g)$

Percent by Mass

7.87 How are each of the following % m/m solutions prepared?
(a) 399 g of 2.95% $NaNO_2(aq)$
(b) 43.8 g of 1.31% LiOH(aq)
(c) 3.77 kg of 0.0296% $NH_4ClO_3(aq)$

7.88 Calculate the mass of concentrated HCl solution (37.0% m/m) that contains the following masses of HCl.
(a) 4.44 g HCl
(b) 542 g HCl
(c) 0.188 kg HCl
(d) 3.91 mg HCl

7.89 Concentrated ammonia, NH_3, is sold as 29% m/m $NH_3(aq)$. Its density is 0.90 g/cm^3. What mass of NH_3 is contained in each of the following volumes of concentrated ammonia solutions? (a) 11 L, (b) 63 mL, (c) 0.0040 mL

7.90 What is the maximum total mass of 2.10% m/m KI solution that could be prepared from 5.05 g KI(s)?

7.91 Calculate the mass of water in 167.5 g of 1.304% m/m Na_2SO_4 solution.

7.92 A solution is prepared by dissolving 6.53 g of solute in 284 g of water. What is the concentration of the solution in % m/m?

7.93 (a) Initially, 85.0 g of a 9.90% m/m ammonium acetate solution is placed in a beaker. What is the concentration of the solution after 145.0 g of water is added to dilute the ammonium acetate? (b) What mass of ammonium acetate solid must be added to the diluted solution to change the concentration back to the original concentration, 9.90%?

Molarity

7.94 Explain how each of the following solutions is prepared.
(a) 50.0 mL of 0.232 M $Mg(NO_3)_2$
(b) 210.0 mL of 0.1919 M NH_3
(c) 5.66 L of 2.08 M $C_6H_{12}O_6$
(d) 9.11×10^6 mL of 5.00 M H_3PO_3.

7.95 What are the molarities of the solutions prepared by dissolving the following amounts of solute in enough water to give 180.0 mL total volume.
(a) 1.441 mol $(NH_4)_2SO_4$
(b) 2.662 mmol $Cu(NO_3)_2$
(c) 12.33 g H_2SO_4
(d) 8.331 mg HBr

7.96 What is the molarity of each of the following solutions?
(a) 5.42 g C_2H_6O in 82.8 mL of solution
(b) 0.994 g Na_2SO_4 in 3.10 L of solution
(c) 834.3 mg K_2CO_3 in 41.75 mL of solution
(d) 8.90 kg NH_4Cl in 526 L of solution

7.97 Calculate the molarity of each of the following 1 solutions:
(a) 70% m/m HNO_3; density = 1.42 g/cm^3
(b) 36% acetic acid, $C_2H_4O_2$; density = 1.045 g/cm^3

7.98 To what total volume should 1.50 L of 15.9 M HNO_3 be diluted in order to produce the following concentrations?
(a) 13.5 M HNO_3
(b) 2.50 M HNO_3
(c) 0.00349 M HNO_3

7.99 Calculate the number of moles of solute particles in each of the following solutions.
(a) 287 mL of 0.444 M RbOH
(b) 17.3 mL of 0.0114 M HI
(c) 497.1 L of 4.290 M KNO_2

7.100 (a) What is the molar concentration of a solution that contains 104 g $AgNO_3$ per liter of solution? (b) What volume of this solution contains 0.837 mol $AgNO_3$? (c) What volume of this solution contains 1.00×10^{23} $AgNO_3$? (d) What is the molar concentration of the solution after it is diluted to 2.45 L?

7.101 (a) A 27% m/m H_2SO_4 solution has a density of 1.2 g/cm^3. Calculate the molar concentration of the solution.
(b) A 1.0% K_2SO_4 solution has a density of 1.01 g/cm^3. Calculate the molar concentration of the solution.
(c) A 12.0% KOH solution has a density of 1.09 g/cm^3. Calculate the molarity of the solution.
(d) A 5.00% $K_2Cr_2O_7$ solution has a density of 1.03 g/cm^3. Calculate the molarity of the solution.

7.102 (a) How can 30.4 mL of 0.855 M $CuCl_2$ be diluted to 0.177 M $CuCl_2$? (b) How can 4.29 L of 1.50 M $HClO_4$ be diluted to

0.150 M HClO₄?

7.103 To what total volume would 182.0 mL of 0.5000 M HI solution have to be diluted in order to produce a 0.2949 M HI solution?

7.104 (a) What volume of 2.85 M NaOH is required to produce 81.7 mL of 0.400 M NaOH? (b) Explain how this solution is prepared.

7.105 If 25.0 mL of water is added to 59.6 mL of 1.04 M HC₂H₃O₂ (CH₃COOH), what is the resulting molar concentration of HC₂H₃O₂? Assume the volumes are additive.

Additional Exercises

7.106 (a) What mass of sodium phosphate, Na₃PO₄, contains the same number of formula units as are in 9.971 g KOH? (b) What mass of sodium phosphate contains the same number of Na atoms as 4.506 g of elemental sodium, Na?

7.107 An impure sample of AgNO₃ contains 59.5% Ag. Calculate the percent by mass of pure AgNO₃ in the sample.

7.108 Various minerals are composed of two or more compounds bonded to each other. Find the empirical formula of a mineral that contains 60.7% SiO₂, 27.2% MgO, and 12.1% H₂O.

7.109 Penicillin G is an antibiotic. It has a molecular formula of C₁₆H₁₈N₂O₄S. (a) Calculate the percent by mass (three significant figures) of C in penicillin. (b) What mass of penicillin contains 1.00 g of carbon? (c) How many carbon atoms are in a 1.00-g sample of penicillin? (d) What mass of penicillin contains 4.19 × 10²³ atoms of hydrogen?

7.110 Saccharin is an artificial sweetener. A 1.000-g sample of saccharin is analyzed and is found to contain 0.459 g C, 0.0275 g H, 0.262 g O, 0.175 g S, and 0.0765 g N. The molecular mass of saccharin is 183.2. Calculate the molecular formula of saccharin.

7.111 Progesterone, C₂₁H₃₀O₂, is a steroid hormone. (a) How many moles of progesterone are in a 4.44-mg sample? (b) What mass of progesterone contains 25 mmol H? (c) What mass of glucose, C₆H₁₂O₆, has the same number of C atoms as a 0.0386-g sample of progesterone?

7.112 Iodine pentafluoride, IF₅, is a colorless liquid that has a density of 3.252 g/cm³. (a) Calculate the volume of 4.31 mol IF₅. (b) How many moles of F atoms are in 2.65 L IF₅? (s) What volume of IF₅ contains 4.821 × 10²³ atoms of F?

7.113 The psychoactive chemical in marijuana, THC, is composed of 71.23% C, 12.95% H, and 15.81% O. Calculate its empirical formula.

7.114 Hemoglobin is the molecule in the blood that transports oxygen to the cells. Its molecular mass is 64,456, and it contains 0.35% O iron by mass. (a) What mass of hemoglobin contains 1.00 g of iron? (b) How many iron atoms are found in a 4.33-g sample of hemoglobin? (c) How many moles of Fe are contained in a 9.11-mg sample of hemoglobin? (e) How many iron atoms in one hemoglobin molecule?

7.115 (a) What mass of 24 carat gold (100% pure) could be obtained from exactly 1 lb of 18 carat (75% pure) gold? (b) How many gold atoms are there in this sample?

7.116 Carbon atoms have a diameter of about 1.5 × 10⁻⁸ cm. If they are placed in a straight line 10.0 cm long, what is their mass?

7.117 Citric acid is an important compound in cellular metabolism and is a component of citrus fruits. A 4.256-g sample of citric acid contains 1.596 g C and 2.481 g O, and the remainder is H. (a) What is the empirical formula of citric acid? (b) If the molecular mass of citric acid is 192.1, calculate the molecular formula of citric acid?

7.118 Trinitrotoluene (TNT), C₇H₅N₃O₆, is a commonly used explosive. (a) What is the percent by mass of hydrogen in TNT? (b) What is the mass of each element in a 3.94 g sample of TNT?

7.119 A compound is found to have the formula XBr₂, in which X is an unknown element. Bromine is found to comprise 71.55% of the mass of the compound. (a) What is the atomic mass of X? (b) What is the name of element X?

7.120 Carbon tetrachloride, CCl₄, is one of the components of dry-cleaning fluids. Its density is 1.587 g/cm³. (a) What volume of carbon tetrachloride contains 9.56 ×

10^{26} chlorine atoms? (b) How many carbon tetrachloride molecules are there in a 48.3-mm³ sample? (c) What is the volume of one carbon tetrachloride molecule?

7.121 What is the number of atoms in a pound mole, the atomic mass in pounds? (Hint: 1 lb = 454 g)

7.122 Nicotine, $C_{10}H_{14}N_2$ is a mild stimulant found in tobacco products. It is a highly toxic compound and was once used as a pesticide. (a) What is the empirical formula of nicotine? (b) If a cigarette has a mass of 1.48 g and it contains 2.1% nicotine by mass, how many nicotine molecules are in the cigarette?

7.123 A solution of perchloric acid, $HClO_4$, is 11.7 M and has a density of 1.67 g/cm³. (a) Calculate the percent by mass of 11.7M $HClO_4$. (b) To what volume would you dilute 255 mL of 11.7 M $HClO_4$ to produce a 5.95 M $HClO_4$ solution? (c) If 81.2 mL of 11.7 M $HClO_4$ is diluted to 10.6 L, what is the new molar concentration?

7.124 (a) Calculate the percent by mass of a 6.26 M acetic acid ($HC_2H_3O_2$) aqueous solution. The density of this solution is 1.045 g/cm³. (b) Explain how 50.0 mL of this solution is diluted to 1.76 M acetic acid? (c) What is the resulting molar concentration of a solution prepared by mixing 37.4 mL of water with 25.0 mL of 6.26 M acetic acid? Assume the volumes are additive.

Notes and Calculations:

Chapter 7 Pretest Assignment

1.   Complete each of the following statements with the correct word, number, or phase.

   a. _____ is Avogadro's number.

   b. _____ is the atomic mass in grams.

   c. The _____ is the sum of the atomic masses.

   d. The _____ is the simplest ratio of whole numbers of the elements in a compound.

   e. The _____ states that the elements in a compound are in a fixed mass ratio.

   f. The _____ is the mass percents of the elements in a compound.

   g. _____ is the concentration unit that expresses the number of moles of solute per liter of solution.

2.   What is the mass of 8.62×10^{24} molecules of CS_2?

3.   How many Cl atoms are in a 8.0-g sample of $AlCl_3$?

4.   What is the percent composition of $Zn(NO_3)_2$?

5.   A 60.0-g sample of a C, H, and O compound contains 32.7 g C, 5.50 g H, and the remainder is O. Find the empirical formula of the compound.

6.   What mass of C_8H_{18} contains the same number of H atoms as a 1.35-g sample of C_3H_8?

7.   (a) What is the percent by mass of solution prepared by dissolving 50 g $C_6H_{12}O_6$ in 175 g of water?

        (b) What is the percent by mass of this solution after adding 100 g of water to the solution?

8.   What mass of $Ca(NO_3)_2$ is contained in 188 mL of 0.0555M $Ca(NO_3)_2$?

9.   (a) Explain how 500 mL of 4.00M CH_3CH_2OH is prepared.

        (b) What is the concentration of CH_3CH_2OH after this solution is diluted to 900 mL?

CHAPTER 8

Molecules, Compounds, and Chemical Bonding

8.1 COMPOUNDS

Compounds are most often classified into two major groups: ionic compounds and covalent compounds. As we will soon learn, the names given to these groups are derived from the two different kinds of chemical bonds that hold the particles in formula units and molecules.

WWWolfe 1
(See WWWolfe section at the end of the chapter.)

Ionic Compounds
Ionic compounds usually result when metallic elements combine with nonmetallic elements.

Metal + nonmetal → ionic compound

Before we consider representative ionic compounds, let's learn how the names of simple ionic compounds are assigned. We will begin with **binary ionic compounds,** those that contain two different elements. First write the name of the metal, and then write the name of the nonmetal, replacing its ending with *ide*.

1. Write the name of the metal.
2. Write the name of the nonmetal, replacing its ending with the ending *ide*

How do we write the name of NaCl? Notice that Na is an alkali metal and Cl is a halogen, a nonmetal. First, write the name of the metal, *sodium,* and then write the name of the nonmetal, dropping its ending and replacing it with *ide*: Chlorine – *ine* + *ide* = chloride. Sodium chloride is, therefore, the name of NaCl.

> Endings dropped from nonmetals:
> **ox**ygen, nit**rogen**, carb**on**, sulf**ur**, phosph**orus**, fluor**ine**, chlor**ine**, brom**ine**, and iod**ine**

Other examples of how to write the names of binary ionic Compounds are given in Example Problem 8.1.

Example Problem 8.1
Write the names for each of the following ionic compounds: (a) KF, (b) CaO, (c) Mg_3N_2.

Solution
(a) KF

     Metal = potassium

     Nonmetal – ending + *ide* = fluorine – *ine* + *ide*

     Name = **potassium fluoride**

(b) CaO

> CaO is also called lime. The expression "being in the limelight" stems from the fact that when lime is heated a brilliant white light is released.

     Metal = calcium

     Nonmetal – ending + *ide* = oxygen – *ygen* + *ide*

     Name = **calcium oxide**

(c) Mg_3N_2

     Metal = magnesium

     Nonmetal – ending + *ide* = nitrogen – ~~oxygen~~ *ogen* + *ide*

     Name = **magnesium nitride**

Exercise

Write the name of Li_3P. (Lithium phosphide)

Ionic compounds share many common properties. At 25°C they are solids with relatively high melting and boiling points. Most are hard, but brittle. Ionic substances are poor conductors of electricity, except in the molten (liquid) state, when they are good conductors. Dissolved in water, their structure is broken apart liberating ions that help conduct an electric current. Table 8.1 presents the properties of six selected ionic compounds.

TABLE 8.1 PROPERTIES OF SELECTED BINARY IONIC COMPOUNDS

Compound	Physical state, 25°C	Color	Melting point, °C	Boiling point, °C	Density, g/cm³	Solubility, g/100 cm³ water
NaCl	Solid	White	801	1413	2.17	35.7 (0°C)
LiF	Solid	White	846	1717	2.64	0.13 (25°C)
$CaCl_2$	Solid	White	772	1940	2.15	42 (20°C)
Fe_2O_3	Solid	Red brown	1462		5.24	Insoluble
CoF_2	Solid	Pink	1127	1737	4.46	1.36 (20°C)
ZnS	Solid	Grayish	1722		4.09	Insoluble

Covalent Compounds

Covalent compounds result when two or more nonmetals combine chemically.

Nonmetal + nonmetal → covalent compound

Frequently encountered covalent compounds include water, H_2O; ammonia, NH_3; carbon dioxide, CO_2; and methane, CH_4. In each of these binary covalent compounds two different nonmetallic elements are chemically combined.

A different set of rules is used when writing the names of binary covalent compounds. If there is only one atom per molecule of the nonmetal that appears first in the formula, write that name of this nonmetal with no change. The name of the second nonmetal is modified in two ways: A prefix is added to it to indicate how many atoms of that element there are in the molecule, and its ending is replaced with *ide*.

Consider CO_2 as an example for writing the name of a binary covalent compound. Start by writing the name of the nonmetal listed first in the formula, *carbon*. Then modify the name of the second nonmetal, oxygen: Add the prefix *di*, which means "two," drop its ending, *ygen*, and replace it with *ide*. Thus, the name of CO_2 is carbon dioxide.

$$CO_2 = \text{carbon (di + oxygen} - ygen + ide) = \text{carbon dioxide}$$

A prefix that shows the number of atoms is required in the names of covalent compounds because two nonmetals can usually combine in more than one way. For example, CO, carbon monoxide, is a second oxide of carbon. The prefix *mono*, or simply *mon*, is added to indicate that this oxide of carbon contains only one O atom.

> Carbon monoxide, CO, is a poisonous gas that kills by not allowing O_2 to reach the hemoglobin in the blood. The affinity of CO for hemoglobin is approximately 200 times greater than that of O_2.

Table 8.2 lists the most commonly used prefixes in the names of covalent compounds.

TABLE 8.2 PREFIXES USED IN THE NAMES OF COVALENT MOLECULES

Prefix	Number of atoms
mono	1
di	2
tri	3
tetra	4
penta	5
hexa	6
hepta	7
octa	8
nona	9
deca	10

In some covalent compounds more than one atom of each nonmetal is found. For example, two N atoms and four O atoms are in a molecule of N_2O_4. To write the names of such compounds, a prefix is added to each nonmetal to tell how many atoms are in the formula. The name of N_2O_4 is dinitrogen tetroxide. The prefix *di is* added to nitrogen to indicate the presence of two N atoms, and the prefix *tetr* is added to oxide to indicate that four O atoms are present. Example Problem 8.2 shows three examples of how to write the names of binary covalent compounds.

Example Problem 8.2
Write the names for each of the following covalent compounds: (a) OCl_2, (b) SF_6, (c) P_2O_5.

Solution
(a) OCl_2 = oxygen (*di* + chlorine – *ine* + *ide*) = **oxygen dichloride**

(b) SF_6 = sulfur (*hexa* + fluorine – *ine* + *ide*) = **sulfur hexafluoride**

(c) P_2O_5 = (*di* + phosphorus) + (*pent* + oxygen – *ygen* + *ide*) = **diphosphorus pentoxide**

      In the last example, *pent* rather than *penta* is added as the prefix for *oxide* to generate a word that is easier to pronounce. If adding the prefix produces a double vowel, such as *oo or ao,* the vowel contributed by the prefix is usually dropped.
Exercise
Write the name of PBr_5. (Phosphorus pentabromide)

      Covalent compounds are markedly different from ionic compounds. Most covalent compounds are either liquids or gases; some are rather soft solids. Compared with average ionic compounds, covalent compounds have lower melting and boiling points and lower densities. Covalent compounds are poor conductors of both heat and electricity. Most do not form ions when dissolved in water. Table 8.3 lists properties of selected covalent compounds. ❖

REVIEW EXERCISES
8.1 What types of elements combine to produce (a) ionic compounds, (b) covalent compounds?

8.2 Write the names of each of the following ionic compounds.

(a) KI
(b) Li_2O
(c) SrO
(d) Cs_3N
(e) Ca_3P_2

8.3 (a) List four properties of ionic compounds.

(b) List four properties of covalent compounds.

8.4 Write the names of each of the following covalent compounds.

(a) OF$_2$

(b) NI$_3$

(c) NO

(d) XeF$_4$

(e) P$_4$O$_{10}$

8.5 Compare the properties of NaCl with those of H$_2$O.

8.2 (a) Potassium iodide, (b) lithium oxide, (c) strontium oxide, (d) cesium nitride, (e) calcium phosphide; 8.4 (a) Oxygen difluoride, (b) nitrogen triiodide, (c) nitrogen monoxide, (d) xenon tetrafluoride, (e) tetraphosphorus decoxide; 8.5 NaCl is a crystalline ionic solid with high melting and boiling point. H$_2$O is a covalent liquid with lower melting and boiling points.

TABLE 8.3 PROPERTIES OF SELECTED COVALENT COMPOUNDS

Compound	Physical state	Color	Melting point, °C	Boiling point, °C	Density
Methane, CH$_4$	Gas	Colorless	–182	–162	0.55 g/L
Hydrogen fluoride, HF	Gas	Colorless	–83.1	19.4	0.98 g/L
Ammonia, NH$_3$	Gas	Colorless	–74.3	–31.1	0.77 g/L
Water	Liquid	Colorless	0.0	100	1.0 g/cm^3
Carbon tetrachloride, CCl$_4$	Liquid	Colorless	–23.0	76.8	1.6 g/cm^3
Tetraphosphorus, decoxide, P$_4$O$_{10}$	Solid	White	340	360 (sublimes)	2.3 g/cm^3
Sulfur dioxide, SO$_2$	Gas	Colorless	–75.5	–10.0	2.72 g/L
Ethanol, CH$_3$CH$_2$OH	Liquid	Colorless	–114	78.3	0.789 g/cm^3
Benzene, C$_6$H$_6$	Liquid	Colorless	5.53	80.1	0.874 g/cm^3

8.2 CHEMICAL BONDS

What is a Chemical Bond?

Chemical bonds are the attractive forces that hold atoms or ions together. In this section we will attempt to understand what drives atoms to combine and produce chemical bonds.

One of the driving forces of nature is the tendency of matter to reach the lowest possible energy state. Generally, a lower energy state implies greater stability. A stable body is more resistant to change than a less stable body.

WWWolfe 2
(See WWWolfe
section at the end of
the chapter.)

Elements can be ranked according to their degree of stability. Elements such as sodium, Na, and chlorine, Cl, are ranked as highly reactive (unstable) because they tend to undergo chemical changes and liberate energy. More stable elements remain unaltered, even under extreme conditions. As a group, the noble gases are quite stable. Helium and neon, for example, do not form any stable compounds.

Certain nonmetallic elements are so unstable that they do not exist in nature as individual atoms, but rather as diatomic molecules (molecules composed of two atoms). Included in this group are hydrogen, H_2; nitrogen, N_2; oxygen, O_2; plus all of the halogens: fluorine, F_2; chlorine, Cl_2; bromine, Br_2; iodine, I_2; and astatine, At_2. More stable elements, such as the noble gases, all exist monatomically ("monatomically" means "as single atoms").

> In addition to the diatomic elements, solid sulfur is found as S_8 molecules, and phosphorus exists as P_4 molecules.

Let's consider molecular hydrogen, H_2. All samples of hydrogen gas, at 25°C, are composed of H_2 molecules. How is this explained? One way to answer the question is to consider the stability of two H atoms compared to that of an H_2 molecule. The H_2 molecule is more stable, and the individual H atoms are less stable. When individual H atoms are combined, they release energy:

$$H\cdot + H\cdot \rightarrow H_2 + 436 \text{ kJ}$$

For each mole of H_2 that forms, 436 kJ of energy is released. This energy is initially in the two H atoms but is released when the atoms combine. Thus, one mole of diatomic hydrogen molecules is 436 kJ more stable than two moles of hydrogen atoms (Fig. 8.1).

As an analogy, you should think of a boulder on the ground relative to one on the top of a hill. Which one has more potential energy? The boulder on the hill has more energy because kinetic energy was added to the boulder, and stored as potential energy, when it was carried to the top of the hill (Fig. 8.2). A boulder on top of a hill has the capacity to fall spontaneously to the ground, whereas the opposite is not true. You would be amazed to see a boulder jump from the ground to the top of a cliff. The two H atoms are at the top of an energy "cliff" and the H_2 molecule is at the bottom.

Figure 8.1 When 2 mol of H atoms bond to form 1 mol of H_2, 436 kJ of energy is released. The same quantity of energy, 436 kJ, is required to break the bonds in 1 mol of H_2.

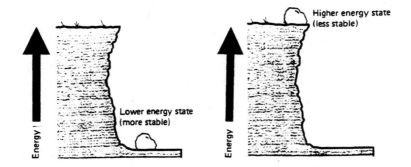

Figure 8.2 A rock on the ground is in a lower energy state and is more stable than a rock on the top of a cliff. Energy must be added to the rock on the ground to move it to the top of the cliff. Thus, at the top of the cliff it is in a higher energy state and is less stable.

Why don't noble gases form diatomic molecules? Using a similar argument to the one just used, we can say that individual noble gas atoms exist at a lower energy state (at the bottom of the hill because of their stability) compared to diatomic noble gas molecules (at the top of the hill) (Fig. 8.3). This is verified by the fact that a large amount of energy is required to produce a diatomic noble gas compound, exactly the opposite of what was found for the formation of diatomic hydrogen, in which energy is released. He_2 does not exit.

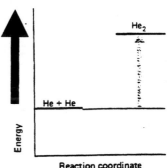

Figure 8.3 Energy must be added to He atoms to produce He_2, if possible. Thus, He_2 is less stable than unbonded He atoms. He_2 does not exist because it is so unstable.

Bonding Theories

During the twentieth century, scientists have attempted to develop and refine a theory that explains why some atoms bond and others do not. This bonding theory also tries to explain the degree of stability of compounds, and to account for the arrangement of atoms within molecules.

In 1916, G. N. Lewis was one of the first scientists to propose that bonding was directly related to the electronic arrangement of atoms. Since then, a large body of information has been collected to show that chemical bonding is adequately explained in terms of the outer-shell, or valence, electrons. This bonding theory is known as the **valence bond theory.** Due to certain limitations of the valence bond theory, a second bonding theory, known as the **molecular orbital theory,** has also developed. In the molecular orbital theory all the electrons in the atoms are considered in bond formation. As a result of the complexity and the quantitative nature of the molecular orbital theory, it is not included in this beginning discussion of chemical bonds—we will consider only the fundamentals of the valence bond theory.

Throughout the development of the principal concepts of the valence bond theory, never lose sight of the fact that a bonding theory attempts to explain the structure and reactivity of molecules. A common misunderstanding is that the theoretical arguments of scientists are the facts and the components of the real world are the supporting evidence. If we reach an exception to a rule or guideline, it is not a discrepancy in the natural world, but a flaw in the theory. Bonding theories are nothing more than models produced by scientists to describe molecular systems.

Types of Bonds

Valence bond theory explains chemical bonds in terms of electron "transfers" and electron "sharing." When one or more electrons are transferred from one atom to another while forming a bond, the resultant bond is called an **ionic bond.** If there is no electron transfer, but "sharing" of electrons occurs between two atoms, the resultant bond is classified as a **covalent bond.**

While it is convenient to classify bonds in such a manner, most bonds are not purely ionic or covalent. Just as most occurrences in the world are not "black" or "white," most bonds have varying degrees of ionic and covalent character. Ionic compounds have bonds with a higher degree of ionic character, and covalent compounds have bonds with a greater degree of covalent character. ❖

> NaCl, an ionic substance, has 67% ionic character and 33% covalent character.

REVIEW EXERCISES

8.6 What is the chemical bond?

8.7 List two everyday phenomena that illustrate the tendency of objects to seek spontaneously their lowest energy states.

8.8 What groups of elements in the periodic table are classified as (a) more stable and (b) less stable? Give specific examples.

8.9 List five elements that exist as diatomic molecules at 25°C.

8.10 Provide an explanation for the fact that diatomic helium molecules do not exist.

8.11 (a) What type of bond results when electrons are shared between two atoms?

(b) What type of bond results when electrons are transferred between atoms?

8.9 N_2, O_2, Cl_2, Br_2, I_2; 8.11 (a) Covalent, (b) ionic

8.3 IONIC (ELECTROVALENT) BONDING

When electrons are transferred from a metal to a nonmetal, an **ionic bond** (sometimes called an **electrovalent bond**) is produced. In this section, we will consider the formation and nature of ionic bonds. Before we begin our discussion of ionic bonds, we must consider an important property of bonded atoms called electronegativity.

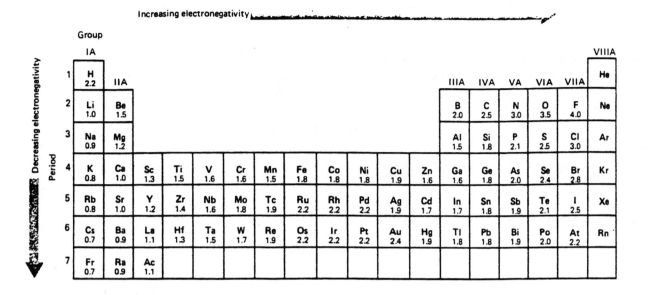

Figure 8.4 Within a period, the electronegativities of atoms increase with increasing atomic number, excluding the noble gases. Within a group, the electronegativities decrease going from top to bottom.

Electronegativity

Electronegativity is a measure of the power of an atom to attract electrons in a chemical bond. An element with a high electronegativity has a greater capacity to attract bonded electrons than one with a lower electronegativity. Three or four scales of electronegativity exist, but the original scale developed by Linus Pauling (1901-1995) is still one of the most popular in beginning chemistry courses.

Pauling collected data on most of the elements, performed various calculations, and produced an electronegativity scale based on the element fluorine, F. Pauling assigned the electronegativity value of 4.0 to fluorine, the most electronegative element.

> Linus Pauling wrote one of the most significant chemistry books of the twentieth century entitled *The Nature of the Chemical Bond.* He was awarded two Nobel prizes. In 1954, he received the Nobel prize for chemistry. Nine years later he received the Nobel peace prize for his work leading to the banning of atmospheric testing of nuclear bombs.

On the Pauling electronegativity scale (Figure 8.4) two trends are evident: (1) From left to right across a period, electronegativities increase (excluding the noble gases), and (2) with increasing atomic mass within a chemical group, electronegativities decrease. Francium, Fr, the element located at the bottom left corner of the periodic table, is the least electronegative element. The closer an element is to fluorine on the periodic table, the higher its electronegativity. Oxygen is the second most electronegative element with a value of 3.5.

Trends in electronegativity directly parallel those in ionization energy, and are indirectly related to trends in atomic size. In other words, elements with high ionization energies, those composed of small atoms, are the most electronegative (excluding the noble gases). Elements with low ionization energies, those composed of large atoms, have lower electronegativities.

Ionic Bonding in Sodium Chloride, NaCl

To illustrate ionic bonding, let's consider sodium chloride, NaCl. When sodium combines with chlorine, the ionic salt sodium chloride is the product. Sodium is an alkali metal with one valence electron:

$$Na \ 1s^2 2s^2 2p^6 3s^1$$

The Lewis symbol for sodium is

$$Na\cdot$$

Chlorine is a halogen with seven outer electrons:

$$Cl \ 1s^2 2s^2 2p^6 3s^2 3p^5$$

The Lewis symbol for chlorine is

$$:\overset{\cdot\cdot}{\underset{\cdot\cdot}{Cl}}\cdot$$

Sodium is a reactive metal and chlorine is a reactive nonmetal. Sodium has a low ionization energy (little energy is needed to remove its $3s^1$ electron) and a lower electronegativity. Chlorine, in contrast, has a relatively high ionization energy and high electronegativity. Sodium is the largest atom in the third period, while chlorine is one of the smallest atoms.

Whenever a sodium atom encounters a chlorine atom, the loosely held valence electron ($3s^1$) of sodium is pulled away by the more compact chlorine atom, creating two ions. In terms of electronegativity, we say that the highly electronegative Cl atom (3.0) attracts the valence electron of sodium because of its low electronegativity (0.9). A Na atom loses an electron and becomes a cation (a positive ion), and a Cl atom gains the electron and becomes an anion (a negative ion).

$$Na\cdot \ + \ :\overset{\cdot\cdot}{\underset{\cdot\cdot}{Cl}}\cdot \ \longrightarrow \ Na^+ \left[:\overset{\cdot\cdot}{\underset{\cdot\cdot}{Cl}}: \right]^-$$

$$Na \ (1s^2 2s^2 2p^6 3s^1) \rightarrow e^- + Na^+ \ (1s^2 2s^2 2p^6 3s^0)$$

$$Cl \ (1s^2 2s^2 2p^6 3s^2 3p^5) + e^- \rightarrow Cl^- \ (1s^2 2s^2 2p^6 3s^2 3p^6)$$

Na^+ and Cl^- have one thing in common; they possess a noble gas electron configuration. A Na^+ ion possesses 10 electrons and has the same electron configuration as Ne. In other words, Na^+ is isoelectronic to Ne. Cl^- has 18 electrons and is isoelectronic to Ar.

CHEM TOPIC: Sodium Chloride

When most people ask for salt, they are referring to sodium chloride. Dissolved sodium chloride, NaCl, is a component of each cell in our bodies. We need a constant source of sodium chloride to replenish the salt that we excrete and lose through our sweat glands. NaCl is also required for the production of hydrochloric acid, HCl(aq), which is a component of gastric juice in our stomachs.

In desert regions salt has always been a valuable commodity. Animals travel great distances to find salt. Salt was an important item in the military baggage of the ancient Roman soldiers. Our word "salary" is derived from the Latin word samarium, which originally meant "money for salt."

Today, salt is readily available in a highly refined form. Many people in the United States consume from 5 to 10 g of sodium chloride per day. These amounts are far in excess of the amounts that are nutritionally sound. Recommended dietary allowances indicate that 1 to 3 g of salt are required to maintain maximum health. Too much salt in one's diet leads to high blood pressure (hypertension) and can cause a fluid imbalance. An elevated concentration of sodium ions in the blood is called hypernatremia.

An ionic bond is the force of attraction between unlike charged ions, in this case Na^+ and Cl^-. Remember that unlike charged particles always attract each other, but it is not the simple attraction of a pair of Na^+ and Cl^- ions that is significant. Ionic compounds like NaCl exist in a *crystal lattice,* a three-dimensional array of Na^+ ions surrounded by Cl^- ions, and vice versa. Figure 8.5 shows the crystal lattice structure of sodium chloride. Each Na^+, except those on the surface, is surrounded and attracted by six Cl^- ions, and each inner Cl^- ion is surrounded and attracted by six Na^+ ions.

In Fig. 8.5, note that the Na^+ ions are smaller than the Cl^- ions. After a Na atom loses its outer $3s^1$ electron, the inner, core electrons are held tightly by the nucleus because there are more protons than electrons. In contrast, Cl^- has one more electron than proton; thus, the electrons are not held as tightly by the nucleus. A measure of the size of an ion is its **ionic radius.** Figure 8.6 shows a comparison of the atomic sizes and ionic radii of alkali metals and halide ions.

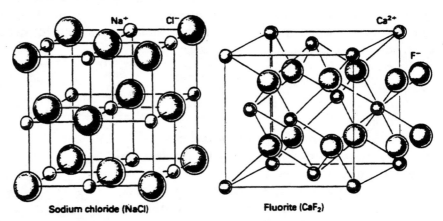

Sodium chloride (NaCl)   Fluorite (CaF₂)

Figure 8.5 ionic solids are composed of regular patterns of alternating ions and cations. This figure shows segments of the crystal lattices of sodium chloride, NaCl, and calcium fluoride, CaF₂.

What drives Na and Cl atoms to combine to form NaCl? When Na and Cl combine they release energy.

$$Na(g) + \tfrac{1}{2}Cl_2(g) \rightarrow NaCl(g) + 623 \text{ kJ}$$

If energy is released in chemical reactions, the products are more stable (lower-energy) than the reactants. In NaCl, both atoms achieve the stable noble gas configuration—the most stable electronic configuration possible for atoms.

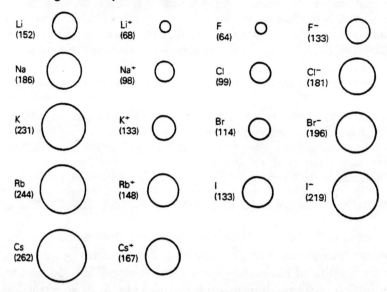

Figure 8.6 Ionic radii of alkali metal cations are smaller than the radii of corresponding alkali metal atoms. The decrease in size is the result of losing the valence electron. Ionic radii of halide anions are larger than the radii of the corresponding halogen atoms. The increase in size is a result of gaining one electron. The radii are measured in picometers (1 pm = 10^{-12} m)

The reaction of Na with Cl is a model for the combination of an alkali metal atom (group IA (1) atom) with a halogen (group VIIA (17) atom). All combinations of alkali metals and halogens yield compounds that have ionic bonds with formula units of *MX*, in which *M* is any alkali metal and *X* is any halogen. *M* and *X* combine in a 1-to-1 ratio because each obtains the stable noble gas electronic configuration after transferring one electron.

> Some other ionic compounds with an alkali metal and halogen are KI, CsBr, RbCl and LiF.

A convenient rule to follow is that atoms are most stable when they are isoelectronic to a noble gas. This rule is often called the **octet rule**, but is better named the **noble gas rule**. A word of caution when applying the octet/noble gas rule: *It is only a generalization that can be applied in many, but not all, cases.* ❖

> "Octet" refers to eight things, a group of eight electrons in this case.

REVIEW EXERCISES

8.12 What is the electronegativity of an atom?

8.13 (a) What is an ionic bond? (b) How is it different from a covalent bond?

8.14 Use Lewis symbols to illustrate the electron transfer that occurs when potassium and fluorine atoms combine to produce potassium fluoride.

8.15 Write the formulas for a cation and an anion that are isoelectronic to each of the following noble gas atoms.

(a) Xe
(b) Kr
(c) He
(d) Ne

8.16 What is the octet or noble gas rule, and how is it applied when considering the formation of ionic bonds?

8.15 (a) Cs^+, I^-; (b) Sr^{2+}, Br^-; (c) Li^+, H^-; (d) Mg^{2+}, O^{2-}

Ionic Bonding in Calcium Fluoride, CaF₂

What happens when Ca atoms bond to F atoms? Calcium belongs to group IIA (2), the alkaline earth metals. Each group IIA element has two loosely held valence electrons. Fluorine is a halogen with seven

> Calcium fluoride, commonly called fluorite, is a high-melting solid (1360°C) that has a low water solubility.

valence electrons. Because fluorine is the most electronegative element, it can remove an electron from a Ca atom and obtain a noble gas configuration. However, two electrons must be removed from a Ca atom for it to obtain a noble gas configuration. Hence, two F atoms accept one electron each from Ca, allowing the Ca atom to obtain the noble gas configuration of Ar.

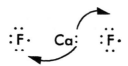

After the two electrons are transferred, Ca obtains a 2+ charge and each F possesses a 1– charge. Both Ca^{2+} and F^- are isoelectronic to noble gases. Ca^{2+} is isoelectronic to Ar, and F^- is isoelectronic to Ne.

$$Ca \ (1s^2 2s^2 2p^6 3s^2 3p^6 4s^2) \rightarrow 2e^- + Ca^{2+} \ (1s^2 2s^2 2p^6 3s^2 3p^6 4s^0)$$

$$F \ (1s^2 2s^2 2p^5) + e^- \rightarrow F^- \ (1s^2 2s^2 2p^6)$$

The Lewis structure for calcium fluoride is as follows:

$$Ca^{2+} \ 2 \left[\ :\overset{..}{\underset{..}{F}}: \ \right]^-$$

A Lewis structure is used to show the bonds in a formula unit or molecule. Figure 8.7 shows the crystal structure of calcium fluoride. Compare its structure to that of sodium chloride.

Again we can generalize: alkaline earth metals (except Be, whose compounds have little ionic character) and halogens combine to yield ionic compounds with the formula MX_2,

Ionic Bonding in Magnesium Oxide, MgO

Magnesium, Mg, belongs to group IIA (2). Oxygen, O, is a member of group VIA (16), the chalcogens. In the formation of magnesium oxide, MgO, a Mg atom must lose two electrons and an O atom must gain two electrons to obtain stable noble gas configurations. Thus, two electrons transfer from Mg, which has a low electronegativity, to O, which has a high electronegativity:

> Magnesium oxide is also called magnesia. It is produced when magnesium carbonate, $MgCO_3$, is heated

$$Mg\!\cdot + \overset{\cdot\cdot}{\underset{\cdot\cdot}{O}}\!: \longrightarrow Mg^{2+} \left[:\overset{\cdot\cdot}{\underset{\cdot\cdot}{O}}: \right]^{2-}$$

Both elements achieve the noble gas electronic configuration of Ne.

$$Mg\ (1s^2 2s^2 2p^6 3s^2) \rightarrow Mg^{2+}\ ((1s^2 2s^2 2p^6 3s^0) + 2e^-$$

$$O\ (1s^2 2s^2 2p^4) + 2e^- \rightarrow O^{2-}\ ((1s^2 2s^2 2p^6)$$

The formula unit of magnesium oxide is MgO because one pair of electrons transfers from the Mg to the O. All members of group IIA combine with nonmetallic members of group VIA in a 1-to-1 ratio.

Ionic Bonding in Potassium sulfide, K₂S

Potassium, K, an alkali metal atom with one valence electron, and sulfur, a chalcogen atom with six valence electrons, combine in a 2-to-1 ratio. After a K atom loses one electron, it achieves the noble gas configuration of Ar, but after gaining an electron, the S atom would only have seven valence electrons. Hence, the S atom removes an electron from a second K atom to obtain the noble gas configuration of Ar:

> Potassium sulfide is a yellow-brown solid that melts at 840°C

$$K\!\cdot\ +\ :\!\overset{\cdot\cdot}{S}\!:\ +\ K\!\cdot \longrightarrow 2K^+ \left[:\overset{\cdot\cdot}{\underset{\cdot\cdot}{S}}: \right]^{2-}$$

Ionic Compound Summary

Table 8.4 lists all possible nontransition metal and nonmetal group combinations that produce binary ionic compounds. Note that in each case both the metal and nonmetal obtain a noble gas configuration, and each compound is electrically neutral; the sum of positive charges equals the sum of negative charges.

TABLE 8.4 SUMMARY OF THE FORMULAS OF IONIC COMPOUNDS

Metal group	Nonmetal group	Formula*	Examples
IA (1)	VIIA (17)	MX $(M^+ X^-)$	NaBr, KI, CsF, RbI, LiCl
IA (1)	VIA (16)	M_2X $(2M^+ X^{2-})$	Li_2O, Na_2S, K_2Se, Rb_2O
IA (1)	VA (15)	M_3X $(3M^+ X^{3-})$	Na_3N, K_3P, Cs_3As
IIA (2)	VIIA (17)	MX_2 $(M^{2+} 2X^-)$	$MgCl_2$, BaF_2, CaI_2, $SrBr_2$
IIA (2)	VIA (16)	MX $(M^{2+} X^{2-})$	CaO, MgS, SrO
IIA (2)	VA (15)	M_3X_2 $(3M^{2+} 2X^{3-})$	Ca_3N_2, Mg_3P_2, Ba_3N_2
IIIA (3)	VIIA (17)	MX_3 $(M^{3+} 3X^-)$	AlF_3, $GaCl_3$
IIIA (3)	VIA (16)	M_2X_3 $(2M^{3+} 3X^{2-})$	Al_2O_3, In_2O_3
IIIA (3)	VA (15)	MX $(M^{3+} X^{3-})$	AlN, GaAs

*M = metal; X = nonmetal

As we discussed previously, all ionic substances have a three-dimensional crystal lattice structure composed of alternating cations and anions. Many different crystal lattice patterns exist. Each has an orderly array of cations surrounded by anions, and vice versa. Figure 8.7 shows three different cubic crystal lattice structures.

> Crystal structures are elucidated through x-ray diffraction analysis.

While the properties of ionic substances are similar, they vary depending on (1) the charge on the ions, (2) the distance between ions, and (3) the pattern of ions within the crystal lattice. For example, more highly charged ions in the crystal lattice generally produce stronger ionic bonds: more energy is needed to break them apart. Ionic bonds in magnesium chloride, $MgCl_2$ (Mg^{2+} $2Cl^-$), are stronger than those in NaCl (Na^+ Cl^-). A greater force of attraction between cations and anions with higher charges creates stronger ionic bonds. ❖

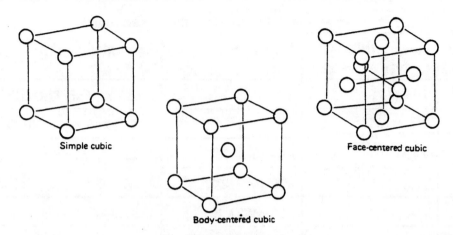

Figure 8.7 Simple cubic, body-centered cubic, and face-centered cubic crystal lattice patterns are shown. Many other geometric arrangements of ions are found in crystal lattices.

REVIEW EXERCISES

8.17 Write the complete electronic configurations for each of the following.

(a) S^{2-}
(b) Rb^+
(c) N^{3-}
(d) Ba^{2+}

8.18 Write the Lewis structures for each of the following ionic substances.

(a) BaS
(b) $SrBr_2$
(c) Li_2O

8.19 What is the formula unit for each of the following ionic compounds?

(a) calcium nitride
(b) rubidium oxide
(c) magnesium phosphide
(d) cesium sulfide

8.17 (a) $1s^2 2s^2 2p^6 3s^2 3p^6$, (b) $1s^2 2s^2 2p^6 3s^2 3p^6 4s^2 3d^{10} 4p^6$, (c) $1s^2 2s^2 2p^6$, (d) $1s^2 2s^2 2p^6 3s^2 3p^6 4s^2 3d^{10} 4p^6 5s^2 4d^{10} 5p^6$; 8.19 (a) Ca_3N_2, (b) Rb_2O, (c) Mg_3P_2, (d) Cs_2S

8.4 INTRODUCTION TO COVALENT BONDING

Many molecules are bonded as a result of "shared" valence electrons between two atoms. In this case, the properties of the atoms involved are such that one atom cannot remove an electron from the other. A chemical bond that forms without the transfer of electrons is a **covalent bond**.

WWWolfe 3
(See WWWolfe
section at the end of
the chapter.)

Covalent Bonding in Hydrogen, H₂

To begin our discussion of covalent bonding, it is easiest to start with the simplest molecule: diatomic hydrogen, H_2. Hydrogen gas is composed of H_2 molecules, rather than discrete H atoms. When one H atom bonds with another H atom, an electron transfer cannot take place because each H atom has the same electronegativity. Instead H atoms must share their

> Hydrogen gas, H_2, is a colorless, highly combustible gas. Its melting point is –259°C and its boiling point is –253°C.

electrons to reach the noble gas configurations of two electrons (isoelectronic to He).

$$H\cdot + H\cdot \rightarrow H:H$$

At first glance this might not seem to be an effective means of bonding the two hydrogen atoms. But in fact the covalent bond between two H atoms is relatively strong; 436 kJ/mol is required to break this bond.

Covalent bonds result when the outermost orbital of one atom overlaps with the outermost orbital of another atom. The 1s orbital of one H atom overlaps with the 1s orbital of the other H atom (Fig. 8.8). Overlapping orbitals are regions between two nuclei where a high probability exists of finding two electrons. Covalent bonds, like ionic bonds, result from the attraction of positive and negative particles. The positively charged nuclei attract the negative region of overlapping orbitals.

Whenever a pair of electrons is located principally in a region of space between two nuclei where orbitals overlap, we say that electrons are shared. In a Lewis structure, shared electrons are illustrated by placing the symbols for the atoms close together and inserting two dots, representing two

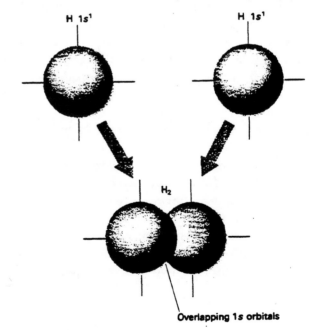

Figure 8.8 In the formation of a covalent bond between two H atoms the 1s orbitals from each H atom overlap producing a negative region between the two nuclei. The force of attraction of the nuclei of the two H atoms for the electrons in the overlapping orbitals is the covalent bond.

electrons, between them. Frequently the electron pair is replaced by a dash (—) which is interpreted as a shared electron pair, a single covalent bond.

$$H—H = H:H$$

Covalent Bonding in Fluorine, F_2

Fluorine gas is composed of diatomic fluorine molecules, F_2. In a manner similar to H_2, F_2 is formed when two atoms with the same electronegativity combine. Neither atom can remove an electron from the other; therefore, the bond between F atoms in F_2 is a covalent bond.
      Let's consider the electronic configuration of fluorine:

$$F \quad 1s^2 2s^2 2p^5$$

If an F atom shares an electron with another F atom, both F atoms obtain the noble gas configuration.

$$:\overset{..}{F}\cdot \;+\; \cdot\overset{..}{F}: \;\longrightarrow\; :\overset{..}{F}:\overset{..}{F}:$$

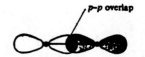

After bonding, both F atoms have eight valence electrons, making them isoelectronic to Ne. The covalent bond in fluorine is similar to the one that bonds H atoms in H_2, except the orbitals that overlap. In a F atom, the valence electrons reside in $2p$ orbitals. Accordingly, a $2p$ orbital that contains one electron from an F atom overlaps with a $2p$ orbital that contains one electron from a second F atom to produce the covalent bond (Fig. 8.9).

Figure 8.9 In the formation of a covalent bond between two F atoms, the p orbitals from each F atom overlap, producing a negative region between the two nuclei.

Multiple Covalent Bonds—Double and Triple Bonds

Whenever one pair of electrons is shared between two nuclei, as was the case in both F_2 and H_2, the bond is classified as a **single covalent bond.** In molecules with more than one pair of electrons is shared between two nuclei, the bonds are classified as **multiple covalent bonds.** In double covalent bonds four electrons are shared; in triple covalent bonds six electrons are shared. A double bond is represented in a Lewis structure by showing four dots or two dashes between two atoms (A).

$$A::A \text{ or } A=A$$
Double covalent bond

A triple bond is represented by six dots or three dashes between two atoms (A).

$$A⋮A \text{ or } A≡A$$
Triple covalent bond

As an example of a multiple covalent bond in a diatomic molecule, let's consider the bond between the two N atoms in diatomic nitrogen, N_2. The electronic configuration of a N atom is

$$N \ 1s^2 2s^2 2p^3$$

For an N atom to gain the stability of a noble gas configuration, it must share three of its electrons with another N atom. The original five valence electrons plus the three shared electrons give each N atom the noble gas configuration of Ne.

> N_2 was discovered in 1772 by Daniel Rutherford (1749-1819), a Scottish chemist. N_2 comprises about 77% of the volume of the atmosphere. It is a relatively inert gas because of its strong N—N triple bond.

$$:N::N: \quad\quad :N{\equiv}N:$$

The triple covalent bond in N_2 is a strong bond.

Double covalent bonds are generally stronger than single bonds between the same atoms. In other words, more energy is required to break them totally. Four negative electrons between two positive nuclei produce a stronger attractive force than two electrons between the same nuclei. Triple bonds are even stronger than double bonds because six electrons are found between the two nuclei. The energy needed to cleave a bond is called the **bond dissociation energy** (bond energies). Most frequently, bond dissociation energies are measured in kilojoules per mole. Table 8.5 lists the bond dissociation energies for selected bonds.

TABLE 8.5 BOND DISSOCIATION ENERGIES FOR SELECTED BONDS

Single bond	Bond energy, kJ/mol	Multiple bond	Bond energy, kJ/mol
H—H	436	N≡N	946
F—F	159	C≡O	1075
Cl—Cl	243	C≡C	839
Br—Br	192	O=O	498
I—I	151	N=N	418
F—Cl	255	C=C	614
C—C	347	C=N	615

Not all atoms can form multiple bonds. O, N, C, and S are the atoms that most readily produce multiple bonds. Atoms such as H or the halogens (F, Cl, Br, and I) obtain a noble gas configuration by sharing one electron with another atom; consequently, they do not form multiple covalent bonds.

Polar Covalent Bonds: Unequal Sharing of Electrons

In the molecules that we have discussed, both of the bonded atoms were the same, resulting in the equal sharing of electrons. When the bonded atoms are the same, their electronegativities are equal; thus, neither atom has a greater attraction for the shared electron pair. A covalent bond in which both atoms have the same electronegativity is called a **nonpolar covalent bond.**

In most cases, however, the atoms forming covalent bonds have different electronegativities, and, as a result, one atom exerts a greater force of attraction on the electrons than the other. Generally, when two different atoms bond, unequal sharing results. A covalent bond in which the electrons are not shared equally is called a **polar covalent bond.**

The term *polar* implies that a charge separation, or dipole, exists. In other words, one end of the bond is more negative than the other end. As an illustration of a molecule that has a polar covalent bond, let's consider the hydrogen chloride molecule, HCl.

Covalent Bonding in Hydrogen Chloride, HCl

An H atom shares its one electron with one of the electrons in a Cl atom. The electronegativity of chlorine (3.0) is greater than that of hydrogen (2.2). Consequently, whenever a H atom bonds with a Cl atom, a single polar covalent bond results.

$$H \cdot \ + \ :\!\overset{\cdot\cdot}{\underset{\cdot\cdot}{Cl}}\!\cdot \ \longrightarrow \ H:\!\overset{\cdot\cdot}{\underset{\cdot\cdot}{Cl}}\!:$$

Hydrogen becomes isoelectronic to He, and chlorine becomes isoelectronic to Ar. Because the electronegativity of a Cl atom is greater than that of a H atom, the shared pair of electrons is more strongly attracted to the nucleus of the Cl atom (Fig. 8.10). In effect the shared electrons spend a larger percent of the time near the Cl nucleus than near the H nucleus. To show that a dipole exists, we write the symbol lowercase delta, δ, followed by a plus or minus to indicate which atom is more positive and which is more negative:

$$\overset{\delta+}{H}\!-\!\overset{\delta-}{Cl}$$

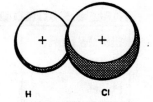

The delta is read as "partial." So δ– means that an atom has a partial negative charge, and δ+ indicates a partial positive charge.

Don't confuse a partial charge (δ+ or δ–) with the full positive (+) or negative (–) charge that we assigned to ions in ionic compounds. Metals have low electronegativities, and nonmetals have high electronegativities; consequently, a more complete transfer of electrons occurs in ionic compounds.

In polar covalent bonds a transfer of electrons does not occur; instead a pair (or pairs) of electrons is shared unequally. Ionic compounds can be thought of as extremely polar covalent compounds, to the point where minimal sharing occurs. The properties of polar covalent compounds are significantly different from those of ionic compounds.

Figure 8.10 In the HCl molecule, the $3p$ orbital of the Cl atom overlaps with the $1s$ orbital of the H atom. Because a Cl atom has a higher electronegativity than an H atom, the Cl atom has a stronger force of attraction for the shared pair of electrons.

Covalent Bonding in Bromine Monochloride, BrCl

Bromine monochloride, BrCl, is another example of a molecule with a polar covalent bond. The electronegativity of Cl (3.0) is greater than that of bromine (2.8). Accordingly, the Cl atom has a slightly greater capacity to attract the shared electron pair than does the Br atom. Thus, the electrons spend a slightly larger percent of the time closer to the Cl nucleus. Whenever the Lewis structure of bromine monochloride is written, a δ– is placed above the Cl and a δ+ is placed above the Br. ❖

$$\overset{\delta+}{Br}-\overset{\delta-}{Cl}$$

REVIEW EXERCISES

8.20 Describe how a covalent bond is different from an ionic bond.

8.21 How many electrons are shared in (a) a single, (b) a double, and (c) a triple covalent bond?

8.22 Draw the Lewis structures for each of the following.

(a) H_2
(b) F_2
(c) N_2
(d) I_2

8.23 Explain the difference between a nonpolar and a polar covalent bond, and give examples of each.

8.24 Draw the Lewis structures for each of the following polar molecules, and indicate the partial charges using δ+ and δ–.

(a) HI   (b) IF

8.21 (a) $2e^-$, (b) $4e^-$, (c) $6e^-$

8.5 LEWIS STRUCTURES FOR COVALENT MOLECULES

A systematic procedure is usually required to write Lewis structures for larger and more complex covalent molecules. Most Lewis structures for covalent molecules are obtained by following a set of five steps.

Step 1 Calculate the total number of valence electrons, V, in all atoms in the molecule.

WWWolfe 4
(See WWWolfe
section at the end of
the chapter.)

Use the periodic table to find the number of valence electrons in each atom, and then add these numbers to obtain the total. For example, CF_4 has a total of 32 valence electrons ($V = 32$) because C has 4 valence electrons and four F atoms each have 7 valence electrons.

Step 2 Identify the central atom (or atoms), and write the symbols for all other atoms around the symbol for the central atom (Fig. 8.11).

The central atom of a molecule is bonded to two or more other atoms and is the atom that determines the overall shape of small molecules. Identifying it is not difficult, and after a little practice this becomes a trivial matter. B, C, Si, N, P, and S are among the most common central atoms encountered.

Hydrogen is never a central atom because it has only one electron to share with another atom, and thus only forms one bond. For the same reason, halogens are usually not central atoms in the simple molecules we will encounter. Nonetheless, except for F, halogens may be central atoms in molecules when they are bonded to more than one oxygen or another halogen. Cl is the central atom in each of the following molecules: $HClO_3$, ClF_3, ClO_2, and Cl_2O_7.

In binary compounds, oxygen is found as the central atom only when it is bonded to H or halogen atoms. In most other binary compounds, and in compounds with three or more elements, oxygen is rarely a central atom.

It is standard when writing the name or molecular formula of a compound to write the central atom first, unless the compound is an acid (HNO_3, H_2SO_4, H_3PO_4, etc.) when the central atom is written second in the formula. In each of the following examples, the central atom is written first: CO_2, OF_2, NH_3, and PBr_3.

Step 3 Place a pair of electrons (single bond) between the central atom and each of the other atoms in the molecule. Then, subtract the number of electrons you have written into the Lewis structure so far from the total number of electrons obtained in Step 1 (V). The resulting number, R, is the quantity of electrons that remain to complete the noble gas configurations of each atom.

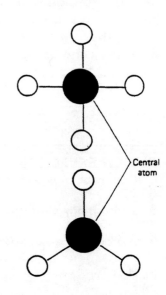

Central atom

Figure 8.11 The central atom in a molecule is bonded to two or more atoms. In binary covalent compounds, the central atom is usually written first in the formula and is often the atom with a lower electronegativity.

Step 4 Calculate the number of electrons needed for all atoms to achieve the valence noble gas configuration (N), and subtract the result from the number of remaining electrons, R, (determined in Step 3), yielding B.

$$B = R - N$$

The value obtained, B, tells you the type of covalent bond in the molecule. If these numbers are equal (N = R), than B equals zero. Whenever B is zero, all of the bonds in the molecule are single covalent bonds. Hence, place the appropriate number of dots around each symbol so that every atom has a noble gas configuration. When you write dots into the formula, ask yourself this question: How many valence electrons does the atom have, and how many does it need to obtain a noble gas configuration?

If the number of electrons available, R, is smaller than the number of electrons needed to obtain the valence noble gas configuration, N, then there must be a multiple bond in the molecule. In other words, whenever B is less than zero or a negative value, then the molecule has one or more multiple bonds. Generally, if the deficit is two electrons ($B = -2$), the molecule has a double bond; a shortage of four electrons ($B = -4$) indicates two double bonds or a triple bond. Table 8.6 summarizes the relationship between B and the type of bonds in a molecule.

TABLE 8.6 TYPES OF BONDS IN COVALENT MOLECULES

$B (R - N)$	Type of Bond(s)
0	Single bond
–2	Double bond
–4	Triple bond
–4	Two double bonds
–6	Triple and double bond
–6	Three double bonds

Step 5 Check the final Lewis structure in two ways: (1) Count the total number of electrons and confirm that the correct number, V, has been written into the formula, and (2) verify that each atom has a noble gas configuration.

An easy way to check the number of electrons that surround each atom is to circle the electrons around each atom. You should include the electrons that belong to the atom and those shared. In most cases, there should be either eight or two electrons. Then and only then are you sure that the Lewis structure is correct (assuming that it is possible for all atoms to achieve a noble gas configuration).

In summary, when writing the Lewis structure of a covalent compound:

Step 1   Calculate the total number of valence electrons, V.

Step 2   Identify the central atom, and write the symbols for all other atoms around the symbol for the central atom.

Step 3   Place a pair of electrons between the central atom and each of the other atoms. Calculate the quantity of electrons that remain, R, to be written into the structure by subtracting the number of electrons already in the formula from the total, V.

Step 4   Calculate the number of electrons required for all atoms to achieve the valence configuration of a noble gas N, and subtract it from the number of electrons that remain, R. This gives the value for B.

$$B = R - N$$

1. If the number of electrons required to complete the noble gas configuration for all atoms equals the number available ($B = 0$), place the electrons around each symbol ($N = R$), completing the octets. The molecule contains only single bonds.

2. If the number of electrons needed, N, is greater than the quantity remaining, R, at least one multiple bond is in the molecule. A shortage of two electrons ($B = -2$) indicates a double bond, and a shortage of four electrons ($B = -4$) indicates either a triple bond or two double bonds. Locate the atoms that have a multiple bond, write in the correct number of electrons around each of their symbols, and then complete the valence shells of all other atoms.

Step 5   Check the Lewis structure to see that each atom has a noble gas configuration, and that the total number of electrons equals the total in Step 1, V.

The five rules for writing Lewis structures are general guidelines that may be used for many, but not all, molecules. Nevertheless the Lewis structures of most molecules that you will encounter in this book can be successfully written using these rules.

Covalent Bonding in Water, H_2O

Water is the most important liquid on earth. A significant quantity of the earth's surface is covered with water, and living tissues contain approximately 80% water.

The properties of water are unique among low-molecular-mass liquids. The special properties of water cannot be understood until we learn how the water molecule is bonded.

We will use the five steps just outlined to write the Lewis structure of water.

Step 1 Calculate the total number of valence electrons, V.

$$
\begin{aligned}
\text{H } 2 \text{ atoms} \times 1 \text{ e}^-/\text{atom} &= 2 \text{ e}^- \\
\text{O } 1 \text{ atom} \times 6 \text{ e}^-/\text{atom} &= +6 \text{ e}^- \\
V(H_2O) &= 8 \text{ e}^-
\end{aligned}
$$

Step 2 Identify the central atom, and write the symbols for all other atoms around the symbol for the central atom. By default the central atom in water is the O atom. Hydrogen atoms are never central atoms. Therefore, write O with the two adjacent H atoms.

H O
H

It does not matter how the atoms are written around the central atom; Lewis structures do not usually illustrate the spatial arrangement of atoms in a molecule.

Step 3 Place a pair of electrons between the central atom and each of the other atoms. Calculate the quantity of electrons that remain, R, to be written into the structure by subtracting the number of electrons already in the formula from the total, V.

$$H : \overset{\displaystyle ..}{O}$$
$$H$$

Four electrons have been written into the Lewis structure, which leaves four electrons.

Remaining e⁻ (R) = Valence e⁻ (V) - electrons already in formula

$$R = 8 \, e^- - 4 \, e^- = 4 \, e^-$$

Step 4 Calculate the number of electrons required for all atoms to achieve the valence configuration of a noble gas N, and subtract it from the number of electrons that remain, R, yielding the value for B.

Four more electrons are needed to complete the octet around O, because, by sharing two electrons from each of the two H atoms, the O has four electrons. Each H atom already has a noble gas configuration of two electrons.

Four electrons are required to complete the noble gas configuration, N = 4, and four electrons remain to be placed into the formula, R = 4. To obtain the value of B subtract N from R.

$$B = R - N = 4 \, e^- - 4 \, e^- = 0$$

This means that only single bonds are in the water; thus, place the four electrons around the O to complete its octet.

$$H : \overset{\displaystyle ..}{\underset{\displaystyle ..}{O}} :$$
$$H$$

Step 5 Check to see the formula has the proper number of electrons.

1. Check to see that each atom has a noble gas configuration: Each H atom has two electrons, and the O atom has eight electrons.
2. Count the total number of electrons in the Lewis structure: There are eight electrons in the Lewis structure, which corresponds to the total number of valence electrons in two H atoms and one O atom.

The Lewis structure of water shows that a water molecule has two covalent bonds. Each bond is classified as a polar covalent bond, because the electronegativity of O (3.5) is greater than that of H (2.2). Besides the electrons in the two bonds, the central oxygen has two pairs of electrons that are not bonded. These electrons are termed **lone pair electrons.**

Because all members of group VIA (16), the chalcogens, have six valence electrons, you might expect that they would bond in a manner similar to oxygen. In simple covalent molecules, this is true. For example, consider the Lewis structure of hydrogen sulfide, H_2S.

$$H : \overset{\displaystyle ..}{\underset{\displaystyle ..}{S}} :$$
$$H$$

Sulfur is the element directly below O on the periodic table; therefore, the bonding in an

H_2S molecule is similar to that in an H_2O molecule. H_2S is a toxic, yellowish gas with the unpleasant odor of rotting eggs. H_2Se and H_2Te also have Lewis structures similar to those of water and hydrogen sulfide.

Covalent Bonding in Ammonia, NH_3

Ammonia, NH_3, is a gas at room temperature. Water solutions of ammonia are commonly used as household cleaners, and ammonia vapors are used to revive people who have passed out. We will write the Lewis structure of ammonia, using it as an illustration of the covalent bonding of atoms in group VA (15).

Following our rules, we first calculate the total number of valence electrons, V, in an ammonia molecule (Step 1):

$$
\begin{array}{lll}
\text{H} & 3 \text{ atoms} \times 1 \text{ e}^-/\text{atom} & = 3 \text{ e}^- \\
\text{N} & 1 \text{ atom} \times 5 \text{ e}^-/\text{atom} & = \underline{+5 \text{ e}^-} \\
\text{V(NH}_3\text{)} & & = 8 \text{ e}^-
\end{array}
$$

The central atom of the NH_3 molecule is N because H atoms are never central atoms. In Step 2 we write the symbol for N with three H atoms placed around it.

$$\text{H N H}$$
$$\text{H}$$

After an electron pair is written between each H and the N. Six electrons are accounted for out of the eight total electrons, which leaves two electrons to complete the octet of the N atom (Step 3). Stated differently, the value of R is 2 e⁻.

$$\text{H}\!:\!\underset{\cdot\cdot}{\text{N}}\!:\!\text{H}$$
$$\text{H}$$

Remaining e⁻ (R) = Valence e⁻ (V) - electrons already in formula

$$R = 8 \text{ e}^- - 6 \text{ e}^- = 2\text{e}^-$$

Each H atom has a noble gas configuration, and the N atom needs only two more electrons to complete its octet. Two electrons are needed (N), and two electrons remain (R) to be placed in the structure; consequently, the value of B is zero.

$$B = R - N = 2 \text{ e}^- - 2 \text{ e}^- = 0$$

Therefore, the remaining electrons are placed next to the N atom to complete its valence shell.

$$\text{H}\!:\!\overset{\cdot\cdot}{\underset{\cdot\cdot}{\text{N}}}\!:\!\text{H}$$
$$\text{H}$$

Each atom in a molecule of ammonia has a noble gas configuration, either two or eight, and the total number of valence electrons equals eight. The Lewis structure of ammonia reveals a molecule with three polar covalent bonds and one lone pair.

Bonding in phosphine, PH_3, is similar to the bonding in ammonia because P is the atom directly below N on the periodic table. Both have five valence electrons. Try to write the Lewis structure of phosphine, following each of the five steps. The Lewis structure of phosphine is

$$H \!:\! \overset{\cdot\cdot}{\underset{\cdot\cdot}{P}} \!:\! H$$
$$H$$

All of the group VA hydrides (binary hydrogen compounds) have analogous Lewis structures. These compounds include NH_3, PH_3, AsH_3, and SbH_3.

Covalent Bonding in Nitrogen Trifluoride, NF₃

Nitrogen trifluoride, NF_3, is a colorless gas that is the most stable of the nitrogen halides. Let's draw its Lewis structure.

Step 1 Calculate the total number of valence electrons, V.

$$
\begin{array}{lll}
\text{F} & 3 \text{ atoms} \times 7 \text{ e}^-/\text{atom} & = \;\; 21 \text{ e}^- \\
\text{N} & 1 \text{ atom} \times 5 \text{ e}^-/\text{atom} & = +\, 5 \text{ e}^- \\
\text{V(NF}_3) & & = \;\; 26 \text{ e}^-
\end{array}
$$

Step 2 Identify the central atom, and write the symbols for the other atoms around it. The central atom in NF_3 is N, because F atoms only form one bond and therefore F cannot be a central atom.

$$F \;\; N \;\; F$$
$$F$$

Step 3 Place a pair of electrons between the central atom and each of the other atoms, and calculate the number of electrons that remain, R, to be written into the structure by subtracting the number of electrons already in the formula from the total, V.

$$F \!:\! \overset{}{\underset{\cdot\cdot}{N}} \!:\! F$$
$$F$$

Remaining e^- (R) = Valence e^- (V) - electrons already in formula

$$R = 26e^- - 6e^- = 20e^-$$

Step 4 Calculate the number of electrons required for all atoms to achieve the valence configuration of a noble gas, N, and subtract it from the number of electrons that remain, R, yielding the value for B. Each F atom requires six electrons to complete its octet, and the N atom requires two electrons ($8e^- - 6e^- = 2e^-$). Hence, 6×3, or 18, electrons are needed for the F atoms, and adding the 2 electrons for N gives 20 electrons. Thus, N is 20 e^-. Because N and R equals 20 e^-, then the value of B is zero. Hence, this molecule only has single bonds. Write the 20 available electrons into the Lewis structure to complete the octets of all atoms.

$$:\overset{\cdots}{F}:\overset{\cdots}{N}:\overset{\cdots}{F}:$$
$$:\overset{\cdots}{F}:$$

Step 5 Check the Lewis structure to make sure you have the correct number of electrons. Each F atom has 8 electrons, as does the N, and the total number of electrons equals 26; consequently, the Lewis structure is written correctly.

Covalent Bonding in Methane, CH₄

Methane, CH_4, commonly called swamp or marsh gas, is the principal component of natural gas. Methane is produced when plants are decomposed by various species of microorganisms.

After following the five steps for writing a Lewis structure, we obtain the following structure for methane:

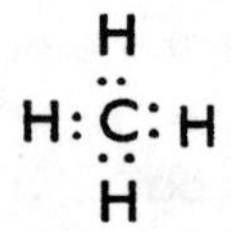

$$\begin{array}{c} H \\ H:\overset{\cdots}{C}:H \\ H \end{array}$$

Verify the Lewis structure of methane by going through the five steps. Note that this structure shows that methane molecules have four single polar covalent bonds and no lone pair electrons.

Carbon tetrachloride, CCl_4, at one time was used in fire extinguishers (it is a noncombustible liquid that smothers fires) and was also a component of many cleaning fluids and spot removers. However, research studies showed that CCl_4 was toxic and inhalation of its vapors caused liver damage. CCl_4 was also found to be carcinogenic, i.e., to cause cancer. The Lewis structure of carbon tetrachloride is

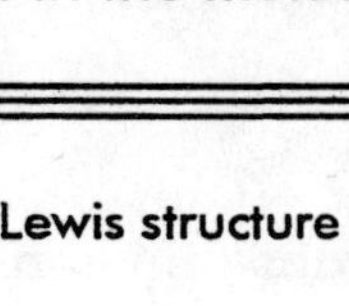

$$:\overset{\cdots}{Cl}:$$
$$:\overset{\cdots}{Cl}:\overset{}{C}:\overset{\cdots}{Cl}:$$
$$:\overset{\cdots}{Cl}:$$

Again verify the Lewis structure by following each of the five steps. Note that the only difference between the Lewis structures for CF_4, CBr_4, and Cl_4 and the one shown here for CCl_4 is the symbol for the halogen atom in the molecule. ❖

REVIEW EXERCISES

8.25 List the five steps followed in writing the Lewis structure for a covalent molecule.

8.26 Illustrate the method for writing Lewis structures using each of the following molecules.
(a) OCl_2
(b) NF_3
(c) Cl_4
(d) AsH_3
(e) SiH_4
(f) H_2Se

8.6 ADDITIONAL COVALENT BONDING CONSIDERATIONS

If the number of electrons that remain, R, after the initial drawing of electron pairs in the structure (Step 3) is less than the number needed to complete the octets of all atoms, N, then one or more **multiple bonds** are in the molecule. We will consider carbon dioxide, CO_2, as an example of such a molecule.

Covalent Bonding in Carbon Dioxide, CO_2

Carbon dioxide, CO_2, is a gas at room temperature. It is an important gas because it is a by-product of cellular respiration in animals—the means by which animals produce energy. Carbon dioxide is also a product of the combustion of materials that contain C. Carbonated beverages contain dissolved CO_2, and become "flat" when the CO_2 escapes.

To write the Lewis structure of CO_2, we begin by calculating the total number of valence shell electrons, V. A C atom has 4 electrons, and two O atoms have 12 electrons, which gives a total of 16 electrons ($V = 16$). Carbon is the central atom. Rarely will you encounter a compound that has O as its central atom. After placing the pairs of electrons between the O atoms and the C atom we get

$$O:C:O$$

Subtracting 4 electrons from the total of 16 electrons leaves us with 12 electrons ($R = 12$ e⁻). But to complete the octets of one C atom and two O atoms we need 16 electrons—4 for the C atom and 6 for each O atom ($N = 16$ e⁻). The electron deficit is 16 e⁻ – 12 e⁻, or 4 e⁻, electrons ($B = -4$), which indicates that there are either two double bonds or a triple bond in CO_2. Usually, it is best to select the more symmetrical arrangement of bonds because the more symmetrical arrangements occur more frequently in nature; thus, we would predict that CO_2 has two double bonds and not one triple and one single bond. If we write in two more electrons between the C and each O, and write the remaining eight electrons around the O atoms, four each, the Lewis structure becomes

$$:\ddot{O}::C::\ddot{O}: \quad \text{or} \quad :\ddot{O}=C=\ddot{O}:$$

In the second formula, we use two dashes to indicate a double covalent bond, composed of four shared electrons.

Covalent Bonding in Formaldehyde, H_2CO

Formaldehyde, H_2CO, a gas at 25°C, is an important industrial chemical. Formaldehyde molecules also have multiple bonds. The central atom in formaldehyde is C, and it is bonded to two H atoms and one O atom. Following the five steps for writing a Lewis structure, we find a shortage of two electrons ($B = -2$), which indicates a double bond in the molecule. The Lewis structure of formaldehyde is

> A water solution of formaldehyde is called formalin. Formalin is used to preserve dead biological specimens. Formaldehyde is a cancer-causing agent.

$$H:\overset{..}{\underset{H}{C}}::\overset{..}{O} \quad \text{or} \quad H-\overset{H}{\underset{|}{C}}=\overset{..}{O}:$$

Verify this structure by going through each of the five steps.

Covalent Bonding in Acetylene, C_2H_2

Acetylene, C_2H_2, is a gas that has many uses. A mixture of C_2H_2 and O_2 in an oxyacetylene torch is used to weld and cut metals. Acetylene is also the principal starting material in the synthesis of various polymers, long-chain molecules that make up plastics and other synthetic materials.

To write the Lewis structure for acetylene, we first find that the total number of valence electrons, V, is 10 e⁻. After using four electrons to bond the two H atoms to the central C atoms and two electrons to bond the C atoms, only four electrons remain. This means the R value is 4 e⁻. Checking each atom reveals that eight electrons are needed to complete the noble gas configurations of the C atoms ($N = 8$ e⁻). Subtracting N from R gives a value of –4, which means that this molecule has either two double bonds or one triple bond. Because H atoms can only form single bonds, a triple bond is located between the two C atoms. The Lewis structure for acetylene is as follows.

$$H:C:::C\ H \quad \text{or} \quad H-C\equiv C-H$$

Resonance: Delocalized Bonding

We have assumed that in all of the molecules discussed the electrons are localized between two nuclei. However, in some molecules this is not true. For example, let's consider the Lewis structure of the gas sulfur dioxide, SO_2. Sulfur dioxide is released into the atmosphere when sulfur-containing fossil fuels are burned. It is a major contributor to the production of acid rain. Following the five steps yield two correct Lewis structures.

$$\overset{..}{S}=\overset{..}{O}: \qquad \text{and} \qquad \overset{..}{S}-\overset{..}{O}:$$
$$\underset{:\overset{..}{O}:}{|} \qquad\qquad\qquad \underset{:\overset{..}{O}:}{||}$$

I   II

In structure I the double bond is between the S atom and the O atom on the right, and in structure II the double bond is between the S atom and the O atom below. Experimental evidence shows that neither structure I nor structure II can explain the properties of the SO_2 molecule. According to the valence bond theory, when such a situation arises, one of the bonding pairs of electrons is spread out over all three atoms. We say that these electrons are **delocalized**. A better way to represent the bonded electrons in sulfur dioxide is as follows:

> Delocalization of electrons occurs only in molecules that have multiple bonds.

A dashed line indicates a partial bond in which the electron pair is spread out over the entire molecule as opposed to being localized between the nuclei of two atoms. From this structure we see that the bond in SO_2 molecules is neither a single nor a double bond. Instead, the bond is intermediate between a single and double bond. Molecules such as SO_2 with delocalized electrons do not have one unique Lewis structure. Instead, these molecules have two or more Lewis structures that differ only with respect to the placement of the electrons. When this situation is encountered, we say that the molecule exhibits **resonance.** Each possible Lewis structure for a molecule is called a **contributing or resonance structure.** The arrangement of atoms in each contributing structure is the same; only the electrons are in different places. The actual arrangement of electrons in molecules that exhibit resonance most closely resembles the average of all contributing structures. To symbolize resonance, the contributing structures are separated by a double headed arrow,

> If a covalent bond forms in which one atom donates both electrons, as is the case in SO_2, the bond is classified as a coordinate covalent bond. After they form, coordinate bonds have the same properties as other covalent bonds.

Another example of a molecule that exhibits resonance is the nitrous oxide molecule, N_2O. The two contributing structures that best represent N_2O are as follows:

$$: N = N = \overset{\cdot\cdot}{O} : \quad \longleftrightarrow \quad : N \equiv N - \overset{\cdot\cdot}{\underset{\cdot\cdot}{O}} :$$

I   II

Because the distribution of electrons is the average of the contributing structures I and II, we see that the bond between the two N atoms is intermediate between a double and a triple bond, and the bond between the N and O atoms is intermediate between a single and double bond.

> The structure of a molecule that exhibits resonance is considered a blend of all contributing structures.

It is unfortunate that the term "resonance" has a different meaning in physics. Do not confuse the meaning of the term "resonance" as defined in physics with the definition used by chemists. "Resonance" in chemistry refers to delocalization of electrons—these electrons are not resonating back and forth as might be implied from the physics definition.

Molecules that exhibit resonance are more stable than similar molecules that do not exhibit resonance. The greater stability of molecules that exhibit resonance results directly from the delocalization of electrons over more than two atoms. Generally, the more localized the electrons are within a molecule, the more unstable it is.

Polyatomic Ions

A **polyatomic ion** is an ion with more than one atom. The atoms in polyatomic ions are bonded by covalent bonds. Examples of common polyatomic ions include (1) hydroxide, OH^-; (2) nitrate, NO_3^-; (3) sulfate, SO_4^{2-}; (4) phosphate, PO_4^{3-}; and (5) ammonium, NH_4^+. A polyatomic ion bonds ionically to another ion. For example, in sodium hydroxide, NaOH, the negative polyatomic ion hydroxide bonds to the positive sodium ion.

> Poly is a prefix that means "many."

When you write the Lewis structures for polyatomic ions, it is necessary to add or subtract the number of electrons indicated by the charge on the ion in Step 1. For example, phosphate has a 3– charge; it possesses three extra electrons besides the valence electrons of the P and O atoms. A total of 32 valence electrons are in phosphate.

> The "extra" electrons in polyatomic ions can come from metals and other polyatomic ions.

To illustrate the procedure for writing the Lewis structures of polyatomic ions, let's write the Lewis structure for the nitrate ion, NO_3^-.

Step 1 Calculate the total number of valence electrons, V.

$$
\begin{array}{lll}
\text{N} & 1 \text{ atoms} \times 5 \text{ e}^-/\text{atom} & = 5 \text{ e}^- \\
\text{O} & 3 \text{ atom} \times 6 \text{ e}^-/\text{atom} & = 18 \text{ e}^- \\
& \text{Additional e}^- & = \underline{+1 \text{ e}^-} \\
V(NO_3^-) & & = 24 \text{ e}^-
\end{array}
$$

Step 2 Place the three O atoms around the central N atom.

$$
\begin{array}{cc}
& O \\
O & N \\
& O
\end{array}
$$

Steps 3 and 4 Six electrons are required to bond the three O atoms to the N atom; thus, 18 electrons remain to be written into the structure. To complete the octets of all atoms, 20 electrons are needed ($3 \times 6e^-/O$ atom $= 18$ $e^- + 2$ e^-/N atom $= 20$ e^-). A shortage of two electrons is found ($B = -2$), indicating a double bond. Consequently, three contributing structures can be written for the nitrate ion, an ion that exhibits resonance. Each of the contributing structures differs with respect to the placement of the double bond.

I   II   III

Step 5 Check to see that there are 24 electrons in each contributing structure, and that each atom has a noble gas electronic configuration.

Lewis structures of polyatomic ions are enclosed in square brackets with their charges as superscripts to the right. This notation is used to show that they represent ions that cannot exist alone. Table 8.7 lists some of the more common polyatomic ions and shows their Lewis structures.

TABLE 8.7 LEWIS STRUCTURES OF SELECTED POLYATOMIC IONS

Name	Molecular formula	Structural formula	Name	Molecular formula	Structural formula
Borate	BO_3^{3-}		Ammonium	NH_4^+	
Carbonate	CO_3^{2-}		Nitrate	NO_3^-	
Hydrogencarbonate (bicarbonate)	HCO_3^-		Nitrite	NO_2^-	
			Hydroxide	OH^-	
Acetate	$C_2H_3O_2^-$		Phosphate	PO_4^{3-}	
Cyanide	CN^-		Sulfate	SO_4^{2-}	
Chromate	CrO_4^{2-}		Sulfite	SO_3^{2-}	

Molecules With Atoms That Do Not Achieve a Noble Gas Configuration

The rules we have been using to write Lewis structures are somewhat artificial generalizations that apply to simple molecular systems. Some molecules do not follow these rules. Remember that this is not the fault of the natural world; it is a limitation of using a system of artificial rules.

Some molecules possess a bonded atom with less than eight electrons. Boron trifluoride, BF_3, is an example of such a molecule. Its Lewis structure is

The central B atom has only six valence electrons. Is BF_3 a stable molecule? No! Boron trifluoride is reactive and combines with almost any molecule or ion that can donate an electron pair.

Numerous molecules exist with a central atom that has more than eight valence electrons. These molecules contain an atom with an *expanded octet*. Only certain elements in the third period and beyond have the capacity to accommodate more than eight valence electrons after

> Noble gas compounds were first synthesized by Neil Bartlett in 1962. At that time it was thought that noble gases could not form stable compounds. Xenon hexaflouroplatinate, $XePtF_6$, was the first noble gas compound synthesized

bonding. Some of these molecules have atoms with 10, 12, and 14 valence electrons. Noble gas compounds are good examples of molecules with expanded octets; examples include XeF_2, XeF_4, XeF_6, $XeOF_4$, and XeO_3. The structures of XeF_2 ane XeF_4 are best represented as follows.

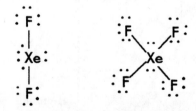

Xenon difluoride   Xenon tetrafluoride

Still other molecules possess an odd number of valence electrons, which precludes the possibility of drawing a structure with eight valence electrons in all atoms. Attempt to draw the Lewis structures of nitric oxide (nitrogen(II) oxide), NO, or nitrogen dioxide (nitrogen(IV) oxide), NO_2, and you will discover that the total number of valence electrons is 11 and 17, respectively. Also you will find that more than one Lewis structure can be written for each of these oxides of nitrogen: NO and NO_2 exhibit resonance. ❖

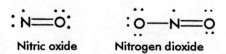

Nitric oxide   Nitrogen dioxide

REVIEW EXERCISES

8.27 Draw the Lewis structure for carbon monoxide, CO, a molecule with a multiple bond.

8.28 (a) What are delocalized electrons?

(b) Write a definition for resonance.

(c) Illustrate resonance by drawing the Lewis structures for the three contributing structures of sulfur trioxide, SO_3.

8.29 Draw the Lewis structures for each of the following polyatomic ions.

(a) OH^-
(b) PO_4^{3-}
(c) CO_3^{2-}
(d) CN^-

8.30 Which of the following molecules do not obey the octet rule: (a) BeF_2, (b) PF_3, (c) IF_3, (d) NO_2?

8.27 :C ⋮ ⋮ O:; 8.28 SO_3 has two S—O single bonds and one double bond; 8.29 BeF_2, IF_3, NO_2

8.7 PROPERTIES OF MOLECULES

Molecular Geometry

The three-dimensional structure of a molecule is called its **molecular geometry.** More simply, molecular geometry refers to the average shape of a molecule. One way to predict the shape of a simple molecule is to consider the total number of bonding and lone pair electrons on its central atom. The best prediction of the molecular geometry of a molecule is the shape that maximizes the distance between the electron pairs on the central atom. Electron pairs, either bonding pairs or lone pairs, are negative regions of space; thus, they repel each other and attempt to be as far as possible from each other. This method of predicting the shape of a molecule is called the **valence shell electron pair repulsion** method, or the **VSEPR method** for short.

WWWolfe 4
(See WWWolfe section at the end of the chapter.)

To illustrate the VSEPR method, let us first consider the beryllium fluoride, BeF_2, molecule. To use the VSEPR method, first write the Lewis structure of the molecule.

$$: \overset{..}{\underset{..}{F}} — Be — \overset{..}{\underset{..}{F}} :$$

Then count the number of bonding pairs and lone pairs on the central atom. On the Be atom we find two bonding pairs and no lone pairs. The angle that minimizes the electron repulsions when there are two bonding pairs on the central atoms is 180°, which means that the molecular geometry of BeF_2 is **linear.** Figure 8.12 shows a diagram of a linear molecule. All the atoms in a linear molecule are in a straight line.

As a second example let's consider boron trifluoride, BF_3. After writing the Lewis structure for BF_3, we find that the central B atom has three bonding pairs and no lone pairs.

Three bonding pairs can be at a maximum distance from each other when they are separated by 120° and all the atoms are in the same plane. This is **trigonal planar geometry** (Fig. 8.12). All molecules with three bonding pairs and no lone pairs have trigonal planar geometry.

Three different molecular geometries can result from four electron pairs on the central atom. For example, the Lewis structure of methane, CH_4, shows four bonding pairs and no lone pairs on the central C atom.

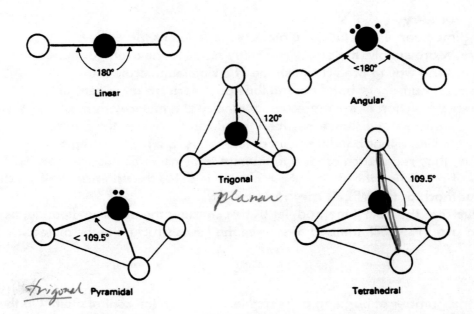

Figure 8.12 In linear molecules, all the atoms are in a straight line (180° bond angle). In angular molecules, two atoms form an angle less than 180°. Trigonal planar molecules are composed of three atoms that are in the same plane. Each atom bonded to the central atom in a trigonal planar molecule is separated by 120° from the other two atoms. Trigonal pyramidal molecules have three bonded atoms and one lone pair around the central atom. Tetrahedral molecules have four atoms bonded to a central atom separated by an angle of 109.5°.

$$
\begin{array}{c}
H \\
| \\
H-\!\!\!\!\underset{|}{C}\!\!\!\!-H \\
| \\
H
\end{array}
$$

To minimize the repulsions of four bonding pairs of electrons, the maximum angle between H atoms is 109.5°, which gives the molecule a **tetrahedral** geometry (Fig. 8.12). Whenever some combination of four bonding and lone pairs are found on a central atom, the geometry of the *electron pairs* is tetrahedral with approximately a 109.5° angle between them.

If a molecule has three bonding pairs and one lone pair, such as is found in ammonia molecules,

$$
\begin{array}{c}
\cdot\cdot \\
N \\
H \quad | \quad H \\
H
\end{array}
$$

the molecular geometry of the molecule becomes **trigonal pyramidal** (pyramid-like) (Fig. 8.12). The angles between the H atoms in ammonia are slightly less than the theoretical maximum angle of 109.5° because lone pairs are diffuse and they tend to compress the angles of the bonding pairs.

> The word "pyramidal" is often mispronounced. It is correctly pronounced py·ram´·id·al.

Angular, or V-shaped, geometry is found in molecules such as water that have two bonding pairs and two lone pairs.

$$
\begin{array}{c}
\cdot\cdot \\
O \\
H \quad \cdot\cdot \quad H
\end{array}
$$

Because two lone pairs are found on the O atom, the bond angle in water is only 104.5° as a result of the greater force of repulsion by the two lone pairs on the two bonding pairs.

Multiple bonds are treated in the same manner as single bonds when applying the VSEPR method. For example, carbon dioxide, CO_2, has the following Lewis structure.

$$
:\!\ddot{O}\!=\!C\!=\!\ddot{O}\!:
$$

CO_2 is a linear molecule because it has no lone pairs to prevent the two double bonds to the C atom from being at a maximum distance from each other. If we reconsider the sulfur dioxide molecule, which has the Lewis structure

$$
\begin{array}{c}
\ddot{S}\!=\!\ddot{O}\!: \\
| \\
:\!\ddot{O}\!:
\end{array}
$$

as one of its contributing structures, we find that it has an angular, or V-shaped, geometry because it has two bonds and one lone pair on the central S atom. Three negative regions are at a maximum distance when they are 120° from each other in the same plane.

Table 8.8 summarizes the principal geometries of molecules that have two, three, and four electron pairs on the central atom.

Table 8.8 MOLECULAR GEOMETRIES of MOLECULES

Number of electrons pairs on central atom			Geometry	Examples
Total	Bonding pairs	Lone pairs		
2	2	0	Linear	BeH_2, $BeCl_2$, CO_2
3	3	0	Trigonal planar	BF_3, $AlCl_3$, CO_3^{2-}
3	2	1	Angular (V-shaped)	SO_2, $SnCl_2$, NO_2^-
4	4	0	Tetrahedral	CH_4, SiH_4, CF_4
4	3	1	Trigonal pyramidal	NH_3, PF_3, AsH_3
4	2	2	Angular (V-shaped)	H_2O, H_2S, OCl_2

Properties of Bonds

Four properties of bonds are commonly considered when studying molecules: (1) bond distance (also called bond length), (2) bond order, (3) bond angle, and (4) bond energy (Fig. 8.13).

Bond distance is the average distance between two nuclei of atoms in a covalent bond. For example, C—C single bonds are approximately 154 pm (1 pm = 1×10^{-12} m). Carbon-carbon double and triple bonds are even shorter: 133 pm and 120 pm, respectively. Bond distance is an average because the atoms that make up a bond vibrate back and forth.

Indirectly related to bond distance is bond order. **Bond order** is the number of covalent bonds that link two atoms. A single covalent bond has a bond order of 1, a double bond has a bond order of 2, and a triple bond has a bond order of 3. In resonance structures,

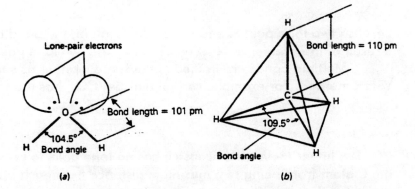

Figure 8.13 Water is composed of angular (V shaped) molecules that have two bonding pairs and two lone pairs on the O atom. The bond angle in water is 104.5° and the O—H bond distance is 101 pm. (b) Methane is composed of tetrahedral molecules. The bond angle between each pair of atoms in methane is 109.5°, and the C—H bond distance is 110 pm.

fractional bond orders are found; e.g., 1.5 and 1.33 are encountered.

As we have already discussed, a **bond angle** is the angle between two imaginary lines passing through the nucleus of the central atom and the nuclei of two atoms bonded to the central atom. For example, the bond angle (H—O—H) between H atoms in the water molecule is 104.5°, and the bond angle between H atoms in the methane molecule is 109.5°.

We have already briefly mentioned **bond energy** which is short for **bond dissociation energy.** It is the energy required to break one mole of a specific bond in the gas phase. Bond energies are related to how strong a bond is. In general, bond energies for triple bonds are higher than those for double bonds, which are higher than those for single bonds. Carbon-carbon triple bonds have bond energies in excess of 800 kJ/mol. Whereas most C—C double bond energies are near 600 kJ/mol, only 350 kJ/ mol is required to break C—C single bonds. ❖

REVIEW EXERCISES

8.31 What are the most common molecular geometries exhibited by simple molecules?

8.32 Use the VSEPR method to predict the shapes of the following molecules.

(a) NCl_3
(b) CCl_4
(c) OF_2
(d) CS_2

8.33 Compare single, double, and triple bonds between two C atoms with respect to (a) bond order, (b) bond length, (c) bond energy.

8.34 What bond angles are in each of the following molecular geometries?

(a) tetrahedral
(b) linear
(c) trigonal planar

8.32 (a) Trigonal pyramidal, (b) tetrahedral, (c) angular, (d) linear; 8.34 (a) 109.5°, (b) 180°, (c) 120°

WorldWideWolfe CHEMISTRY LINKS

Connect to WorldWideWolfe at

http://www.mindspring.com/~drwolfe/WWWolfe_hcc_1025_links.htm

and link to the following sites.

Compounds, Molecules, and Bonding

1. Molecules Compounds A good overview of molecules, ions, and compounds. It has Learning Objectives, Before You Start, Nomenclature, Lecture Notes , and References and Resources.

2. Chemical Bonding A discussion of ionic, covalent, and coordinate covalent bonds. Do not be concerned that the author goes crazy with hyphens.

3. Introduction to Chemical Bonds A thorough introduction to all aspects of chemical bonding. This is a good place to begin your study of chemical bonds.

4. How to Draw Lewis Structures A tutorial that shows you how to draw Lewis structures. It is recommended. However, be patient.

Writing Lewis Structures A good introduction on how to write the Lewis structure for a molecule.

Writing Lewis Structures Shows a procedure for determining the correct Lewis structure for a molecule. It is similar but different to the one that I show you.

SUMMARY

Compounds are divided into two groups: (1) ionic and (2) covalent. **Ionic compounds** form when a metal combines with a nonmetal or a polyatomic ion. **Covalent compounds** result when two or more nonmetals combine.

The properties of ionic compounds differ from those of covalent compounds. Generally, ionic compounds have higher melting points, boiling points, and densities than covalent compounds. All ionic compounds are solids at room temperature, while covalent compounds are more frequently liquids and gases. Both groups are nonconductors of electricity, although ionic compounds do conduct an electric current in the liquid state.

A **chemical bond** is the force of attraction that results when atoms either transfer or share electrons. If atoms transfer electrons in the formation of a chemical bond, the bond is classified as an ionic bond, and if electrons are shared, the bond is classified as a **covalent bond.**

After one or more electrons are transferred from a metal to a nonmetal, two ions result. The metal atom loses electrons and becomes a cation, and the nonmetal atom gains electrons and becomes an anion. Both ions achieve the configuration of a noble gas. Cations attract anions and vice versa, creating the network of ionic bonds in ionic compounds.

Covalent compounds share electrons through overlapping valence orbitals in order to obtain the stable electronic configuration of a noble gas. A covalent bond in which the electrons are equally shared is called a **nonpolar bond.** If the electrons are shared unequally, the bond is classified as a **polar covalent bond.** The polarity of a bond is predicted from the electronegativities of the atoms that make up the bond. **Electronegativity** is the capacity of atoms to attract electrons in chemical bonds.

To identify the bonds in a molecule, we write its Lewis structure. A **Lewis structure** accounts for all valence electrons in a molecule. Most often, the atoms in a Lewis structure achieve the noble gas electron configuration. A series of five steps is usually required to write Lewis structures of molecules.

Covalent molecules contain single, double, and triple bonds. A **single covalent bond** has one shared electron pair. Double bonds have two pairs of shared electrons, and

triple bond have three pairs of shared electrons. Molecules can have any combination of single, double, or triple covalent bonds.

To predict the shapes of molecules, chemists use the **valence shell electron pair repulsion method, VSEPR, method.** The Lewis structure is written, and the predicted molecular geometry is the one in which the electron pairs on the central atom are at a maximum distance from each other. When studying molecules, chemists are most concerned with bond distances, bond orders, bond energies, and bond angles.

KEY TERMS

bond order	ionic radius
bond angle	ionic compound
bond distance (length)	molecular geometry
chemical bond	multiple bond
contributing structure	nonpolar covalent bond
covalent compound	polar covalent bond
crystal lattice	polyatomic ion
delocalized electrons	resonance
electronegativity	stability
electrovalent bond	

STUDY GUIDELINES

After completing Chapter 8, you should be able to

1. Contrast the properties of ionic and covalent compounds

2. Write the names of simple binary ionic and covalent compounds

3. Discuss the reason why atoms combine to form molecules

4. Describe the electron transfer that takes place when an ionic bond forms given the names of a specific metal and nonmetal that combine

5. Write Lewis structures for ionic substances

6. Write the formula unit of an ionic compound given the chemical group numbers of the metal and nonmetal on the periodic table

7. Determine if one chemical species is isoelectronic to another

8. Define electronegativity and describe its importance

9. Rank elements according to their electronegativity using the periodic table

10. Discuss the reason why some nonmetallic elements exist as diatomic molecules instead of as single atoms

11. Apply the steps for writing the Lewis structures of simple covalent molecules

12. Identify and discuss the nature of single, double, and triple bonds

13. Write a Lewis structure for a molecule, and determine if the bonds are polar or nonpolar

14. Identify and draw Lewis structures of simple polyatomic ions

15. Use the valence shell electron pair repulsion method to determine the molecular geometry of a molecule

16. Distinguish among bond order, bond distance, bond energy and bond angle

---

EXERCISES

8.35 Define each of the following: ionic compounds covalent compound, chemical bond, stability, valence electron, electrovalent bond, ionic radius, crystal lattice, electronegativity, nonpolar covalent bond, polar covalent bond, multiple bond, delocalized electrons, resonance, contributing structure, polyatomic ion, bond order, bond distance, bond angle, molecular geometry.

Compounds

8.36 How do the rules for writing names of ionic compounds differ from those used to write names of covalent compounds? Give an example.

8.37 Write the names of the following ionic compounds.
(a) NaBr   (b) MgO
(c) RbI   (d) Ba_3P_2
(e) SrF_2 (f) PbS
(g) AgBr   (h) GaP

8.38 How do the properties of ionic compounds differ from those of covalent compounds? Give specific examples.

8.39 What quantity of atoms do each of the following prefixes refer to? (a) tetra, (b) hexa, (c) di, (d) octa, (e) tri, (f) mono, (g) penta

8.40 Write the name of each of the following covalent compounds.
(a) N_2O (b) PF_3
(c) N_2O_4 (d) XeF_4
(e) S_2Cl_2 (f) AsF_5
(g) IF_3 (h) $SeBr_4$.

8.41 Write the name of each of the following compounds.
(a) I_2O_4 (b) K_2S
(c) Cl_2O_7 (d) I_4O_9
(e) Al_2O_3 (f) CaI_2
(g) Te_2F_{10} (h) SeF_6.

8.42 Predict whether an ionic or a covalent compound has, on average, a higher (a) melting point, (b) boiling point, (c) density.

8.43 Explain why ionic substances conduct an electric current in the molten state but are nonconductors when in the solid state.

Chemical Bonding

8.44 (a) Describe the energy change that occurs when two H atoms bond to form a diatomic hydrogen molecule. (b) Describe the energy change that occurs when a diatomic hydrogen molecule is split into two H atoms.

8.45 (a) What are the names of the two theories of chemical bonding? (b) Which one is used to explain the properties of molecules in this textbook?

8.46   Explain why nitrogen gas is composed of diatomic nitrogen molecules instead of individual N atoms.

8.47   How do chemists measure the stability of a chemical bond? Give an example.

8.48   What is incorrect about the following statement: "The bond that joins Na^+ and Cl^- ions is purely ionic"?

8.49   What accounts for the fact that diatomic noble gas compounds, such as Ne_2, Ar_2, or Xe_2, are not found at 25°C?

Ionic Bonding

8.50   (a) What two trends are observed in the electronegativities of atoms? (b) Which atoms have the highest and lowest electronegativities?

8.51   Why are electronegativity values generally not assigned to atoms of the noble gases?

8.52   From each of the following groups, select the element with the lowest electronegativity.
(a) F, Cl, Br, I
(b) Ge, As, Sn, Sb
(c) K, Rb, Cs, Fr
(d) Al, Si, P, S
(e) Se, Br, Te, I

8.53   Arrange the following sets of atoms in order of decreasing electronegativity (highest to lowest).
(a) P, As, Sb
(b) Be, Li, B
(c) Rb, Sr, Cs, Ba.

8.54   What noble gas is isoelectronic to each of the following ions?
(a) Ca^{2+} (b) N^{3-}
(c) Br^- (d) Rb^+
(e) Te^{2-} (f) Na^+
(g) P^{3-} (h) O^{2-}

8.55   Write the complete electronic configuration for each of the following ions.
(a) Sr^{2+} (b) P^{3-}
(c) Se^{2-} (d) Rb^+
(e) I^- (f) Sr^{2+}
(g) Ga^{3+}

8.56   Select the ion with the largest ionic radius from each of the following sets.
(a) O^{2-}, S^{2-}, Se^{2-};
(b) N^{3-}, O^{2-}, F^-
(c) Na^+, Mg^{2+}, Al^{3+}
(d) Na, Mg^{2+}, K^+, Ca^{2+}

8.57   Use Lewis structures to illustrate the electron transfers that occur when the

following ionic substances form.
(a) K_2O (b) $MgBr_2$
(c) Al_2O_3 (d) CaS
(e) Cs_3P

8.58   Draw the Lewis structures for the following ionic compounds.
(a) NaI   (b) $MgBr_2$
(c) SrO   (d) Rb_2S
(e) Ba_3N_2 (f) AlN
(g) K_2Se

8.59   What is the formula unit of the ionic compound that results from combination of each of the following metals-nonmetals pairs?
(a) Aluminum-oxygen
(b) Strontium-sulfur
(c) Magnesium-bromine
(d) Gallium-oxygen
(e) Sodium-fluorine
(f) Lithium-selenium
(g) Aluminum-fluorine
(h) Calcium-phosphorus

8.60   (a) What is a crystal lattice? (b) Give three examples.

Covalent Bonding

8.61   (a) Draw a diagram showing the orbitals that overlap in F_2. (b) Explain how the F atoms are attracted to each other in the fluorine molecule. (c) Describe the energy change when two F atoms bond.

8.62   Explain how electron sharing leads to the formation of a chemical bond. Give an example in your explanation.

8.63   In what electron subshells does sharing occur in each of the following covalent molecules?
(a) HI   (b) IBr
(c) SiI_4 (d) NCl_3
(e) OBr_2 (f) NH_3

8.64   Label each of the following diatomic molecules as polar or nonpolar.
(a) BrCl   (b) O_2
(c) CO   (d) NO
(e) I_2 (f) ICl
(g) F_2

8.65   Write the Lewis structure for BrF, and indicate the partial positive and negative charges in the molecule.

8.66   Write the Lewis structures for each of the following molecules using the suggested five-step procedure.
(a) CBr_4 (b) OF_2
(c) H_2Te,   (d) PF_3

(e) SF_2 (f) N_2Cl_4
(g) $C_2H_2Br_2$ (h) Si_2Cl_6
(i) H_2O_2,   (j) H_4SiO_4
(each H atom is bonded to an O atom)

8.67 Write the Lewis structures for each of the following ions.
(a) OH^- (b) CN^-
(c) NH_4^+ (d) BH_4^-
(e) ClO_4^- (f) O_2^{2-}
(g) SO_4^{2-} (h) $C_2H_3O_2^-$

8.68 Write the Lewis structures for three different compounds that contain two C atoms. (a) C_2H_6, (b) C_2H_4, (c) C_2H_2

8.69 Write the Lewis structures for each of the following acids (the H atoms are bonded to the O atoms).
(a) carbonic acid, H_2CO_3
(b) sulfuric acid, H_2SO_4
(c) phosphoric acid, H_3PO_4
(d) nitric acid, HNO_3
(e) chlorous acid, $HClO_2$
(f) sulfurous acid, H_2SO_3.

8.70 Give an example of a molecule that contains each of the following.
(a) a single and a double bond
(b) two double bonds
(c) a triple bond
(d) a triple and a single bond
(e) an atom with less than eight valence electrons.

8.71 Which of the following molecules contain atoms with expanded octets?
(a) Cl_4 (b) PF_5
(c) IF_5 (d) $SnBr_4$
(e) SF_6 (f) PCl_3
(g) $C_2H_2Cl_2$

8.72 Draw all of the contributing structures for each of the following.
(a) HCO_3^- (b) CO_3^{2-}
(c) NO_2^- (d) O_3
(e) N_2O

8.73 Explain why molecules with delocalized electrons are more stable than similar molecules in which the electrons are not delocalized. Give examples.

8.74 Predict the molecular geometries of each of the following molecules.
(a) NF_3 (b) H_2S
(e) SiF_4 (d) $AlCl_3$
(e) BeF_2 (f) SO_3
(g) HCN (h) AsH_3

8.75 Predict the shapes of each of the following polyatomic ions.
(a) NO_2^- (b) NO_3^-

(c) CO_3^{2-} (d) HS^-
(e) SO_4^{2-} (f) BO_3^{3-}

8.76 Explain why triple bonds are shorter than double bonds. (Hint: Consider the number of electrons in the bonds.)

8.77 What is the bond order in each of the following diatomic molecules? (a) N_2, (b) F_2, (c) HBr, (d) I_2

8.78 What accounts for the fact that the average bond distance of a Si—O bond, 166 pm, is longer than that of a C—O bond, 143 pm.

Additional Exercises

8.79 Correct the following incorrect statements.
(a) In covalent bonds, electrons are always equally shared.
(b) Electronegativity is a measure of the force of attraction between a nucleus and its electrons.
(c) Average bond energies are higher for single covalent than for double covalent bonds.
(d) Ionic compounds result when two nonmetals combine.
(e) The name of the compound SO_3 is sulfur oxide.
(f) Calcium chloride molecules have the formula $CaCl_2$.
(g) The one electron in a H atom is transferred to a F atom in hydrogen fluoride.
(h) All nonpolar covalent bonds result when atoms of the same element bond.

8.80 (a) One form of elemental phosphorus exists as P_4 molecules. Write two contributing structures for P_4. (b) Is P_4 a polar or a nonpolar molecule? Explain.

8.81 Write Lewis structures for molecules described as follows.
(a) Is diatomic with a bond order of 3
(b) has tetrahedral geometry, but does not contain C or Si
(c) has a single, double, and triple bond
(d) has two bonded O atoms
(e) has both ionic and covalent bonds
(f) is a noble gas compound
(g) has B, F, N, and H atoms

8.82 Acetone, C_3H_6O, is a molecule with a C atom bonded to two C atoms and one O atom. (a) Draw the Lewis structure for acetone. (b) What is the molecular geometry around each C atom in acetone? (c) Does acetone exhibit resonance? Explain. (d) Write the Lewis structure for another molecule that has the same molecular formula as acetone.

8.83 Write the Lewis structure for the following.
(a) NaOH   (b) NH_4Cl
(c) $Ca(ClO)_2$ (d) $Mg_3(PO_4)_2$
(e) NH_2OH

8.84 (a) Acetic acid, $C_2H_4O_2$, has a C—C single bond, and each O atom is bonded to one C atom. Write the Lewis structure for acetic acid. (b) Draw two additional Lewis structures of compounds with the molecular formula $C_2H_4O_2$.

8.85 (a) Write all contributing structures for the formate ion, CHO_2^-. (b) Discuss the delocalization of electrons in the formate ion. (c) Draw a structure that best represents the structure of the formate ion.

8.86 In a through d, compare bond energy, bond distance, and bond order for the two bonds shown.
(a) C—C and Si—Si
(b) Cl—Cl and F—F
(c) N—N and N=N
(d) C=C and C—C

8.87 (a) Write the Lewis structure for NO_2^+. (b) What bond angle is found between the O atoms in NO_2^+? (c) Describe the N–O bonds in NO_2^+. (d) Compare the structure of NO_2^+ with that of NO_2.

8.88 Write the Lewis structures for each of the following. (a) H_2NOH, (b) HONO, (c) O_2SCl_2, (d) N_3^-, (e) H_2CNN

8.89 Propane, C_3H_8, is a fuel used to heat houses. Write the Lewis structure for propane.

8.90 (a) Write reasonable contributing structures for the thiocyanate anion, SCN^-. (b) Describe the S—C and C—N bonds in SCN^-.

8.91 Ozone, O_3, is an air pollutant and a component of the upper atmosphere. (a) Draw all contributing structures of ozone. (b) What is the bond order for the O—O bonds in ozone? (c) Predict the molecular geometry of ozone. (d) What is the approximate bond angle in ozone?

8.92 Isomers are compounds that have the same molecular formula but have a different arrangement of atoms within the molecules. Write the Lewis structures for three isomers of $C_2H_2I_2$.

8.93 A compound has 26.6% K, 35.4% Cr, and 38.1% O. (a) Calculate the empirical formula of the compound. (b) A 0.0191-mol sample of the compound has a mass of 5.63 g. What is the molecular formula of the compound? (c) Is this compound ionic or covalent? Explain.

Notes and Calculations

Chapter 8 Pretest Assignment

1.   Complete each of the following statements with the correct word, number, or phase.

a. A(n) _____ results when an electron is transferred from a metal to a nonmetal.

b. _____ is the power of atoms to attract electrons in chemical bonds.

c. A(n) _____ bond has six shared electrons.

d. A(n) _____ bond results when electrons are shared equally.

e. A(n) _____ ion is composed of more than one atom.

f. _____ is the energy needed to break a bond.

g. _____ is the number of covalent bonds between two nonmetal atoms.

2.   Write the names for the following compounds.

a. K_2S _____

b. MgO _____

c. PBr_5 _____

d. Al_2S_3 _____

e. Cl_2O_7 _____

3.   Draw the Lewis structure for each of the following.

a. Na_2O b. AlP

c. SCl_2 d. C_2I_4

e. H_2CS f. $C_2H_3O_2^-$

4.   Give an example of a molecule and draw the Lewis structure with the following properties.

a. polar covalent molecule containing H and Br

b. tetrahedral molecule with C and F

c. molecule with H, C, and N that has a triple bond.

d. ionic compound with Ca and N

5.   Write a paragraph that explains why two H atoms bond to each other.

6.   Give an example of a molecule that has the following molecular geometries.

a. tetrahedral   _____

b. linear   _____

c. angular   _____

CHAPTER 9

Chemical Nomenclature

Chemical nomenclature is the means by which chemists assign names to atoms and compounds. A systematic method is needed to name the vast number of known compounds, and the new ones

> Our system of chemical nomenclature must generate names for more substances than there are words in the English language.

synthesized each day. Our standards for naming compounds are established by the **International Union of Pure and Applied Chemistry, IUPAC** for short. IUPAC adopted the **Stock System of Nomenclature** for assigning names to inorganic compounds. We will learn part of the Stock system along with some common names that are frequently used by nonchemists.

Before we can discuss the specifics of inorganic nomenclature, we need to learn a method for keeping track of the apparent charge, called the oxidation number, that an atom has within a compound.

WWWolfe 1
(See WWWolfe section at the end of the chapter.)

9.1 OXIDATION NUMBERS (OXIDATION STATES)

Oxidation numbers, sometimes called oxidation states, are signed numbers assigned to atoms in molecules and ions. They allow us to keep track of the electrons associated with each atom. Oxidation numbers are often used to write chemical formulas, predict properties of compounds, and help balance equations in which electrons are transferred (oxidation-reduction reactions).

Knowledge of the oxidation state of an atom gives us an idea about its positive or negative character. In themselves, oxidation numbers have no physical meaning; they are used to simplify tasks

> Oxidation numbers are the result of the stated rules, nothing more. They cannot be measured experimentally.

that are more difficult to accomplish without them.

To assign oxidation numbers the following set of rules is used.

Rule 1   All pure elements are assigned the oxidation number of zero.

Rule 2   All monatomic ions are assigned oxidation numbers equal to their charges.

Rule 3   Certain elements usually possess a fixed oxidation number in compounds.

1. The oxidation number of O in most compounds is –2.

2. The oxidation number of H in most compounds is +1.

3. The oxidation number of halogens in many, but not all, binary compounds is –1.

4. The oxidation numbers of alkali metals and alkaline earth metals are +1 and +2, respectively.

Rule 4   The sum of all oxidation numbers in a compound equals zero, and the sum of oxidation numbers in a polyatomic ion equals the ion's charge.

Let's now discuss each rule. **Rule 1** states that all uncombined elements are assigned the oxidation number of zero, no matter how they exist in nature—by themselves, diatomically, or in larger aggregates (e.g., P_4 and S_8). It is common practice to write oxidation numbers above the symbols of the atoms.

$$\overset{0}{Na} \quad \overset{0}{Fe} \quad \overset{0}{H_2} \quad \overset{0}{O_2} \quad \overset{0}{F_2} \quad \overset{0}{Ne} \quad \overset{0}{P_4} \leftarrow \text{Oxidation numbers}$$

Rule 2 states that all monatomic ions are assigned oxidation numbers equal to their charge. When you write an oxidation number, the sign comes before the magnitude of the charge. Charges on atoms are written with the magnitude before the sign. Some examples of oxidation numbers of monatomic ions are as follows:

$$\overset{-1}{Cl^-} \quad \overset{+3}{Al^{3+}} \quad \overset{+2}{Cu^{2+}} \quad \overset{-2}{O^{2-}} \quad \overset{+1}{K^+} \quad \overset{+2}{Mg^{2+}}$$

Rule 3 tells us that some atoms have fixed oxidation numbers. These atoms usually have oxidation numbers that correspond to the number of electrons that they lose or gain when forming a binary ionic compound. For example, halogens gain one electron, chalcogens gain two electrons, alkali metals lose one electron, and alkaline earth metals lose two electrons to obtain noble gas configurations when they form ionic compounds.

Rule 3 has a few exceptions. For example, in peroxides, the oxidation number of an O atom is –1, not –2. Peroxides are compounds with an O—O single bond. Two peroxides are hydrogen peroxide, H_2O_2, and sodium peroxide,

> If an O atom is bonded to two F atoms, the O atom has a +2 oxidation state because F atoms have a higher electronegativity.

Na_2O_2. Another exception is found for metallic hydrides, which are compounds with an H atom bonded to a metal with a lower electronegativity. The oxidation number of H is –1 in metallic hydrides. Examples of metallic hydrides include sodium hydride, NaH, and calcium hydride, CaH_2.

Through the application of **Rule 4**, we can identify the oxidation numbers of all elements in a compound. For example, we can calculate the oxidation number of N in NO. The oxidation number of O is –2, and the sum of the oxidation numbers in NO equals zero. Thus, the oxidation number of N in NO is +2:

Total oxidation numbers →	? −2 = 0	+2−2 = 0
	NO	NO
Individual oxidation numbers	−2	−2

To keep track of oxidation numbers, write the known oxidation states for individual atoms below the formula and the total oxidation number for all elements of that type above the symbol.

What is the oxidation number of S in SO_2? Again following Rule 4, we assign −4 to the two O atoms; hence, the oxidation number of S is +4 in order for the sum to equal zero.

$$? -4 \qquad +4 -4$$
$$SO_2 \qquad SO_2$$
$$-2 \qquad -2$$

For a polyatomic ion the reasoning is the same except that the sum of the oxidation numbers equals the charge on the ion. To illustrate this, let's calculate the oxidation number of a P atom in PO_4^{3-}. Four O atoms have a total oxidation number of −8, so the oxidation state of P must be +5 for the sum to equal the charge of −3.

$$? -8 = -3 \qquad +5 -8 = -3$$
$$PO_4^{3-} \qquad PO_4^{3-}$$
$$-2 \qquad -2$$

Example Problem 9.1 presents additional illustrations of how to assign oxidation numbers.

Example Problem 9.1
Find the oxidation states for the elements in each of the following: (a) CuF_2, (b) HNO_3, (c) SO_4^{2-}, (d) $C_{12}H_{22}O_{11}$.

Solution
(a) CuF_2. Halogens such as F have an oxidation number equal to −1; two F atoms have a total oxidation number of −2; therefore, it follows that the oxidation number of Cu is +2.

$$+2 \ -2$$
$$CuF_2$$
$$-1$$

(b) HNO_3. The oxidation number of H is +1, and three O atoms have a total oxidation number of −6; thus, the oxidation number of N is +5 in order for the total to be 0.

$$+1+5-6$$
$$HNO_3$$
$$+1 \ -2$$

(c) SO_4^{2-}. The oxidation number of each O atom is −2, so four O atoms have a total oxidation number of −8. To make the sum of the oxidation numbers equal to −2, the charge on SO_4^{2-}, the oxidation number of S is +6.

$$\overset{+6\ -8}{SO_4{}^{2-}}$$
$$\underset{-2}{}$$

(d) $C_{12}H_{22}O_{11}$. The total oxidation number of 22 H atoms is +22 (22 × +1), and the total for 11 O atoms is –22 (11 × –2). Therefore, the 12 C atoms have a total oxidation number of 0, which means that each C has an oxidation number equal to zero.

$$\overset{0\ \ +22\ -22}{C_{12}H_{22}O_{11}}$$
$$\underset{+1\ \ -2}{}$$

Exercise
What is the oxidation state of C in $(NH_4)_2C_2O_4$?   (+3)

Group																		
	IA(1)																	VIIIA(18)
1	1 H +1	IIA(2)											IIIA(13)	IVA(14)	VA(15)	VIA(16)	VIIA(17)	2 He
2	3 Li +1	4 Be +2											5 B +3	6 C ±4,+2	7 N ±3,5,4,2	8 O –2,1	9 F –1	10 Ne
3	11 Na +1	12 Mg +2	IIIB(3)	IVB(4)	VB(5)	VIB(6)	VIIB(7)	(8) VIIIB (9)	(10)	IB(11)	IIB(12)		13 Al +3	14 Si +4	15 P ±3,5,4	16 S ±2,4,6	17 Cl ±1,3,5,7	18 Ar
4	19 K +1	20 Ca +2	21 Sc +3	22 Ti +4,3	23 V +5,4,3,2	24 Cr +6,3,2	25 Mn +7,6,4,3,2	26 Fe +2,3	27 Co +2,3	28 Ni +2,3	29 Cu +1,2	30 Zn +2	31 Ga +3	32 Ge +4	33 As ±3,5	34 Se –2,4,6	35 Br ±1,5	36 Kr
5	37 Rb +1	38 Sr +2	39 Y +3	40 Zr +4	41 Nb +5,3	42 Mo +6,5,4,3,2	43 Tc +7	44 Ru +8,6,4,3,2	45 Rh +4,3,2	46 Pd +2,4	47 Ag +1	48 Cd +2	49 In +3	50 Sn +4,2	51 Sb ±3,5	52 Te –2,4,6	53 I ±1,5,7	54 Xe
6	55 Cs +1	56 Ba +2	57 La +3	72 Hf +4	73 Ta +5	74 W +6,5,4,3,2	75 Re +7,6,4,2	76 Os +8,6,4,3,2	77 Ir +6,4,3,2	78 Pt +2,4	79 Au +1,3	80 Hg +2,1	81 Tl +1,3	82 Pb +4,2	83 Bi +3,5	84 Po +2,4	85 At ±1,3,5,7	86 Rn
7	87 Fr +1	88 Ra +2	89 Ac +3	104 Unq	105 Unp	106	107	108											

58 Ce +3,4	59 Pr +3,4	60 Nd +3	61 Pm +3	62 Sm +2,3	63 Eu +2,3	64 Gd +3	65 Tb +3,4	66 Dy +3	67 Ho +3	68 Er +3	69 Tm +2,3	70 Yb +2,3	71 Lu +3

90 Th +4	91 Pa +4,5	92 U +6,5,4,3	93 Np +6,5,4,3	94 Pu +6,5,4,3

Figure 9.1 The most common oxidation states of each element are listed under its symbol. This table does not list all of the oxidation states for an element only the most common ones.

With the exception of the metals in groups IA (1), IIA (2), and IIIB (3), metals generally can exist in more than one oxidation state. Chromium, Cr, for example, is found in the +6, +3, and +2

> A large percent of the elements exist in two or more oxidation states.

oxidation states. Gold is found in both +3 and +1 oxidation states. Nonmetals, except F, also exhibit a range of oxidation states. For example, the oxidation states of S include +6, +4, +2, and –2. Figure 9.1 presents a periodic table with the most common oxidation states of the elements. ❖

REVIEW EXERCISES

9.1 What is chemical nomenclature?

9.2 (a) What does the oxidation number of an element within a compound represent?

(b) Explain why the oxidation number for an element is not always equal to the charge of an atom in a compound.

9.3 List the four rules employed to assign oxidation numbers to elements in compounds.

9.4 What are the oxidation numbers for all elements in each of the following compounds?

(a) PBr_3
(b) MnO_2
(c) AlF_3
(d) N_2O
(e) P_2O_5

9.5 Find the oxidation states for all elements except O in the following polyatomic ions.

(a) $C_2O_4^{2-}$
(b) NO_2^{-}
(c) BrO_3^{-}
(d) CO_3^{2-}
(e) $C_2H_3O_2^{-}$

9.4 (a) P +3, Br –1, (b) Mn +4, O –2, (c) Al +3, F –1, (d) N +1, O –2, (e) P +5, O –2; 9.5 (a) C +3, (b) N +3, (c) Br +5, (d) C +4, (e) C 0, H +1.

9.2 NAMES AND FORMULAS OF BINARY INORGANIC COMPOUNDS

Binary compounds are those with two different elements. **Ternary compounds**, discussed in the next section, are composed of three different elements. Each of these groups of compounds is divided into subgroups that have their own specific rules of nomenclature. Figure 9.2 outlines the most general classes of binary and ternary inorganic compounds.

WWWolfe 2
(See WWWolfe
section at the end of
the chapter.)

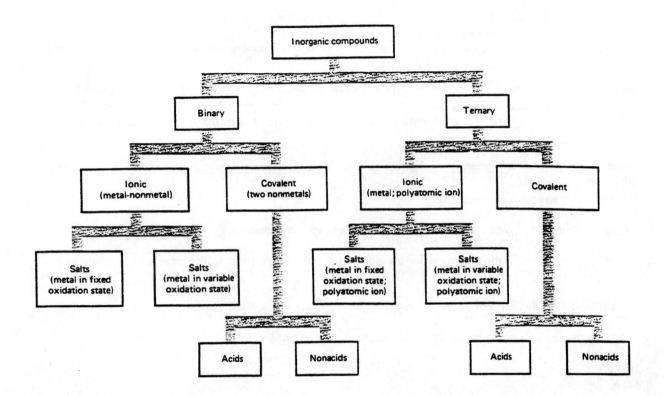

Figure 9.2 Inorganic compounds are first classified as binary or ternary. Both binary and ternary compounds are subdivided into ionic compounds or covalent compounds. Ionic compounds contain a metal in either a fixed or variable oxidation state. Covalent substances may be divided into acids and nonacids.

When you write the name of a compound, first identify what class of compound is being named. Using the flowchart in Fig. 9.3, decide if the compound is binary or ternary. Then decide if the compound is ionic or covalent. Ionic compounds are most commonly composed of a metal and a nonmetal, a metal and a polyatomic ion, or a polyatomic ion and a nonmetal. Covalent compounds are composed of two or more nonmetals.

Binary Ionic Compounds That Contain Metals with Fixed Oxidation States
In Chap. 8, we learned the rules for naming simple binary ionic compounds, i.e., those composed of a metal ion with a fixed oxidation state and a nonmetal ion. To review: First write the name of the metal, and then write the name of the nonmetal, removing its ending and adding the suffix *ide*.

Name = metal + (nonmetal – ending + *ide*)

If you have forgotten how to name these compounds, refer to Sec. 8.1.

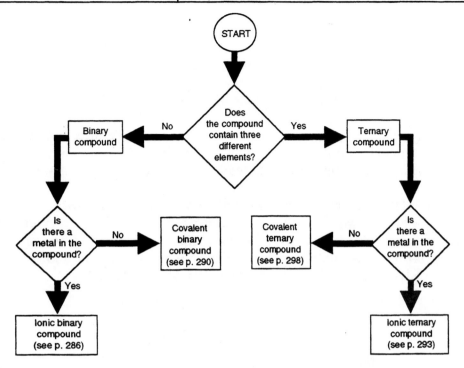

Figure 9.3 To use the nomenclature flowchart, begin at the top and answer each question, concerning the compound of interest. When you answer either yes or no, the chart poses another question or gives the type of compound.

Binary Ionic Compounds That Contain Metals with Variable Oxidation States

What if the metal ion component of a binary ionic substance has a variable oxidation state? We mentioned that metals can exist in more than one oxidation state; consequently, more than one binary compound can result when such a metal combines with a nonmetal. For example, two chlorides of copper are known, $CuCl$ and $CuCl_2$. Our naming system must provide a means of distinguishing between the two. In the Stock system, we modify the above rules for naming ionic substances to include the oxidation state of the metal ion.

Specifically, we write the full name of the metal followed by its oxidation number written in roman numerals in parentheses:

Metal name(oxidation number)

The left parenthesis is written next to the last letter in the name of the metal, and the oxidation state is written in roman numerals, followed by the right parenthesis. Accordingly, the two oxidation states of copper are expressed as follows:

$$Cu^+ = copper(I)$$

$$Cu^{2+} = copper(II)$$

To write the complete names of $CuCl$ and $CuCl_2$, it is only necessary to append the modified name of the nonmetal (nonmetal – ending + *ide*), chloride. Therefore, $CuCl$ is copper(I) chloride, and $CuCl_2$ is copper(II) chloride.

$$CuCl = copper(I) \text{ chloride}$$

$$CuCl_2 = copper(II) \text{ chloride}$$

Note, a space is between the right parenthesis and the nonmetal name, but no space is between the left parenthesis and the end of the metal name. When reading names expressed this way, state the metal name followed by the number: "copper-one" and "copper-two."

The old system of nomenclature assigns names to metals that exist in more than one oxidation state in a different way. To write the names of the chlorides of copper, two endings, *ic* and *ous,* are added to the old name for copper, *cuprum.* The ending *ic* designates the higher oxidation state, while *ous* identifies the lower oxidation state of the metal. For CuCl, in which Cu is in the +1 state, we add *ous* to cuprum – *um,* which gives "cuprous":

$$Cu^+ = cuprum - um + ous = cuprous$$

In a similar manner, *ic* is affixed to cuprum – *um,* which yields "cupric":

$$Cu^{2+} = cuprum - um + ic = cupric$$

In the old system, the names of the chlorides of Cu are cuprous chloride, CuCl, and cupric chloride, $CuCl_2$.

The following table lists old Latin names for some common metals.

> CuCl is a white solid that melts at 130°C. $CuCl_2$ is a yellow-brown solid that melts at 520°C.

Modern name	Old name
Antimony	Stibum
Copper	Cuprum
Gold	Aurum
Iron	Ferrum
Lead	Plumbum
Potassium	Kalium
Silver	Argentum
Tin	Stannum

To write the names of binary compounds using the Stock system, one needs to know only the oxidation states of the elements in the compound. Additional knowledge (the old names for metals) is required when using the old system. Table 9.1 lists both the old and new names of frequently encountered metal ions with variable oxidation states. In this textbook we will principally use the Stock system.

Initially, refer to Table 9.1 when writing the names of metals with more than one oxidation state. Example Problem 9.2 illustrates how to write the names of compounds with metals that have variable oxidation states.

EXAMPLE PROBLEM 9.1
Write the Stock and old names for each of the following binary compounds: (a) HgI_2, (b) PbO_2, (c) SnF_2, (d) FeO.

Solution
(a) HgI_2. Identify the oxidation state of Hg in HgI_2, using the rules for assigning oxidation numbers. Iodine is a halogen with an oxidation number of –1 in binary compounds; two I atoms have a total oxidation number of –2. Consequently, the oxidation state of Hg is +2 (the higher oxidation state of Hg), which is mercury(II) in the Stock system and mercuric in the old system. To modify the name of iodine, remove the *ine* and add *ide*.

Stock name = mercury(II) iodide

Old name = mercuric iodide

(b) PbO_2. The total oxidation number for two O atoms is –4. In order for the oxidation numbers to add up to zero, the oxidation state of Pb must be +4. The +4 oxidation state of lead is the higher one, necessitating that is be placed at the end of the metal's old name, *plumbum*.

Stock name = lead(IV) oxide

Old name = plumbic oxide

(c) SnF_2. After following the general rules, we find that Sn is in the +2 oxidation state, its lower oxidation state. Consequently, the two names for SnF_2 are

Stock name = tin(II) fluoride

Old name = stannous fluoride

(d) FeO. The oxidation number for an O atom is –2; therefore, the oxidation number of Fe is +2. The Stock name for iron in this compound is thus iron(II), and the old name ferrous, because +2 is the lower oxidation state. To the names of the metal ion we add the modified name of oxygen, which is oxide.

> Some compounds have an element that exists in two different oxidation states. Fe_3O_4 is a combination of FeO and Fe_2O_3; hence, it is best named iron (II,III) oxide.

Stock name = iron (II) oxide

Old name = ferrous oxide

Exercise

What are the Stock and old names of TiS_2? (Titanium(IV) sulfide, titanic sulfide)

TABLE 9.1 NAMES OF SELECTED METALS WITH MULTIPLE OXIDATION STATES

Metal	Oxidation state	Stock name	Old name
Copper	+1	Copper(I)	Cuprous
	+2	Copper(II)	Cupric
Mercury	+1	Mercury(I)*	Mercurous
	+2	Mercury(II)	Mercuric
Iron	+2	Iron(II)	Ferrous
	+3	Iron(III)	Ferric
Chromium	+2	Chromium(II)	Chromous
	+3	Chromium(III)	Chromic
Cobalt	+2	Cobalt(II)	Cobaltous
	+3	Cobalt(III)	Cobaltic
Tin	+2	Tin(II)	Stannous
	+4	Tin(IV)	Stannic
Lead	+2	Lead(II)	Plumbous
	+4	Lead(IV)	Plumbic
Titanium	+3	Titanium(III)	Titanous
	+4	Titanium(IV)	Titanic

*Mercury(I) is a diatomic cation; i.e., it exists in pairs–Hg_2^{2+}. Whenever mercury(I) is written, it indicates a pair of mercury ions.

Binary Covalent Compounds

In Sec. 8.1, we discussed the rules for writing the names of covalent binary compounds. To review: The name of the nonmetal in the positive oxidation state (the nonmetal with the lower electronegativity) is written first unchanged. The ending of the nonmetal in a negative oxidation state (the nonmetal with the higher electronegativity) is dropped and *ide* is added. A prefix is attached to this name to show the number of atoms with each nonmetal in the formula. Examples of covalent binary compounds include sulfur trioxide, SO_3; dinitrogen pentoxide, N_2O_5; and carbon tetrafluoride, CF_4.

Binary Acids

Some covalent binary hydrogen compounds are classified as acids. When dissolved in water, acids ionize and add hydrogen ions, H^+ and anions to water. In the following equation, hypothetical acid HA dissociates and forms H^+ and A^- (anion).

$$HA \xrightarrow{\text{water}} H^+(aq) + A^-(aq)$$

Acids are important compounds and have thousands of uses. They have a set of common properties. Acids taste sour, change the color of acid-base indicator dyes such as litmus, react with bases (metallic hydroxides) to produce salts, and may combine with active metals to liberate hydrogen gas.

When you write the names of binary acids, the prefix *hydro* is added to the nonmetal name, the ending is usually dropped, and *ic acid* is attached in its place.

Acid name = *hydro* + nonmetal – ending + *ic acid*

For example, the binary acid with chlorine, HCl(aq), is called hydrochloric acid. *Hydro* is added to "chlorine – ine + *ic acid*" to generate the name. Additional examples of binary acids include hydrosulfuric acid, H_2S(aq); hydrofluoric acid, HF(aq); and hydrobromic acid, HBr(aq).

> If a binary acidic substance is not in aqueous solution, it is named in the same way as any other binary compound. For example, HCl(g) is hydrogen chloride gas.

Writing Formulas of Binary Compounds

To write the formula of a binary compound, given its name, you must first determine if the compound is ionic or covalent. If it is covalent, the actual number of atoms is specified in the formula. Therefore, you write the formula with the subscripts indicated by the prefixes—for example, carbon disulfide, CS_2, dinitrogen tetroxide, N_2O_4, and carbon tetrabromide, CBr_4.

To write the formula of an ionic compound, write each ion with its correct oxidation state, and then determine the quantity of each ion that produces a zero oxidation state for the compound. To illustrate this procedure, let's write the formula for chromium(III) oxide. Given the Stock name, the oxidation state of the metal is indicated by the roman numeral. Oxygen belongs to group A VIA (16) and has an oxidation number of –2 in

> The sum of the oxidation numbers of all the elements in a compound is zero.

binary compounds. Write both elements with their oxidation numbers:

$$\overset{+3}{Cr} \quad \overset{-2}{O}$$

Because the sum of all oxidation numbers adds up to zero, ask yourself what numbers of Cr and O atoms give the same total oxidation number. This is easily accomplished by finding the lowest common multiple for the two oxidation numbers; for Cr and O the lowest common multiple is 6. Then, divide each individual oxidation number into the lowest common multiple to obtain the correct formula subscript.

Lowest common multiple = 6

$$\overset{+3}{Cr}\quad\overset{-2}{O}$$

$$\frac{6}{3}=2\qquad\frac{6}{2}=3$$

Thus two chromium ions and three oxide ions are in chromium(III) oxide.

$$Cr_2O_3$$

Example Problem 9.3 shows additional examples of how to write formulas of compounds given their names. ❖

Example Problem 9.3

Write the formulas for each of the following: (a) lead(II) chloride, (b) titanium(III) sulfide, (c) cobaltous oxide.

Solution

(a) Lead(II) chloride. Lead(II) is Pb^{2+}, and chloride, Cl^-, is a halide ion with an oxidation number of –1. Two chloride ions are needed to balance the Pb^{2+}; hence, the formula of lead(II) chloride is $PbCl_2$.

$$PbCl_2$$

(b) Titanium(III) sulfide. The oxidation number of titanium(III) is +3, and that of sulfur is –2. The lowest common multiple of +3 and –2 is 6. Thus, two Ti atoms and three S atoms are needed to give a zero oxidation state for titanium(III) sulfide.

$$Ti_2S_3$$

(c) Cobaltous oxide. Referring to Table 9.1, we find that cobaltous is Co^{2+}, and we know that an O atom has an oxidation number of –2; thus, the formula of cobaltous oxide is CoO. Co and O are found in a 1-to-1 ratio in cobaltous oxide.

$$CoO$$

Exercise
What is the formula of platinum(VI) oxide?   (PtO_3)

REVIEW EXERCISES

9.6 Write the old name that corresponds to each of the following Stock names for metal ions.

(a) copper(II)
(b) manganese(II)
(c) lead(IV)
(d) iron(II)
(e) tin(II).

9.7 Write the Stock names for each of the following.

(a) Fe_2S_3
(b) Cu_3N
(c) PbO
(d) Hg_2F_2
(e) MnF_3
(f) $HBr(aq)$
(g) AlF_3

9.8 Write the formulas for each of the following.

(a) tin(II) bromide
(b) gold(III) oxide
(c) nickel(II) nitride
(d) plumbic iodide
(e) copper(I) sulfide
(f) sulfur dichloride

9.6 (a) Cupric, (b) manganous, (c) plumbic, (d) ferrous, (e) stannous; 9.7 (a) Iron(III) sulfide, (b) copper(I) nitride, (c) lead(II) oxide, (d) mercury(I) fluoride, (e) manganese(III) fluoride, (f) hydrobromic acid, (g) aluminum fluoride; 9.8 (a) $SnBr_2$, (b) Au_2O_3, (c) Ni_3N_2, (d) PbI_4, (e,) Cu_2S, (f) SCl_2

9.3 NAMES OF TERNARY INORGANIC COMPOUNDS

A ternary compound is one with three elements. Referring to Figs. 9.2 and 9.3, it should be apparent that ternary compounds are classified in a similar manner to binary compounds. First decide if the ternary compound is ionic or covalent. If it is ionic, check to see if the metal has a fixed or variable oxidation state. If it is covalent, determine whether it is an acid.

We will concentrate on the names of ternary compounds composed of (1) a metal and a polyatomic ion (ionic) or (2) an H atom bonded to a polyatomic ion (acid). Polyatomic ions were first introduced in Chap. 8. They are ions composed of more than one atom; some examples are hydroxide, OH^-; nitrate, NO_3^-; and sulfate, SO_4^{2-}. Rules for naming ionic ternary compounds are similar to those for binary compounds, except that the name of a polyatomic ion is found in place of either the metal ion or nonmetal ion name. Table 9.2 lists 14 frequently encountered polyatomic ions. *Learning the formulas, charges, and names of these polyatomic ions will simplify the writing of names of ternary compounds.* When you learn these polyatomic ions, do not forget their charges. **It is of no value to learn the ions without their charges.** A more complete listing of ions, including polyatomic ions, is found an appendix at the end of the book.

To write the name of an ionic ternary compound, first determine if the metal has a fixed or variable oxidation number. Depending on what metal is found, the compound is named in a similar manner to an ionic binary compound except for the name of the polyatomic ion.

Let's illustrate the procedure for writing the name of ionic ternary compounds by considering $Co(NO_3)_2$. Cobalt is a transition metal with a variable

WWWolfe 3
(See WWWolfe section at the end of the chapter.)

> **Study Hint:** Write the formula of the polyatomic ion on one side of an index card, and the name on the other side. Flip through the cards learning names of formulas; then, turn the deck over and proceed in the opposite direction, learning formulas of names.

oxidation state. Thus, find the oxidation state of Co and write it in parentheses: cobalt(II). Then identify the polyatomic ion, NO_3^-, nitrate, and add its name to the name of the metal: cobalt(II) nitrate.

$$Co(NO_3)_2 = \text{cobalt(II) nitrate}$$

The oxidation state of Co is determined from the charge on the nitrate ion, which is –1. Because two nitrate ions are in the formula, the cobalt exists in the +2 oxidation state.

> If more than one polyatomic ion of the same kind is found in a compound, it is placed in parentheses with the appropriate subscript.

Example Problem 9.4 shows how to write the names of several other ternary ionic compounds.

TABLE 9.2 IMPORTANT POLYATOMIC IONS

Name of ion	Formula
Acetate	$C_2H_3O_2^-$ $(CH_3CO_2^-)$
Ammonium	NH_4^+
Arsenate	AsO_4^{3-}
Borate	BO_3^{3-}
Carbonate	CO_3^{2-}
Chlorate	ClO_3^-
Chromate	CrO_4^{2-}
Cyanide	CN^-
Dichromate	$Cr_2O_7^{2-}$
Hydroxide	OH^-
Nitrate	NO_3^-
Permanganate	MnO_4^-
Phosphate	PO_4^{3-}
Selenate	SeO_4^{2-}
Sulfate	SO_4^{2-}

Example Problem 9.4

Write the Stock names for each of the following compounds: (a) $K_2Cr_2O_7$, (b) $(NH_4)_2S$, (c) $FeCO_3$, (d) $Mn_3(PO_4)_2$.

Solution

(a) $K_2Cr_2O_7$. The metal is potassium, an alkali metal with a fixed oxidation state, and the polyatomic ion is dichromate. Thus

$$K_2Cr_2O_7 = \text{potassium dichromate}$$

A number is not written after potassium in the name because potassium exists in only one oxidation state, $+1$.

(b) $(NH_4)_2S$. In this compound, we find the ammonium ion in place of a metal ion along with the nonmetal sulfur. Remove the ending from sulfur and add *ide*:

$$(NH_4)_2S = \text{ammonium sulfide}$$

(c) $FeCO_3$. Iron is a metal with a variable oxidation state; consequently, the name must indicate the oxidation state of iron. Carbonate, CO_3^{2-}, has a charge of -2; thus, to sum to zero, the oxidation number of Fe is $+2$. Accordingly,

$$FeCO_3 = \text{iron(II) carbonate}$$

(d) $Mn_3(PO_4)_2$. Again, the oxidation state of the metal has to be expressed because manganese exists in a variety of states. Phosphate has a charge of $3-$; therefore, two phosphates have a total charge of $6-$. So the three Mn atoms' total oxidation number is $+6$, or each Mn has an oxidation number of $+2$.

$$Mn_3(PO_4)_2 = \text{manganese(II) phosphate}$$

Exercise
What are the stock names of $AlAsO_4$ and $Au_2(SO_4)_3$? (Aluminum arsenate and gold(III) sulfate)

To write the formula of a ternary compound, given its name, follow the same procedures used when writing formulas of binary compounds, as shown in Example Problem 9.5.

Example Problem 9.5

Write the formulas of (a) zinc(II) hydroxide, (b) silver(I) cyanide, and (c) cobaltic sulfate.

Solution

(a) Zinc(II) hydroxide. Zinc(II) is Zn^{2+}, and hydroxide is OH^-. To produce a compound with a zero oxidation state, two hydroxide ions are required per each zinc(II) ion.

$$Zn^{2+} \quad OH^-$$
$$\text{Zinc(II) hydroxide} = Zn(OH)_2$$

(b) Silver(I) cyanide. Silver(I) is Ag^+, and cyanide is CN^-. Because they have equal but opposite charges, they combine in a l-to-1 ratio.

$$Ag^+ \quad CN^-$$
$$\text{Silver(I) cyanide} = AgCN$$

(c) Cobaltic sulfate. "Cobaltic" is the old name for the higher oxidation state of Co, which is Co^{3+}. The formula for sulfate is SO_4^{2+}. The lowest common multiple of 3 and is 6; accordingly, the formula of cobaltic sulfate becomes $Co_2(SO_4)_3$.

$$Co^{3+} \quad SO_4^{2-}$$
$$\text{Cobaltic sulfate} = Co_2(SO_4)_3$$

Exercise
What is the formula of mercury(I) selenate? (Hg_2SeO_4)

Oxyanions
A group of polyatomic ions exists with one less O atom than some of those listed in Table 9.2. For example, in addition to sulfate, SO_4^{2-}, an ion with the formula SO_3^{2-} also exists. How is this ion named? If a polyatomic ion has one less O atom than the ion ending in *ate*, it is given an *ite* ending. SO_3^{2-} is the *sulfite* ion because it has one less O atom than sulfate, SO_4^{2-}. Table 9.3 lists additional examples of *ite* **oxyanions,** i.e., polyatomic ions that contain oxygen. Note that both *ate* and *ite* oxyanions have the same charge.

> Some people have allergic reactions to sulfites used as preservatives in foods

TABLE 9.3 SELECTED OXYANIONS: *ate* VERSUS *ite* ENDINGS

Oxyanion	Name
SO_4^{2-}	Sulfate
SO_3^{2-}	Sulfite
NO_3^-	Nitrate
NO_2^-	Nitrite
PO_4^{3-}	Phosphate
PO_3^{3-}	Phosphite
AsO_4^{3-}	Arsenate
AsO_3^{3-}	Arsenite
SeO_4^{2-}	Selenate
SeO_3^{2-}	Selenite

Once the formula for the *ate* ion is learned, it is only necessary to subtract an O atom from the formula and replace the ending of the name with *ite* to obtain the correct formula and name of the *ite* oxyanion. Example Problem 9.6 shows how the names of such compounds are derived.

Example Problem 9.6
Write the Stock names for the following compounds: (a) $Fe_3(PO_3)_2$, and (b) $Ba(NO_2)_2$.

Solution
(a) $Fe_3(PO_3)_2$. Looking at the oxyanion, we notice that it has one less O atom than phosphate, PO_4^{3-}; thus, it is the phosphite ion, PO_3^{3-}. Because two phosphite ions are in the formula, each with a charge of 3–, the total charge or oxidation number is 6–. Each iron ion must have a charge of 2+ (3 × 2+ = 6+) to balance the charge of the phosphite ions. Accordingly, the name of $Fe_3(PO_4)_2$ is iron(II) phosphite

$$Fe_3(PO_3)_2 = \text{iron(II) phosphite}$$

(b) $Ba(NO_2)_2$. Barium is an element in group IIA (2); thus, it has a fixed charge of 2+. NO_2^- has one less O atom than nitrate, NO_3^-, so its name is nitrite. Thus,

$$Ba(NO_2)_2 = \text{barium nitrite}$$

Exercise
What is the Stock name of Au_2SeO_3? (Gold(I) selenite)

Oxyanions With Halogen Atoms
The oxyanions that have a halogen atom, X, (Cl, Br, and I) can form four different ions: XO_4^-, XO_3^-, XO_2^-, and XO^-. Let us consider the oxyanions of Cl. You should recall from Table 9.2 that chlorate has the formula of ClO_3^-. As you just learned, the oxyanion of Cl with one less O atom, ClO_2^-, is assigned the name chlorite. A third oxyanion of Cl has one less O atom then chlorite. Its formula is written either as ClO^- or OCl^-. To name oxyanions with one less O atom than the *ite* ion, add *hypo*, a prefix that means under, to the beginning of the *ite* ion name. This produces the name hypochlorite.

$$ClO^- (OCl^-) = \text{hypochlorite}$$

The fourth oxyanion of Cl has the formula ClO_4^-. Its name is obtained by adding the prefix *per* to the name of the *ate* ion. Thus, ClO_4^- is perchlorate.

$$ClO_4^- = \text{perchlorate}$$

The oxyanions for the other halogens are named in a similar fashion. BrO_4^-, BrO_3^-, BrO_2^-, and BrO^- are name perbromate, bromate, bromite, and hypobromite, respectively. IO_4^-, IO_3^-, IO_2^-, and IO^- are name periodate, iodate, iodite, and hypoiodite, respectively.

REVIEW EXERCISES

9.9 Identify each of the following polyatomic ions.

(a) BO_3^{3-}
(b) ClO_3^-
(c) MnO_4^-
(d) CrO_4^{2-}
(e) PO_4^{3-}
(f) $C_2H_3O_2^-$

9.10 Write the formula for each of the following.

(a) ammonium ion
(b) carbonate ion
(c) nitrate ion
(d) cyanide ion
(e) phosphite ion
(f) selenite ion

9.11 Write the names for each of the following compounds.

(a) Cs_2CO_3
(b) $Sr(ClO_3)_2$
(c) Ag_2CrO_4
(d) $Hg_2(NO_3)_2$
(e) Na_3PO_4
(f) $Co(NO_2)_2$

9.12 Write the formulas for each of the following.

(a) ammonium chromate
(b) iron(II) sulfite
(c) aluminum cyanide
(d) nickel(II) nitrite
(e) manganic phosphate
(f) sodium arsenate

9.11 (a) Cesium carbonate, (b) strontium chlorate, (c) silver chromate, (d) mercury(I) nitrate, (e) sodium phosphate, (f) cobalt(II) nitrite; 9.12 (a) $(NH_4)_2CrO_4$, (b) $FeSO_3$, (c) $Al(CN)_3$, (d) $Ni(NO_2)_2$, (e) $MnPO_4$, (f) Na_3AsO_4

Covalent Ternary Compounds

Because we will encounter few covalent ternary compounds that are not acids, only acids are discussed in this section. Examples of ternary acids include sulfuric acid, $H_2SO_4(aq)$; nitric acid, $HNO_3(aq)$; phosphoric acid, $H_3PO_4(aq)$; chloric acid, $HClO_3(aq)$; and boric acid, $H_3BO_3(aq)$.

Oxyacids

Oxyacids are ternary acids with one or more O atoms. Such compounds have H ions, H^+, bonded to an oxyanion. For example, if two H ions bond to sulfate, SO_4^{2-}, the resulting acid, H_2SO_4, is called sulfuric acid. This name was obtained by adding *ic acid* to the end of the nonmetal name contained in sulfate.

$$\text{Sulfuric acid} = \text{sulfur} + ic\ acid$$

Oxyanions that end in *ate* when bonded to H ions, form oxyacids whose names are derived from the name of the nonmetal, with *ic acid* as the ending. Table 9.4 presents examples of other ic *acids*.

TABLE 9.4 NAMES OF SELECTED OXYACIDS

Oxyacid name	Oxyacid	Oxyanion	Name
Boric acid	$H_3BO_3(aq)$	BO_3^{3-}	Borate
Carbonic acid	$H_2CO_3(aq)$	CO_3^{2-}	Carbonate
Chloric acid	$HClO_3(aq)$	ClO_3^-	Chlorate
Chromic acid	$H_2CrO_4(aq)$	CrO_4^{2-}	Chromate
Nitric acid	$HNO_3(aq)$	NO_3^-	Nitrate
Selenic acid	$H_2SeO_4(aq)$	SeO_4^{2-}	Selenate
Sulfuric acid	$H_2SO_4(aq)$	SO_4^{2-}	Sulfate

If the nonmetal in the oxyacid exists in more than one oxidation state, then at least two oxyacids exist, each with a different number of bonded O atoms. For example, two oxyacids contain one S atom:

$$\underset{+6}{H_2SO_4} = \text{sulfuric acid}$$

$$\underset{+4}{H_2SO_3} = \text{sulfurous acid}$$

The S atom in sulfuric acid, H_2SO_4, is in the +6 oxidation state, whereas the S atom in sulfurous acid, H_2SO_3, is in the lower +4 state. If two oxyacids exist that contain the same nonmetal, the acid that contains the nonmetal in the higher oxidation state is given the *ic acid* ending (corresponding to the oxyanion sulfate, SO_4^{2-}) and the acid that contains the nonmetal in the lower oxidation state is given the *ous acid* ending (corresponding to the oxyanion sulfite, SO_3^{2-}).

Nitric acid, HNO_3, and nitrous acid, HNO_2, are the two oxyacids that contain a single N atom. The nitrogen in nitric acid is found in the +5 oxidation state, and the nitrogen in nitrous acid is in the +3 oxidation state.

> The name given to nitric acid by the alchemists was *aqua fortis*, which means strong water.

$$\underset{+5}{HNO_3} = \text{nitric acid}$$

$$HNO_2 = \text{nitrous acid}$$
$$\overset{+3}{}$$

The name of the oxyacid depends on the name of the oxyanion in the molecule. Nitrate, NO_3^-, is the oxyanion in HNO_3; accordingly, *ic acid* is added to the stem *nitr* from nitrogen, which gives nitric acid. The nitrite ion, NO_2^-, is the oxyanion in nitrous acid; thus, *ous acid is* added to the stem *nitr,* which gives nitrous acid.

Four oxyacids can result from oxyanions that contain halogen atoms. For example, the four oxyacids that contain Cl are as follows.

$$\overset{+7}{HClO_4}, \text{perchloric acid (Cl)}$$

$$\overset{+5}{HClO_3}, \text{chloric acid (Cl)}$$

$$\overset{+3}{HClO_2}, \text{chlorous acid (Cl)}$$

$$\overset{+1}{HClO}, \text{hypochlorous acid (Cl)}$$

Here, in addition to the acids with just the *ic* and *ous* endings, two other acids exist, one with a Cl atom in a still higher oxidation state, and another with the Cl in a still lower state. When this situation arises, the acid that contains the nonmetal in the highest oxidation state (the acid that has one more O than the *ic acid*) is named by placing *per* as a prefix in H front, and adding *ic acid* to the end. Similarly, the acid with the nonmetal in the lowest oxidation state (the acid that has one less O than the *ous acid*) is given the prefix *hypo,* with the *ous acid* ending.

> Perchloric acid is one of the strongest mineral acids. It is also a strong oxidizing agent, one that adds O atoms to other compounds. Perchloric acid must be treated with great care: solutions with concentrations above 60% are unstable and often explode!

When perchloric acid, $HClO_4$, gives up an H^+, the ClO_4^-, or perchlorate ion results. Acids with *per* as the prefix and ending in *ic acid* contain polyatomic ions named by dropping the *ic acid* and adding *ate.* Similarly, acids with *hypo* and *ous acid* contain the *hypo . . . ite* ion. Thus, when HOCl (HClO) loses an H^+, a hypochlorite ion, OCl^-, results.

> Per. . .ic oxyacids contain one more O atom than *ic acids,* and hypo. . .ous acids contain one less O atom than *ous acids.*

Example Problem 9.7 shows another example of a nonmetal that can exist in four different oxidation states.

Example Problem 9.7

Write the names for the following series of oxyacids and the names for the polyatomic ions in the following compounds: (a) $HBrO_4$, (b) $HBrO_3$, (c) $HBrO_2$, (d) HBrO (HOBr).

Solution

(a) The Br atom in $HBrO_4$ is in the +7 oxidation state, the highest of the series. Thus, its name is perbromic acid, and it contains the perbromate ion, BrO_4^-.

(b) The Br atom in $HBrO_3$ is in the +5 state, and it is given the name bromic acid. The bromate ion, BrO_3^-, is the polyatomic ion in bromic acid.

(c) The Br atom in $HBrO_2$ is in the +3 oxidation state. The name of the acid is bromous acid, and it contains a bromite ion, BrO_2^-.

(d) The Br atom in HBrO (HOBr) is +1; thus, the acid is hypobromous acid, and the BrO^- ion is the hypobromite ion.

Exercise

Write the name of the following acid and identify its polyatomic ion: HIO_3. (Iodic acid, iodate ion)

Unfortunately, no easy way exists to know which oxyacids exist for a particular nonmetal. It is a matter of sitting down and learning the most important ones and referring to a table of oxyacids for the others. Table 9.5 gives a partial listing of additional common oxyacids.

Acids with more than one H atom (e.g., H_2SO_4, H_3PO_4, . . .) can donate some or all of their H^+ ions in chemical reactions. If H_2SO_4 loses one H^+, the resulting ion is HSO_4^-:

$$H_2SO_4 \rightarrow H^+(aq) + HSO_4^-(aq)$$

HSO_4^- is assigned the name hydrogensulfate (Stock name) or bisulfate (old name). In the Stock system, it is only necessary to affix the word *hydrogen* to the name of the polyatomic ion *sulfate* (SO_4^{2-}). In the common name, the prefix *bi* is used in place of the word hydrogen.

Phosphoric acid, H_3PO_4, can release one, two, or three H^+ ions. If one H^+ is lost, then $H_2PO_4^-$, dihydrogenphosphate, is produced. If two H^+ ions are lost, then HPO_4^{2-}, hydrogenphosphate (also called monohydrogenphosphate), results, and if three H^+ are lost, the phosphate ion is produced:

> Pure phosphoric acid is a white solid that melts at 42°C. Phosphoric acid is generally sold as an 80 to 85% aqueous solution.

$$H_3PO_4 \rightarrow H^+(aq) + H_2PO_4^-(aq) \quad \text{(dihydrogenphosphate)}$$

$$H_3PO_4 \rightarrow 2H^+(aq) + HPO_4^{2-}(aq) \quad \text{(hydrogenphosphate)}$$

$$H_3PO_4 \rightarrow 3H^+(aq) + PO_4^{3-}(aq) \quad \text{(phosphate)}$$

The names of polyatomic ions that contain H atoms are incorporated into the names of compounds in the same way as those of the other polyatomic ions. To write the name of $NaHCO_3$, it is only necessary to write sodium hydrogencarbonate (or sodium bicarbonate). If $CaHPO_4$ is given, the name calcium hydrogenphosphate.

> The common names for sodium hydrogen-carbonate are baking soda and bicarbonate of soda. When an acid combines with $NaHCO_3$, $CO_2(g)$ is liberated which helps bread and other foods rise.

TABLE 9.5 SELECTED OXYACIDS

Nonmetal	Oxyacid	Formula
As	Arsenic acid	H_3AsO_4
	Arsenous acid	H_3AsO_3
B	Boric acid	H_3BO_3 ✓
C	Carbonic acid	H_2CO_3 ✓
P	Phosphoric acid	H_3PO_4 ✓
	Phosphorous acid	H_3PO_3
	Hypophosphorous acid	H_3PO_2
Se	Selenic acid	H_3SeO_4
	Selenous acid	H_3SeO_3
Si	Silicic acid	H_4SiO_4

Hydrates

Some binary and ternary ionic compounds form weak bonds with water molecules and produce a group of compounds known as **hydrates.** For example, barium chloride, $BaCl_2$, bonds with two water molecules to produce a hydrate that is expressed as follows:

$$BaCl_2 \cdot 2H_2O$$

The two water molecules are separated from the formula of $BaCl_2$ with a raised dot to indicate that the water molecules are only loosely bonded. To write the name of the hydrate, you first write the name of the ionic compound; you then attach the prefix that corresponds to the number of water molecules to the word *hydrate* (from the Greek for "water"). Thus, the name of $BaCl_2 \cdot 2H_2O$ is barium chloride dihydrate. If the water molecules are removed from the hydrate, the resulting compound is called an *anhydrous salt*. In our example, $BaCl_2$ is the anhydrous salt. Additional examples of hydrates are gypsum, $CaSO_4 \cdot 2H_2O$; epsom salt, $MgSO_4 \cdot 7H_2O$; Glauber's salt, $Na_2SO_4 \cdot 10H_2O$, and borax, $Na_2B_4O_7 \cdot 10H_2O$. ❖

REVIEW EXERCISES

9.13 What is the name of each of the following oxyacids?

(a) HNO_3
(b) H_3PO_3
(c) H_2SO_3
(d) $HClO$

9.14 Write the formulas for each of the following.

(a) boric acid
(b) selenic acid
(c) chlorous acid
(d) carbonic acid

9.15 Write the formulas for each of the following.

(a) potassium arsenate
(b) rubidium hydrogensulfite
(c) magnesium borate
(d) iron(III) dihydrogenphosphate

9.16 Write the names for each of the following compounds.

(a) Na_2SO_3
(b) $Sr(NO_2)_2$
(c) $CsHSO_3$
(d) $KBrO_2$
(e) $CuClO$
(f) $CuSO_4 \cdot 5H_2O$
(g) $Fe(NO_3)_2 \cdot 6H_2O$

9.17 Write formulas for each of the following.

(a) sodium chlorite
(b) nickel(III) hydrogencarbonate
(c) mercurous selenite
(d) magnesium perbromate
(e) lead(IV) dihydrogenphosphate
(g) sodium acetate trihydrate

9.13 (a) Nitric acid, (b) phosphorous acid, (c) sulfurous acid, (d) hypochlorous acid; 9.14 (a) H_3BO_3, (b) H_2SeO4, (c) $HClO_2$, (d) H_2CO_3; 9.15 (a) K_3AsO_4, (b) $RbHSO_3$, (c) $Mg_3(BO_3)_2$, (d) $Fe(H_2PO_4)_3$; 9.16 (a) Sodium sulfite, (b) strontium nitrite, (c) cesium hydrogensulfite, (d) potassium bromite, (e) copper(I) hypochlorite, (f) Copper(II) sulfate pentahydrate, (g) iron(II) nitrate hexahydrate; 9.17 (a) $NaClO_2$, (b) $Ni(HCO_3)_3$, (c) Hg_2SeO_3, (d) $Mg(BrO_4)_2$, (e) $Pb(H_2PO_4)_4$, (f) $NaC_2H_3O_2 \cdot 3H_2O$

9.4 Organic Compounds

Modern **organic chemistry** is the study of the properties and reactions of carbon compounds. In the past, chemists did not define organic chemistry in this way. In 1807, Berzelius proposed that compounds derived from living things were "organic" and all others were "inorganic," not derived from life. Such a definition appealed to scientists of the time, especially when it was well known that organic substances could easily be converted to inorganic substances by heating or treatment with acids in the laboratory. They felt that the opposite conversion, from inorganic to organic, was not possible.

Early nineteenth century scientists were certain that organic compounds could be produced only within living systems. At that time it was thought that living things possessed a "vital force" that changed inorganic substances to organic ones. Scientists believed that without the vital force inorganic compounds could not be converted to an organic compound. In 1828, Friedrich Wohler (1800-1882) stunned the world of science and shattered the vital force theory (also called vitalism) by synthesizing an organic compound from an inorganic salt.

Wohler heated the inorganic salt ammonium cyanate NH_4OCN, and analyzed the products; he discovered that urea, NH_2CONH_2, was one of the reaction products.

$$NH_4OCN \rightarrow H_2NCONH_2$$

Urea is a byproduct of protein metabolism found in urine. Wohler communicated his finding to his former professor, Berzelius, who then realized that his own ideas concerning the definition of organic chemistry would have to be modified in light of Wohler's new evidence.

Organic chemistry is one of the most exciting areas of chemistry because of the importance of compounds that contain C. Organic compounds are the major components of living systems, and life as we

> Friedrich Wohler studied medicine and received his degree as a physician before becoming a chemist. Besides making his famous discovery, Wohler was one of the first to investigate how compounds are metabolized in living things.

know it could not exist without these compounds. The food that we eat, the gasoline we use in our cars, and most of our possessions are principally composed of organic compounds.

Organic compounds differ significantly from inorganic compounds. Most organic compounds have lower densities, melting points, and boiling points than do most inorganic compounds. Many organic substances are flammable, an uncommon property of inorganic compounds. Finally, most organic compounds are less water-soluble and more soluble in nonpolar solvents than most inorganic compounds.

Some carbon-containing substances are not classified as organic compounds because their properties more closely resemble those of inorganic compounds. For example, carbon dioxide, CO_2, carbon monoxide, CO, carbon disulfide, CS_2, and hydrogen cyanide, HCN, are inorganic compounds. In addition, salts that contain carbonate, CO_3^{2-}, bicarbonate, HCO_3^-, thiocyanate, SCN^-, and cyanate, OCN^-, are also classified as inorganic compounds.

Organic compounds are divided into two major classes, hydrocarbons (*hydro*, hydrogen) and hydrocarbon derivatives. **Hydrocarbons** are compounds composed exclusively of C and H. **Hydrocarbon derivatives** are those compounds that contain C, usually H, and at least one other element. Hydrocarbon derivatives normally possess one or more of the following elements besides C and H: O, N, S, P, halogens (*X*), and various metals. ❖

9.5 HYDROCARBONS AND HYDROCARBON DERIVATIVES

Hydrocarbons are divided into four groups: (1) alkanes, (2) alkenes, (3) alkynes, and (4) aromatics. The **alkanes**, **alkenes**, and **alkynes** are together known as **aliphatic hydrocarbons**. Aromatics possess a special structure called an aromatic ring that makes them chemically distinct. Accordingly, organic chemists place them in a separate group called the aromatic hydrocarbons.

WWWolfe 4
(See WWWolfe
section at the end of
the chapter.)

Alkanes

Alkanes are hydrocarbons that possess C atoms bonded to the maximum number of H atoms possible. Alkanes do not have multiple bonds. Since alkanes cannot chemically add any more H atoms, they are frequently called the **saturated hydrocarbons**— saturated with respect to the number of H atoms in the molecule. In alkanes, C atoms are bonded in chains and rings. First, we will consider alkanes composed of molecules with C chains.

Methane, CH_4, is the simplest alkane. It has four H atoms bonded tetrahedrally to the central C atom (Fig. 9.4). The bond angle between H atoms in methane and in the other alkanes is 109.5°. Methane is a colorless, odorless gas with a melting point of –183°C and a normal boiling point of –162°C. Such low melting and boiling points indicate that the intermolecular forces (forces between the molecules) among methane molecules are weak (London forces). They result because methane is a nonpolar covalent molecule.

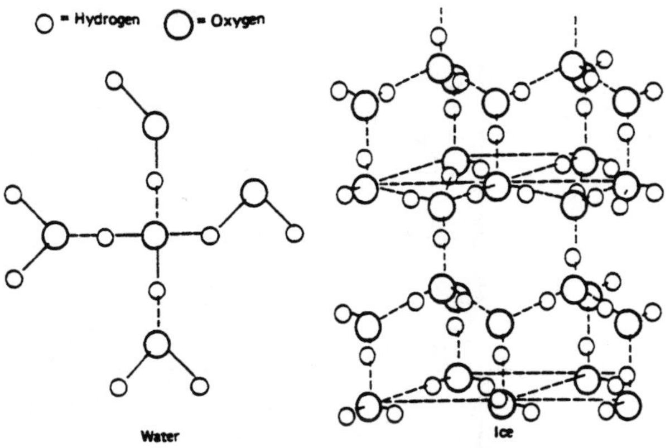

Figure 9.4 Methane molecules are tetrahedral with 109.5° bond angles. Each C—H bond is polar, but due to its symmetry the molecule is nonpolar.

Methane, like many organic compounds, is referred to by one or more common names. For example, methane is frequently called swamp gas. When plants decay in the absence of oxygen, a quantity of methane is produced. Such conditions exist in swamps and marshlands where decaying plant matter is covered with water. Methane is the principal component of natural gas. Natural gas is used for heating and cooking. Because natural gas is odorless, a small quantity of an organic sulfur compound with a distinct odor is added so that gas leaks can be detected.

To alleviate the problem of having more than one name for a compound, organic chemists have adopted the IUPAC systematic procedure for naming organic compounds. IUPAC stands for the International Union of Pure and Applied Chemistry, an international organization that oversees the naming of chemical substances. Table 9.6 lists the accepted names for the first 10 alkanes.

> Many more organic compounds exist than there are words in the English language. The task of properly naming such an immense number of compounds is not an easy task.

Each name is composed of two parts: stem and suffix. The stem indicates the number of C atoms in a molecule. For example, *eth* tells us that two C atoms are in a molecule. The stem *prop* means three C atoms, and *but* indicates four C atoms. The suffix tells what class of organic compound to which the molecule belongs. The alkanes are designated by the ending *ane*. Each class of organic compound has its own unique suffix.

Alkanes have the general formulas C_nH_{2n+2}. If n C atoms are in the molecule, then $2n + 2$ H atoms are attached. An alkane with 20 C atoms, for example, will have 42 (($2 \times 20) + 2$) hydrogen atoms. Alkanes are an example of a homologous series of compounds. A **homologous series** is a group of compounds in which one member differs from the compound that immediately precedes or follows it by a fixed amount, in this case by a CH_2

unit. If we select ethane, C_2H_6, it differs from both methane, CH_4, and propane, C_3H_8, by a CH_2 unit. Homologous series have observable trends in physical properties and exhibit similar chemical properties.

TABLE 9.6 NAMES OF THE FIRST 10 ALKANES

Molecular formula	Condensed formula*	IUPAC name
CH_4	CH_4	Methane
C_2H_6	CH_3CH_3	Ethane
C_3H_8	$CH_3CH_2CH_3$	Propane
C_4H_{10}	$CH_3(CH_2)_2CH_3$	Butane
C_5H_{12}	$CH_3(CH_2)_3CH_3$	Pentane
C_6H_{14}	$CH_3(CH_2)_4CH_3$	Hexane
C_7H_{16}	$CH_3(CH_2)_5CH_3$	Heptane
C_8H_{18}	$CH_3(CH_2)_6CH_3$	Octane
C_9H_{20}	$CH_3(CH_2)_7CH_3$	Nonane
$C_{10}H_{22}$	$CH_3(CH_2)_8CH_3$	Decane

*A condensed formula is one in which the number of bonded hydrogen atoms is written to the right of each carbon atom. This is a shorthand way to express organic structural formulas.

The first four members of the alkane series, methane to butane, are gases at room temperature. Pentane to heptadecane, $C_{17}H_{36}$, are liquids, and the remaining alkanes, those with 18 or more carbon atoms, are waxy solids. Such a trend shows a gradual increase in boiling and melting points with increased molecular mass. The alkanes as a group are inert, and only react under the proper conditions with substances such as the halogens or oxygen.

Besides the alkanes composed of molecules with unbranched chains, alkanes exist with branches in the chain. For example, the molecular formula of butane is C_4H_{10}. Molecules of butane have four C atoms in a continuous chain.

$$CH_3—CH_2—CH_2—CH_3$$

Another compound with the same molecular formula but with a different structural formula is

$$
\begin{array}{c}
CH_3 \\
| \\
CH_3—CH—CH_3
\end{array}
$$

This molecule has a branch in the C chain.

There are 75 isomers of decane, 366,319 isomers of eicosane ($C_{20}H_{42}$), and 4,111,846,763 isomers of triacontane ($C_{30}H_{62}$).

These two compounds are **structural isomers (constitutional isomers),** i.e., compounds with the same molecular formula but with a different arrangement of C atoms (different structural formulas). Each has its own unique set of physical and chemical properties.

The IUPAC has established specific rules for naming the alkanes with branches in the chain. These rules are as follows:

Rule 1 Find the longest continuous chain of C atoms in the molecule.

This is accomplished by starting at one end of the molecule and counting C atoms that are consecutively bonded. The name of the molecule is derived from the name of the alkane with the same number of C atoms in the longest continuous chain. This is called the **parent alkane.** All of the other C atoms in the molecule are considered branches off the main chain, and are called **substituent groups**. In the above example the longest continuous chain is three C atoms; hence, the parent alkane is propane.

Rule 2 Number the longest continuous chain so the lowest possible number is given to the C atom to which the substituent group is bonded.

Our example has only one substituent group, which is in the center of the longest chain. Thus, it does not matter in which direction the three-carbon chain is numbered.

$$
\begin{array}{ccc}
 & CH_3 & \\
1 & 2| & 3 \\
CH_3 & \!\!\!\!-CH- & \!\!\!\!CH_3
\end{array}
$$

Rule 3 Identify each substituent group in the chain, and the carbon to which it is attached.

A name is required for the substituent group CH_3. This group is the first in a series of what are called **alkyl groups.** An alkyl group is an alkane minus one H atom ($CH_4 - H = CH_3-$) bonded to a C chain or other organic structure. To name alkyl groups, remove the *ane* ending and replace with *yl*. Therefore, a CH_3- group is a *methyl* group (methane – *ane* + *yl*). If an H atom is removed from ethane, a C_2H_6, an ethyl group, C_2H_5-, results. Methyl and ethyl groups are the only alkyl groups that we will consider in this brief introduction to organic compounds. Nonetheless, organic compounds have propyl (C_3H_7-), butyl (C_4H_9-), pentyl ($C_5H_{11}-$), and hexyl ($C_6H_{13}-$) groups.

In our example, a methyl group is bonded to the second C atom of the three-carbon chain.

Rule 4 Write the name of the compound by first writing the number of the C atom to which the substituent group is bonded, followed by a hyphen connected to the name of the substituent group and the name of the parent hydrocarbon.

Thus, the name of the hydrocarbon we are considering is **2-methylpropane** or methylpropane, for short. If we analyze the name, we see that on the second C atom of a three-carbon chain is a methyl group, CH_3-.

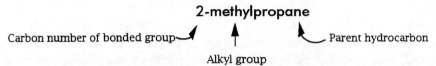

Often the "2" is not included in the name of 2-methylpropane because it is the only C atom that can bond to the methyl group without changing the molecule.

To illustrate both structural isomers and IUPAC naming, let us identify and name all of the structural isomers of pentane, C_5H_{12}. Starting with pentane, the unbranched chain is

$$CH_3CH_2CH_2CH_2CH_3 = pentane$$

Next we can write a four-carbon chain with one substituent group.

$$
\begin{array}{cccc}
& & CH_3 & \\
& & |2 & \\
4 & 3 & | & 1 \\
CH_3 & -CH_2 & -CH & -CH_3
\end{array}
$$

To write the name of this compound, follow each of the above steps: (1) Identify the longest continuous chain: four C atoms are in the longest chain. (2) Number the chain, starting from the end closest to the substituent group. (3) Identify substituent groups and the C atom to which they are bonded: A methyl group is bonded to the second C atom. (4) Write the name of the compound, starting with the number of the C atom to which the substituent group is bonded, followed by the names of the alkyl group and the parent hydrocarbon. Thus, the name of this compound is **2-methylbutane.**

The compound 2-methylbutane is the only pentane isomer with butane as the parent hydrocarbon. If we write the structure with the methyl group bonded to the next carbon in the chain, we have just found another way of writing 2-methylbutane. Following the rules, the chain should be numbered starting from the end closest to the substituent group.

$$
\begin{array}{cccc}
& CH_3 & & \\
& |2 & & \\
1 & | & 3 & 4 \\
CH_3 & -CH & -CH_2 & -CH_3
\end{array}
$$

The remaining structural isomer of pentane has a parent chain of three C atoms with two methyl groups bonded to the second C atom.

$$
\begin{array}{ccc}
& CH_3 & \\
& |2 & 3 \\
1 & | & \\
CH_3 & -C & -CH_3 \\
& | & \\
& CH_3 &
\end{array}
$$

Following the rules, we find that three C atoms form the longest continuous chain, with two methyl groups attached at the second carbon. To indicate that two groups are bonded to the chain, the prefix *di* is placed in front of methyl, and to indicate that both methyl groups are bonded to the second C atom, the number 2 is written twice separated by a comma. A hyphen is used to attach these numbers to the name. The correct name for the compound is **2,2-dimethlylpropane.**

Example Problem 9.1 shows another example of how write the name of an alkane.

Example Problem 9.1

Draw the structures and write the names of all pentane isomers of heptane.

Solution

The molecular formula of heptane is C_7H_{16}. The pentane isomers have five C atoms in their longest continuous chains. Hence, two C atoms and their H atoms must be attached to the five-carbon chain. To begin writing the isomers, let bond two methyl groups to the second C atom. Note that no methyl groups can be bonded to the first C atom because it will extend the length of the chain. This compound is **2,2-dimethylpentane**.

$$CH_3 - CH_2 - CH_2 - \underset{\underset{CH_3}{|}}{\overset{\overset{CH_3}{|}}{C}} - CH_3$$

One of the methyl groups can be moved to the third C atom, producing **2,3-dimethylpentane**.

$$CH_3 - CH_2 - \overset{\overset{CH_3}{|}}{CH} - \overset{\overset{CH_3}{|}}{CH} - CH_3$$

Placing methyl groups on the second and fourth C atoms gives **2,4-dimethylpentane**.

$$CH_3 - \overset{\overset{CH_3}{|}}{CH} - CH_2 - \overset{\overset{CH_3}{|}}{CH} - CH_3$$

Both methyl groups can bond to the third C atom, resulting in the molecule **3,3-dimethylpentane**.

$$CH_3 - CH_2 - \underset{\underset{CH_3}{|}}{\overset{\overset{CH_3}{|}}{C}} - CH_2 - CH_3$$

Finally, an ethyl group, CH_3CH_2-, can bond to the third C atom. This produces **3-ethylpentane**.

$$CH_3 - CH_2 - \underset{}{\overset{\overset{CH_3}{\overset{|}{\underset{|}{CH_2}}}}{CH}} - CH_2 - CH_3$$

Hence, five structural pentane isomers of heptane exist.

Exercise

Write the names of all hexane isomers of octane. (2,2-dimethylhexane, 2,3-dimethylhexane, 2,4-dimethylhexane, 2,5-dimethylhexane, 3,3-dimethylhexane, 3,4-dimethylhexane, 3-ethylhexane)

Cycloalkanes

So far we have seen that alkanes exist as chains and branched chains. They can also exist as ring structures. An alkane ring structure, or **cycloalkane,** is one in which each C atom is bonded to two other C atoms and usually two H atoms. A three-carbon cycloalkane is the smallest ring structure:

Cyclopropane

To write the names of cycloalkanes, we place the prefix *cyclo* in front of the name of the parent alkane. Consequently, a three-carbon cycloalkane is called cyclopropane. The next compound in the homologous series is cyclobutane. Its structure is

> Cyclopropane is an excellent anesthetic, but it must be handled carefully for it is explosive.

Cyclobutane

Next in the series are cyclopentane, cyclohexane, and cycloheptane

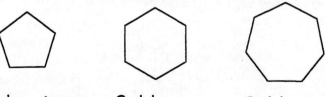

Cyclopentane   Cyclohexane   Cycloheptane

Note that the general formula of the cycloalkanes is different from that of the alkanes in chains. Cycloalkanes have the general formula C_nH_{2n}. Cycloalkanes can also have alkyl groups bonded to the ring. Consider the following examples: methylcylopentane and 1,2-diethylcyclohexane.

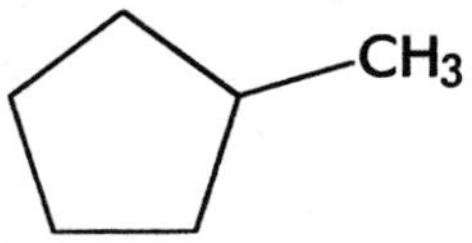

Methylcyclopentane 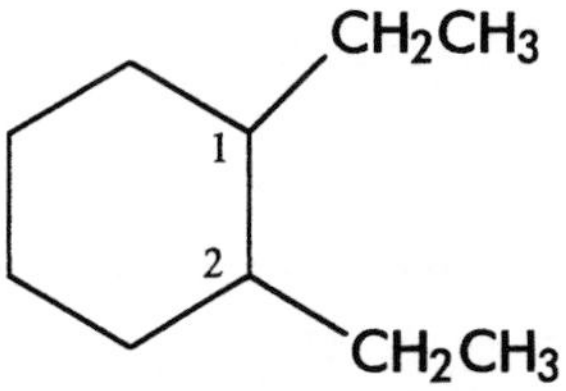   1,2-Diethylcyclohexane

REVIEW EXERCISES

9.18 What are the four classes of hydrocarbons?

9.19 Write the names of the unbranched alkanes with the following numbers of C atoms in the molecule.

(a) two
(b) four
(c) five
(d) seven
(e) nine

9.20 What are the molecular formulas of the following compounds?

(a) methane
(b) propane
(c) pentane
(d) hexane
(e) decane

9.21 Write the condensed formulas for the following structures.

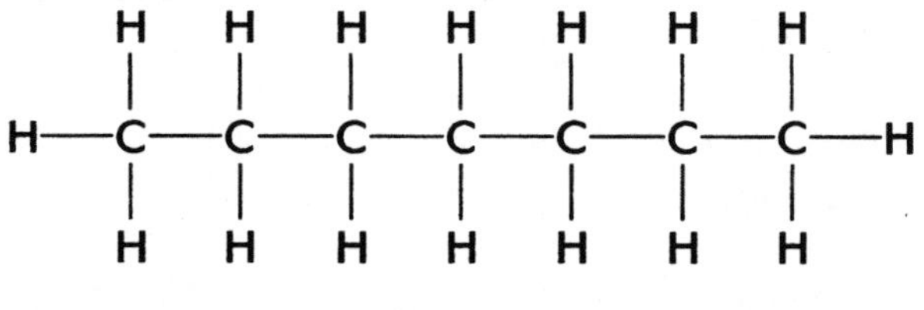

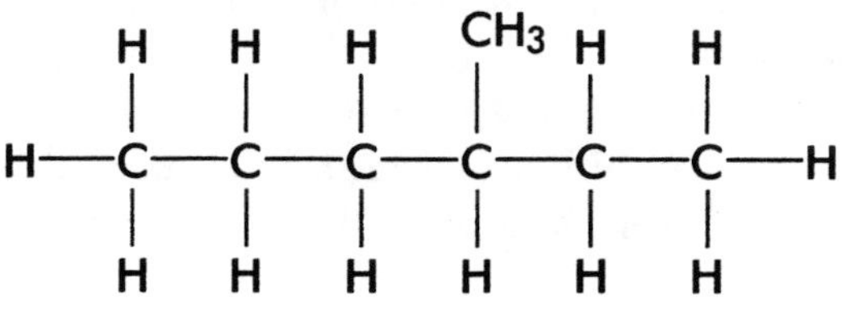

9.22 Draw the structures and write the IUPAC names for all five isomers of hexane.

9.23 (a) Draw the structure of the simplest cycloalkane.

(b) How is the structure of this molecule different from that of its parent molecule that does not have a ring?

9.21 (a) $CH_3(CH_2)_5CH_3$, (b) $CH_3CH_2CH_2CH(CH_3)CH_2CH_3$; 9.22 Hexane, 2-methylpentane, 3-methylpentane, 2,2-dimethylbutane, 2,3-dimethylbutane; 9.23 (b) It is a ring structure with the formula C_3H_6. The parent is composed molecules that are chains that have the formula C_3H_8.

Alkenes

Alkenes are hydrocarbons that contain a C—C double bond. Alkenes are classified as unsaturated hydrocarbons. **Unsaturated hydrocarbons** undergo hydrogenation reactions (reaction with H_2 gas in the presence of a catalyst) and add at least one mole H_2 per one mole of compound. After adding H_2, they become saturated and produce alkanes.

> The general formula for alkenes is C_nH_{2n}

$$\begin{array}{ccc} \text{Alkene} & & \text{Alkane} \\ \text{(Unsaturated)} & & \text{(Saturated)} \end{array}$$

The simplest alkene has two C atoms joined by a double bond.

$$H_2C=CH_2$$
Ethene

All alkenes are given the ending *ene* in the IUPAC naming system. Thus, the simplest alkene is ethene, C_2H_4. (A common name, ethylene, is used most often.) Following ethene in the alkene homologous series is the three-carbon alkene, propene, C_3H_6:

$$H_2C=CHCH_3$$
Propene

Both ethene and propene are gases at room temperature; they have normal boiling points of $-102°C$ and $-48°C$, respectively. The low boiling points of the alkenes are due to the weak forces (London forces) between their molecules.

Butene, C_4H_8, is the next alkene in the series. Two structural isomers of butene exist. With four C atoms in the chain, the double bond can be either between the first and second C atoms or between the second and third C atoms. The structures of the two butene isomers are as follows:

$$\overset{4}{C}H_3-\overset{3}{C}H_2-\overset{2}{C}H=\overset{1}{C}H_2 \qquad \overset{4}{C}H_3-\overset{3}{C}H=\overset{2}{C}H-\overset{1}{C}H_3$$
1-Butene   2-Butene

To distinguish between these two isomers, a number that indicates the position of the double bond is placed before the name of the compound. Thus, in 1-butene the C—C double bond is between C_1 and C_2, whereas in 2-butene the double bond is between C_2

and C_3.

The number added to the names of alkenes tells you the first C atom in the chain that has the double bond. Consider the structure of 2-heptene.

$$CH_3CH{=}CHCH_2CH_2CH_2CH_3$$
2-Heptene

As with the alkanes, no limit exists for the number of C atoms that can be in an alkene chain. Like alkanes, alkenes can also be composed of branched chains and rings. An example of a cycloalkene is cyclohexene.

Cyclohexene

An alkene molecule can also possess more than one double bond. Those alkenes containing two double bonds are called **alkadienes, or dienes,** for short. One interesting alkadiene is 2-methyl-1,3-butadiene, commonly called isoprene.

$$\begin{array}{c} CH_3 \\ | \\ H_2C{=}C{-}CH{=}CH_2 \end{array}$$

Isoprene (2-methyl-1,3-butadiene)

Under the proper conditions, isoprene, like many alkenes, combines with itself forming high-molecular-mass compounds collectively called **polymers.** Substances containing long chains of connected isoprene molecules resemble natural rubber (*cis*-polyisoprene).

Polymers result when one or more monomers (small molecules) combine to form long chains of bonded monomer units. Common polymers include polyethylene, polyvinylchloride (PVC), polystyrene, nylon, and Teflon.

Alkynes

Alkynes are molecules that have a C—C triple bond and, like alkenes, are unsaturated hydrocarbons. One mole of an alkyne combines with two moles of $H_2(g)$ to form a saturated hydrocarbon. Ethyne is the simplest alkyne:

> The general formula for alkynes is C_nH_{2n-2}.

$$HC{\equiv}CH$$
Ethyne

Alkynes are named in a similar manner to alkenes except that *yne* is placed after the stem to indicate that a triple bond is in the molecule.

Ethyne (or acetylene, as it is more often called) is industrially the most significant alkyne. It is relatively inexpensive to synthesize. Lime, CaO, is heated with C to produce calcium carbide, CaC_2, which is combined with water to produce acetylene.

$$CaO + 3C \rightarrow CaC_2 + CO$$

$$CaC_2 + 2H_2O \rightarrow HC \equiv CH + Ca(OH)_2$$

Acetylene is combusted in oxyacetylene torches, which are used to weld and cut through metals.

Aromatic Hydrocarbons

Aromatic hydrocarbons are those that possess the general properties and structure of benzene, C_6H_6.

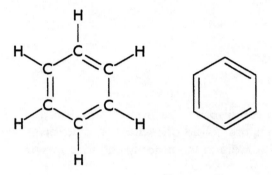

Complete structure   Shorthand structure

Benzene

Many structures are classified as aromatic hydrocarbons. However, in our cursory discussion, we will consider only the benzenelike aromatics.

In 1865, August Kekule' first proposed the cyclic structure of benzene. It was purportedly the result of a dream he had in which he saw a snake bite its own tail.

Benzene is unique with respect to the classes of hydrocarbons already discussed. In the structure that we draw for benzene, it appears as if benzene is a cyclic molecule with alternating double and single bonds. Nevertheless, benzene molecules exhibit **resonance.** Molecules that exhibit resonance have delocalized electrons which means that the actual structure of benzene resembles the average of the resonance structures.

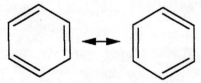

Two resonance structures of benzene

Benzene molecules actually have no double or single bonds. Instead, each bond in benzene is intermediate between a single and a double bond, and has a bond order of 1.5. Accordingly, most chemists represent a molecule of benzene by drawing a six-membered ring with a circle in the center.

Benzene

Other aromatic hydrocarbons have the benzene structure with substituent groups attached. If a methyl group is bonded to the ring, toluene, also known as methylbenzene, results.

CH₃

Toluene (methylbenzene)

The series continues with ethylbenzene, which has an ethyl group bonded to the ring.

CH₂CH₃

Ethylbenzene

More than one group can bond to a benzene ring. In fact any combination of up to six substituent groups can bond to a benzene ring. If, for example, two methyl groups (or two of any substituent group) are bonded to a benzene ring, three different structural isomers are possible.

| 1,2-Dimethylbenzene | 1,3-Dimethylbenzene | 1,4-Dimethylbenzene |
| o-Xylene | m-Xylene | p-Xylene |

In the first structure, the two methyl groups are attached to C_1 and C_2, giving 1,2-dimethylbenzene. The second structure has the two methyl groups attached to the C_1 and C_3 positions, resulting in 1,3-dimethylbenzene. In the third structure, the methyl groups are attached to C_1 and C_4, and this compound is 1,4-dimethylbenzene. Another name for the three isomers of dimethylbenzene is xylene. Three terms are used to represent the placement of two substituents on a benzene ring: (1) *ortho or o,* attachment at C atoms 1 and 2; (2) *meta or m,* attachment at C atoms 1 and 3; and (3) *para or p,* attachment at C atoms 1 and 4. Many people call the dimethylbenzenes o-xylene, *m*-xylene, and *p*-xylene.

Hydrocarbon Derivatives

Hydrocarbon derivatives are organic compounds that also have atoms such as oxygen, nitrogen, sulfur, phosphorus, and halogens. Each class of hydrocarbon derivative is characterized by a functional group. **Functional groups** are a specific arrangement of atoms that give a class of organic compounds their characteristic chemical properties. Functional groups, themselves, are bonded to a carbon chain or ring. Table 9.7 lists the primary **hydrocarbon derivatives** with their functional groups. The symbol R is employed in organic chemistry to represent any alkyl group.

TABLE 9.7 HYDROCARBON DERIVATIVES

Class	Functional group	Structural formula	Condensed structural formula
Alcohol	—OH	R—OH	ROH
Ether	—O—	R—O—R′	ROR′
Aldehyde	$\overset{\displaystyle O}{\overset{\|}{—C—H}}$	$\overset{\displaystyle O}{\overset{\|}{R—C—H}}$	RCHO
Ketone	$\overset{\displaystyle O}{\overset{\|}{R—C—R'}}$	$\overset{\displaystyle O}{\overset{\|}{R—C—R'}}$	RCOR′
Carboxylic acid	$\overset{\displaystyle O}{\overset{\|}{—C—OH}}$	$\overset{\displaystyle O}{\overset{\|}{R—C—OH}}$	RCOOH
Ester	$\overset{\displaystyle O}{\overset{\|}{—C—OR'}}$	$\overset{\displaystyle O}{\overset{\|}{R—C—OR'}}$	RCOOR′
Amide	$\overset{\displaystyle O}{\overset{\|}{—C—NH_2}}$	$\overset{\displaystyle O}{\overset{\|}{R—C—NH_2}}$	$RCONH_2$
Amine	$—NH_2$	$R—NH_2$	RNH_2
Nitrile	—CN	R—CN	RCN
Thiol	—SH	R—SH	RSH
Thioether	—S—	R—S—R′	RSR′
Halide	—X (X = F, Cl, Br, I)	R—X	RX

*R′ indicates that the second alkyl group does not necessarily have to be the same as the first, although it can be.

WorldWideWolfe CHEMISTRY LINKS

Connect to WorldWideWolfe at

http://www.mindspring.com/~drwolfe/WWWolfe_hcc_1025_links.htm

and link to the following sites.

Inorganic Compounds

1. Determining Oxidation Numbers A tutorial that shows how to determine the oxidation numbers of atoms in molecules.

2. Nomenclature and Formula Writing of Inorganic Compounds Discusses names and formulas of inorganic compounds. It also goes over the names and formulas of acids and their salts.

Naming Compounds Takes you through the names of binary ionic, binary covalent, ternary ionic, and acid names. It also has practice problems.

3. Ion Nomenclature This page presents the most important polyatomic ions.

Organic Compounds

4. Introduction to Organic Chemistry This page discusses the beginning of modern organic chemistry. It then discusses: alkanes, alkenes, alkynes, and aromatic hydrocarbons. It concludes with discussion of some of the more important hydrocarbon derivative groups.

SUMMARY

Oxidation numbers are used to help keep track of the electrons associated with elements in compounds Oxidation numbers are needed to write formulas and equations, but they are not an actual, measurable property of elements.

     Binary compounds are those with two different elements. The names of ionic binary compounds are assigned by writing the name of the metal and then modifying the nonmetal name by dropping its ending and adding *ide*. If the compound has a metal that can exist in more than one oxidation state, then the Stock name includes roman numerals in parentheses after the metal name; these indicate the exact oxidation number of the metal.

     An old system for naming binary compounds is still employed by many people; this system requires knowledge of the Latin names for metals. Using the old name as the stem, either *ic* or *ous* is appended as a suffix, denoting the metal in its higher and lower oxidation states, respectively.

     Ternary compounds contain three different elements. Most are composed of a metal and a polyatomic ion and are named in a similar manner to that of binary compounds except that the name of the polyatomic ion is written in place of that of the nonmetal. Examples of polyatomic ions include chromate CrO_4^{2-}; nitrate, NO_3^-; cyanide,

CN^-; and hydroxide, OH^-.

Acids are substances that donate H^+ to water. Binary acids are named by attaching the prefix *hydro* and the ending *ic acid* to the stem of the name of the nonmetal. Many ternary acids are oxyacids; i.e., they contain an O atom in addition to the nonmetal and hydrogen. Oxyacid names have the endings *ic* or *ous*, depending on the oxidation state of the nonmetal. Oxyanions derived from acids are named in a systematic fashion. If the resulting ion is from an *ic acid,* the ending *ate* is placed at the end of the oxyanion; *ite* is the suffix given to oxyanions produced from *ous* acids.

Organic compounds can be divided into two categories: hydrocarbons and hydrocarbon derivatives. **Hydrocarbons** are compounds with only C and H. **Hydrocarbon derivatives** are organic compounds with halogens, oxygen, nitrogen, sulfur, or phosphorus in addition to C and H.

Alkanes, alkenes, alkynes, and, aromatics are the four classes of hydrocarbons. **Alkanes** are called the saturated hydrocarbons because they have the maximum number of H atoms bonded to their C atoms and thus have only C—C single bonds. Alkane molecules exist in chains, branched chains, and rings. Methane, CH_4, is the simplest alkane, and ethane, C_2H_6, is the next member of the series. Each succeeding member of the alkanes differs only by a —CH_2— group. Such a series of compounds is called **a homologous series.**

Alkenes have a C—C double bond and, as a result, are unsaturated hydrocarbons. **Alkynes** are also unsaturated, however, they contain a triple covalent bond. **Aromatic hydrocarbons** have a special set of properties that resemble the properties of benzene, C_6H_6. Most aromatics have a stable, benzenelike ring structure as part of their molecules.

Each class of **hydrocarbon derivative** is identified by its functional group. A **functional group** is a specific arrangement of atoms that gives a compound its a characteristic chemical properties. For example, the functional group in all alcohols is an —OH group.

KEY TERMS

alcohol	functional group
aldehyde	homologous series
alkane	hydrate
alkene	hydrocarbon derivative
alkyl group	hydrocarbon
alkyl halide	isomer
alkyne	IUPAC
amide	ketone
anhydrous salt	organic chemistry
aromatic hydrocarbons	oxidation number
binary compound	oxyacid
binary acid	oxyanion
chemical nomenclature	polyatomic ion
cyclic structure cycloalkane	R group
ester	saturated hydrocarbon
ether	Stock system

substituent group   ternary compound
ternary acid   unsaturated hydrocarbon

STUDY GUIDELINES

After completing Chapter 9, you should be able to

1. State the rules used to assign oxidation numbers and assign oxidation numbers for elements in compounds

2. Write the formulas or names of ionic binary compounds that contain metals with either fixed or variable oxidation states

3. Write the formulas or names of covalent binary compounds

4. Identify the principal oxidation states, and write names of frequently encountered ions.

5. Distinguish a binary compound from a ternary compound

6. Write the names and formulas of at least 14 polyatomic ions

7. Write names and formulas of ionic ternary compounds

8. Write names and formulas of oxyacids

9. Distinguish between binary and ternary acids

10. Name ternary acids that contain nonmetals that exist in variable oxidation states

11. Write the name of an oxyanion given the acid that it is derived from and vice versa

12. Write the name of a hydrate given its formula and vice versa

13. List the major classes of organic compounds

14. Write IUPAC names for simple alkanes

15. Draw the structures and write the names of isomers of alkanes

16. Identify and give examples of unsaturated hydrocarbons

17. Identify the basic structure of aromatic hydrocarbons

18. Give examples of important hydrocarbons from each major group

19. Write the functional groups in common hydrocarbon derivatives

EXERCISES

9.30   Define each of the following: chemical nomenclature, IUPAC, oxidation number, oxidation-reduction reaction, binary compound, ternary compound, Stock system, polyatomic ion, binary acid, ternary acid, oxyacid, oxyanion, hydrate, anhydrous salt.

Oxidation Numbers
9.31   What are the oxidation numbers of all elements in the following compounds?
(a) F_2 (b) H_2O,   (c) MgS
(d) NCl_3 (e) N_2O_5 (f) PCl_5
(g) Al_2S_3 (h) Cl_4.

9.32   What is the oxidation state of S in each of the following compounds?
(a) SO_3 (b) SO_2
(c) H_2SO_4 (d) H_2SO_3
(e) S_8 (f) $H_2S_2O_7$
(g) S_2O_3 (h) S_2F_{10}

9.33   What is the oxidation state of N in each of the following compounds?
(a) N_2,   (b) N_2O
(c) N_2O_4 (d) N_2O_3
(e) $NOCl$ (f) HNO_3
(g) $H_2N_2O_2$ (h) N_2H_4

9.34   Calculate the oxidation number of each element in the following compounds.
(a) $K_2Cr_2O_7$ (b) Na_2GeO_3
(c) Na_2UO_4 (d) $RbHSO_4$
(e) $Ca(HS)_2$ (f) U_3O_8
(g) $K_4V_2O_7$ (h) $Na_2C_2O_4$
(i) $Cu(CN)_2$ (j) Na_2O_2 (a peroxide)
(k) MgH_2 (a hydride).

9.35   Find the oxidation states of the metals in the following compounds.
(a) $CePO_3$ (b) Sb_2O_5
(c) $Zn(OH)_2$ (d) $Cr_2(SO_4)_3$
(e) $MoSeO_4$ (f) Cu_2SO_4
(g) MnH_2PO_4 (h) Hg_2CO_3
(i) $Pr_2(MoO_4)_3$ (j) $Ni(NO_3)_2 \cdot 6H_2O$

Names and Formulas of Binary Compounds
9.36   Write the name of each of the following covalent substances.
(a) CO_2 (b) N_2O
(c) CCl_4 (d) PBr_3
(e) OF_2 (f) SiO_2
(g) XeO_4 (h) IF_7

9.37   Write the names of each of the following.
(a) $SnBr_2$ (b) CoN
(c) PbS (d) Cu_3P
(e) HgO (f) Na_2Se
(g) $MgCl_2$ (h) Sc_2O_3
(i) CdI_2.

9.38   Write the formulas for each of the following.
(a) iron(III) bromide
(b) manganese(II) sulfide
(c) copper(I) iodide
(d) chromium(II) fluoride
(e) magnesium oxide
(f) barium carbide
(g) mercury(I) fluoride
(h) tin(II) nitride
(i) palladium(II) selenide
(j) rubidium phosphide.

9.39   Write the formulas of the following oxides.
(a) thallium(III) oxide
(b) uranium(IV) oxide
(c) gold(I) oxide
(d) molybdenum(V) oxide
(e) manganese(VII) oxide
(f) ruthenium(IV) oxide
(g) tungsten(VII) oxide
(h) vanadium(IV) oxide
(i) scandium(III) oxide
(j) tin(IV) oxide.

Names and Formulas of Ternary Compounds
9.40   Complete the table on the next page by writing the name of the compound that is a combination of the anion listed horizontally and the cation listed vertically.

	$C_2H_3O_2^-$	PO_4^{3-}	MnO_4^-	CN^-	CO_3^{2-}	OH^-	S^{2-}
NH_4^+							
Mg^{2+}							
Fe^{2+}							
Hg^{2+}							
Al^{3+}							
Sn^{4+}							
Rb^+							
Au^{3+}							

9.41 Complete the following table by writing the formula of the compound that is a combination of the anion listed horizontally and the cation listed vertically.

	Hydroxide	Acetate	Sulfate	Chlorate	Selenate	Nitride
Calcium						
Aluminum						
Lead(IV)						
Cobaltous						
Ammonium						
Germanium(IV)						
Tin(II)						

9.42 In the following table, the common name for a compound is given, with either its formula or modern name. Complete the table by writing the formula or modern name of the compound:

Old Name	Formula	Stock Name
Alunogenite		Aluminum sulfate
Aragonite	$CaCO_3$	
Baking soda		Sodium hydrogencarbonate
Blue vitriol	$CuSO_4 \cdot 5H_2O$	
Celestrite		Strontium sulfate
Chrome yellow	$PbCrO_4$	
Cyanoauric acid		Gold(III) cyanide
Glauber's salt	Na_2SO_4	
Hemimorphite		Zinc(II) silicate
Nitrobarite	$Ba(NO_3)_2$	

9.43 Write the formula of the compound that results when the ammonium ion is combined with each of the following ions.
(a) selenate   (b) sulfite
(c) nitrite   (d) periodate
(e) chlorate   (f) hydrogencarbonate
(g) bromite   (h) hypochlorite
(i) hydrogensulfite

9.44 Write the formulas of the compounds that result when acetate ions combine with each of the following ions.
(a) lithium   (b) zinc(II)
(c) ferrous   (d) cupric
(e) gallium(III)   (f) thallium(III),
(g) plumbic   (h) iridium(IV)

Acids

9.45 Write the name of each of the following binary acids.
(a) $HBr(aq)$ (b) $HI(aq)$
(c) $H_2Se(aq)$.   (d) $H_2S(aq)$

9.46 Write the name of each of the following oxyacids.
(a) H_3BO_3 (b) $HClO$
(c) HIO_3 (d) H_3AsO_4
(e) H_2CO_3 (f) $HBrO_4$

9.47 Lactic acid, $HC_3H_5O_3$, a weak organic acid, ionizes to a small extent in water, producing the $C_3H_5O_3^-$ ion. What is the name of the ion?

9.48 Write the names of the following acids.
(a) HIO_4 (b) $HC_2H_3O_2$
(c) H_2SeO_3 (d) HIO
(e) HCN

9.49 Write the name of the polyatomic ion in each acid in Exercise 9.48.

9.50 Write the name of each of the following polyatomic ions and the name of the acid from which it is derived.
(a) HSO_3^- (b) HPO_3^{2-}
(c) HSO_4^- (d) HCO_3^-

Additional Inorganic Exercises

9.51 Identify the oxidation states of the elements in each of the following

sodium compounds.
(a) $NaHF_2$ (b) $Na_2S_2O_6 \cdot 2H_2O$
(c) $NaBF_4$ (d) Na_2MoO_4
(e) Na_2SiF_6 (f) Na_3AsS_4

9.52   Write the name and formula of a member of each of the following classes of compounds.
(a) ternary ionic compound
(b) binary covalent compound
(c) oxyacid
(d) hydrate
(e) binary ionic compound
(f) ternary covalent compound
(g) binary acid
(h) binary metallic sulfide.

9.53   What do the following endings indicate about a compound?
(a) ite   (b) ate
(c) ide   (d) ic
(e) ous

9.54   Write the names of each of the following oxyacids.
(a) H_3AsO_4
(b) HIO_3
(c) H_2SeO_4

9.55   Write the names of each of the following hydrates.
(a) $CrPO_4 \cdot 6H_2O$
(b) $Ga_2O_3 \cdot H_2O$
(c) $In(ClO_4)_3 \cdot 8H_2O$
(d) $FePO_4 \cdot 2H_2O$
(e) $LiI \cdot 3H_2O$
(f) $Na_2CO_3 \cdot 10H_2O$.

9.56   Write the formulas of each of the following hydrates.
(a) sodium borate tetrahydrate
(b) thorium(IV) selenate nonahydrate
(c) nickel(II) phosphate octahydrate
(d) mercury(II) bromate dihydrate
(e) manganese(II) acetate tetrahydrate
(f) lead(II) bromate monohydrate.

9.57   Write the names of each of the following compounds:
(1) $(NH_4)_2S$ (2) SbI_3
(3) H_3AsO_4 (4) As_2O_3
(5) $BaCrO_4$ (6) $BeSeO_3$
(7) $BiCl_4$ (8) BN
(9) BrO_2 (10) $Cd(BrO_3)_2$
(11) $Ca(ClO)_2$ (12) S_2F_{10}
(13) $Ce(OH)_3$ (14) $CsHCO_3$
(15) Cl_2O_7 (16) $Cr_2(SO_3)_3$
(17) CoF_3 (18) $CuSeO_4$
(19) $GaCl_3$ (20) GeS_2
(21) $HCN(g)$ (22) $HCN(aq)$
(23) $HIO_3(aq)$ (24) IF_5
(25) Ir_2S_3 (26) $Fe(H_2PO_2)_3$
(27) $Pb(AsO_2)_2$ (28) $LiClO_3$
(29) $Mg(NO_3)_2$ (30) $MnAs$
(31) $Hg(BrO_3)_2$ (32) $Mo(SO_3)_3$
(33) Si_3Cl_8 (34) OsO
(35) $Pd(NO_3)_2$ (36) PBr_5
(37) $Pt(OH)_2$ (38) KH_2AsO_4
(39) $RaCO_3$ (40) ReF_6
(41) $Rh_2(SO_4)_3$ (42) Rb_2SeO_4
(43) Sc_2O_3 (44) SeF_4
(45) Ag_2TeO_3 (46) NaH_2PO_3
(47) $Sr(MnO_4)_2$ (48) S_2F_2
(49) $TlCN$ (50) $Sn(SO_4)_2$

9.58   Write the formula for each of the following:
(1) titanium(III) chloride
(2) tungsten(VI) bromide
(3) zinc(II) chromite
(4) zirconium(IV) iodide
(5) ammonium sulfite
(6) sodium hydroxide
(7) magnesium sulfate
(8) barium hypobromite
(9) cesium hydrogenphosphate
(10) bismuth(III) bromide
(11) cuprous hypochlorite
(12) aluminum nitrate
(13) ferrous arsenide
(14) lead(IV) chlorate
(15) lithium hydrogenphosphite
(16) manganese(II) oxide
(17) mercuric telluride
(18) molybdenum(IV) iodide
(19) nickel(III) bicarbonate
(20) dinitrogen tetroxide
(21) palladium(IV) silicide
(22) osmium(II) sulfate
(23) lithium chlorate
(24) hypophosphorous acid
(25) tetraphosphorus heptasulfide
(26) potassium iodate
(27) rhenium(VI) chloride
(28) tin(IV) phosphate
(29) rubidium chlorite
(30) scandium(III) sulfate
(31) silicon nitride
(32) silicic acid
(33) silver(I) phosphate
(34) sodium hydrogensulfite
(35) strontium iodate
(36) tantalum(III) nitride
(37) thallous sulfate
(38) stannic iodide

(39) zinc(II) cyanide
(40) cobalt(II) phosphate
(41) ammonium bromite
(42) aluminum nitride
(43) calcium carbide
(44) hypochlorous acid
(45) ferric acetate
(46) manganese(II) carbonate
(47) mercury(II) sulfide
(48) hydrocyanic acid
(49) potassium permanganate
(50) cerium(III) carbonate

9.59 A 5.000-g sample of a compound is found to contain 2.247 g of lead; what remains is iodine. The molecular mass of the compound is 461. (a) What is the molecular formula of the compound? (b) What is the name of the compound?

9.60 A hydrate of magnesium phosphate is found to have 25.5% water by mass. Its molecular mass is 353. (a) What is the formula of the hydrate? (b) What is the name of the hydrate?

9.61 Three sulfides of phosphorus are analyzed and found to contain 43.70% (molecular mass = 220), 64.49% (molecular mass = 348), and 72.13% S by mass (molecular mass = 444). What are the names of these phosphorus sulfides?

9.62 What is the percent composition of tungsten(VI) bromide?

Hydrocarbons

9.63 (a) What scientist is credited with the discovery that organic compounds could come from nonliving things? (b) How did he prove his point?

9.64 What is the difference between a hydrocarbon and a hydrocarbon derivative?

9.65 What distinguishes each class of hydrocarbon from the others?

9.66 How many C atoms are in each of the following hydrocarbons: (a) heptane, (b) butane, (c) decane, (d) ethane, and (e) octane?

9.67 Draw the complete structural formulas from the following condensed formulas:
(a) $CH_3CH_2CH_2CH_2CH_2CH_3$
(b) $CH_3CH_2CH_2CH_2CH_2CH_2CH_2CH_2CH_3$
(c) $CH_3CH_2CH(CH_3)CH_2CH_2CH_2CH_3$
(d) $(CH_3)_3CCH_2CH_2CH_2CH_2CH_2CH_3$

9.68 For each of the hydrocarbons in Exercise 9.67, write the name of the unbranched isomer.

9.69 Write the names of the following alkanes:

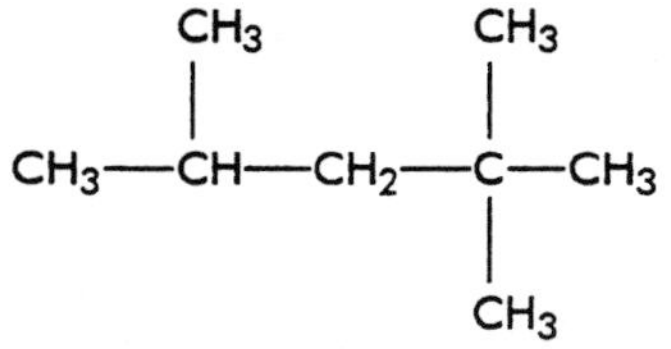

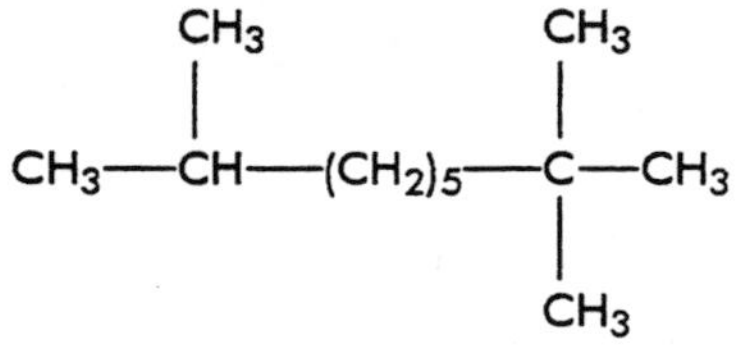

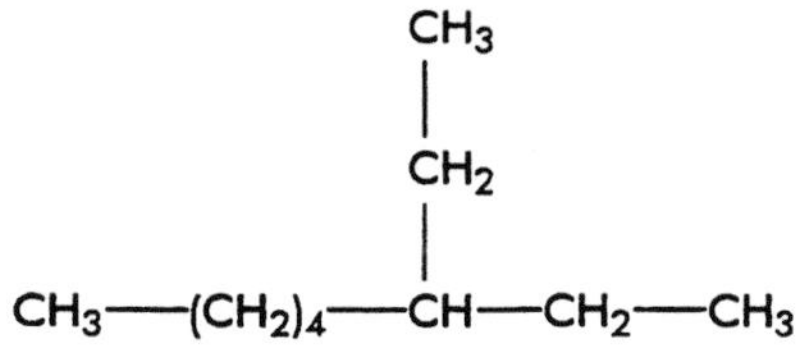

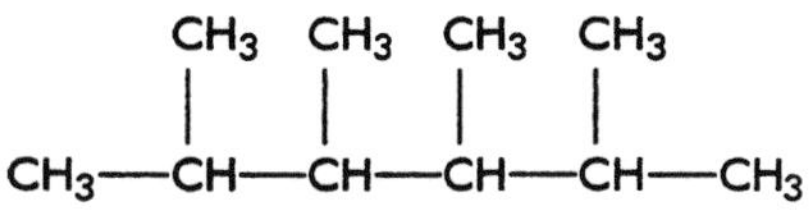

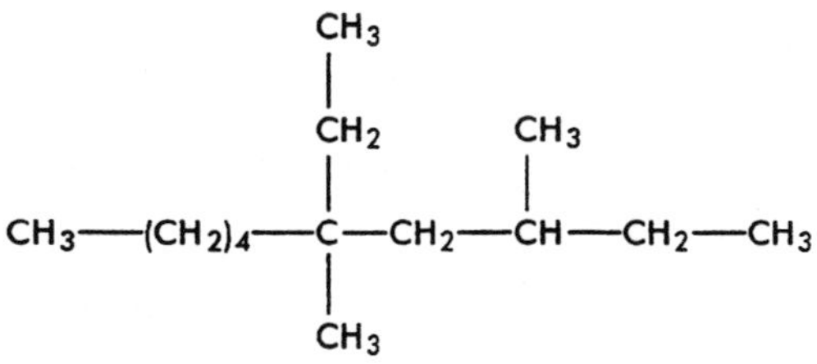

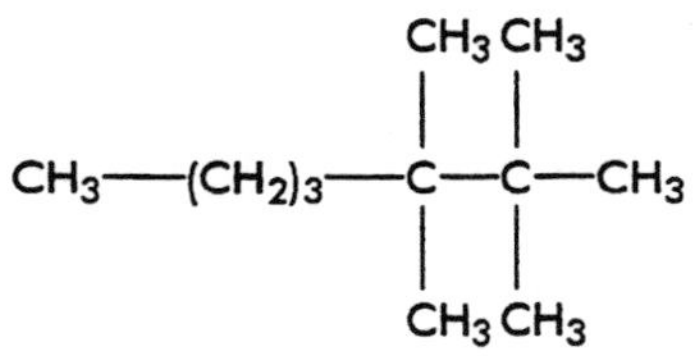

9.70 Draw the structures of:
(a) 3-methylheptane
(b) 2,2-dimethylpentane
(c) 3-ethyl-4-methyldecane
(d) 2,2,4-trimethyloctane
(e) 2,2,3,3-tetramethylhexane
(f) 4-ethylnonane
(g) ethylcyclopentane
(h) 1,2,3-triethylcyclooctane

9.71 Draw the structures and write the IUPAC names for all isomers of heptane.

9.72 Explain why a trend of increasing boiling points is found in an homologous series.

9.73 Write the names of the following cycloalkanes:

(a)

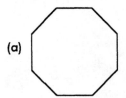

(b)

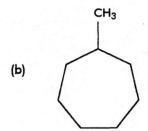

(c)

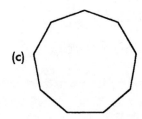

(e)

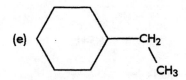

9.74 If there are *n* carbon atoms in a cycloalkane, how many H atoms are also in the molecule?

9.75 Draw the structures of the following unsaturated hydrocarbons: (a) a four-carbon alkene, (b) a six-carbon cycloalkene, (c) two unbranched five-carbon alkenes, (d) two four-carbon alkadienes, (e) all cyclic six-carbon alkadienes.

9.76 How many H atoms are in (a) 2-methylbutane, (b) nonene, (c) methylcyclopentane, (d) butyne, (e) benzene, (f) 3-methylheptane?

9.77 Draw the structures and write the names of all isomers of C_5H_{10}. Do not forget about cyclic structures.

9.78 (a) What is the general formula of the alkynes? (b) What is the general formula of cycloalkenes?

9.79 Draw the structures of the three diethylbenzenes, and write a name for each.

9.80 (a) Determine how many different trimethylbenzenes exist. (b) Draw the structure and name each trimethylbenzene.

Hydrocarbon Derivatives

9.81 What type of hydrocarbon derivative is each of the following: (a) RCOOR, (b) RX, (c) RCOR, (d) RSH, (e) $RCONH_2$, (f) RCOOH, (g) RNH_2, (h) ROR?

9.82 What functional group is in each of the following: (a) aldehydes, (b) acids, (c) amines, (d) thioethers, (e) esters?

9.83 Circle and identify each functional group in the following molecules:

(a)

$$CH_3-\underset{\underset{OH}{|}}{C}H-\underset{\underset{O}{\|}}{C}-O-CH_2-\underset{\underset{Cl}{|}}{C}\underset{OH}{\overset{O}{\diagup}}$$

(b) $Cl-CH_2-\underset{\underset{CHO}{|}}{C}H-\underset{\underset{NH_2}{|}}{C}H-CH_2-CH_2-CH_2-OCH_3$

(c)

9.84   Draw the structures of the following: (a) a four-carbon alcohol, (b) a three-carbon aldehyde, (c) a four-carbon carboxylic acid, (d) a six-carbon ketone, (e) an eight-carbon amine, (f) a cyclic five-carbon ester.

Notes and Calculations:

Chapter 9 Pretest Assignment

1. Complete each of the following statements with the correct word, number, or phase.

    a. _____ are numbers used to keep track of the electrons associated
    with atoms in molecules.

    b. A(n) _____ increases the H ion concentration when dissolved in
    water.

    c. A(n) _____ compound consists of a metal and a polyatomic ion.

    d. _____ is the oxidation state of S in S_8.

    e. _____ is the oxidation state of Cr in $(NH_4)_2Cr_2O_7$.

    f. _____ is an amorphous form of carbon.

    g. _____ is a molecule that has one or more loosely bonded water
    molecules.

    h. The _____ of nomenclature is principally used by chemists to write
    names and formulas of inorganic compounds.

    i. _____ is an example of an oxyanion that contains sulfur.

    j. _____ is the formula of the acetate ion.

    k. _____ is the formula of the borate ion.

    l. _____ are the intermolecular forces between water molecules.

    m. The _____ is the collective name given to the alkanes, alkenes,
    and alkynes.

    n. _____ is the general formula for the cycloalkanes.

    o. _____ are compounds with the same molecular formula but
    have different structural formulas.

    p. _____ is the common name for the simplest alkyne.

    q. _____ different isomers of diethylbenzene exist.

2. Write the names for each of the following.

    a. KNO_3 _____
    b. $(NH_4)_2O$ _____
    c. N_2O_5 _____
    d. $HBr(aq)$ _____
    e. $Fe(MnO_4)_3$ _____

f. $H_2SO_3(aq)$ _____

g. $Co(IO)_2$ _____

h. $CuSO_4 \cdot 5H_2O$ _____

i. Li_3P _____

j. $Al(CN)_3$ _____

3.   Write the formulas for each of the following.

a. perbromic acid   _____
b. sodium hydrogencarbonate   _____
c. mercuric arsenate   _____
d. tetraphosphorus decoxide   _____
e. stannic hydroxide   _____
f. palladium(IV) sulfide   _____
g. cuprous dihydrogenphosphate   _____
h. hydrosulfuric acid   _____
i. hypochlorous acid   _____
j. ammonium phosphite   _____

4.   Draw the structure for each the following.

a. 2,4-dimethylnonane   b. 1,1,4-trimethylcyclohexane

c. simplest aromatic compound   d. two five-carbon alkenes

5.   (a) Draw all pentane isomers of octane.

(b) Write the names for each pentane isomer of octane.

CHAPTER 10

Chemical Reactions

Chemical changes occur when substances undergo changes in their composition. When a substance undergoes a chemical change, we say that "a chemical reaction has taken place." In this chapter, we will consider some of the principal inorganic and organic chemical reactions. We will begin our discussion by considering chemical equations.

10.1 COMPONENTS OF A CHEMICAL EQUATION

It is inconvenient and time consuming to express what happens during chemical reactions by writing the complete names of all substances involved (a word equation); instead, chemists write a concise statement, called a **chemical equation,** using the symbols of the elements and the formulas of compounds. Other special symbols are added to the equation to express exactly what changes occur during chemical changes.

WWWolfe 1
(See WWWolfe section at the end of the chapter.)

A chemical equation has two parts: (1) reactants and (2) products. **Reactants,** sometimes called starting materials, are all substances present prior to the chemical change. The symbols for all reactants are listed, separated by plus signs. All reactants are written to the left of an arrow ($\rightarrow$) that separates the reactants from the products.

All **products,** substances produced after the chemical change occurs, are written to the right of the arrow, and are separated from each other by plus signs. Hence, chemical equations have the following format:

$$\text{Reactants} \rightarrow \text{products}$$

or

$$A + B \rightarrow C + D$$

In our example, hypothetical substances A and B are the reactants, and C and D are the products of the reaction. The above equation is translated as "reactant A reacts with reactant B to yield product C and product D." Note that the arrow is read as "to yield" or "yield" or "gives."

Frequently, other information is added to the equation. For example, it is important to know the physical states of the reactants and products. Four symbols are employed to indicate physical states: solid, (s); liquid, (l); gas, (g); and water, or aqueous, solution, (aq). Enclosed in parentheses, these symbols are written next to the formula. Consider the following example:

$$A(g) + B(l) \rightarrow C(aq) + D(s)$$

Translating to a word equation gives: "Reactant A, in the gas phase, combines with reactant B. in the liquid phase, yielding product C, which is dissolved in water, and product D, in the solid phase."

Conditions required for the reaction to take place are also written into a chemical equation. They are placed either above or below the arrow. If heat is needed for the chemical change, the word "heat" or more commonly the Greek uppercase delta, Δ, is written above or below the arrow. Sometimes the actual temperature is expressed.

$$A(s) \xrightarrow{\Delta} B(g) + C(s)$$

$$A(s) \xrightarrow{heat} B(g) + C(s)$$

Both equations are read as "solid reactant A is heated to yield gaseous product B and solid product C." Besides the addition of heat, some reactions occur only in the presence of a particular type of electromagnetic radiation, e.g., infrared (ir) or ultraviolet (uv).

Various reactions require **catalysts,** substances that increase the rates of reactions and are usually recovered chemically unchanged after the reaction. The word "catalyst," the abbreviation "cat," or the actual name of the catalyst is written above or below the arrow. Any special conditions (high or low pressure, presence or absence of light, etc.) are also written near the arrow. Table 10.1 summarizes the symbols used in writing chemical equations. ❖

> Most chemical reactions in living tissues are catalyzed by complex protein structures called enzymes.

TABLE 10.1 SUMMARY OF SYMBOLS USED IN CHEMICAL EQUATIONS

Symbol	Meaning
$\longrightarrow$	Yields, produces, gives
+	Separates compounds and elements
(s)	Solid state
(l)	Liquid state
(g)	Gaseous state
(aq)	Aqueous solution
$\xrightarrow{\Delta}$	Reaction requires heat
$\xrightarrow{cat}$	Reaction requires a catalyst
$\xrightarrow{uv}$	Reaction requires ultraviolet light

REVIEW EXERCISES

10.1 (a) What is a chemical change?

(b) How is a chemical change different from a physical change?

10.2 Collectively, what are the substances called that are (a) to the right of the arrow and (b) to the left of the arrow in a chemical equation?

10.3 What is the exact meaning of the following symbols used in chemical equations?

(a) +
(b) Δ
(c) (aq)
(d) $\rightarrow$

10.4 Translate the following chemical equation into a word equation:

$$C(s) + O_2(g) \rightarrow CO_2(g)$$

10.4 Solid carbon reacts with gaseous molecular oxygen yielding gaseous carbon dioxide

10.2 BALANCING CHEMICAL EQUATIONS

When an equation is written, it must obey the **law of conservation of mass,** i.e., matter cannot be created or destroyed. Specifically, the number of atoms of each different element in an equation must be the same on the left and right sides of the arrow. After a chemical change, the same types and number of atoms are present; they are merely rearranged. More simply, atoms are conserved in reactions.

WWWolfe 2
(See WWWolfe
section at the end of
the chapter.)

To obey the law of conservation of mass, an equation must be **balanced**. Balancing an equation involves placing coefficients in front of all reactants and products so that the same number of atoms of each element appears on either side of the equation.

Simple equations are balanced using the *inspection method,* which involves equalizing the number of atoms of each element by placing **coefficients** in front of all elements and compounds in the equation.

Let us illustrate how to balance equations by the **inspection method,** using the combination reaction in which hydrogen gas, $H_2(g)$, combines with oxygen gas, $O_2(g)$, to yield water vapor, $H_2O(g)$. First write the unbalanced equation, including all reactants and products.

> Coefficients are the numbers that precede the symbols and formulas in a chemical equation.

$$H_2(g) + O_2(g) \rightarrow H_2O(g) \text{ (Unbalanced)}$$

After writing the unbalanced equation, we readily see that the number of O atoms is not the same on both sides of the equation. Two O atoms appear on the left side, and only one on the right side. To balance the O atoms, we place a 2 as the coefficient of water. Two water molecules contain two O atoms.

We cannot place a 2 as a subscript next to the O atom in water because it would change the composition of water. **Never change subscripts when you balance chemical equations.** If you incorrectly place a 2 as the subscript for

> **Do not change the subscripts when you balance equations.**

oxygen, it gives a new product of the reaction, H_2O_2—hydrogen peroxide. The properties of hydrogen peroxide are vastly different from those of water!

After balancing the O atoms, we are left with the following partially balanced equation:

$$H_2(g) + \underline{O}_2 (g) \rightarrow 2H_2\underline{O}(g)$$

By balancing the O atoms, we have learned the number of H atoms needed. Two water molecules contain four H atoms ($2 \times H_2O = 4$ H and 2 O). Therefore, we place a 2 as the coefficient of $H_2(g)$ on the left side of the equation, which gives four H atoms.

$$2\underline{H}_2(g) + \underline{O}_2 (g) \rightarrow 2\underline{H}_2\underline{O}(g)$$

The last step, an important one, is to check to see that you have correctly balanced all of the atoms. If the same number of atoms of each type appears on both sides, the equation is properly balanced. If you are off by one atom, then the equation is not balanced. In our example, we find that four H atoms and two O atoms on either side of the arrow, which indicates a correctly balanced equation. It is convenient to check off or underline each atom as you verify that the equation is balanced:

> H_2 combines explosively with O_2; this reaction should not be demonstrated on a large scale unless it is carefully controlled.

$$2\underline{H}_2(g) + \underline{O}_2 (g) \rightarrow 2\underline{H}_2\underline{O}(g) \text{ (Balanced)}$$

The coefficients in a balanced equation show the ratio in which the reactants and products combine and form. Our equation now reads: "Two molecules of hydrogen gas combine with one molecule of oxygen gas to yield two molecules of water vapor." Figure 10.1 shows how hydrogen and oxygen combine to produce water. As we will learn in Chap. 12, the coefficients also indicate mole relationships in chemical reactions.

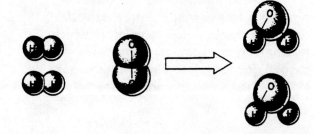

Figure 10.1 In the reaction of H_2 and O_2, two H_2 molecules combine with one O_2 molecule to produce two H_2O molecules.

Let us tackle a more complex equation to illustrate balancing by inspection. Balance the equation for the reaction in which methane gas, $CH_4(g)$, combines with oxygen gas, $O_2(g)$, to yield carbon dioxide gas, $CO_2(g)$, and water vapor, $H_2O(g)$. Methane is the principal component of natural gas, which is a widely used fuel. As before, write the unbalanced equation:

$$CH_4(g) + O_2(g) \rightarrow CO_2(g) + H_2O(g) \text{ (Unbalanced)}$$

When you balance an equation in which one element appears in many reactants and products, it is best to balance that atom last. Here, and in many equations, this atom is oxygen. Oxygen is frequently the last atom balanced, and in many cases H is balanced next to last. Thus, we should start by balancing C atoms. Because one C atom is on each side of the arrow, the C atoms are balanced as written:

$$\underline{C}H_4(g) + O_2(g) \rightarrow \underline{C}O_2(g) + H_2O(g)$$

We find four H atoms on the left side and two H atoms on the right side. A 2 is placed in front of H_2O to give four H atoms on the right:

$$\underline{C}\underline{H}_4(g) + O_2(g) \rightarrow \underline{C}O_2(g) + 2\underline{H}_2O(g)$$

All that remains is to balance the O atoms. Because we have balanced all of the products, we now know the total number of O atoms. One CO_2 molecule has two O atoms, and two H_2O molecules have two O atoms, which gives a total of four O atoms; therefore, four O atoms must be in the reactants. Looking at the left side of the equation, we only find two O atoms. Ask yourself, what number times 2 gives 4? The answer is 2, so place a 2 as the coefficient of O_2 to complete the balancing of the equation.

$$\underline{C}\underline{H}_4(g) + 2\underline{O}_2(g) \rightarrow \underline{C}O_2(g) + 2\underline{H}_2\underline{O}(g) \text{ (Balanced)}$$

Finally, check to see that all atoms are balanced. We find one C, four H. and four O atoms on each side of the equation. Our equation states, "One molecule (or mole) of methane gas combines with two molecules (moles) of oxygen gas to produce one molecule (mole) of carbon dioxide gas and two molecules (moles) of water vapor." Figure 10.2 shows this reaction diagrammatically.

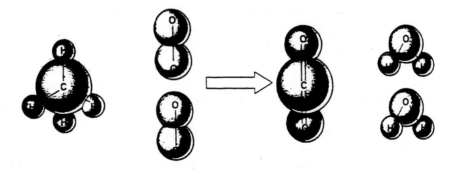

Figure 10.2 In the reaction of CH_4 and O_2, one CH_4 molecule combines with two O_2 molecules, producing one CO_2 molecule and two H_2O molecules.

A summary of the rules that can be followed to balance most chemical equations follows:

Rule 1 Write an unbalanced equation that includes the correct formulas of all reactants and products.

This first step is most significant, because one incorrect formula alters the way the equation is balanced or sometimes makes it impossible to balance. Always double-check to see that the unbalanced equation is written properly.

Rule 2 Determine a logical sequence for balancing the atoms in the equation, leaving those atoms that appear in more than one compound on each side for last.

It is frequently best to start with metals, especially those that only appear in one molecule on each side of the equation. Then proceed to nonmetals that also occur in one molecule on each side; then balance the remaining nonmetals found in more than one molecule. Step 2 is a planning step that simplifies the entire procedure and makes for an orderly approach to the problem.

> Instead of balancing equations haphazardly, think first of a "plan of attack," and then execute it.

Rule 3 Balance the atoms one at a time by placing the appropriate coefficients in front of the atoms and molecules in the equation. If possible, proceed in the predetermined order arrived at in Step 2.

After balancing an atom, underline it on both sides of the equation to indicate to yourself that it has been balanced. When all atoms are underlined, the equation should be balanced. If after balancing a couple of atoms you see that your predetermined order for balancing the atoms is not the most efficient, drop it, and proceed in a more efficient way to successfully balance the equation.

Rule 4 Check to see that all atoms are balanced in the equation. If an equal number of atoms of each type are on each side of the equation, then the equation is balanced; if not, repeat Step 3. These four steps are summarized in Figure 10.3.

Other helpful hints to consider when you balance equations are:

1. Although whole numbers are generally preferred, using fractional coefficients is correct. Certain equations are more easily balanced if one fraction is included as a coefficient. Consider the following correctly balanced equation for the reaction of sodium with water:

$$Na(s) + H_2O(l) \rightarrow NaOH(aq) + \tfrac{1}{2}H_2(g)$$

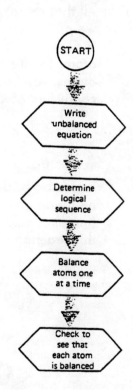

Figure 10.3 Steps to follow when you balance an equation

To remove the fraction, the coefficient of each substance in the equation is multiplied by 2.

$$2Na(s) + 2H_2O(l) \rightarrow 2NaOH(aq) + H_2(g)$$

2. If all of the coefficients are divisible by a small whole number, divide by that number to reduce them to their lowest possible whole-number values. Balanced equations are correct when they are expressed using the lowest possible multiple of coefficients. For example,

$$4C(s) + 2O_2(g) \rightarrow 4CO(g) \text{ (Incorrectly balanced)}$$

is incorrect because the coefficients can be divided by 2. The correct balanced equation is

$$2C(s) + O_2(g) \rightarrow 2CO(g)$$

3. If polyatomic ions are part of reactant molecules and if they are unchanged after the reaction, they can be balanced as a unit. For example, if two nitrate ions, NO_3^-, are within a reactant, you can place a 2 in front of a product that contains one NO_3^- to balance them. Such is the case in the following balanced equation.

$$Ca(NO_3)_2 + Na_2CO_3 \rightarrow 2NaNO_3 + CaCO_3$$

4. If an odd number of atoms of one type appear on one side and an even number of atoms are found on the other side, multiply the odd number by 2 to give an even number.

Example Problem 10.1 gives two additional examples of how to balance equations by the inspection method. ❖

Example Problem 10.1
Balance the following equations by inspection:
(a) $NH_3(g) + O_2(g) \rightarrow NO(g) + H_2O(g)$
(b) $C_2H_6(g) + O_2(g) \rightarrow CO_2(g) + H_2O(g)$

Solution
(a) $NH_3(g) + O_2(g) \rightarrow NO(g) + H_2O(g)$ (Unbalanced)
Because O atoms are in all but one compound, balance them last. If the H atoms are balanced first, then we will know the total number of N atoms in the equation. Therefore, balance H atoms and N atoms before O atoms.

First balance the H atoms by finding the lowest common multiple of 3 and 2, which is 6. Place 2 as the coefficient of NH_3, and 3 as the coefficient of H_2O.

$$2N\underline{H}_3(g) + O_2(g) \rightarrow NO(g) + 3\underline{H}_2O(g)$$

Because two NH_3 molecules are required, we know the number of N atoms needed—two. If we place a 2 in front of the NO, it will give a total of five O atoms—an odd number.

$$2\underline{N}H_3(g) + O_2(g) \rightarrow 2\underline{N}O(g) + 3\underline{H}_2O(g)$$

We can balance the O atoms in O_2 by using a fraction, 2.5.

$$2\underline{N}H_3(g) + 2.5\underline{O}_2(g) \rightarrow 2\underline{N}O(g) + 3\underline{H}_2O(g) \text{ (Balanced)}$$

The fraction in the equation can be eliminated by multiplying the equation by 2.

$$4\underline{N}H_3(g) + 5\underline{O}_2(g) \rightarrow 4\underline{N}O(g) + 6\underline{H}_2O(g) \text{ (Balanced)}$$

Check to see that 4 N, 12 H, and 10 O atoms are in this equation, and half that number in the previous equation with a fractional coefficient. Both equations are correctly balanced.

 This reaction, the oxidation of ammonia to produce NO and H_2O, is the first step in the Ostwald process for the production of nitric acid. To obtain good yields in this reaction, NH_3 is reacted with an excess amount of air heated to out 650°C and then passed over a special metal catalyst

(b) $C_2H_6(g) + O_2(g) \rightarrow CO_2(g) + H_2O(g)$ (Unbalanced)
In this equation it is convenient to start with C atoms, proceed to H atoms, and balance O atoms last.

 There are two C atoms on the left side, and they are balanced by writing a 2 as the coefficient of CO_2.

$$\underline{C}_2H_6(g) + O_2(g) \rightarrow 2\underline{C}O_2 + H_2O(g)$$

The six H atoms in C_2H_6 are balanced by placing a 3 in front of the H_2O.

$$\underline{C}_2H_6(g) + O_2(g) \rightarrow 2\underline{C}O_2 + 3\underline{H}_2O(g)$$

Seven O atoms are in the products, four in $2CO_2$ and $3H_2O$. Because two O atoms are on the left, ask yourself: "What number multiplied by 2 gives 7?" The answer is 7/2 or 3.5; thus; the coefficient is 3.5.

$$\underline{C}_2H_6(g) + 3.5\underline{O}_2(g) \rightarrow 2\underline{C}O_2 + 3\underline{H}_2O(g) \text{ (Balanced)}$$

 A check of the coefficients shows that both the reactants and the products have a total of 2 C, 6 H, and 7 O atoms; thus, the equation is balanced.

REVIEW EXERCISES
10.5 Balance each of the following equations:

(a) $N_2O_4 \rightarrow NO_2$
(b) $Al + F_2 \rightarrow AlF_3$
(c) $P_4 + Br_2 \rightarrow PBr_3$
(d) $ZnS + O_2 \rightarrow Zn + SO_2$
(e) $C + SO_2 \rightarrow CS_2 + CO$
(f) $Al + H_2SO_4 \rightarrow Al_2(SO_4)_3 + H_2$

10.6 Change the following word equation to a correctly balanced chemical equation: Calcium phosphide, Ca_3P_2, combines with water, H_2O, to yield calcium hydroxide, $Ca(OH)_2$, and phosphine, PH_3.

10.7 Translate the following word equation to a balanced chemical equation:
Aqueous sulfuric acid combines with solid aluminum hydroxide, producing liquid water and aqueous aluminum sulfate. (Hint: Start by writing the correct formula for each compound.)

10.5 (a) $N_2O_4 \rightarrow 2NO_2$, (b) $2Al + 3F_2 \rightarrow 2AlF_3$, (c) $P_4 + 6Br_2 \rightarrow 4PBr_3$, (d) $ZnS + O_2 \rightarrow Zn + SO_2$, (e) $5C + 2SO_2 \rightarrow CS_2 + 4CO$, (f) $2Al + 3H_2SO_4 \rightarrow Al_2(SO_4)_3 + 3H_2$; 10.6 $Ca_3P_2 + 6H_2O \rightarrow 3Ca(OH)_2 + 2PH_3$; 10.7 $3H_2SO_4(aq) + 2Al(OH)_3(s) \rightarrow 6H_2O(l) + Al_2(SO_4)_3(aq)$

10.3 INORGANIC CHEMICAL REACTIONS

Classification of Inorganic Reactions

Inorganic chemical reactions can be classified in many different ways. A simple, relatively common grouping of inorganic reactions is as follows.

1. Combination reactions

2. Decomposition reactions

3. Single replacement (displacement) reactions

4. Metathesis (double replacement) reactions

You should realize that this classification is an artificial grouping of reactions that help chemists to understand chemical reactions. Not all inorganic reactions fit into this simple grouping, and overlap occurs in some groups.

Do not lose sight of the fact that all of the information presented in this section is the result of studying each reaction experimentally (in the laboratory). Products obtained in chemical reactions depend mainly on the specific conditions: different conditions give different products.

It is helpful to organize and study the various classes of inorganic reactions in a systematic fashion. Many students find that placing general and specific equations on small index cards greatly assists in learning this information. Write an equation on one side of the card, and the reaction type on the other side (Figure 10.4). This is an effective technique for learning chemical equations.

Combination Reactions

Combination reactions (sometimes called addition reactions) have the following general form:

$$A + X \rightarrow AX$$

In all combination reactions, two reactants, A and X, combine to produce one product, AX.

Three different possibilities exist for combination reactions, defined by the types of substances that combine. Two elements, an element and a compound, or two compounds can be united in a combination reaction. Let's look at each case individually.

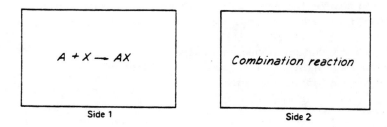

Figure 11.4 One way to learn the types of chemical reactions is to write the general equation on one side of a small index card and the name of the reaction type on the other side of the card. Prepare one card for each reaction to be learned.

Equations 1 through 3 are examples of combination reactions in which two elements combine:

$$2H_2(g) + O_2(g) \rightarrow 2H_2O(g) \tag{1}$$

$$P_4(s) + 5O_2(g) \rightarrow P_4O_{10}(s) \tag{2}$$

$$U(s) + 3F_2(g) \rightarrow UF_6(g) \tag{3}$$

In Equations 1 and 2, two nonmetals react with O_2 and form nonmetal oxides. In both reactions the nonmetals, H_2 and P_4 are oxidized, which means that they lost electrons to O_2. In Equation 3, the metal uranium reacts with F_2, producing the metal fluoride, UF_6. In this reaction the U is oxidized by the F_2. **Oxidation** occurs when a substance loses electrons. Whenever an oxidation occurs, another

Uranium hexafluoride, $UF_6(g)$, is used to separate U isotopes through a gaseous diffusion process. The UF_6 molecules with heavier isotopes (e.g., $^{238}UF_6$) diffuse more slowly than those with lighter ones (e.g., $^{235}UF_6$).

substance must undergo **reduction**, the gaining of electrons. When substances add O atoms or lose H atoms, they lose electrons; thus, they are oxidized. When substances lose O atoms or gain H atoms, they gain electrons; thus, they are reduced.

The second category of combination reactions includes the combination of an element with a compound. Equations 4 and 5 are examples of such reactions.

$$CO(g) + \frac{1}{2}O_2(g) \rightarrow CO_2(g) \tag{4}$$

$$K_2O(s) + \frac{1}{2}O_2(g) \rightarrow 2KO_2(s) \tag{5}$$

In Equations 4 and 5, O_2 combines with a nonmetal and metal oxide, respectively, yielding products with a larger number of O atoms per molecule than the reactant compounds. These two equations are also examples of **oxidation-reduction**

KO_2 is potassium superoxide. It is used by miners in special survival masks. Water from the breath of the miner reacts with KO_2 releasing life-sustaining O_2, and producing KOH which combines with exhaled CO_2 to form $KHCO_3$.

reactions.

In the third type of combination reaction, two compounds combine. Equations 6 to 8 illustrates this class of reaction.

$$SO_3(g) + H_2O(l) \rightarrow H_2SO_4(aq) \tag{6}$$

$$BaO(s) + H_2O(l) \rightarrow Ba(OH)_2(s) \tag{7}$$

$$MgO(s) + CO_2(g) \rightarrow MgCO_3(s) \tag{8}$$

In Equation 6, a nonmetal oxide, SO_3, combines with water to produce sulfuric acid, H_2SO_4. Many nonmetal oxides, when added to water, produce acids. Most metal oxides such as BaO in Equation 7, in contrast, combine with water to form bases (metal hydroxides). Equation 8 shows a

> Metal oxides are sometimes called basic anhydrides—bases without water. Many metal oxides combine with water and produce basic solutions. Similarly nonmetal oxides are called acidic anhydrides.

nonmetal oxide, CO_2, that combines with a metal oxide, MgO, to produce a salt. A **salt** is an ionic compound that does not contain OH^- or O_2^-.

Table 10.3 summarizes each of the different types of combination reactions.

Decomposition Reactions

Decomposition reactions have the general form

$$AX \rightarrow A + X$$

in which AX is a compound and A and X are either elements or compounds. Only one reactant is in a **decomposition reaction,** and under the proper conditions it breaks down to two or more products. Decomposition reactions always have a compound as the reactant; elements cannot be decomposed chemically.

Many decomposition reactions are initiated by heat, which is required to break the bonds in the starting materials. Certain less stable compounds spontaneously decompose without added heat. Other compounds require electricity, light, or catalysts to decompose.

Examples of decomposition reactions are shown in Equations 9 to 12.

$$2H_2O(l) \xrightarrow{\text{elec}} 2H_2(g) + O_2(g) \tag{9}$$

$$2N_2O(g) \xrightarrow{\Delta} 2N_2(g) + O_2(g) \tag{10}$$

$$2HgO(s) \xrightarrow{\Delta} 2Hg(l) + O_2(g) \tag{11}$$

$$CaCO_3(s) \xrightarrow{\Delta} CaO(s) + CO_2(g) \tag{12}$$

In Equations 9 through 11, compounds are decomposed to elements. With the addition of energy (heat or electricity), O_2 gas is driven off. Equation 12 shows a carbonate, $CaCO_3$, that decomposes to two oxides, CaO and CO_2, a characteristic reaction of carbonate salts.

Hydrated salts release water when heated. For example, consider Equation 13, in which calcium sulfate dihydrate is decomposed to calcium sulfate and water.

$$CaSO_4 \cdot 2H_2O(s) \xrightarrow{\Delta} CaSO_4(s) \ + \ 2H_2O(g) \qquad (13)$$

$$\text{Hydrated salt} \qquad\qquad\qquad \text{Anhydrous salt}$$

On heating, the hydrated salt, $CaSO_4 \cdot 2H_2O$, is dehydrated, resulting in the anhydrous salt, $CaSO_4$, (i.e., the salt without water).

Table 10.3 summarizes the principal types of decomposition reactions.

Single Replacement Reactions

A **replacement reaction** (also called a **displacement reaction** or **substitution reaction**) occurs when an element takes the place of another element in a compound. For example, consider the following general equation for a single replacement reaction.

$$A + BX \ \rightarrow AX + B$$

Here, element A replaces element B in compound BX. Typically in replacement reactions, a metal displaces another metal or hydrogen in the compound with which it combines. Equations 14 to 16 show representative examples of single replacement reactions.

$$Zn(s) + Pb(NO_3)_2(aq) \ \rightarrow Zn(NO_3)_2(aq) + Pb(s) \qquad (14)$$

$$Mg(s) + H_2SO_4(aq) \ \rightarrow MgSO_4(aq) + H_2(g) \qquad (15)$$

$$2K(s) + 2HOH(l) \ \rightarrow 2KOH(aq) + H_2(g) \qquad (16)$$

In Equation 14, a metal, Zn, replaces a lead ion, Pb^{2+}, that is initially associated with nitrate ions in an aqueous solution of $Pb(NO_3)_2$. During the reaction, solid lead, $Pb(s)$, is produced, the zinc is dissolved in water and becomes $Zn^{2+}(aq)$. In Equation 15, Mg metal replaces hydrogen ions, H^+, in sulfuric acid, H_2SO_4, yielding the dissolved salt $MgSO_4(aq)$ and hydrogen gas, H_2. As shown in Equation 16, more reactive metals, such as K, displace hydrogen in water. In this reaction, K replaces hydrogen in water and produces aqueous potassium hydroxide, $KOH(aq)$, and hydrogen gas, $H_2(g)$.

> When (aq) is written next to an ionic substance, MX, it indicates that the substance is dissociated into ions surrounded by many water molecules.

Metals are ranked according to their ability to displace other metals and hydrogen from compounds. This ranking is called the **activity series of metals.** A partial activity series is shown in Table 10.2. Metals on the left side of the list displace metals farther to the right. For example, Ni replaces Pb^{2+} from compounds, but Pb is unable to displace Ni^{2+} from its compounds.

$$Ni(s) + Pb(NO_3)_2(aq) \rightarrow Ni(NO_3)_2(aq) + Pb(s) \qquad (17)$$

$$Pb(s) + Ni(NO_3)_2(aq) \rightarrow \text{no reaction (NR)} \qquad (18)$$

Metals such as Li, K, Ba, Sr, Ca, and Na are the most active metals and can liberate H_2 gas when placed in cold water, steam, or acid. Less active metals, such as Mg, Al, Mn, Zn, and Fe, only liberate H_2 from steam or acid. Ni, Sn, and Pb only displace hydrogen in acidic solutions, and do not displace H atoms when combined with water. The least active metals are Hg, Ag, Pt. and Au. This group does not displace hydrogen in water or acids.

TABLE 10.2 ACTIVITY SERIES OF SELECTED METALS

Most Active <-- Least Active			
Li K Ba Sr Ca Na Mg Al Mn Zn Fe Ni Sn Pb **H** Cu Hg Ag Pt Au			
Liberates H_2 in cold H_2O, steam, or acid	Liberates H_2 in steam or acid	Liberates H_2 in acidic solution	

Halogens (not included in Table 10.2) have the capacity to displace certain halide ions. A halide ion is a halogen atom in the –1 oxidation state—e.g., fluoride, F^-; chloride, Cl^-; and bromide, Br^-. Equations 19 and 20 show that both Cl_2 and Br_2 (halogens) can displace the iodide ion, I^-, in sodium iodide.

$$Cl_2(g) + 2NaI(aq) \rightarrow 2NaCl(aq) + I_2(s) \qquad (19)$$

$$Br_2(l) + 2NaI(aq) \rightarrow 2NaBr(aq) + I_2(s) \qquad (20)$$

The order of reactivity of the halogens in such reactions is $F_2 > Cl_2 > Br_2 > I_2$. Consequently, Cl_2 displaces both Br^- and I^-, but Br_2 only displaces I^-.

All of the single replacement reactions that we have discussed can also be classified as oxidation-reduction reactions. We have already stated that an electron transfer occurs in all oxidation-reduction reactions (redox, for short). For example, let's reconsider Equation 15, in which Mg displaces hydrogen in sulfuric acid. Initially, Mg is in the zero oxidation state because it is a free metal. After the reaction, Mg^{2+} is present; thus, the oxidation state of magnesium has changed from zero to +2. Whenever the oxidation number of a substance increases, the substance has undergone oxidation; electrons (negative particles) have been lost.

$$\underset{0}{Mg} \rightarrow \underset{+2}{Mg^{2+}} + 2e^- \text{ (Oxidation)}$$

If a substance oxidizes, then another substance must be reduced. In Equation 15, the sulfuric acid is reduced. Initially, the oxidation state of the H ions in aqueous sulfuric acid is +1, but after the reaction the H atoms are a component of H_2: they have been *reduced* to the zero oxidation state. Whenever the oxidation state of a substance decreases, it has undergone reduction; it has accepted electrons.

$$2H^+ + 2e^- \rightarrow \qquad H_2 \text{ (Reduction)}$$
$${+I} 0$$

Table 10.3 summarizes the principal single replacement reactions.

Metathesis Reactions (Double Replacement Reactions)

Two substances are replaced in **metathesis reactions** (sometimes called **double replacement or double displacement** reactions). Consider the following general equation for metathesis reactions.

$$AY + BX \rightarrow AX + BY$$

In this equation, A is initially bonded to Y, and B is bonded to X. A and B are elements in positive oxidation states; X and Y are in negative oxidation states. When AY and BX combine, A replaces B from BX and B then attaches to Y, yielding AX and BY. In all metathesis reactions the more positive component of one reactant bonds with the more negative component of the other reactant.

Many reactions in aqueous solution are classified as metathesis reactions. Two of the more important aqueous reactions occur when either a solid, insoluble substance, a **precipitate**, or a gaseous product form. Equations 21 and 22 are examples of aqueous metathesis reactions in which a precipitate forms, and Equations 23 and 24 are examples of gas formation reactions.

$$NaBr(aq) + AgNO_3(aq) \rightarrow AgBr(s) + NaNO_3(aq) \tag{21}$$

$$BaCl_2(aq) + K_2SO_4(aq) \rightarrow BaSO_4(s) + 2KCl(aq) \tag{22}$$

$$2HCl(aq) + Na_2CO_3(aq) \rightarrow 2NaCl(aq) + CO_2(g) + H_2O(l) \tag{23}$$

$$KCN(aq) + HNO_3(aq) \rightarrow KNO_3(aq) + HCN(g) \tag{24}$$

In Equation21, aqueous solutions of sodium bromide and silver nitrate are mixed. The Ag^+ ion combines with the Br^- ion and produces the insoluble solid, AgBr (a precipitate).

$$Ag^+(aq) + Br^-(aq) \rightarrow AgBr(s)$$

The Na^+ and NO_3^- ions do not combine and remain dissolved in solution. AgBr is a pale-yellow solid that settles out of solution. In Equation 22, $BaSO_4$ precipitates when the Ba^{2+} combines with SO_4^{2-}.

$$Ba^{2+}(aq) + SO_4^{2-}(aq) \rightarrow BaSO_4(s)$$

The reactions in Equations 23 and 24 are gas-formation reactions, in which a gas bubbles up from the solution. In both reactions an acid (HCl and HNO_3) combines with an ionic compound to yield a gaseous product: $CO_2(g)$ in Equation 23 and HCN(g) in Equation 24. At first glance Equation 23 might not look like a metathesis reaction. Initially,

$H_2CO_3(aq)$, carbonic acid, results when two H^+ ions from 2HCl combine with the carbonate ion from sodium carbonate.

$$2H^+(aq) + CO_3^{2-}(aq) \rightarrow [H_2CO_3(aq)]$$

The carbonic acid, H_2CO_3, is placed in brackets to indicate that it is unstable and immediately decomposes to produce gaseous CO_2 and liquid H_2O.

$$[H_2CO_3(aq)] \rightarrow CO_2(g) + H_2O(l)$$

Another type of metathesis reaction occurs when acids combine with bases to form salts and often water. The members of this very important class of metathesis reaction are called **neutralization reactions.**

$$Acid + base \rightarrow salt + water$$

You should recall that acids, HA, are substances that donate hydrogen ions to water and bases are metallic hydroxides, MOH, that donate OH^- ions to water. In a neutralization reaction the H^+ and OH^- combine to produce water.

$$H^+(aq) + OH^-(aq) \rightarrow H_2O(l)$$

The remaining ions remain in solution, M^+, and A^-. Recall that when a metal cation and nonmetal anion combine, they produce a salt. The overall neutralization reaction is as follows.

$$HA(aq) + MOH(aq) \rightarrow MA(aq) + H_2O(l)$$

Equations 25 to 27 are specific examples of neutralization reactions.

$$HCl(aq) + NaOH(aq) \rightarrow NaCl(aq) + H_2O(l) \tag{25}$$

$$HNO_3(aq) + KOH(aq) \rightarrow KNO_3(aq) + H_2O(l) \tag{26}$$

$$H_2SO_4(aq) + Mg(OH)_2(aq) \rightarrow MgSO_4(aq) + 2H_2O(l) \tag{27}$$

TABLE 10.3 SUMMARY TABLE OF SELECTED INORGANIC REACTIONS

1. Combination reactions ($A + X \rightarrow AX$)
   A. Metal + nonmetal $\rightarrow$ salt
   B. Metal + oxygen $\rightarrow$ metal oxide (basic oxide)
   C. Nonmetal + oxygen $\rightarrow$ nonmetal oxide (acidic oxide)
   D. Metal + hydrogen $\rightarrow$ metal hydride
   E. Nonmetal + hydrogen $\rightarrow$ nonmetal hydride
   F. Metal oxide + water $\rightarrow$ base (metal hydroxide)
   G. Nonmetal oxide + water $\rightarrow$ acid (oxyacid)
   H. Metal oxide + nonmetal oxide $\rightarrow$ salt

II. Decomposition reactions ($AX \rightarrow A + X$)
  A. Oxide $\rightarrow$ element + oxygen gas
  B. Oxide $\rightarrow$ compound + oxygen gas
  C. Carbonate $\rightarrow$ oxide + carbon dioxide
  D. Hydrogencarbonate $\rightarrow$ carbonate + carbon dioxide + water
  E. Hydrate $\rightarrow$ anhydrous salt + water

III. Single replacement reactions ($A + BX \rightarrow AX + B$)
  A. Active metal + water $\rightarrow$ hydroxide (or oxide) + hydrogen gas
  B. Metal + acid $\rightarrow$ salt solution + hydrogen gas
  C. Metal + salt solution $\rightarrow$ displaced metal + new salt solution
  D. Metal + salt solution $\rightarrow$ gas + new salt solution
  E. Halogen + halide solution $\rightarrow$ displaced halogen + new halide solution

IV. Metathesis reactions ($AY + BX \rightarrow AX + BY$)
  A. Acid + base $\rightarrow$ salt + water
  B. Two aqueous solutions $\rightarrow$ precipitate + salt solution
  C. Two aqueous solutions $\rightarrow$ gas + salt solution
  D. Acid + carbonate solution $\rightarrow$ salt solution + carbon dioxide + water
  E. Metal oxide + acid $\rightarrow$ salt + water

REVIEW EXERCISES

10.8 Write the general form for each of the following reactions.

(a) single replacement
(b) decomposition
(c) metathesis
(d) combination

10.9 Write a balanced equation that illustrates each of the following.

(a) combination of two compounds
(b) decomposition of a metal oxide
(c) displacement of hydrogen by a metal
(d) decomposition of a hydrate

10.10 Explain how a metathesis reaction is different from a single replacement reaction. Give two examples of each.

10.11 Write three equations that illustrate different types of metathesis reactions.

10.12 Identify the reaction class to which each of the following belongs:

(a) $H_2O_2(l) \rightarrow H_2O(l) + 2O_2(g)$
(b) $Na(s) + H_2O(l) \rightarrow NaOH(aq) + \frac{1}{2}H_2(g)$
(c) $P_4O_{10}(s) + 6H_2O(l) \rightarrow 4H_3PO_4(aq)$
(d) $2Al(s) + 3Zn(NO_3)_2(aq) \rightarrow 2Al(NO_3)_3(aq) + 3Zn(s)$
(e) $CaCl_2(aq) + Na_2CO_3(aq) \rightarrow CaCO_3(s) + 2NaCl(aq)$

10.12 (a) Decomposition, (b) single replacement, (c) combination, (d) single replacement, (e) metathesis

10.4 WRITING EQUATIONS FOR METATHESIS REACTIONS

Writing equations is an important skill developed only through experience and practice. In this section we will concentrate on predicting the products of metathesis reactions, given the reactants, and then balancing the equation.

Precipitation Reactions

To illustrate how to write metathesis equations, let us consider the precipitation reaction when an aqueous solution of sodium phosphate, $Na_3PO_4(aq)$, combines with an aqueous solution of cobalt(II) chloride, $CoCl_3(aq)$.

$$Na_3PO_4(aq) + CoCl_3(aq) \rightarrow$$

(handwritten: Correction ✓) *(handwritten: (III))*

WWWolfe 3
(See WWWolfe
section at the end of
the chapter.)

In a precipitation metathesis reaction, the positive ion from one compound can potentially bond to the negative ion from the other compound and form a precipitate, a solid insoluble substance. The remaining ions stay in solution.

To begin, first write individually all of the ions in the reactants. Na_3PO_4 is composed of Na^+ and PO_4^{3-}, and $CoCl_3$ is composed Co^{3+} and Cl^-.

$$Na_3PO_4(aq) + CoCl_3(aq) \rightarrow$$
$$Na^+ \; PO_4^{3-} \qquad Co^{3+} \; Cl^-$$

This means that either the Na^+ and Cl^- or the Co^{3+} and PO_4^{3-} combine to produce the precipitate. When Na^+ and Cl^- combine, they produce NaCl.

$$Na^+ + Cl^- \rightarrow NaCl$$

When Co^{3+} and PO_4^{3-} combine, they produce $CoPO_4$.

$$Co^{3+} + PO_4^{3-} \rightarrow CoPO_4$$

Both products are in a 1-to1 ratio because the charges on the cations and anions are the same. If you have forgotten how to write formulas, refer to Section 9.2.

Which of the two products, NaCl or $CoPO_4$, precipitates from the solution? The answer to this question is obtained from a water solubility table. **Solubility** is the degree to which a substance dissolves in a solvent at a constant temperature. Table 10.4 is a solubility table that lists the general solubilities of different types of inorganic compounds. To use Table 10.4, find the class of compound of interest and determine if it is soluble or insoluble. Then check to see if the compound is one of the exceptions. *If the class of compound is soluble, the exceptions are insoluble and if the class of compound is insoluble, the exceptions are soluble.*

Remember that only five types of compounds produce insoluble substances and thus precipitate. They insoluble groups are carbonates, hydroxides, phosphates, sulfides, and sulfites. Also note that all exceptions for soluble substances will precipitate. For example, chlorides are soluble but AgCl, Hg_2Cl_2, and $PbCl_2$ will precipitate.

In our problem, we must check the table to determine whether NaCl or $CoPO_4$ will precipitate. Knowing that chlorides are soluble and sodium is not an exception, we can conclude that it will not precipitate. Hence, we add (aq) to the formula of sodium chloride, $NaCl(aq)$. Again checking the table, we see that phosphates are insoluble and cobalt is not an exception; therefore, $CoPO_4$ precipitates. Thus, add (s) to the formula of cobalt(III) phosphate, $CoPO_4(s)$. Next write $NaCl(aq)$ and $CoPO_4(s)$ as the products of reaction.

$$Na_3PO_4(aq) + CoCl_3(aq) \rightarrow CoPO_4(s) + NaCl(aq) \text{ (Unbalanced)}$$

Finally, balance the equation by placing a 3 as the coefficient of NaCl.

$$Na_3PO_4(aq) + CoCl_3(aq) \rightarrow CoPO_4(s) + 3NaCl(aq) \text{ (Balanced)}$$

Therefore, to write precipitation metathesis reactions successfully you should:

Step 1 Write the reactants of the metathesis reaction.

Step 2 Write the individual ions that make up each reactant under their formulas.

Step 3 Determine the formulas of the two products.

Step 4 Using Table 10.4, determine which compound precipitates, if any.

Step 5 Write (s) next to the precipitate and (aq) next to the other compound, and write both as products of the reaction.

Step 6 Balance the equation

Consider Example Problem 10.2 as another example of how to write a precipitation reaction.

Example Problem 10.2
Write the balanced equation for the reaction of $(NH_4)_2S(aq)$ and $Fe(NO_3)_3(aq)$.

Solution
Step 1 Write the reactants of the metathesis reaction.

$$(NH_4)_2S(aq) + Fe(NO_3)_3(aq) \rightarrow$$

Step 2 Write the individual ions that make up each reactant under their formulas.

$$(NH_4)_2S(aq) + Fe(NO_3)_3(aq) \rightarrow$$
$$NH_4^+ \ S^{2-} \qquad Fe^{3+} \ NO_3^-$$

Step 3 Determine the formulas of the two products.

The ammonium ion and nitrate have equal but opposite charges; thus, they combine in a 1-to-1 ratio.

$$NH_4NO_3$$

TABLE 10.4 SOLUBILITIES OF SELECTED INORGANIC COMPOUNDS IN WATER

Compound	Formula	Soluble	Insoluble	Exceptions*
Acetates	$C_2H_3O_2^-$	✔		
Ammonium	NH_4^+	✔		
Bromides	Br^-	✔		$AgBr$, Hg_2Br_2, $HgBr_2$, $PbBr_2$
Carbonates	CO_3^{2-}		✔	Group IA, $(NH_4)_2CO_3$
Chlorates	ClO_3^-	✔		
Chlorides	Cl^-	✔		$AgCl$, Hg_2Cl_2, $PbCl_2$
Group IA (1)	M^+	✔		
Hydroxides	OH^-		✔	Group IA, $Ca(OH)_2$, $Ba(OH)_2$, $Sr(OH)_2$
Iodides	I^-	✔		AgI, Hg_2I_2, HgI_2, PbI_2
Nitrates	NO_3^-	✔		
Phosphates	PO_4^{3-}		✔	Group IA, $(NH_4)_3PO_4$
Sulfates	SO_4^{2-}	✔		$CaSO_4$, $SrSO_4$, $BaSO_4$, $PbSO_4$, Hg_2SO_4, Ag_2SO_4
Sulfides	S^{2-}		✔	Group IA and IIA, $(NH_4)_2S$
Sulfites	SO_3^{2-}		✔	Group IA, $(NH_4)_2SO_3$

*When groups IA and IIA are listed, the table refers to the ionic compounds of all members of these groups.

The iron ion has a 3+ charge, Fe^{3+}, and the sulfide has a 2− charge, S^{2-}. The lowest common multiple between 3+ and 2− is six. Thus, to equalize the charges, two iron(III) ions and three sulfide ions make up iron(III) sulfide.

$$Fe_2S_3$$

Step 4 Using Table 10.4, determine which compound precipitates, if any.

Table 10.4 shows that ammonium and nitrate compounds are usually soluble, but sulfides are insoluble. Checking exceptions to the insolubility of sulfides does not include iron(III). Therefore, Fe_2S_3 precipitates, $Fe_2S_3(s)$ and NH_4NO_3 and remains in solution, $NH_4NO_3(aq)$.

Step 5 Write (s) next to the precipitate and (aq) next to the other compound, and write both as products of the reaction.

$$(NH_4)_2S(aq) + Fe(NO_3)_3(aq) \rightarrow Fe_2S_3(s) + NH_4NO_3(aq)$$

Step 6 Balance the equation

$$3(NH_4)_2S(aq) + 2Fe(NO_3)_3(aq) \rightarrow Fe_2S_3(s) + 6NH_4NO_3(aq)$$

Exercise

Write the balanced equation for the reaction of $NH_4Cl(aq)$ and $AgNO_3(aq)$.

$(NH_4Cl(aq) + AgNO_3(aq) \rightarrow AgCl(s) + NH_4NO_3(aq))$

Gas-Formation Reactions

Gas-formation reactions are the least common of the three classes of metathesis reactions. Gas-formation reactions occur when an acid, HA, reacts with a carbonate, bicarbonate, sulfide, or cyanide. In each case the H^+ from the acid combines with the designated *ion or* polyatomic ion and produces a gaseous product. Table 10.5 summarizes the reactions that produce gases.

Therefore, to write gas-formation it is only necessary that an acid is present with carbonate, bicarbonate, sulfide, or cyanide. The steps to follow are similar to those for a precipitation reaction. Example Problem 10.3 shows how to write a gas-formation equation.

TABLE 10.5 GAS-FORMATION REACTIONS

Reactants	Ionic equation for gas formation
Acid + carbonate	$2H^+(aq) + CO_3^{2-}(aq) \rightarrow [H_2CO_3](aq) \rightarrow CO_2(g) + H_2O(l)$
Acid + bicarbonate	$H^+(aq) + HCO_3^-(aq) \rightarrow [H_2CO_3](aq) \rightarrow CO_2(g) + H_2O(l)$
Acid + sulfide	$2H^+(aq) + S^{2-}(aq) \rightarrow H_2S(g)$
Acid + cyanide	$H^+(aq) + CN^-(aq) \rightarrow HCN(g)$

Example Problem 10.3

Write the equation for the reaction of $H_2SO_4(aq)$ and $LiHCO_3(aq)$.

Solution

Step 1 Write the reactants of the gas-formation metathesis reaction.

$$H_2SO_4(aq) + LiHCO_3(aq) \rightarrow$$

Step 2 Write the individual ions that make up each reactant under their formulas.

$$H_2SO_4(aq) + LiHCO_3(aq) \rightarrow$$
$$H^+ \ SO_4^{2-} \qquad Li^+ \ HCO_3^-$$

Step 3 Determine the formulas of the products

In this equation we find the combination of an acid and a bicarbonate; thus, the H^+ ions react with HCO_3^- and produce $CO_2(g)$ and $H_2O(l)$ (Table 10.5). The other combination of ions, Li^+, and SO_4^{2-}, combine in a 2-to-1 ratio to produce a neutral compound, Li_2SO_4. Looking at the solubility table, Table 10.4, we see that Li_2SO_4 is soluble, $Li_2SO_4(aq)$.

Step 4 Write (g) next to the gas and (aq) next to the other compound, and write both as products of the reaction.

$$H_2SO_4(aq) + LiHCO_3(aq) \rightarrow Li_2SO_4(aq) + CO_2(g) + H_2O(l)$$

Step 5 Balance the equation

$$H_2SO_4(aq) + 2LiHCO_3(aq) \rightarrow Li_2SO_4(aq) + 2CO_2(g) + 2H_2O(l)$$

Exercise
Write the equation for the reaction of $H_3PO_4(aq)$ and $KCN(aq)$.
($H_3PO_4(aq) + 3KCN(aq) \rightarrow 3HCN(g) + K_3PO_4(aq)$)

Neutralization Reactions
In a neutralization reaction, an acid reacts with a base and produces a salt and water. Therefore, determine if a neutralization reaction occurs by checking to see if an acid and base are present as reactants. Recall that the general formulas of acids and bases are HA and MOH, respectively. The overall reaction that occurs in a neutralization reaction is as follows.

WWWolfe 4
(See WWWolfe
section at the end of
the chapter.)

$$HA(aq) + MOH(aq) \rightarrow MA(aq) + H_2O(l)$$

To predict the products of a neutralization reaction, determine the formula of the salt, MA, and then, in most cases, add water. Example Problem 10.4 shows the steps required to write neutralization reactions. ❖

Example Problem 10.4
Write the equation for reaction of $HBr(aq)$ and $Al(OH)_3(s)$.

Solution
In this reaction, an acid, HBr, reacts with a base, $Al(OH)_3$; hence, this is a neutralization reaction.

Step 1 Write the reactants of the neutralization metathesis reaction.

$$HBr(aq) + Al(OH)_3(s) \rightarrow$$

Step 2 Write the individual ions that make up each reactant under their formulas.

$$HBr(aq) + Al(OH)_3(s) \rightarrow$$
$$H^+ \ Br^- \qquad Al^{3+} \ OH^-$$

Step 3 Determine the formulas of the two products.
The H^+ and OH^- produce water, $H_2O(l)$. The aluminum ion has a 3+ charge and the bromide ion has a 1– charge. The lowest common multiple of 3+ and 1– is 3; thus, the

formula of this product is $AlBr_3$. The solubility table, Table 10.4, shows that $AlBr_3$ is soluble which means that (aq) is written next to the formula, $AlBr_3(aq)$.

Step 4 Write the products of the reaction.

$$HBr(aq) + Al(OH)_3(s) \rightarrow AlBr_3(aq) + H_2O(l)$$

Step 5 Balance the equation

$$3HBr(aq) + Al(OH)_3(s) \rightarrow AlBr_3(aq) + 3H_2O(l)$$

Exercise
Write the balanced equation for the reaction of $H_2SO_3(aq)$ and $Mg(OH)_2(s)$.
($H_2SO_3(aq) + Mg(OH)_2(s) \rightarrow MgSO_3(s) + 2H_2O(l)$)

REVIEW EXERCISE
10.13 Predict the products of the following reactions, and write a complete balanced equation:

(a) $(NH_4)_3PO_4(aq) + Cu(NO_3)_2(aq) \rightarrow$
(b) $KClO_4(aq) + Fe(NO_3)_2(aq) \rightarrow$
(c) $Pb(NO_3)_2(aq) + K_2SO_4(aq) \rightarrow$

10.13 (a) $2(NH_4)_3PO_4(aq) + 3Cu(NO_3)_2(aq) \rightarrow Cu_3(PO_4)_2(s) + 6NH_4NO_3(aq)$, (b) no reaction, (c) $Pb(NO_3)_2(aq) + K_2SO_4(aq) \rightarrow PbSO_4(s) + 2KNO_3(aq)$

10.5 ENERGY CONSIDERATIONS IN CHEMICAL REACTIONS
So far, we have concentrated on the changes that matter undergoes during chemical reactions. In addition, we must consider the energy requirements for reactions because reactions only take place when the proper amount of energy is present.

Heat, and other sources of energy, are extremely important to chemical reactions. Heat is either absorbed or liberated during the course of reactions. When heat from the surroundings is absorbed, the reaction is classified as an **endothermic reaction** ("endothermic" means "taking in heat"). The opposite of an endothermic reaction is an **exothermic reaction,** which is one that releases heat to its surroundings (Fig. 10.6).

To understand endothermic and exothermic reactions, think of the reactants as having a fixed quantity of stored chemical energy. If an endothermic

Figure 10.6 If heat flows from the surroundings to the reaction, it is classified as an endothermic reaction. If heat flows from a chemical reaction to the surroundings, the reaction is classified as an exothermic reaction.

An exothermic reaction releases heat to the surroundings. An endothermic reaction absorbs heat from the surroundings.

reaction occurs, energy is absorbed by the reactants and is ultimately stored in the products. Therefore, the products have more stored chemical energy than the reactants. In contrast, if an exothermic reaction takes place, the reactants lose energy to the surroundings, producing products with a smaller amount of stored chemical energy. A measure of the chemical energy of the reactants and products is called **enthalpy, H**. Figure 10.7 shows the changes in enthalpy that occur in endothermic and exothermic reactions.

Endothermic reactions are sometimes expressed as follows:

$$A + B + heat \rightarrow C + D$$
(endothermic reaction)

This equation tells us that heat is added to the reactants, A and B, and stored in the products, C and D. In other words, the total enthalpy of the products is greater than that of the reactants. In equations for exothermic reactions, heat is written as a product:

$$A + B \rightarrow C + D + heat$$
(exothermic reaction)

Heat is liberated in this hypothetical reaction, indicating that the enthalpy of the products is less than that of the reactants (Fig. 10.7).

In actual equations the word "heat" is not written; instead, the

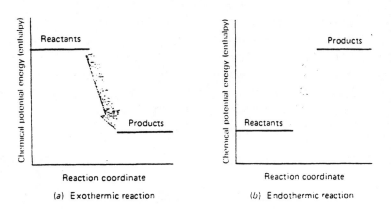

Figure 10.7 If the enthalpy of the products is less than the enthalpy of the reactants, an exothermic reaction has taken place. If the enthalpy of the products is greater than the enthalpy of the reactants, an endothermic reaction has taken place.

actual number of kilojoules released or absorbed is written. Consider the following equations:

$$CH_4(g) + 2O_2(g) \rightarrow CO_2(g) + 2H_2O(g) + 891 \text{ kJ}$$

$$2Ag_2O(s) + 61.9 \text{ kJ} \rightarrow 4Ag(s) + O_2(g)$$

Methane, CH_4, in the first equation, reacts with oxygen, O_2, producing carbon dioxide, CO_2; water vapor, H_2O; and 891 kJ of heat. This is one of the more significant reactions that occurs when natural gas burns. Natural gas is used to heat houses and as a fuel for industry. Heat is by far the most valuable product of this reaction. In the second reaction, silver oxide decomposes to pure silver. To decompose 2 moles of Ag_2O, 61.9 kJ of heat is required. Many ores that contain metal oxides and sulfides must be heated to release the metals.

Exothermic reactions such as the burning of methane are called combustion reactions. A **combustion reaction** occurs when a substance combines rapidly with oxygen and releases heat and light. Combustible substances are those that undergo combustion reactions. The amount of heat liberated per mole of combustible substance is called either the **enthalpy or heat of combustion.** Enthalpies of combustion for selected substances are listed in Table 10.6.

Generally, exothermic reactions are more spontaneous and self-sustaining than endothermic reactions. Heat produced by an exothermic reaction provides a constant source of energy to sustain the reaction. In contrast, endothermic reactions continue only when heat is applied, and after the heat is removed, the reaction usually ceases.

Heat is absorbed or released by chemical reactions as a result of the breaking and formation of chemical bonds. The cleaving of chemical bonds is an endothermic process, while bond formation is an exothermic process. Therefore, exothermic reactions are those that release more heat as a result of bond formation than is required to break bonds. In other words, stronger bonds are found in the products than in the reactants. Endothermic reactions are the opposite: more energy is required to break bonds in the reactants than is given off during the reaction—the bonds are stronger in the reactants than in the products. ❖

> Bond breaking is an endothermic process. In contrast, bond formation is exothermic.

TABLE 10.6 ENTHALPIES Of COMBUSTION FOR SELECTED SUBSTANCES

Substance	Formula	State	Enthalpy of combustion, –kJ/mol
Benzene	C_6H_6	Liquid	3270
Carbon	C	Solid	400
Hydrogen	H_2	Gas	240
Octane	C_8H_{18}	Liquid	5450
Propane	C_3H_8	Gas	2200

REVIEW EXERCISES

10.14 How is an exothermic reaction different from an endothermic reaction?

10.15 On what side of the arrow is the heat written in (a) an exothermic and (b) an endothermic reaction?

10.16 Classify each of the following as either an exothermic or an endothermic reaction.

(a) $H_2 + Cl_2 \rightarrow 2HCl + 184$ kJ
(b) $Cu_2O + 167$ kJ $\rightarrow 2Cu + 2O_2$
(c) $I_2 + Br_2 + 84$ kJ $\rightarrow 2IBr$
(d) $C + O_2 \rightarrow CO_2 + 393$ kJ

10.17 Explain what happens, in terms of bond breaking and formation, when an endothermic reaction occurs.

10.15 (a) right, (b) left; 10.16 (a) exothermic, (b) endothermic, (c) endothermic, (d) exothermic

CHEM TOPIC: Greenhouse Effect

Over the past 40 years many scientists have become concerned with the possibility that an increase in the concentration of CO_2 in the atmosphere could have dire environmental effects. Their concern stems from the fact that the CO_2 concentration in the air has increased greater than 13 percent in the past 200 years and most of the increase is the result of the increased combustion of fossil fuels. Whenever fossil fuels such as gasoline and coal are burned they release CO_2 to the atmosphere. These fuels are mixtures of hydrocarbons. During burning the C in hydrocarbons is principally oxidized to CO_2 and the H is oxidized to H_2O.

Carbon dioxide has a central role in the regulation of the temperature of the atmosphere. It is essentially transparent to the visible light from the sun but can effectively block the infrared radiation (ir) released by the earth. Thus, an increased concentration of CO_2 in the atmosphere helps trap ir radiation normally radiated to outer space. Such an effect results when the glass of a greenhouse allows light in but does not allow the ir radiation out. The result is an increase in temperature inside the greenhouse—the greenhouse effect. On the global scale some scientists believe that too high a concentration of CO_2 in the atmosphere can result in the warming of the earth. It has been calculated that a 1- to 2-degree increase in the average temperature of the earth could raise the level of the oceans as much as 5 m. An increase of this magnitude would inundate the coastal regions, flooding the most heavily populated regions of the earth. Additionally the greenhouse effect would change weather patterns causing the temperature zones of the earth to move further north. Canada and the Soviet Union might have milder climates but the United States would be more arid and desertlike.

However, other scientists are skeptical about the greenhouse effect. They point out that the average temperature of the earth dropped slightly between 1940 and the early 1970s. Such a drop in temperature could possibly be explained by the increase in particulate matter (particles) thrown into the atmosphere when fossil fuels are burned. These particles help reflect energy from the sun. Therefore in upcoming years environmentalists must carefully monitor the CO_2 concentration in the atmosphere and the temperature of the earth so that they might warn the appropriate people before a disaster can result.

WorldWideWolfe CHEMISTRY LINKS

Connect to WorldWideWolfe at

http://www.mindspring.com/~drwolfe/WWWolfe_hcc_1025_links.htm

and link to the following sites.

Chemical Reactions

1. Principles of Reactivity: Chemical Reactions Brief discussion of chemical reactions and equations. It has many links to other sites.

2. Balancing Chemical Equations Shows you how to balance simple equations.

Chemical Reactions Covers all of the basic principles regarding chemical equations and reactions.

Determining What Is Reacting Reviews chemical equations, balancing, equations, stoichiometry, and limiting reactants (covered in Chapter 11).

3. Precipitation Reactions Discusses precipitation reactions and selective precipitation.

4. Acid/Base Reactions - Basics Describes the nature of acid-base reactions and acid-base titrations.

SUMMARY

Chemical equations are a shorthand notation that chemists use to indicate what happens during chemical reactions. Each equation shows formulas of substances separated by an arrow (which means "yields").

All substances written to the left of the arrow are called **reactants**, and all substances to the right of the arrow are called **products**. Each chemical equation is initially worked out in the laboratory; chemists perform experiments to determine what products result from a given set of reactants and conditions.

Chemical equations obey the law of conservation of mass; this law states that matter cannot be created or destroyed during normal chemical changes. This law is obeyed when an equation is balanced. A **balanced** equation shows the ratio in which the reactants combine to yield the products, as well as the ratio in which the products are formed. Equations are balanced by changing the coefficients of each substance in the equation. Usually, the correct coefficients are determined by comparing the number of atoms of each different element on either side of the equation, using what is called the **inspection method.**

To understand inorganic reactions, chemists group similar equations into a general class. Elementary inorganic reactions are normally placed into four classes. They are (1) combination, (2) decomposition, (3) single replacement, and (4) metathesis. **Combination reactions** are those in which two or more reactants unite to produce a single product. **Decomposition reactions** are the opposite of combination reactions. A single reactant is broken into two or more products. **Single replacement** reactions are those in which an element replaces another element within a compound, resulting in a compound of the initially free element. Finally, in **metathesis reactions** (double replacements), two compounds react and the more positive part of one combines with the negative part of the other.

Reactions are classified according to whether heat is released or taken in during the course of the reaction. Those reactions in which heat is absorbed are salted **endothermic reactions.** Reactions in which there is a net release of heat energy are called exothermic reactions.

KEY TERMS

acid-catalyzed reaction   catalyst
activity series   chemical equation
aqueous solution   combination reaction

decomposition reaction
endothermic reaction
enthalpy
equation balancing
exothermic reaction
metathesis reaction
oxidation
oxide

oxidizing agent
precipitation
product
reactant
redox reduction
single replacement reaction

STUDY GUIDELINES

After completing Chapter 11, you should be able to

1. Identify the reactants and products in a chemical equation

2. Identify and write all common symbols found in chemical equations

3. Explain the meaning of the abbreviations (g), (l), (s) and (aq)

4. Explain why subscripts in formulas cannot be changed when balancing a chemical equation

5. Balance chemical equations using the inspection method

6. Translate a word equation into a correctly balanced chemical equation

7. List the four classes of inorganic reactions.

8. Write a general equation for each class of inorganic reaction

9. Write balanced chemical equations that illustrate each type of inorganic reaction

10. Identify (a) combination, (b) decomposition, (c) single replacement, and (d) metathesis reactions

11. Use the activity series to decide when a single replacement reaction occurs

12. Predict what substance precipitates, what gas is released, or what salt forms when two aqueous salt solutions undergo a metathesis reaction

13. Describe the difference between endothermic and exothermic reactions

14. Identify endothermic and exothermic reactions from their chemical equations given the

heat released or absorbed

15. Explain, in terms of bond breaking and formation, what happens in endothermic and exothermic reactions

---

EXERCISES

10.18 Define each of the following terms: chemical equation, reactant, product, aqueous solution, catalyst, equation balancing, combination reaction, decomposition reaction, single replacement reaction, metathesis reaction, oxidation, reduction, oxide, hydride, hydrate, activity series, precipitation, exothermic, endothermic, enthalpy.

Format of Chemical Equations

10.19 What is the meaning of each of the following symbols in chemical equations: (a) (aq), (b) (g), (c) →?

10.20 Write the names of all reactants and products in the following reaction:
$CaCl_2 + (NH_4)_2CO_3 \rightarrow CaCO_3 + 2NH_4Cl$

10.21 Write a word equation for each of the following chemical equations:
(a) $2SO_3(g) \rightarrow 2SO_2(g) + O_2(g)$
(b) $Hg(l) + Cl_2(g) \rightarrow HgCl_2(s)$
(c) $N_2(g) + 3H_2(g) \rightarrow 2NH_3(g)$
(d) $Al_2S_3(s) + 6H_2O(l) \rightarrow 2Al(OH)_3(s) + 3H_2S(aq)$

Balancing Equations by Inspection

10.22 Balance each of the following equations:
(a) $P_4 + O_2 \rightarrow P_2O_5$
(b) $Mg + N_2 \rightarrow Mg_3N_2$
(c) $Li_2O + H_2O \rightarrow LiOH$
(d) $Cl_2 + KI \rightarrow I_2 + KCl$
(e) $Cu + O_2 \rightarrow CuO$
(f) $FeO + SiO_2 \rightarrow FeSiO_3$
(g) $Na_2CO_3 + C \rightarrow Na + CO$
(h) $WO_3 + H_2 \rightarrow W + H_2O$
(i) $B_2O_3 + H_2O \rightarrow H_3BO_3$
(j) $H_2S + O_2 \rightarrow SO_2 + H_2O$

10.23 Balance each of the following equations:
(a) $C_4H_{10} + O_2 \rightarrow CO_2 + H_2O$
(b) $POF_3 + H_2O \rightarrow H_3PO_4 + HF$
(c) $Cu(NO_3)_2 \rightarrow CuO + NO_2 + O_2$
(d) $CaCO_3 + H_3PO_4 \rightarrow Ca_3(PO_4)_2 + CO_2 + H_2O$
(e) $FeS_2 + O_2 \rightarrow FeO + SO_2$

(f) $Al + CuSO_4 \rightarrow Al_2(SO_4)_3 + Cu$
(g) $LiH + AlCl_3 \rightarrow LiAlH_4 + LiCl$
(h) $Cr_2O_3 + C \rightarrow Cr + CO$
(i) $(NH_4)_2Cr_2O_7 \rightarrow Cr_2O_3 + N_2 + H_2O$
(j) $C_{10}H_{22} + O_2 \rightarrow CO_2 + H_2O$

10.24 Balance each of the following equations:
(a) $B_3N_3H_6 + O_2 \rightarrow N_2O_5 + B_2O_3 + H_2O$
(b) $IBr + NH_3 \rightarrow NH_4Br + NI_3$
(c) $KAlSi_3O_8 + H_2O + CO_2 \rightarrow K_2CO_3 + Al_2Si_2O_5(OH)_4 + SiO_2$
(d) $Co_3O_4 + Al \rightarrow Co + Al_2O_3$
(e) $Al(OH)_3 + NaOH \rightarrow NaAlO_2 + H_2O$
(f) $C_7H_6O_2 + O_2 \rightarrow CO_2 + H_2O$
(g) $HClO_4 + P_4O_{10} \rightarrow H_3PO_4 + Cl_2O_7$
(h) $XeF_2 + H_2O \rightarrow Xe + O_2 + HF$
(i) $Na_2H_3IO_6 + AgNO_3 \rightarrow Ag_5IO_6 + NaNO_3 + HNO_3$
(j) $XeF_4 + SF_4 \rightarrow Xe + SF_6$
(k) $K_4Fe(CN)_6 + H_2SO_4 + H_2O \rightarrow K_2SO_4 + FeSO_4 + (NH_4)_2SO_4 + CO$
(l) $Au + KCN + H_2O + O_2 \rightarrow KAu(CN)_4 + KOH$

10.25 Translate each of the following word equations into a balanced chemical equation:
(a) Sodium bromide solution + silver nitrate solution yield aqueous sodium nitrate + silver(I) bromide solid
(b) Aluminum hydroxide solution + nitric acid yield aqueous aluminum nitrate + water
(c) Chlorine gas + rubidium iodide solution yield aqueous rubidium chloride + iodine solid
(d) Iron(III) acetate solution + sodium sulfide solution yield aqueous sodium acetate + iron(III) sulfide solid
(e) Silicon tetrafluoride gas + water yield silicon dioxide solid + hydrofluoric acid
(f) Manganese(IV) oxide solid + hydrochloric acid yield manganese(II) chloride + chlorine gas + water
(g) Dinitrogen tetroxide gas, when heated, yields nitrogen dioxide.

(h) Calcium phosphide solid + water yield calcium hydroxide + phosphine (PH_3) gas

(i) On heating, silver(I) nitrate solid yields silver, plus nitrogen dioxide gas, plus oxygen gas.

(j) Aluminum metal + aqueous copper(II) sulfate yield copper metal + aqueous aluminum sulfate

(k) Mercury(I) nitrate solution + potassium chloride solution yield mercury(I) chloride solid + aqueous potassium nitrate

(l) Calcium sulfate dihydrate, when heated, yields calcium sulfate plus water.

(m) Ammonium sulfide solution + cadmium(II) chloride solution yield cadmium(II) sulfide solid + aqueous ammonium chloride

(n) Phosphorous acid + sodium hydroxide solution yield aqueous sodium phosphite + water

(o) Ammonia gas + sulfuric acid yield aqueous ammonium sulfate

(p) Carbon disulfide liquid + chlorine gas yield disulfur dichloride + carbon tetrachloride

(q) Calcium phosphate solution + sulfuric acid yield phosphoric acid + calcium sulfate

(r) Aqueous ammonia + copper(I) oxide yield nitrogen gas + water + copper metal

(s) Ammonium nitrate solid, when heated, yields water and dinitrogen oxide gas

(t) Magnesium hydroxide solution + zinc(II) nitrate solution yield zinc(II) hydroxide solid + aqueous magnesium nitrate

10.26 (a) Classify each of the reactions in Exercise 10.25 as combination, decomposition, single displacement, metathesis, or none of these. (b) Which of the reactions in 10.25 are oxidation-reduction reactions?

Classes of Inorganic Reactions

10.27 Write an equation to illustrate each of the following types of combination reactions. (a) a compound combines with an element, (b) two compounds combine, (c) two elements combine.

10.28 What are the reactants in the combination reaction to produce the following products?
(a) CO   (b) SO_3
(c) NO_2 (d) CS_2
(e) PH_3 (f) MgH_2

10.29 What metal oxide (basic oxide), when added to water, produces each of the following bases?

(a) KOH   (b) $Ba(OH)_2$
(c) $Ca(OH)_2$ (d) $Al(OH)_3$

10.30 What nonmetal oxide (acidic oxide), when added to water, produces each of the following acids?
(a) H_2CO_3 (b) H_2SO_3
(c) H_3PO_4 (d) H_2SO_4

10.31 Write formulas for the compound that decomposes to each of the following sets of products.
(a) $MgO + CO_2$
(b) $KCl + O_2$
(c) $K_2CO_3 + CO_2 + H_2O$
(d) $Ba(NO_2)_2 + H_2O$
(e) $H_2 + O_2$
(f) $NaNO_2 + O_2$
(g) $SO_2 + O_2$

10.32 (a) What is the common feature of all oxidation-reduction reactions? (b) Give an example of an oxidation-reduction reaction.

10.33 For each of the following reactions, determine which reactants undergo oxidation and which undergo reduction:
(a) $2Li + 2HCl \rightarrow H_2 + LiCl$
(b) $Si + 2F_2 + SiF_4$
(c) $H_2 + Cl_2 \rightarrow 2HCl$
(d) $2ZnS + 3O_2 \rightarrow 2SO_2 + 2ZnO$
(e) $Fe_3O_4 + 4H_2 \rightarrow 3Fe + 4H_2O$

10.34 Write a balanced equation for a single displacement reaction that illustrates each of the following. (a) a metal displaces hydrogen from water, releasing $H_2(g)$; (b) a metal replaces hydrogen in an acid, releasing $H_2(g)$; (c) A metal replaces copper in a copper nitrate solution; (d) bromine liquid replaces iodine in a solution of rubidium iodide.

10.35 (a) What substances combine in a neutralization reaction? (b) Give three examples of neutralization reactions.

10.36 Write an equation that illustrates a metathesis reaction in which (a) an insoluble hydroxide forms, (b) carbon dioxide gas is one of the products, (c) an insoluble carbonate results, (d) the soluble salt NH_4I results.

10.37 Use Table 10.4 to predict whether each of the following is soluble or insoluble in water.
(a) K_2SO_4 (b) $Fe(OH)_2$
(c) $MgCO_3$ (d) Hg_2Cl_2
(e) NH_4I (f) $V(CO_3)_2$
(g) $CsC_2H_3O_2$ (h) Al_2S_3

(i) AgI   (j) CaSO$_4$
(k) FeSO$_3$ (l) KBr
(m) (NH$_4$)$_3$PO$_4$.

Writing Metathesis Equations

10.38 Complete and balance the equations for the following aqueous metathesis reactions:
(a) NiCl$_2$(aq) + Ca(OH)$_2$(aq) →
(b) Hg(C$_2$H$_3$O$_2$)$_2$(aq) + K$_2$CO$_3$(aq) →
(c) H$_3$PO$_4$(aq) + AgNO$_3$(aq) →
(d) H$_2$SO$_3$(aq) + Al(OH)$_3$(aq) →
(e) (NH$_4$)$_2$S(aq) + BaI$_2$(aq) →
(f) Cs$_2$CO$_3$(aq) + HC$_2$H$_3$O$_2$(aq) →
(g) Li$_2$SO$_4$(aq) + Co(NO$_3$)$_2$(aq) →
(h) NH$_4$CN(aq) + HBr(aq) →

10.39 Translate each of the following to symbols and formulas, and then complete and balance the equation.
(a) Silver(I) nitrate(aq) + copper(II) chloride(aq) →
(b) Ammonium sulfide(aq) + mercury(II) acetate(aq) →
(c) Potassium hydroxide(aq) + sulfuric acid(aq) →
(d) Nitric acid(aq) + barium carbonate(s) →
(e) Sodium bicarbonate(s) + phosphoric acid(aq) →
(f) Sulfuric acid(aq) + copper(II) hydroxide(s) →
(g) Hydrobromic acid(aq) + lead(II) nitrate(aq) →
(h) Calcium nitrate(aq) + potassium sulfate(aq) →
(i) Ammonium nitrate(aq) + zinc(II) phosphate(s) →
(j) Sodium carbonate(s) + perchloric acid(aq) →
(k) Tin(II) sulfide(s) + hypobromous acid(aq) →
(l) Iron(III) acetate(aq) + potassium sulfide(aq) →
(m) Sodium acetate(aq) + lead(II) acetate(aq) →
(n) mercury(I) nitrate(aq) + ammonium chloride(aq) →
(o) sodium iodide(aq) + silver(I) sulfate(s) →
(p) Cesium carbonate(s) + iron(III) acetate(aq) →
(q) Sulfurous acid(aq) + rubidium hydroxide(aq) →
(r) Magnesium chloride(aq) + silver nitrate(aq) →
(s) Lithium bicarbonate(aq) + phosphorous acid(aq) →

Energy in Chemical Reactions

10.40 Give an example of (a) an exothermic reaction and (b) an endothermic reaction.

10.41 (a) Use the data in Table 10.6 to calculate the amount of heat liberated when 1.00 g of octane is completely combusted. (b) If all of this heat could be transferred to 1.00 kg of water at 25°C, what is the maximum temperature that the water would reach? [The specific heat of water is 4.184 J/(g °C).]

10.42 Compressed propane is used as a fuel in homes and industry. What mass of propane would have to be completely combusted to produce as much heat as the complete combustion of 1.56 kg of octane? (*Hint:* Use Table 10.6.)

10.43 Benzene is an aromatic liquid that is toxic and cancer-causing. (a) Write the equation for the complete combustion of benzene, C$_6$H$_6$. (b) How much heat is released when 9.01 g of benzene is completely combusted? (c) How much heat is produced when 154 g CO$_2$ is released during the complete combustion of benzene? (d) How many grams of benzene must be combusted to increase the temperature of 152 g of water from 0.0°C to 73.9°C?

10.44 Classify each of the following reactions as endothermic or exothermic:
(a) PCl$_5$ + 376 kJ → P + Cl$_2$
(b) CaCO$_3$ + 180kJ → CaO + CO$_2$
(c) FeS + 2H$^+$ → Fe^{2+} + H$_2$S + 13 kJ
(d) C + 2F$_2$ → CF$_4$ + 920 kJ

10.45 (a) What is enthalpy? (b) What enthalpy change occurs in an endothermic reaction? (c) What enthalpy change occurs in an exothermic reaction?

10.46 Most decomposition reactions are endothermic. Write an explanation to account for this observation.

Additional Exercises

10.47 Correct the following **incorrect** statements
(a) Most metal oxides produce acidic solutions when placed in water.
(b) All inorganic reactions belong to one of

four different classes.

(c) Fractional coefficients may never be used to balance chemical equations.

(d) All phosphate salts are insoluble.

(e) Metallic zinc when placed in liquid water, replaces hydrogen and dissolves immediately.

(f) The product of a metathesis reaction is a precipitate.

(g) Substances that undergo endothermic reactions are used as fuels.

(h) When bonds are broken, heat is released.

(i) Oxidation occurs when electrons are accepted.

(j) Endothermic reactions release heat and exothermic reactions absorb heat.

10.48 Write and balance the following equations:

(a) The Haber reaction occurs when nitrogen and hydrogen gases combine at high pressures at 550°C, and with a metal catalyst to produce ammonia gas.

(b) Ammonia, when combusted, gives nitrogen monoxide and water vapor (Ostwald process).

(c) Nitrogen monoxide is further oxidized to nitrogen dioxide.

(d) Nitrogen dioxide is pumped through water to yield both nitric acid and nitrous acid.

10.49 Write and balance equations for Reactions 1 through 7.

(1) Calcium carbonate, when heated to about 850°C, decomposes to calcium oxide and carbon dioxide.

(2) The carbon dioxide is used to manufacture sodium bicarbonate and sodium carbonate. Carbon dioxide is combined with ammonia, water, and sodium chloride to produce sodium bicarbonate plus ammonium chloride (the Solvay process).

(3) Sodium carbonate is formed along with carbon dioxide and water when sodium bicarbonate is decomposed.

(4) The calcium oxide produced in Eq. (1) is combined with carbon at high temperatures to produce calcium carbide and carbon monoxide.

(5) Calcium carbide is then heated with nitrogen gas at 1100°C, producing calcium cyanamid, $CaCN_2$, and carbon.

(6) This calcium cyanamid is combined with carbon and the sodium carbonate

produced in Eq. (3) to give sodium cyanide, NaCN, and calcium carbonate.

(7) Sodium cyanide is the main source of hydrogen cyanide gas. Sodium cyanide is combined with sulfuric acid, producing hydrogen cyanide and sodium sulfate.

10.50 Balance each of the following equations, noting that in each reaction calcium fluorophosphate is one of the reactants:

(a) $Ca(PO_4)_3F + H_2SO_4 \rightarrow HF + H_3PO_4 + CaSO_4$

(b) $Ca(PO_4)_3F + H_3PO_4 \rightarrow HF + Ca(H_2PO_4)_2$

(c) $Ca(PO_4)_3F + H_2SO_4 + H_2O \rightarrow HF + CaSO_4 + Ca(H_2PO_4)_2 \cdot H_2O$

10.51 When acetylene, C_2H_2, is completely combusted, it produces carbon dioxide and water. For each two moles of acetylene combusted, 2602 kJ of energy is released. (a) Write and balance the equation for the combustion of acetylene. (b) Calculate the amount of energy released when 40.0 g of acetylene is combusted. (c) If all the heat released by 40.0 g of acetylene is transferred to 1.35 kg of water at 10.0°C, what is the final temperature of the water? [The specific heat of water is 4.184 J/(g °C).] (d) How many grams of acetylene must be combusted to produce 125 kJ of energy?

Notes and Calculations:

Chapter 10 Pretest Assignment

1.   Complete each of the following statements with the correct word, number, or phase.

     a. _____ is the general form for any metathesis reaction.

     b. In a(n) _____ reaction one element takes the place of another in a compound.

     c. A(n) _____ reaction releases heat to the surroundings.

     d. A(n) _____ reaction has only a single reactant.

     e. _____ is an example of an insoluble carbonate.

     f. _____ , _____ , _____ are three types of metathesis reactions.

     g. _____ reacts with hydrochloric acid and produces CO_2 and H_2O.

2.   Balance the following equations.

     a. ____ XeF_4 + ____ SF_4 → ____ Xe + ____ SF_6

     b. Phosphorous acid + sodium hydroxide solution → aqueous sodium phosphite + water

3.   Predict the products and balance the equation for the following.

     a. $(NH_4)_2CO_3$ + $PbCl_4$ →

     b. $Ca(NO_3)_2(aq)$ + $KOH(aq)$ →

     c. $Mg(HCO_3)_2(s)$ + $HBr(aq)$ →

4.   In what class of reaction is each of the following (e.g., decomposition, metathesis, etc.)?

    a. $CuSO_4 \cdot 5H_2O \rightarrow CuSO_4 + 5H_2O$ _____

    b. $N_2(g) + 3H_2(g) \rightarrow 2NH_3(g)$ _____

    c. $HCl(aq) + NaOH(aq) \rightarrow NaCl(aq) + H_2O(l)$ _____

    d. $Na(s) + H_2O(l) \rightarrow NaOH(aq) + \frac{1}{2}H_2(g)$ _____

5.   Give an example of each of the following reactions:

    a. single replacement reaction   _____

    b. gas-formation reaction   _____

    c. neutralization reaction   _____

    d. combination reaction   _____

    e. precipitation reaction   _____

CHAPTER 11

Stoichiometry

11.1 STOICHIOMETRY

What is stoichiometry (stoy-key-ahm-uh-tree)? **Stoichiometry** is the study of mole, mass, energy, and volume relationships in chemical reactions. The term "stoichiometry" comes from the Greek terms *stoicheion*, which means "element," and *metron*, "to measure." In the study of stoichiometry, we usually consider the quantities of reactants that react to produce various amounts of products.

WWWolfe 1
(See WWWolfe section at the end of the chapter.)

Many industries use stoichiometric relationships to predict the masses of raw materials required to produce the desired amounts of final products. Knowledge of stoichiometry is applied to production problems, e.g., the recovery of metals from ores, the synthesis of medicines and drugs, and the manufacture of explosives.

Stoichiometric relationships are found by investigating a chemical reaction in the laboratory. From this investigation, the ratios in which the reactants combine and the ratios in which the products form are determined.
When these ratios are known, the correct balanced equation is written. As we learned in Chap. 10, the coefficients of symbols and formulas in chemical equations give the theoretical ratio in which reactants combine and products form.

> Jeremias Benjamin Richter (1762-1807) first coined the term "stoichiometry." He applied basic math principles to what was known about the combining masses of compounds to explain how substances reacted quantitatively.

A word of caution is in order before getting to the specifics of stoichiometry. Predictions made from stoichiometric considerations are theoretical; this means our answers are not what *will* necessarily happen, but what *would* happen if the reaction proceeded to completion as written. If we predict the quantity of a product that forms from specified amounts of reactants, our prediction is the theoretical maximum that could result (the theoretical yield); however, only rarely will the maximum quantity be obtained in the laboratory.

Though a chemical equation may appear to represent a simple relationship, it generally does not. Reactants most often have more than one possible pathway they can follow as they react. In other words, one or more "side reactions" may occur at the same time as the principal one, thus decreasing the yield of the product of interest. Small quantities of impurities may alter the pathway of the reaction—sometimes significantly. Additionally, meticulous attention must be given to the energy requirements of a reaction. If these requirements are not met, different products may result or the reaction may not occur at all. ❖

REVIEW EXERCISES

11.1 (a) What is stoichiometry?

(b) How is stoichiometry applied?

11.2 What factors tend to decrease the observed yield of a reaction compared to the computed theoretical yield?

11.2 1. loss of products in experiment, 2. incomplete reactions, 3. formation of side products

11.2 CHEMICAL EQUATION CALCULATIONS

To begin our study of stoichiometry, let's consider a relatively simple chemical reaction, the combination of hydrogen and chlorine gases to produce hydrogen chloride gas:

$$H_2(g) + Cl_2(g) \rightarrow 2HCl(g)$$

In words, the equation states that one hydrogen molecule combines with one chlorine molecule to produce two hydrogen chloride molecules. The reaction is diagramed in Fig. 11.1.

| The formation of HCl is the result of a series of intermediate steps that the reactants follow. These steps are called the reaction mechanism. |

Knowing the coefficients for the equation, we already have a wealth of information. As previously stated, the coefficients show what is happening quantitatively at the molecular level—one H_2 molecule combines with one Cl_2 molecule and produces two HCl molecules.

In the laboratory we cannot work with individual molecules because they are too small, instead, we are concerned with the number of moles of reactants and products. We can move from the molecular level to the mole level by multiplying all components of the equation by Avogadro's number, 6.022×10^{23}. Consequently, 6.022×10^{23} H_2 molecules combine with 6.022×10^{23} Cl_2 molecules

Figure 11.1 One molecule of diatomic hydrogen, H_2, collides with one molecule of diatomic chlorine, Cl_2, producing two molecules of hydrogen chloride, HCl.

to produce 1.204×10^{24} ($2 \times 6.022 \times 10^{23}$) HCl molecules. More simply, 1 mol H_2 combines with 1 mol Cl_2 to yield 2 mol HCl.

$$1 \text{ mol } H_2 + 1 \text{ mol } Cl_2 \rightarrow 2 \text{ mol } HCl$$

Mass relationships follow directly from the mole relationships. Accordingly, 1.0 mol H_2, 2.0 g H_2, combines with 1.00 mol Cl_2, 70.9 g Cl_2, to produce 2.00 mol HCl, 72.9 g HCl. Note that the law of conservation of mass is upheld; the sum of

| Hydrogen chloride is a colorless, poisonous gas. Its melting point is −112°C, and its boiling point is −84°C. If HCl is dissolved in water, it almost totally breaks up into ions—this solution is called hydrochloric acid. |

the masses of the reactants, its 72.9 g (2.0 g H_2 + 70.9 g Cl_2), equals the mass of the product, 72.9 g.

Table 11.1 summarizes the molecule, mole, and mass relationships relevant to the formation of HCl from the elements.

TABLE 11.1 REACTION STOICHIOMETRY FOR THE FORMATION OF HYDROGEN CHLORIDE, HCl

	H_2 +	Cl_2 →	2HCl
Molecules	1 molecule	1 molecule	2 molecules
Molecules	6.02×10^{23} molecules	6.02×10^{23} molecules	$2 \times 6.02 \times 10^{23}$ molecules
Moles	1.00 mol	1.00 mol	2.00 mol
Mass	2.01 g	70.9 g	72.9 g

Given the balanced equation and quantities of starting materials, we can calculate the masses, the numbers of moles, or the numbers of molecules of products (or vice versa). To show this, let's calculate the number of moles of Cl_2 needed to combine with 2 mol H_2, and the number of moles of HCl that result.

Because H_2 and Cl_2 combine in a 1-to-1 mole ratio, the same number of moles Cl_2 as moles of H_2 are required. Thus, 2 mol Cl_2 reacts with 2 mol H_2. For each 1 mol of reactant, 2 mol of product, HCl, forms. Consequently, 4 mol HCl is produced. In terms of mass, 2 mol H_2 (2 mol H_2 × 2.0 g H_2/mol), 4.0 g H_2, combines with 2 mol Cl_2 (2 mol Cl_2 × 70.9 g Cl_2/mol), 141.8 g Cl_2, to produce 4 mol HCl, (4 mol HCl × 36.45 g HCl/mol), 145.8 g HCl.

	H_2 +	Cl_2 →	2HCl
Moles	2.0 mol	2.0 mol	4.0 mol
Mass	4.04 g	141.8 g	154.8 g

It should be apparent that the coefficients of the reactants and products in a chemical equation give the mole ratios in which substances react. Thus, we use the coefficients to generate conversion factors. For example, if we are interested in the number of moles of HCl produced per mole of H_2, it is only necessary to write

$$\frac{2 \text{ mol HCl}}{1 \text{ mol } H_2}$$

A similar conversion factor relates moles of Cl_2 to moles of HCl produced:

$$\frac{2 \text{ mol HCl}}{1 \text{ mol Cl}_2}$$

The mole relationship between the reactants is expressed as follows:

$$\frac{1 \text{ mol Cl}_2}{1 \text{ mol H}_2}$$

Mole-Mole Calculations

Turning our attention to the equation that represents the formation of ammonia, NH_3, from its elements (the Haber reaction), we will illustrate stoichiometry problems that exclusively involve mole relationships.

$$N_2(g) + 3H_2(g) \rightarrow 2NH_3(g)$$

WWWolfe 2
(See WWWolfe section at the end of the chapter.)

In the Haber reaction, 1 mol $N_2(g)$ combines with 3 mol H_2 to yield 2 mol NH_3. How many moles of H_2 are required to combine with 10 mol N_2? Utilizing conversion factors from the equation, we find that 3 mol H_2 is required per 1 mol N_2:

$$\frac{3 \text{ mol H}_2}{1 \text{ mol N}_2}$$

To answer our question, we multiply this conversion factor by the number of moles of N_2 given, 10 mol.

$$\cancel{10 \text{ mol N}_2} \times \frac{3 \text{ mol H}_2}{\cancel{1 \text{ mol N}_2}} = 30 \text{ mol H}_2$$

We find that 30 mol H_2 is required to react exactly with 10 mol N_2.

If 30 mol H_2 is needed to combine with 10 mol N_2, how many moles of NH_3 result? Again, look at the equation, and extract from it the mole relationship between either moles of N_2 and moles of NH_3 produced or moles of H_2 and moles NH_3 produced.

> Fritz Haber (1868-1934), a German chemist, developed a method of reacting N_2 and H_2 under pressure with an iron catalyst to produce ammonia. Unfortunately, this discovery prolonged World War I because ammonia can be converted to explosives.

$$\frac{2 \text{ mol NH}_3}{1 \text{ mol N}_2} \qquad \text{or} \qquad \frac{2 \text{ mol NH}_3}{3 \text{ mol H}_2}$$

Using either of these conversion factors gives us the correct answer:

$$10 \; \cancel{\text{mol N}_2} \times \frac{2 \text{ mol NH}_3}{1 \; \cancel{\text{mol N}_2}} = 20 \text{ mol NH}_3$$

or

$$30 \; \cancel{mol \; H_2} \times \frac{2 \; mol \; NH_3}{3 \; \cancel{mol \; H_2}} = 20 \; mol \; NH_3$$

Thus 20 mol NH_3 is the theoretical maximum yield when 10 mol N_2 combines with 30 mol H_2. Chemists call this calculated amount of product the **theoretical yield.**

Example Problems 11.1 and 11.2 illustrate the application of the factor-label method and our problem-solving techniques to the solution of mole-mole stoichiometry problems. Refer to Fig. 11.2, which graphically illustrates how mole-mole problems are solved.

Theoretical yields are the predicted amounts of products when the principles of stoichiometry are applied.

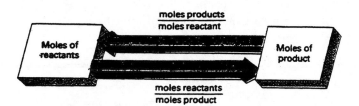

Figure 11.2 To calculate the number of moles of product formed given the number of moles of a reactant, multiply the number of moles of reactant by the conversion factor that gives the number of moles of product per mole of reactant. This conversion factor is obtained from the coefficients of the reactant and product of interest in the balanced equation.

Example Problem 11.1
Calculate the theoretical maximum number of moles of NH_3 that result, the theoretical yield, when 0.55 mol H_2 combines with an excess amount of N_2.

$$N_2(g) + 3H_2(g) \rightarrow 2NH_3(g)$$

Solution
1. What is unknown?   Mol NH_3
2. What is known? 0.55 mol H_2, 2 mol NH_3/3 mol H_2
3. Apply the factor-label method.

$$0.55 \; \cancel{mol \; H_2} \times \frac{2 \; mol \; NH_3}{3 \; \cancel{mol \; H_2}} = ? \; mol \; NH_3$$

4. Perform the indicated math operations.

$$0.55 \; \cancel{mol \; H_2} \times \frac{2 \; mol \; NH_3}{3 \; \cancel{mol \; H_2}} = \textbf{0.37 mol NH}_3$$

Exercise

Calculate the theoretical yield of moles of NH_3 when 25 mol N_2 reacts with excess H_2. (50 mol NH_3)

Theoretically, 0.37 mol NH_3 results when 0.55 mol H_2 reacts with excess N_2 in the Haber reaction. An assumption is made that an excess amount of N_2 is present or at least the exact amount needed to combine with the 0.55 mol H_2; if not, the

If not stated, assume in stoichiometric calculations that sufficient quantities of all substances are present for the reaction to take place.

maximum product yield could not be obtained. If 0.0 g N_2 is present, the reaction does not take place! A common practice is to assume that sufficient quantities of all the other reactants are present unless told otherwise.

Example Problem 11.2

Butane, C_4H_{10}, is a combustible gas used as a fuel and is found in some cigarette lighters. How many moles of butane are required to combine with excess oxygen, O_2, to produce 6.44 mol of carbon dioxide, CO_2, in the following reaction:

Butane is a colorless gas that boils at $-0.3°C$. It is a liquid in lighters only because it is under pressure.

$$C_4H_{10}(g) + 6.5O_2(g) \rightarrow 4CO_2(g) + 5H_2O(g)$$

Solution

1. What is unknown?   Mol C_4H_{10}
2. What is known? 6.44 mol CO_2; 1 mol C_4H_{10}/4 mol CO_2
3. Apply the factor-label method.

$$6.44 \; \cancel{mol \; CO_2} \times \frac{1 \; mol \; C_4H_{10}}{4 \; \cancel{mol \; CO_2}} = ? \; mol \; C_4H_{10}$$

4. Perform the indicated math operations

$$6.44 \; \cancel{mol \; CO_2} \times \frac{1 \; mol \; C_4H_{10}}{4 \; \cancel{mol \; CO_2}} = \textbf{1.61 mol C}_4\textbf{H}_{10}$$

In this reaction, 1.61 mol C_4H, must be present to react with excess oxygen to produce 6.44 mol CO_2.

Exercise

How many moles of C_4H_{10} exactly reacts with 1.00 mol O_2? (0.154 mol C_4H_{10})

REVIEW EXERCISES

11.3 Use the Haber equation to calculate the number of moles of NH_3 produced when 8.73 mol N_2 reacts with excess H_2.

11.4 (a) Calculate the number of moles of O_2 that reacts exactly with 0.922 mol C_4H_{10} to produce CO_2 and H_2O.

(b) How many moles of CO_2 and H_2O are produced from 0.922 mol C_4H_{10}?

(c) Are moles conserved in chemical reactions?

11.5 How many moles of H_2O and CO_2 are released when 7.35×10^{-3} mol C_4H_{10} reacts with excess oxygen in the combustion of butane?

11.3 17.5 mol NH_3; 11.4 (a) 5.99 mol O_2; (b) 3.69 mol CO_2, 4.61 mol H_2O; (c) no; 11.5 0.0368 mol H_2O, 0.0294 mol CO_2

Mole-Mass Calculations

Usually, chemists calculate the masses of reactants and products. One additional conversion factor is needed to find masses, the molar mass of the reactant or product (grams per mole). Figure 11.3 shows the pathway you will follow to solve mole-mass problems.

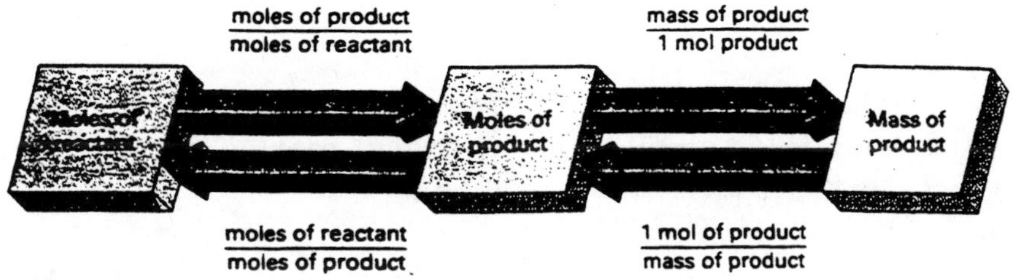

An important industrial reaction is the water gas-formation reaction. Steam, $H_2O(g)$, is passed over red-hot coke, $C(s)$, yielding a mixture of carbon monoxide, $CO(g)$, and hydrogen gas, $H_2(g)$.

Figure 11.3 Two conversion factors are required to calculate the mass of product formed from a given number of moles of reactant. They are moles of product per moles of reactant, obtained from the balanced equation, and molar mass of the product, mass of product per 1 mol product.

$$H_2O(g) + C(s) \rightarrow CO(g) + H_2(g)$$
Water gas

This mixture of CO and H_2, water gas, is burned, releasing a large amount of energy. Let's calculate the mass of CO produced when 125 mol $H_2O(g)$ is reacted with excess coke.

In addition to being used as fuel, water gas is combined with steam on a special catalyst to produce CO_2; in addition, more H_2 is also liberated.

From the equation, we obtain the mole ratio of CO formed to H_2O reacted, a 1-to-1 ratio. Accordingly, we solve the problem in the same way as we have solved prior stoichiometry problems, adding one more conversion factor, one that converts moles of CO to grams of CO.

~~mol H$_2$O~~ × $\dfrac{\text{~~mol CO~~}}{\text{~~mol H$_2$O~~}}$ × $\dfrac{\text{g CO}}{\text{~~mol CO~~}}$ = g CO

124 ~~mol H$_2$O~~ × $\dfrac{\text{1 ~~mol CO~~}}{\text{1 ~~mol H$_2$O~~}}$ × $\dfrac{\text{28.0 g CO}}{\text{1.00 ~~mol CO~~}}$ = 3500 g CO = 3.50×10^3 g CO = 3.50 kg CO

When 125 mol H$_2$O(g) reacts in the water gas-formation reaction, a maximum of 3.50 kg CO results.

Example Problems 11.3 and 11.4 are examples of mole-mass calculations, i.e., stoichiometry problems with the moles and mass of reactants and products.

Example Problem 11.3

Coke, C(s), is produced when coal is heated to drive off its volatile components. Coke is used as fuel and can be converted to graphite. What mass of coke, C(s), must be present to react with 125 mol H$_2$O(g) in the water gas reaction?

$$H_2O(g) + C(s) \rightarrow CO(g) + H_2(g)$$

Solution

1. What is unknown?   Mass of C(s) in g
2. What is known? 125 mol H$_2$O(g); 1 mol C/1 mol H$_2$O; and 12.0 g C/mol C
3. Apply the factor-label method.

125 ~~mol H$_2$O~~ × $\dfrac{\text{1 ~~mol C~~}}{\text{1 ~~mol H$_2$O~~}}$ × $\dfrac{\text{12.0 g C}}{\text{1 ~~mol C~~}}$ = ? g C

4. Perform the indicated math operations.

125 ~~mol H$_2$O~~ × $\dfrac{\text{1 ~~mol C~~}}{\text{1 ~~mol H$_2$O~~}}$ × $\dfrac{\text{12.0 g C}}{\text{1 ~~mol C~~}}$ = **1.50×10^3 g C or 1.50 kg C**

Whenever 125 mol H$_2$O(g) is present, it reacts with exactly 1.50 kg of coke.

Exercise

How many moles of H$_2$ result when 0.555 g C reacts with H$_2$O in the above reaction?
(0.0463 mol H$_2$)

Example Problem 11.4

The common name for MgO is magnesia. It is sometimes used to prepare Mg(OH)$_2$(aq), called milk of magnesia. This solution is used to decrease excess stomach acid. How many moles of magnesium oxide, MgO, form when 65.0 g Fe$_2$O$_3$ reacts with excess magnesium in the following reaction:

$$3Mg + Fe_2O_3 \rightarrow 3MgO + 2Fe$$

Solution

1. What is unknown?   Mol MgO
2. What is known? 65.0 g Fe$_2$O$_3$; 1 mol Fe$_2$O$_3$/159.6 g Fe$_2$O$_3$; 3 mol MgO/1 mol Fe$_2$O$_3$

3. Apply the factor-label method.

$$65.0 \text{ g Fe}_2\text{O}_3 \times \frac{1 \text{ mol Fe}_2\text{O}_3}{159.6 \text{ g Fe}_2\text{O}_3} \times \frac{3 \text{ mol MgO}}{1 \text{ mol Fe}_2\text{O}_3} = ? \text{ mol MgO}$$

4. Perform the indicated math operations.

$$65.0 \text{ g Fe}_2\text{O}_3 \times \frac{1 \text{ mol Fe}_2\text{O}_3}{159.6 \text{ g Fe}_2\text{O}_3} \times \frac{3 \text{ mol MgO}}{1 \text{ mol Fe}_2\text{O}_3} = \textbf{1.22 mol MgO}$$

When 65.0 g Fe_2O_3 reacts with excess Mg, a maximum of 1.22 mol MgO is expected to form.

Exercise
How many moles of Fe results when 65.0 g Fe_2O_3 reacts with excess Mg? (0.815 mol Fe)

Mass-Mass Calculations

Mass-mass calculations are those in which a mass is initially given and the final answer is also a mass. This type of stoichiometric calculation is the one most often encountered. Let's consider examples of such problems.

WWWolfe 3
(See WWWolfe section at the end of the chapter.)

When white phosphorus, P_4, reacts with chlorine gas, Cl_2, a colorless fuming liquid, phosphorus trichloride, PCl_3, results.

$$P_4(s) + 6Cl_2(g) \rightarrow 4PCl_3(l)$$

What mass of PCl_3 forms when 100.0 g P_4 reacts with excess chlorine gas?

First convert the mass of P_4 to moles of P_4. We do this because the balanced equation shows the mole ratio, not the mass ratio. Once the number of moles of P_4 is known, the problem is the same as a mole to mass conversion.

> Phosphorus exists in two different forms. White phosphorus is composed of P_4 molecules, and red phosphorus is made up of long chains of bonded P_4 molecules. White phosphorus is very reactive and spontaneously bursts into flames when exposed to the air. Red phosphorus is much less reactive.

$$100.0 \text{ g P}_4 \times \frac{1 \text{ mol P}_4}{123.9 \text{ g P}_4} \times \frac{4 \text{ mol PCl}_3}{1 \text{ mol P}_4} \times \frac{137.3 \text{ g PCl}_3}{1 \text{ mol P}_4} = 443.3 \text{ g PCl}_3$$

The first conversion factor,

$$\frac{1 \text{ mol P}_4}{123.9 \text{ g P}_4}$$

converts the mass of P_4 to moles. The balanced equation shows that 4 mol PCl_3 forms for each mole of P_4 initially present. Thus, the second conversion factor yields the number of moles of PCl_3 produced. Our problem is completed by changing the number of moles of PCl_3 to grams of PCl_3, using the molar mass of PCl_3, which is 137.3 g/mol.
Carefully go through Example Problems 11.5 and 11.6, which illustrate mass-mass stoichiometry problems. ❖

Example Problem 11.5

What mass of Cl_2 reacts with excess P_4 to yield 0.927 g PCl_3?

$$P_4(s) + 6Cl_2(g) \rightarrow 4PCl_3(l)$$

Solution

1. What is unknown?   Mass of Cl_2 in g
2. What is known? 0.927 g PCl_3; 1 mol PCl_3/137.3 g PCl_3; 4 mol PCl_3/6 mol Cl_2
3. Apply the factor-label method.

$$0.927 \text{ g } PCl_3 \times \frac{1 \text{ mol } PCl_3}{137.3 \text{ g } PCl_4} \times \frac{6 \text{ mol } Cl_2}{4 \text{ mol } PCl_3} \times \frac{70.9 \text{ g } Cl_2}{1 \text{ mol } Cl_2} = ? \text{ g } Cl_2$$

4. Perform the indicated math operations.

$$0.927 \text{ g } PCl_3 \times \frac{1 \text{ mol } PCl_3}{137.3 \text{ g } PCl_4} \times \frac{6 \text{ mol } Cl_2}{4 \text{ mol } PCl_3} \times \frac{70.9 \text{ g } Cl_2}{1 \text{ mol } Cl_2} = \textbf{0.718 g } Cl_2$$

A sample of 0.718 g Cl_2, when combined with an excess of P_4, yields 0.927 g PCl_3.

Exercise

What mass of P_4 reacts with 1.00 g Cl_2 in the above reaction? (0.291 g P_4)

Example Problem 11.6

What mass of oxygen gas, $O_2(g)$, is liberated when a 2.5-g sample of sodium nitrate, $NaNO_3$, is heated?

> The common name for $NaNO_3$ is Chile saltpeter. Both $NaNO_3$ and $NaNO_2$ used to prevent bacterial growth in meats.

$$2NaNO_3(s) \rightarrow 2NaNO_2(s) + O_2(g)$$

Solution

1. What is unknown?   Mass O_2 in g
2. What is known? 2.5 g $NaNO_3$; 85 g $NaNO_3$/mol $NaNO_3$; 1 mol O_2/2 mol $NaNO_3$; and 32 g O_2/mol O_2
3. Apply the factor-label method.

$$2.5 \text{ g } NaNO_3 \times \frac{1 \text{ mol } NaNO_3}{85 \text{ g } NaNO_3} \times \frac{1 \text{ mol } O_2}{2 \text{ mol } NaNO_3} \times \frac{32 \text{ g } O_2}{1 \text{ mol } O_2} = ? \text{ g } O_2$$

4. Perform the indicated math operations.

$$2.5 \text{ g } NaNO_3 \times \frac{1 \text{ mol } NaNO_3}{85 \text{ g } NaNO_3} \times \frac{1 \text{ mol } O_2}{2 \text{ mol } NaNO_3} \times \frac{32 \text{ g } O_2}{1 \text{ mol } O_2} = \textbf{0.47 g } O_2$$

A 2.5-g sample of $NaNO_3$ thermally decomposes to produce 0.47 g O_2.

Exercise
What mass of $NaNO_2$ results when 2.5 g $NaNO_3$ decomposes in the above reaction? (2.0 g $NaNO_2$)

Figure 11.4 shows the steps required to solve mass-mass stoichiometry problems.

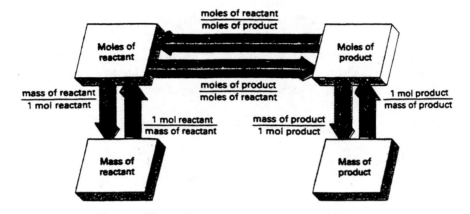

Figure 11.4 Mass-mass problems are solved in a similar manner to mole-mass problems except that a third conversion factor is needed to change the mass of the reactant to moles. This conversion factor is the molar mass of the reactant, mass of reactant per mole of reactant.

REVIEW EXERCISES

11.6 Calculate the number of moles of SO_2 produced when 4.55 g S_8 reacts with excess O_2 in the following reaction.

$$S_8(s) + 8O_2(g) \rightarrow 8SO_2(g)$$

11.7 Consider the following equation:

$$P_4(s) + 6Cl_2(g) \rightarrow 4PCl_3(l)$$

(a) What mass of P_4 is required to combine with 0.398 g Cl_2 to produce PCl_3?

(b) What mass of PCl_3 results when 0.398 g Cl_2 is combined with the calculated mass of P_4?

11.8 (a) Calculate the mass of F_2 required to combine with N_2 to produce 204 kg NF_3 in the following reaction:

$$N_2(g) + 3F_2(g) \rightarrow 2NF_3(g)$$

(b) What mass of N_2 exactly reacts with 25.91 mg F_2?

11.6 0.142 mol SO_2; 11.7 (a) 0.116 g P_4, (b) 0.514 g PCl_3; 12.8 (a) 1.64×10^5 g F_2, (b) 0.006367 g N_2

11.3 QUANTITATIVE ENERGY EFFECTS

As discussed in Chapter 10, heat is either released or absorbed in chemical reactions. Whenever heat is liberated, the reaction is classified as an **exothermic** reaction, and when heat is absorbed, the reaction is classified as an **endothermic** reaction. The amount of heat transferred in chemical reactions is related to the number of moles of reactants that undergo chemical change. A fixed quantity of heat is transferred per mole of reactant consumed. This amount of heat is called the **enthalpy of reaction, ΔH, or heat of reaction.**

Through the application of stoichiometric principles, we can calculate the energy released or absorbed in a chemical reaction. Let us reconsider the reaction in which $HCl(g)$ is synthesized from its elements. This time the heat evolved by the reaction is also shown.

$$H_2(g) + Cl_2(g) \rightarrow 2HCl(g) + 184 \text{ kJ}$$

Besides the two moles of HCl produced, 184 kJ (44 kcal) is released in this exothermic reaction. In other words, for each 1 mol H_2 and 1 mol Cl_2 that react, 2 mol HCl and 184 kJ of heat are produced.

Given the balanced equation and the quantity of heat transferred per mole of reactant, the amount of energy released for any mass of reactant can be calculated. What quantity of heat is liberated when a 1.00-g sample of H_2 reacts with excess Cl_2 to produce HCl? To solve this problem, a conversion factor is needed that relates moles of H_2 to the amount of heat liberated; it is

$$\frac{184 \text{ kJ}}{1 \text{ mol } H_2}$$

We solve for kilojoules, kJ, by calculating the number of moles of H_2 and using the above conversion factor.

$$1.00 \text{ g } H_2 \times \frac{1.0 \text{ mol } H_2}{2.02 \text{ g } H_2} \times \frac{184 \text{ kJ}}{1 \text{ mol } H_2} = 91.1 \text{ kJ}$$

For each gram of H_2 that reacts with Cl_2, 91.1 kJ (21.8 kcal) of heat is liberated to the surroundings.

Example Problems 11.7 and 11.8 are additional examples of problems that deal with energy effects in chemical reactions. Refer to Fig. 11.5, which shows the required steps.

Example Problem 11.7

Acetylene, C_2H_2, is a combustible gas used to cut and weld metals. Formation of one mole of acetylene from its elements requires the addition of 227 kJ of energy.

$$2C(s) + H_2(g) + 227 \text{ kJ} \rightarrow C_2H_2(g)$$

Calculate the amount of heat required to produce 545 g C_2H_2. Assume that sufficient quantities of the reactants are present.

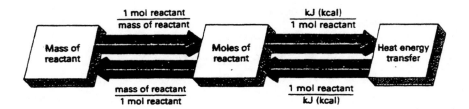

Figure 11.5 To calculate the energy consumed or liberated by a chemical reaction, the conversion factor for the number of moles of reactant and the amount of energy in kilojoules or kilocalories transferred is required. Therefore, if the mass of reactant is given, convert the mass to moles and then multiply by the energy conversion factor.

Solution

1. What is unknown?   Heat transferred in kJ
2. What is known? 545 g C_2H_2; 227 kJ/mol C_2H_2; 26.0 g C_2H_2/ mol C_2H_2
3. Apply the factor-label method.

$$545 \text{ g } C_2H_2 \times \frac{1 \text{ mol } C_2H_2}{26.0 \text{ g } C_2H_2} \times \frac{227 \text{ kJ}}{1 \text{ mol } C_2H_2} = ? \text{ kJ}$$

4. Perform the indicated math operations.

$$545 \text{ g } C_2H_2 \times \frac{1 \text{ mol } C_2H_2}{26.0 \text{ g } C_2H_2} \times \frac{227 \text{ kJ}}{1 \text{ mol } C_2H_2} = 4.76 \times 10^3 \text{ kJ}$$

To produce 545 g C_2H_2, 4.76×10^3 kJ of energy is required in addition to the proper amount of both reactants. As with other fuels, formation of acetylene from its elements is an endothermic process.

Exercise
What mass of C_2H_2 results when 800 kJ of heat is added to sufficient amounts of the reactants in the above reaction? (91.6 kJ)

Example Problem 11.8
Blood sugar, or glucose, $C_6H_{12}O_6$, is one of the main sources of energy in living systems. It is broken down in biological cells to CO_2 and H_2O, releasing 2816 kJ/mol $C_6H_{12}O_6$:

$$C_6H_{12}O_6(s) + 6O_2(g) \rightarrow 6CO_2(g) + 6H_2O(g) + 2816 \text{ kJ}$$

Calculate the number of kilocalories of heat released for each 1.00 g of glucose.

Solution
1. What is unknown?   kcal/1.00 g $C_6H_{12}O_6$

2. What is known? 1.00 g $C_6H_{12}O_6$; 2816 kJ/mol $C_6H_{12}O_6$; 180 g $C_6H_{12}O_6$/mol $C_6H_{12}O_6$, and 4.184 kJ/kcal

3. Apply the factor-label method.

$$1.00 \text{ g } \cancel{C_6H_{12}O_6} \times \frac{1 \text{ mol } \cancel{C_6H_{12}O_6}}{180 \text{ g } \cancel{C_6H_{12}O_6}} \times \frac{2816 \text{ kJ}}{1 \text{ mol } \cancel{C_6H_{12}O_6}} \times \frac{1 \text{ kcal}}{4.184 \text{ kJ}} = ? \text{ kcal}$$

4. Perform the indicated math operations.

$$1.00 \text{ g } \cancel{C_6H_{12}O_6} \times \frac{1 \text{ mol } \cancel{C_6H_{12}O_6}}{180 \text{ g } \cancel{C_6H_{12}O_6}} \times \frac{2816 \text{ kJ}}{1 \text{ mol } \cancel{C_6H_{12}O_6}} \times \frac{1 \text{ kcal}}{4.184 \text{ kJ}} = \textbf{3.74 kcal}$$

For each 1.00 gram of glucose "burned" by your cells, 3.74 kcal of energy is released.

Exercise
What mass of glucose in mg is required to produce 1.0 kJ in the above reaction? (64 mg $C_6H_{12}O_6$)

Calorimetry

Calorimeters are the instruments used to measure heat transfers in chemical reactions (refer to Section 4.6). A **calorimeter** is a reaction vessel constructed so that the heat either evolved or absorbed is detected. You may recall that we previously discussed how calorimeters are used to measure specific heat.

Crude estimates of the heat transferred in chemical reactions can be made with a simple calorimeter made from a Styrofoam cup (Fig. 4.13, page 99). Two solutions are mixed inside the Styrofoam cup. Temperature readings are taken before and after the solutions react. The only other quantity that must be determined is the **heat capacity** of the calorimeter, i.e., the quantity of heat absorbed by the calorimeter to raise its temperature by one degree Celsius. Since the calorimeter is constructed of Styrofoam, which does not absorb too much heat, only the temperature change of the resulting solution is considered. Rough estimates of heat transfers are obtained using Styrofoam cup calorimeters. The instruments used in research laboratories are more sophisticated. One such calorimeter, a bomb calorimeter, is shown in Fig. 11.6.

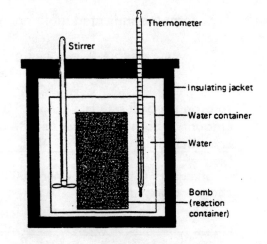

Figure 11.6 A bomb calorimeter is used to obtain the quantity of heat transferred in a chemical reaction at constant volume.

Example Problem 11.9 shows an example of an energy transfer problem in which a calorimeter is used. ❖

Example Problem 11.9

When 0.500 g KOH is placed into 45.6 g H_2O at 25.1°C inside a Styrofoam cup calorimeter, the KOH dissolves and raises the temperature of the water to 27.8°C. Calculate the amount of heat in kJ released per mole of KOH, kJ/mol. This quantity is called the enthalpy of solution, ΔH_{soln}, for KOH. Assume that the specific heat of the resulting solution is 4.18 J/(g °C), and that the calorimeter does not absorb any heat.

Solution
1. What is unknown?   Enthalpy of solution (ΔH_{soln}), kJ/mol
2. What is known? 0.500 g KOH, 56.1 g KOH/mol KOH, 45.6 g H_2O, ΔT = 27.8°C – 25.1°C = 2.7°C, 4.18 J/(g °C), 1000 J/kJ
3. Calculate the amount of heat released, in kJ, to the water

$$q_{water} = m_{water} \times \Delta T \times c_{water} = 45.6 \text{ g} \times 2.7°C \times 4.18 \text{ J/(g °C)} \times 1 \text{ kJ}/1000 \text{ kJ} = 0.51 \text{ kJ}$$

The result tells us that 0.51 kJ of heat is absorbed by the water when 0.500 g KOH dissolves. Because the heat gained by the water is lost by the KOH as it dissolves, then q_{KOH} is –0.51 kJ.
4. Calculate the enthalpy of solution in kJ/mol.
Convert the mass of KOH to moles,

$$0.500 \text{ g KOH} \times \frac{1 \text{ mol KOH}}{56.1 \text{ g KOH}} = 0.00891 \text{ mol KOH}$$

and then divide the moles into the kJ of heat released.

$$\Delta H_{soln} = -0.51 \text{ kJ}/0.00891 \text{ mol} = \textbf{–57 kJ/mol}$$

The enthalpy of solution for KOH is –57 kJ/mol.

Exercise
When 0.500 g NaOH is placed into 45.6 g H_2O at 25.1°C inside a Styrofoam cup calorimeter, the KOH dissolves and raises the temperature of the water to 28.0°C. Calculate the amount of heat in kJ released per mole of NaOH, kJ/mol. Assume that the specific heat of the resulting solution is 4.18 J/(g °C), and that the calorimeter does not absorb any heat. (–45 kJ/mol)

REVIEW EXERCISES
11.9 What mass of Cl_2 reacts with H_2 to produce 812 kJ of energy in the following reaction?

$$H_2(g) + Cl_2(g) \rightarrow 2HCl(g) + 184 \text{ kJ}$$

11.10 How much energy, in kilojoules, is released when 254.0 g $C_6H_{12}O_6$, glucose, reacts with O_2 in human cells?

$$C_6H_{12}O_6 + 6O_2(g) \rightarrow 6CO_2(g) + 6H_2O(g) + 2816 \text{ kJ}$$

11.11 If the heat released from the combustion of 10.00 g CH_4 is totally transferred to 15.0 kg H_2O at 15.00°C, what is the final temperature of the water. The specific heat of water is 4.184 J/(g °C)

$$CH_4 + 2O_2 \rightarrow CO_2 + 2H_2O + 802 \text{ kJ}$$

11.9 313 g Cl_2; 11.10 3.97 × 10³kJ; 11.11 22.99°C

11.4 LIMITING-REACTANT PROBLEMS

So far we have assumed in our calculations that sufficient quantities of all reactants are present to react with the specified mass of one reactant of interest. However, situations arise when masses are given for more than one of the reactants and we must decide which reactant limits the reaction and determines the maximum yield of product; such problems are called **limiting-reactant** or **limiting-reagent** problems.

To illustrate a limiting reactant problem, let us consider the complete oxidation of carbon to carbon dioxide:

> A limiting reactant, sometimes called limiting reagent, is the reactant consumed first, and thus determines the maximum amounts of products formed

$$C(s) + O_2 \rightarrow CO_2(g)$$

One mole of carbon combines with one mole of molecular oxygen to produce one mole CO_2. As long as equal numbers of moles of reactants react, a limiting-reagent situation is not encountered. If 5 mol C and 5 mol O_2 are combined, 5 mol CO_2 forms. However, if 5 mol C reacts with 10 mol O_2, the result is still 5 mol CO_2. After the 5 mol C is consumed, the reaction stops. Carbon is therefore the limiting reagent because after it is consumed, the reaction ceases. Study Table 11.2, which shows stepwise what happens when 5 mol C combines with 10 mol O_2.

TABLE 11.2 LIMITING REACTANT IN THE OXIDATION OF CARBON
$$C(s) + O_2(g) \rightarrow CO_2(g)$$

Moles C present	Moles O_2 present	Moles CO_2 produced	Amount reacted
5	10	0	Initial amount
4	9	1	After 1 mol
3	8	2	After 2 mol
2	7	3	After 3 mol
1	6	4	After 4 mol
0˙	5	5	After 5 mol

˙After the C is consumed, the reaction cannot continue. At that time, 5 mol of unreacted O_2 and 5 mol of CO_2 are in the system. Carbon is the limiting reactant, and oxygen is the reactant in excess.

Some everyday experiences provide good analogies to the situation that occurs in limiting-reactant problems. Take for example the stapling of photocopied pages to produce a pamphlet. If 25 first pages, 50 second pages, and 100 third pages are stapled to produce a three-page pamphlet, how many complete pamphlets could be produced? Here, the first page is the "limiting reagent." Once 25 pamphlets are stapled, no more complete pamphlets can be produced because no first pages remain. It does not matter that 25 second pages and 75 third pages are unstapled; a complete pamphlet cannot be produced without adding more first pages to our supply (Fig. 11.7).

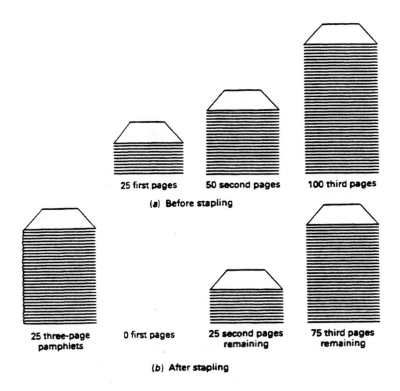

25 first pages   50 second pages   100 third pages

(a) Before stapling

25 three-page   0 first pages   25 second pages   75 third pages
pamphlets   remaining   remaining

(b) After stapling

Figure 11.7 A pamphlet is produced by stapling three pages together. If 25 first pages, 50 second pages, and 100 third pages are initially present, the maximum number of complete pamphlets that can be produced is 25. After the first page runs out, no more completed pamphlets can be produced.

Our initial chemical limiting-reactant example was straightforward because the reactants combined in a l-to-l ratio. What if the reactants combine in another ratio? Again we return to the Haber reaction:

$$N_2(g) + 3H_2(g) \rightarrow 2NH_3(g)$$

What is the limiting reactant, if 6 mol N_2 combines with 6 mol H_2? In the Haber reaction, 3 mol H_2 is consumed for each 1 mol N_2. Initially, 1 mol N_2 combines with 3 mol H_2, which leaves 5 mol N_2 and 3 mol H_2. When the next 1 mol N_2 reacts, it consumes all of the remaining H_2; the reaction then stops for lack of H_2. Hydrogen is therefore the limiting reagent. Consequently, 4 mol unreacted N_2 remains in the reaction vessel with the 4 mol NH_3 produced (Table 11.3).

TABLE 11.3 LIMITING REACTANT IN THE HABER REACTION
$$N_2 + 3H_2 \rightarrow 2NH_3$$

Moles N₂ present	Moles H₂ present	Moles NH₃ formed	Amount reacted
6	6	0	Initial amount
5	3	2	After 1 mol N₂
4	0	4	After 2 mol N₂

As the above examples show, the limiting reactant is found by comparing the numbers of moles of reactants present, while taking into account the mole ratio in which they react. Most often, masses of the reactants are given; thus, it is necessary to convert the masses to moles and then decide which reactant is limiting (consumed first).

What is the limiting reactant when 10.0 g H_2 and 50.0 g O_2 are combined to produce water vapor?

$$2H_2(g) + O_2(g) \rightarrow 2H_2O(g)$$

Calculate the number of moles of each reactant:

$$10.0 \text{ g } H_2 \times \frac{1 \text{ mol } H_2}{2.02 \text{ g } H_2} = 4.95 \text{ mol } H_2$$

$$50.0 \text{ g } O_2 \times \frac{1 \text{ mol } O_2}{32.0 \text{ g } O_2} = 1.56 \text{ mol } O_2$$

After calculating the number of moles of each reactant, select one of the reactants and determine how many moles of the other are needed to combine with it completely. Because it does not matter which reactant we select, let's calculate the number of moles of H_2 required to combine with the O_2 present.

$$1.56 \text{ mol } O_2 \times \frac{2 \text{ mol } H_2}{1 \text{ mol } O_2} = 3.12 \text{ mol } H_2$$

We take the number of moles of O_2 and multiply it by 2 because, in the equation, 2 mol H_2 are required per 1 mol O_2. Looking at the results, we see that 3.12 mol H_2 is required to combine with 1.56 mol O_2. Is there enough H_2 to react with the O_2? Yes, only 3.12 mol H_2 is needed, and 4.95 mol is available. Hence, O_2 is the limiting reactant. After the 1.56 mol O_2 reacts with the excess H_2, the reaction ceases.

Once the limiting reactant is identified, all other calculations are completed using the number of moles of limiting reactant. What total mass of H_2O is produced in the above problem?

$$1.56 \text{ mol } O_2 \times \frac{2 \text{ mol } H_2O}{1 \text{ mol } O_2} \times \frac{18.0 \text{ g } H_2O}{1 \text{ mol } H_2O} = \textbf{56.2 g } \textbf{H}_2\textbf{O}$$

When 10.0 g H_2 and 50.0 g O_2 combine, the theoretical yield of water is 56.2 g.

Note that if you had not chosen the correct limiting reactant, the calculated mass of water would have been larger than the theoretical yield.

$$4.95 \ \cancel{mol \ H_2} \ \times \ \frac{2 \ \cancel{mol \ H_2O}}{2 \ \cancel{mol \ H_2}} \ \times \ \frac{18.0 \ g \ H_2O}{1 \ \cancel{mol \ H_2O}} = 89.1 \ g \ H_2O \ \textbf{(Incorrect answer)}$$

This amount of H_2O, 89.1 g, could only be produced if a sufficient quantity of O_2 is available (2.48 mol O_2). It is impossible for 89.1 g H_2O to form with the stated quantities of starting materials.

Example Problems 11.10 and 11.11 provide additional illustrations of limiting-reagent problems. The steps required to solve limiting-reagent problems are summarized in Fig. 11.8. ❖

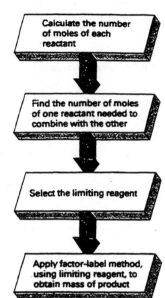

Example Problem 11.10

What mass of SO_3 is produced when 0.600 g SO_2 reacts with 0.400 g O_2?

$$2SO_2(g) + O_2(g) \rightarrow 2SO_3(g)$$

Solution

1. Identify the limiting reactant.
First, calculate which reactant is the limiting reactant by comparing the initial numbers of moles.

Figure 11.8 Steps required to solve limiting reactant problems.

$$0.600 \ \cancel{g \ SO_2} \ \times \ \frac{1 \ mol \ SO_2}{64.1 \ \cancel{g \ SO_2}} = 0.00936 \ mol \ SO_2$$

$$0.400 \ \cancel{g \ O_2} \ \times \ \frac{1 \ mol \ O_2}{32.0 \ \cancel{g \ O_2}} = 0.0125 \ mol \ O_2$$

Calculate the number of moles of SO_2 needed to react with the number of moles of O_2 actually present or vice versa.

$$0.0125 \ \cancel{mol \ O_2} \ \times \ \frac{2 \ mol \ O_2}{1 \ \cancel{mol \ O_2}} = 0.0250 \ mol \ O_2$$

We find that 0.0250 mol SO_2 is required to react with 0.0125 mol O_2. However, only 0.00936 mol of SO_2 is present; consequently, SO_2 is the limiting reactant.
2. Apply the factor-label method.
Complete the problem by using conversion factors to find the mass of SO_3 formed (mole-mass problem).

$$0.00936 \ \cancel{g \ SO_2} \ \times \ \frac{2 \ \cancel{mol \ SO_3}}{2 \ \cancel{mol \ SO_2}} \ \times \ \frac{80.0 \ g \ SO_3}{1 \ \cancel{mol \ SO_3}} = \textbf{0.749 g } SO_3$$

If 0.600 g SO_2 is combined with 0.400 g O_2, 0.749 g SO_3 is the maximum quantity of product produced.

Exercise

If 100 g SO_2 reacts with 24.0 g O_2, what is the theoretical yield of SO_3? (120 g SO_3)

Example Problem 11.11

Gaseous hydrogen, H_2, reacts with nitrogen dioxide to produce ammonia and water. (a) What mass of ammonia results when 25.0 g of molecular hydrogen combines with 185 g of nitrogen dioxide? (b) What mass of excess reactant remains?

Solution

1. Write and balance the equation.

$$H_2(g) + NO_2(g) \rightarrow NH_3(g) + H_2O(g) \text{ (Unbalanced)}$$

$$7H_2(g) + 2NO_2(g) \rightarrow 2NH_3(g) + 4H_2O(g) \text{ (Balanced)}$$

2. Identify the limiting reactant.

$$25.0 \text{ g } H_2 \times \frac{1 \text{ mol } H_2}{2.02 \text{ g } H_2} = 12.4 \text{ mol } H_2$$

$$185 \text{ g } NO_2 \times \frac{1 \text{ mol } NO_2}{46.0 \text{ g } NO_2} = 4.02 \text{ mol } NO_2$$

Calculate the number of moles of NO_2 needed to combine with 12.4 mol H_2

$$12.4 \text{ mol } H_2 \times \frac{2 \text{ mol } NO_2}{7 \text{ mol } H_2} = 3.54 \text{ mol } NO_2$$

Because 3.54 mol NO_2 is needed and 4.02 mol is actually present, H_2 is the limiting reactant. When all 12.4 mol H_2 is combined, an excess of NO_2 remains.

3. Use the limiting reactant to calculate the mass of NH_3 produced.

$$12.4 \text{ mol } H_2 \times \frac{2 \text{ mol } NH_3}{7 \text{ mol } H_2} \times \frac{17.0 \text{ g } NH_3}{1 \text{ mol } NH_3} = \textbf{60.2 g } NH_3$$

After 25.0 g H_2 and 185 g NO_2 react, the theoretical yield of NH_3 is 60.2 g.

4. Calculate the mass of excess reactant.

In Step 2 we found that 3.54 mol NO_2 is needed to react with 12.4 mol H_2; therefore, subtract 3.54 mol NO_2 from 4.02 mol NO_2, the total number of moles of NO_2 present, to find the moles of NO_2 in excess.

$$\text{Excess mol } NO_2 = 4.02 \text{ mol } NO_2 - 3.54 \text{ mol } NO_2 = 0.48 \text{ mol } NO_2$$

To find the mass of NO_2 in excess, we use the molar mass to cancel moles of NO_2.

$$0.48 \; \text{mol NO}_2 \times \frac{46 \text{ g NO}_2}{1 \text{ mol NO}_2} = \textbf{22 g NO}_2$$

After the reaction, 22 g of unreacted NO_2 should be found in the reaction vessel.

Exercise

When 50 g C_4H_8 reacts with 50 g O_2 the products are CO_2 and H_2O. What mass of CO_2 results from this reaction? (46 g CO_2)

REVIEW EXERCISES

11.12 (a) What is the limiting reactant in a chemical reaction?

(b) Explain how to determine which reactant is the limiting reactant.

11.13 For the combination reaction of carbon and oxygen to produce carbon dioxide, determine which is the limiting reactant, carbon or oxygen, given the following amounts:

(a) 6 mol C + 6 mol O_2
(b) 2 mol C + 1 mol O_2
(c) 12.0 g C + 12.0 g O_2
(d) 16 g C + 31 g O_2
(e) 0.0455 g C + 0.205 g O_2

11.14 For each part of 11.13, calculate what mass of excess reactant is present if the reaction is allowed to go to completion.

11.15 (a) What is the maximum mass of sodium fluoride, NaF, that results when 52.9 g of sodium metal combines with 44.8 g of fluorine, F_2?

$$2Na + F_2 \rightarrow 2NaF$$

(b) What mass of excess reactant remains?

11.13 (a) No limiting reactant, (b) 1 mol O_2 is limiting, (c) 12.0 g O_2 is limiting, (d) 31 g O_2 is limiting, (e) 0.0455 g C is limiting; 11.14 (b) 12 g C, (c) 7.5 g C, (d) 4.4 g C, (e) 0.0837 g O_2; 11.15 (a) 96.6 g NaF, (b) 1 g F_2

11.5 THEORETICAL AND ACTUAL YIELDS

Frequently the mass of product obtained in a reaction is less than the predicted theoretical yield. The amount of product isolated is called the **actual yield.** To show the degree to which the theoretical yield is obtained, chemists often report the **percent yield** for products. It is defined as follows:

$$\% \text{ yield} = \frac{\text{actual yield}}{\text{theoretical yield}} \times 100$$

If the theoretical yield of a product is 5 g, and only 4 g is isolated, the percent yield is reported as 80 percent (4 g/5 g × 100). Example Problems 11.12 and 11.13 are examples of percent yield problems. ❖

Example Problem 11.12

Calcium phosphate, $Ca_3(PO_4)_2$, reacts with silicon dioxide, SiO_2, to produce calcium silicate, $CaSiO_3$, and P_4O_{10}. Initially, 50.0 g $Ca_3(PO_4)_2$ reacts with excess SiO_2. After the reaction, 16.9 g P_4O_{10} is isolated; calculate the percent yield of P_4O_{10}.

$$2Ca_3(PO_4)_2 + 6SiO_2 \rightarrow 6CaSiO_3 + P_4O_{10}$$

Solution

1. What is unknown?   % yield = (g P_4O_{10} (actual)/g P_4O_{10} (theoretical)) × 100
2. What is known? 50.0 g $Ca_3(PO_4)_2$, 16.9 g P_4O_{10} (actual), 310.2 g $Ca_3(PO_4)_2$/mol, 284 g P_4O_{10}/mol, 1 mol P_4O_{10}/2 mol $Ca_3(PO_4)_2$
3. Calculate the theoretical yield of P_4O_{10}.

$$50.0 \; \cancel{g \; Ca_3(PO_4)_2} \times \frac{1 \; \cancel{mol \; Ca_3(PO_4)_2}}{310 \; \cancel{g \; Ca_3(PO_4)_2}} \times \frac{1 \; \cancel{mol \; P_4O_{10}}}{2 \; \cancel{mol \; Ca_3(PO_4)_2}} \times \frac{284 \; g \; P_4O_{10}}{1 \; \cancel{mol \; P_4O_{10}}} = 22.9 \; g \; P_4O_{10}$$

Without going through each step, the above factor-label setup gives the mass of P_4O_{10} that forms when 50.0 g of calcium phosphate combines with excess silicon dioxide. Thus, the theoretical yield is 22.9 g P_4O_{10}.

2. Calculate the percent yield.

$$\% \text{ yield} = \frac{\text{actual yield}}{\text{theoretical yield}} \times 100$$

$$= (16.9 \text{ g } P_4O_{10}/22.9 \text{ g } P_4O_{10}) \times 100 = \textbf{73.8\%}$$

An actual yield of 16.9 g P_4O_{10} represents a 73.8% yield. Perhaps during the course of the reaction and isolation of the product, 26.2% of the theoretical yield of P_4O_{10} was lost.

Exercise

Initially, 50.0 g SiO_2 reacts with excess $Ca_3(PO_4)_2$. After the reaction, 27.6 g P_4O_{10} is isolated; calculate the percent yield of P_4O_{10}. (70.1%)

Example Problem 11.13

Chromium metal and aluminum oxide, Al_2O_3, are produced when chromium(III) oxide, Cr_2O_3, is heated with aluminum metal.

$$Cr_2O_3 + 2Al \rightarrow 2Cr + Al_2O_3$$

The maximum percent yield of Cr obtained by this process is found to be 89.3%. Calculate the mass of Cr_2O_3 required to produce 91.3 g Cr, if the maximum percent yield is obtained.

Solution

To solve this problem, we must consider that in this reaction only 89.3% of the theoretical yield is obtained. Thus, we should first calculate the theoretical yield that gives the desired amount of Cr (91.3 g Cr) and then calculate the mass of Cr_2O_3 that produces that amount of Cr.

1. Calculate the theoretical yield of Cr that gives the desired actual yield. The percent yield of the reaction is 89.3%, which means that

$$\% \text{ yield} = \frac{89.3 \text{ g Cr (actual)}}{100 \text{ g Cr (theoretical)}} \times 100$$

Therefore, we should calculate the theoretical yield of Cr that gives 91.3 g Cr as follows:

$$91.3 \text{ g } \cancel{\text{Cr (actual)}} \times \frac{100 \text{ g Cr (theoretical)}}{89.3 \text{ g } \cancel{\text{Cr (actual)}}} = 102 \text{ g Cr (theoretical)}$$

A theoretical yield of 102 g Cr gives an actual yield of 91.3 g Cr.

2. Calculate the mass of Cr_2O_3 needed to produce 102 g Cr.

$$102 \text{ g } \cancel{\text{Cr}} \times \frac{1 \cancel{\text{ mol Cr}}}{59.0 \text{ g } \cancel{\text{Cr}}} \times \frac{1 \cancel{\text{ mol Cr}_2\text{O}_3}}{2 \cancel{\text{ mol Cr}}} \times \frac{152 \text{ g Cr}_2\text{O}_3}{1 \cancel{\text{ mol Cr}_2\text{O}_3}} = \textbf{149 g Cr}_2\textbf{O}_3$$

If 149 g Cr_2O_3 is combined with excess Al, it produces an actual yield of 91.3 g Cr.

Exercise

In the above reaction with a percent yield of 89.3%, calculate the actual mass of Cr that results from 35.0 g Cr_2O_3? (24.3 g Cr)

REVIEW EXERCISE

11.16 Consider the following reaction.

$$CS_2(g) + 3Cl_2(g) \rightarrow CCl_4(l) + S_2Cl_2(g)$$

(a) Initially, 4.29 g of carbon disulfide, CS_2, reacts with excess Cl_2, and 7.83 g CCl_4 is isolated. What is the percent yield for the reaction?

(b) What mass of CCl_4 would be obtained from 4.29 g CS_2 if the percent yield were 61.9%?

11.16 (a) 90.1%, (b) 5.38 g CCl_4

11.5 SOLUTION STOICHIOMETRY

Solution stoichiometry is the study of mole and mass relationships for reactions that take place in solution. To determine the amounts of dissolved reactants, molarity is the principal solution concentration unit used. You should recall from Section 7.4 that molarity is the ratio of moles of solute per liter of solution.

$$\text{Molarity} = \frac{\text{moles solute}}{\text{liters solution}}$$

Therefore, in solution stoichiometry problems the molarities and volumes of the reactant solutions are usually given instead of the masses or number of moles. Otherwise, solution stoichiometry problems are solved in the same way as the problems that we have already considered.

Let us illustrate a solution stoichiometry problem by considering what volume of 0.750 M $AgNO_3$ is needed to react with excess NaCl to produce 2.50 g AgCl(s) in the following reaction.

$$AgNO_3(aq) + NaCl(aq) \rightarrow AgCl(s) + NaNO_3(aq)$$

From the balanced equation, we see that the number of moles of AgCl equals the number of moles of $AgNO_3$. Hence, we should convert the mass of AgCl, 2.50 g, to moles (143 g/mol) because this number equals the number of moles of $AgNO_3$. From the molarity of $AgNO_3$, 0.750 mol $AgNO_3$/L, the volume is determined as follows.

$$2.50 \text{ g AgCl} \times \frac{1 \text{ mol AgCl}}{143 \text{ g AgCl}} \times \frac{1 \text{ mol AgNO}_3}{1 \text{ mol AgCl}} \times \frac{1 \text{ L soln}}{0.750 \text{ mol AgNO}_3} \times \frac{1000 \text{ mL}}{1 \text{ L soln}} = 23.3 \text{ mL}$$

It takes 23.3 mL of 0.750 M $AgNO_3$ to react with excess NaCl to produce 2.50 g AgCl.

Example Problems 11.14 and 11.15 show two additional examples of solution stoichiometry problems. ❖

Example Problem 11.14

Consider the following neutralization reaction.

$$H_2SO_4(aq) + 2KOH(aq) \rightarrow K_2SO_4(aq) + 2H_2O(l)$$

What volume of 0.111M H_2SO_4 is needed to exactly neutralize 100 mL 0.125M KOH?

Solution

1. What is unknown?   Volume in mL of 0.111M H_2SO_4
2. What is known? 100 mL 0.125M KOH, 0.111M H_2SO_4, 2 mol KOH/1 mol H_2SO_4, 1L/1000 mL
3. Apply the factor-label method

$$100 \text{ mL KOH} \times \frac{1 \text{ L KOH}}{1000 \text{ mL KOH}} \times \frac{0.125 \text{ mol KOH}}{1 \text{ L KOH}} \times \frac{1 \text{ mol H}_2\text{SO}_4}{2 \text{ mol KOH}} \times \frac{1 \text{ L H}_2\text{SO}_4}{0.111 \text{ mol H}_2\text{SO}_4} \times$$

$$\frac{1000 \text{ mL H}_2\text{SO}_4}{1 \text{ L H}_2\text{SO}_4} = ? \text{ mL H}_2\text{SO}_4$$

4. Perform the indicated math operations.

100 mL KOH × $\dfrac{1 \text{ L KOH}}{1000 \text{ mL KOH}}$ × $\dfrac{0.125 \text{ mol KOH}}{1 \text{ L KOH}}$ × $\dfrac{1 \text{ mol } H_2SO_4}{2 \text{ mol KOH}}$ × $\dfrac{1 \text{ L } H_2SO_4}{0.111 \text{ mol } H_2SO_4}$ ×

$$\dfrac{1000 \text{ mL } H_2SO_4}{1 \text{ L } H_2SO_4} = \textbf{56.3 mL } \textbf{H}_2\textbf{SO}_4$$

In this reaction, 56.3 mL of 0.111M H_2SO_4 exactly neutralizes 100 mL 0.125M KOH.

Exercise

What volume of 0.250M KOH is needed to neutralize exactly 500 mL 0.250M H_2SO_4? (1.00 L)

Example Problem 11.15

What mass of $PbCl_2$ precipitates when 75.0 mL of 0.275M HCl(aq) is mixed with 100 mL 0.150M $Pb(NO_3)_2$(aq)?

Solution

Before starting this problem, the balanced equation must be written. In this precipitation reaction, $PbCl_2$ and HNO_3 are the products. The balanced equation is as follows.

$$Pb(NO_3)_2(aq) + 2HCl(aq) \rightarrow PbCl_2(s) + 2HNO_3(aq)$$

This is a limiting-reactant problem because the quantities for both reactants are given. Thus, the limiting reactant must be found first to solve this problem.

1. What is unknown?   Mass in g $PbCl_2$
2. What is known? 75.0 mL 0.275M HCl(aq), 100 mL 0.150M $Pb(NO_3)_2$(aq), 1 mol $PbCl_2$/1 mol $Pb(NO_3)_2$
3. Determine the limiting reactant.
This is accomplished by finding which is consumed first.

75.0 mL HCl × $\dfrac{1 \text{ L HCl}}{1000 \text{ mL HCl}}$ × $\dfrac{0.275 \text{ mol HCl}}{1 \text{ L HCl}}$ = 0.0206 mol HCl

100 mL $Pb(NO_3)_2$ × $\dfrac{1 \text{ L } Pb(NO_3)_2}{1000 \text{ mL } Pb(NO_3)_2}$ × $\dfrac{0.150 \text{ mol } Pb(NO_3)_2}{1 \text{ L } Pb(NO_3)_2}$ = 0.0150 mol $Pb(NO_3)_2$

Next determine the number of moles of HCl needed to react with exactly 0.0150 mol $Pb(NO_3)_2$. The balanced equation shows that 2 moles of HCl react with one mole of $Pb(NO_3)_2$.

$$0.0150 \text{ mol } Pb(NO_3)_2 \times \dfrac{2 \text{ mol HCl}}{1 \text{ mol } Pb(NO_3)_2} = 0.0300 \text{ mol HCl}$$

Because more moles of HCl are needed to react with 0.0150 mol $Pb(NO_3)_2$ than are present, HCl is the limiting reactant and the remainder of the problem is solved with the moles of HCl.

$$0.0206 \text{ mol HCl} \times \frac{1 \text{ mol PbCl}_2}{2 \text{ mol HCl}} \times \frac{278 \text{ g PbCl}_2}{1 \text{ mol PbCl}_2} = \textbf{2.86 g PbCl}_2$$

Exercise
What mass of CaS results when 500 mL 0.500M $CaCl_2$ reacts with 500 mL 0.450M Na_2S? (16.2 g CaS)

REVIEW EXERCISES
11.17 What volume of each of the following exactly neutralizes 160 mL 0.100M NaOH?

(a) 0.100M HCl
(b) 0.100M H_2SO_4
(c) 0.100M H_3PO_4
(d) 0.555M CH_3COOH

11.18 What mass of carbon dioxide is liberated when 85 mL 0.75M HBr reacts with 75 mL 0.70M $NaHCO_3$?

11.17 (a) 160 mL HCl, (b) 80.0 mL H_2SO_4, (c) 53.3 mL H_3PO_4, (d) 28.8 mL CH_3COOH; 11.18 2.8 g CO_2

WorldWideWolfe CHEMISTRY LINKS

Connect to WorldWideWolfe at

http://www.mindspring.com/~drwolfe/WWWolfe_hcc_1025_links.htm

and link to the following sites.

Stoichiometry

1. Introduction to Stoichiometry It covers the basic principles of stoichiometry and mole ratios.

2. Stoichiometry Reviews mol-mol, mol-mass, and mass-mass stoichiometry problems.

Chemical Equations and Stoichiometry A complete discussion of the basic principles of stoichiometry.

3. Stoichiometry Tutorial A simple tutorial on the main aspects of mole and mass relationships.

SUMMARY

Stoichiometry is the study of quantitative relationships in chemical reactions. With a balanced equation, mole and mass relationships are easily obtained. Predictions that result from stoichiometric calculations are the theoretical maximum amounts that could be obtained in a reaction.

Commonly, masses of starting materials are given, and the quantities of products are sought. Initially, the masses of reactants are converted to moles because the balanced equation indicates the mole ratio between each reactant and product. After calculating the number of moles of desired product, it is only necessary to convert the moles of product to grams, using the molecular or atomic mass. Stoichiometry problems are ideally suited to be solved by the factor-label method.

The amount of energy transferred may also be predicted from chemical equations. Given the quantity of heat evolved or absorbed per mole of reactant, a conversion factor that relates moles and energy is determined. Energy transfers in chemical reactions are experimentally measured by means of **calorimetry,** i.e., the measurement of heat transfers in chemical reactions using an instrument called a calorimeter.

When the initial quantities of all reactants are given and no assumption is made that one or more reactants is in excess, it is necessary to find the reactant consumed first (the **limiting reactant** or **limiting reagent).** After the limiting reactant is consumed, the reaction stops.

The amounts of products produced in chemical reactions differ from the theoretically predicted amounts. Chemists regularly calculate the **percent yield** of the reaction, which is the ratio of the actual yield to the theoretical yield times 100.

KEY TERMS

actual yield	percent yield
calorimetry	solution stoichiometry
heat capacity	stoichiometry
limiting reactant	theoretical yield

STUDY GUIDELINES

After completing Chapter 11, you should be able to

1. Explain the meaning of a stoichiometric relationship

2. List reasons why chemists obtain experimentally quantities different from those predicted by stoichiometry calculations

3. Determine molecular and mole relationships given a balanced chemical equation

4. Show that, in a correctly balanced equation, the sum of the masses of the reactants equals the sum of the masses of the products

5. Calculate the number of moles or mass of product given either the number of moles or mass of a reactant, or vice versa

6. Calculate the amount of heat liberated or consumed in a reaction given the mass or number of moles of starting material, the balanced equation, and the enthalpy of reaction

7. Explain how heat transfers are measured through calorimetry

8. Find the limiting reactant (limiting reagent) in a reaction

9. Calculate the maximum mass of product formed given the masses of all reactants

10. Calculate the percent yield of a reaction given the actual yield and masses of reactants

11. Calculate the volume of reactants needed or products formed given the molarities of the reactants or products

---

EXERCISES

11.19   Define each of the following terms: stoichiometry, theoretical yield, calorimetry, heat capacity, limiting reactant, actual yield, percent yield.

Quantitative Equation Relationships

11.20   Complete the following table for the reaction in which N_2 and O_2 combine to yield NO.

	N_2 +	O_2 →	2NO
Molecules	5 molecules		
Molecules	6.02×10^{22} molecules		
Moles	5.0 mol		
Mass, g		16.0 g	
Mass, g			19.5

11.21   Complete the following table for the reaction 1 in which pentane, C_5H_{12}, combines with O_2 to produce CO_2 and H_2O.

	C_5H_{12}	+	O_2	→	$5CO_2$	+	$6H_2O$
Molecules	10 molecules						
Molecules	6.02×10^{22} molecules						
Moles	1.00 mol						
Moles			1.00 mol				
Mass, g	85.0 g						

11.22 When Ca combines with F_2, CaF_2 is produced:

$$Ca + F_2 \rightarrow CaF_2$$

Assume that 1 mol Ca and 1 mol F_2 are combined. (a) How many moles of CaF_2 result? (b) What mass of CaF_2 results? (c) Show that the balanced equation illustrates the law of conservation of mass—i.e., show that the sum of the masses of the reactants equals the mass of the product.

11.23 Consider the reaction in which bromine combines with fluorine to form BrF:

$$Br_2 + F_2 \rightarrow 2BrF$$

If 1 mol F_2 combines with 1 mol Cl_2 to produce 2 mol BrF, show that the sum of the masses of the reactants equals the mass of product.

Mole-Mole Relationships

11.24 For the reaction $2Al + 3Cl_2 \rightarrow 2AlCl_3$, calculate the number of moles of $AlCl_3$ produced from each of the following stated quantities of reactant (always assume the other reactant is in excess).
(a) 5.0 mol Al   (b) 8.0 mol Cl_2
(c) 18 mol Al   (d) 33 mol Cl_2
(e) 29 mmol Cl_2.

11.25 For the following equation, write all possible conversion factors that relate the number of moles of each reactant to the number of moles of each product:

$$C_5H_{12} + 8O_2 \rightarrow 5CO_2 + 6H_2O$$

11.26 For the following reaction, calculate the requested quantities:

$$3KCl + 4HNO_3 \rightarrow Cl_2 + NOCl + 2H_2O + 3KNO_3$$

(a) number of moles of Cl_2 produced for each mole of HNO_3 reacted
(b) number of moles of H_2O produced when 5.00 mol KCl reacts
(c) number of moles of HNO_3 reacted to produce 11.0 mol NOCl
(d) number of moles of Cl_2 and KNO_3 produced when 8.59 mol KCl reacts
(e) number of moles of each product produced when 0.0300 mol HNO_3 reacts.

11.27 Consider the equation

$$4FeS_2 + 11O_2 \rightarrow 2Fe_2O_3 + 8SO_2$$

For each of the given molar quantities of reactant, calculate the number of moles of each product produced.
(a) 0.44 mol FeS_2
(b) 29.1 mol FeS_2
(c) 8.200 mol O_2
(d) 19.9 mmol O_2
(e) 0.00345 mol O_2

Mole-Mass Calculations

11.28 A laboratory preparation of O_2 gas is to decompose $KClO_3$ by heating it in the presence of MnO_2, a catalyst:

$$2KClO_3 \rightarrow 2KCl + 3O_2$$

(a) Calculate the mass of O_2 produced when 17.1 mol $KClO_3$ is decomposed.
(b) Calculate the number of moles of O_2 produced when 1.55 g $KClO_3$ is heated.
(c) Find the number of moles of KCl and O_2 produced from 6.20 kg $KClO_3$.
(d) What mass of $KClO_3$ is needed to produce 397 mg O_2?

11.29   Sodium bicarbonate, $NaHCO_3$, reacts with HCl to produce sodium chloride, NaCl, carbon dioxide, CO_2, and water, H_2O.

$$NaHCO_3(aq) + HCl(aq) \rightarrow NaCl(aq) + CO_2(g) + H_2O(l)$$

(a) What mass of HCl must be present to combine totally with 0.150 mol $NaHCO_3$?
(b) How many moles of CO_2 are produced when 4.96 g $NaHCO_3$ combines with excess HCl?
(c) Calculate the mass of NaCl that results when 9.48 mmol HCl combines with excess $NaHCO_3$.
(d) What mass of $NaHCO_3$ is required to produce 8.309×10^3 mol H_2O?

11.30   Copper is isolated from its oxide, Cu_2O, by heating the oxide in the presence of copper(I) sulfide, Cu_2S:

$$2Cu_2O + Cu_2S \rightarrow 6Cu + SO_2$$

Calculate the mass of Cu produced from each of the following quantities of reactant (assume an excess amount of the other reactant).
(a) 9.22 mol Cu_2O
(b) 5.09 mol Cu_2O
(c) 0.00125 mol Cu_2O
(d) 7.92×10^5 mol Cu_2S
(e) 1964 mol Cu_2S
(f) 7.88 mmol Cu_2O

Mass-Mass Calculations

11.31   When silver(I) oxide, Ag_2O, is heated, it readily liberates oxygen, O_2, and leaves free silver, Ag:

$$2Ag_2O(s) \rightarrow 4Ag(s) + O_2(g)$$

What mass of silver results when the following quantities of silver(I) oxide are completely heated?
(a) 0.3811 g Ag_2O
(b) 7.91 kg Ag_2O
(c) 6.22 mg Ag_2O
(d) 54.80 kg Ag_2O

11.32   Lead nitrate, $Pb(NO_3)_2$, on heating decomposes to lead(II) oxide, PbO, oxygen, O_2, and nitrogen dioxide, NO_2:

$$2Pb(NO)_2(s) \rightarrow 2PbO(s) + O_2(g) + 4NO_2(g)$$

What mass of $Pb(NO_3)_2$ must be heated to produce the following masses of product?
(a) 1.002 g PbO
(b) 9341 g O_2
(c) 0.0420 kg NO_2
(d) 900.4 mg PbO

11.33   Carbon tetrachloride, CCl_4, once used as a cleaning fluid and as a fire extinguisher, is produced by heating methane, CH_4, and chlorine, Cl_2:

$$CH_4 + 4Cl_2 \rightarrow CCl_4 + 4HCl$$

(a) What mass of CH_4 is needed to exactly combine with 33.4 g Cl_2?
(b) How many grams of Cl_2 are required to produce 9336 g CCl_4, assuming excess CH_4?
(c) What mass of CH_4 must have reacted if 4.02 mg HCl is liberated?
(d) Calculate the masses of CH_4 and Cl_2 required to produce exactly 800.0 kg CCl_4?

11.34   Pure boron is prepared by combining boron trichloride, BCl_3, with hydrogen gas, H_2, at high temperatures:

$$2BCl_3 + 3H_2 \rightarrow 2B + 6HCl$$

(a) Calculate the mass of boron produced when 0.771 g BCl_3 is combined with excess hydrogen gas. (b) What mass of hydrogen gas is needed to completely combine with 4.9 kg BCl_3?
(c) What mass of BCl_3 must be present to produce 112.5 g B?
(d) Calculate the mass of H_2 that combines exactly with 9.04 kg BCl_3, and calculate how much B and HCl are produced.

11.35   Xenon tetrafluoride, XeF_4, a noble gas

compound, is highly reactive. When mixed with water, XeF_4 undergoes the following reaction:

$$6XeF_4 + 8H_2O \rightarrow 2XeOF_4 + 4Xe + 16HF + 3O_2$$

(a) Calculate the mass of XeF_4 needed to produce 100.0 g $XeOF_4$.
(b) After a measured mass of XeF_4 is placed in water, 0.0984 g HF is released. What mass of XeF_4 was reacted with water?
(c) How much water should be exactly combined with 0.01144 g XeF_4 in the above reaction?
(d) Calculate the mass of each product produced when 3.48 mg XeF_4 is combined with water.

11.36 Nickel chloride hexahydrate, $NiCl_2 \cdot 6H_2O$, on heating in a vacuum, yields nickel chloride, $NiCl_2$, and water, H_2O:

$$NiCl_2 \cdot 6H_2O \rightarrow NiCl_2 + 6H_2O$$

(a) How many grams of the hydrate should be heated to produce 327 g H_2O?
(b) When 0.184 kg of the hydrate is heated, what mass of the anhydrous compound, $NiCl_2$, results?
(c) What mass of hydrate is heated to yield 743 g $NiCl_2$?
(d) Find the mass of each product when 0.853 mg of nickel chloride hexahydrate is heated.

11.37 Potassium nitrate decomposes to potassium nitrite and oxygen.
(a) Write the balanced equation for this reaction.
(b) State all mole relationships for this equation.
(c) How many grams of potassium nitrite form when 581.0 g of potassium nitrate is heated?
(d) What mass of oxygen is liberated when 4.760 kg of potassium nitrate is decomposed?

11.38 Silicon tetrachloride and carbon monoxide are produced when silicon dioxide, carbon, and chlorine gas are heated.
(a) Write the balanced equation for this chemical change.
(b) What mass of silicon tetrachloride is

produced when 171 g of silicon dioxide is combined with excess carbon and chlorine?
(c) How many molecules of carbon monoxide are produced when 0.00201 g of chlorine combines with excess reactants?

11.39 Stibnite, antimony(II) sulfide, when heated with iron undergoes a single replacement reaction, liberating free antimony metal and iron(II) sulfide.
(a) Write the balanced equation for the reaction.
(b) What mass of iron is required to react with 58.5 g of stibnite?
(c) How many grams of antimony are produced when 94.7 kg of stibnite is reacted?
(d) What masses of stibnite and iron should combine to yield 5.097 g of antimony?

Energy Effects

11.40 When hydrogen, H_2, reacts with oxygen, O_2, water vapor forms and 569 kJ of heat is released:

$$2H_2(g) + O_2(g) \rightarrow 2H_2O(g) + 569 \text{ kJ}$$

(a) Rewrite the equation with the energy expressed as kilocalories instead of kilojoules.
(b) What mass of H_2 and O_2 liberate 408 kJ of heat?
(c) If 2.93 mol H_2 is combined with excess O_2, what quantity of heat is liberated?
(d) If 2.93 g O_2 is combined with excess hydrogen, what quantity of heat is liberated?

11.41 Consider the oxidation of nitrogen monoxide:

$$2NO(g) + O_2(g) \rightarrow 2NO_2(g) + 116.7 \text{ kJ}$$

(a) What mass of NO produces 851.2 kJ of heat?
(b) If 11.78 g NO is reacted, what quantity of heat is liberated?
(c) How many moles of oxygen are needed to combine with excess NO to produce 92.52 J?
(d) What mass of NO is required to produce 705.4 kcal of energy?

11.42 When combusted, ethylene, C_2H_4, yields CO_2 and H_2O:

$$C_2H_4(g) + 3O_2(g) \rightarrow 2CO_2(g) + 2H_2O(g) + 1.41 \times 10^3 \text{ kJ}$$

(a) How much heat is liberated per gram of C_2H_4?
(b) What mass of C_2H_4 must be combusted to liberate 646 J?
(c) If 5.96 g O_2 is available, with excess C_2H_4, what quantity of heat is released?
(d) How much C_2H_4 must be combusted to liberate 2.75 kcal of energy?

11.43 The decomposition of aluminum oxide in the following reaction requires 3.34×10^3 kJ:

$$2Al_2O_3(s) + 3.34 \times 10^3 \text{ kJ} \rightarrow 4Al(s) + 3O_2(g)$$

(a) How much energy is required to decompose 77.6 mol Al_2O_3?
(b) What quantity of heat is needed to decompose 478 kg Al_2O_3?
(c) If 9.48 g of Al metal is obtained, what quantity of heat is required to decompose the Al_2O_3?
(d) How many kilocalories of energy are required to decompose 76.7 g Al_2O_3?

11.44 When 1.001 g of calcium carbonate is decomposed to calcium oxide and carbon dioxide, 1.78 kJ of energy is needed.
(a) Write a balanced equation for the reaction, including the energy (in kilojoules) required per mole of calcium carbonate.
(b) Rewrite the equation with the energy expressed in kilocalories.

11.45 In a simple calorimeter, two 150.0-g solutions of reacting chemicals are poured together, each initially at 23.8°C. After they are allowed to react, the final temperature of the resulting mixture is 41.7°C. Assuming that all of the heat released by the reaction is absorbed by the water, and knowing that the heat capacity of the solution is 4.18J/(g °C), calculate the amount of heat released by the reaction.

11.46 When 0.750 g $NH_3(g)$ is bubbled into 100 g H_2O at 22.2°C inside of a Styrofoam cup calorimeter, the NH_3 dissolves and raises the temperature of the water to 25.4°C. Calculate the amount of heat, in kJ, released per mole of NH_3, kJ/mol. Assume that the specific heat of the resulting solution is 4.18 J/(g °C), and that the calorimeter does not absorb any heat.

Limiting-Reagent Problems

11.47 Consider the following equation:

$$H_2(g) + I_2(g) \rightarrow 2HI(g)$$

(a) Calculate the mass of HI that forms when 1.53 g H_2 combines with 126 g I_2.
(b) What is the maximum yield of HI when 8.87 g H_2 combines with 1025 g I_2?
(c) What mass of excess reactant remains when 0.3462 g H_2 and 45.92 g I_2 combine?

11.48 Phosgene, $COCl_2$, reacts with water to produce carbon dioxide, CO_2, and hydrochloric acid, HCl:

$$COCl_2(g) + H_2O(l) \rightarrow CO_2(g) + 2HCl(aq)$$

(a) What mass of CO_2 is produced when 6.41 g $COCl_2$ is combined with 1.78 g H_2O?
(b) Calculate the mass of HCl formed when 3.09 kg of each reactant is combined?
(c) What mass of excess reactant remains in the reaction in part by

11.49 Consider the following equation:

$$2NaCl + H_2SO_4 \rightarrow Na_2SO_4 + 2HCl$$

(a) How many grams of Na_2SO_4 are produced when 970.0 g of each reactant is combined?
(b) Find the mass of Na_2SO_4 that forms when 35.7 g NaCl and 21.9 g H_2SO_4 combine.
(c) What mass of HCl results when 12.2 kg NaCl and 9.74 kg H_2SO_4 combine?
(d) What mass of excess reactant remains in the reaction in part c?

11.50 A lead(II) nitrate solution combines with a solution of potassium iodide to yield a precipitate, lead(II) iodide, and aqueous potassium nitrate.
(a) Write the balanced equation for this aqueous reaction.

(b) What mass of lead iodide precipitates from solution if 49.11 g of lead(II) nitrate combines with 49.60 g of potassium iodide.
(c) Calculate the mass of reactant in excess.

11.51 If sodium carbonate reacts with carbon and nitrogen gas, carbon monoxide and sodium cyanide result. (a) What mass of sodium cyanide results when 36.5 g of carbon, 81.4 g of sodium carbonate, and excess nitrogen gas are combined? (b) What mass of nitrogen gas is consumed in this reaction?

Percent Yield

11.52 When benzene, C_6H_6, reacts with chlorine, Cl_2, chlorobenzene, C_6H_5Cl, and hydrogen chloride gas, HCl, are produced.
(a) If 13.0 g of benzene reacts with excess chlorine, what is the theoretical yield of chlorobenzene?
(b) If 10.4 g of chlorobenzene is isolated after the reaction, calculate the percent yield of chlorobenzene.
(c) What mass of chlorobenzene results if the percent yield is 64.3% and the initial mass of benzene is 2.87 g?
(d) What mass of benzene is required to produce 4.92 g of chlorobenzene, if the percent yield is 59.2%?

11.53 Rare germanium metal is isolated by heating GeO_2 in the presence of pure carbon:

$$GeO_2 + 2C \rightarrow Ge + 2CO$$

(a) After 729 g GeO_2 is reacted with carbon, 435 g Ge is obtained; calculate the percent yield of germanium.
(b) Starting with 61.0 kg GeO_2 and excess carbon, what mass of Ge results if a 91.2% yield is obtained? (c) What mass of GeO_2 is required to produce 33.7 g Ge, if the percent yield is 91.2%.

11.54 Calcium cyanamide, $CaCN_2$, combines with carbon, C, and sodium carbonate, Na_2CO_3, to produce calcium carbonate, $CaCO_3$, and sodium cyanide, NaCN.
(a) What mass of calcium cyanamide is needed to produce 2.953 g of sodium cyanide, if the percent yield of the reaction is 70.1%?

(b) What mass of calcium cyanamide is required to produce 40.47 kg of sodium cyanide, if the percent yield is 83.9%?

Solution Stoichiometry
11.55 Consider the following aqueous reaction.

$$Na_2CO_3(aq) + FeCl_2(aq) \rightarrow FeCO_3(s) + 2NaCl(aq)$$

What mass of iron(II) carbonate precipitates when the following solutions are mixed with excess $FeCl_3$? (a) 10.0 mL 0.400M Na_2CO_3
(b) 14.0 mL 0.444M Na_2CO_3
(c) 195 mL 1.40M Na_2CO_3

11.56 Consider the following aqueous reaction.

$$Na_2CO_3(aq) + 2HCl(aq) \rightarrow CO_2(g) + 2NaCl(aq) + H_2O$$

What mass of CO_2 results when the following solutions are mixed with excess HCl?
(a) 10.0 mL 0.400M Na_2CO_3,
(b) 14.0 mL 0.444M Na_2CO_3
(c) 195 mL 1.40M Na_2CO_3

11.57 What volume of 0.100M KOH exactly neutralizes each of the following solutions?
(a) 5.00 mL 0.122M nitric acid
(b) 5.00 mL 0.122M sulfurous acid
(c) 5.00 mL 0.122M phosphoric acid

11.58 What mass of sodium nitrate results when 75.0 mL 0.155M nitric acid reacts with each of the following?
(a) 75.0 mL 0.155M NaOH
(b) 65.0 mL 0.165M NaOH
(c) 85.0 mL 0.145M NaOH

11.59 What masses of product result from the reaction of 200 mL 1.50M Na_3PO_4 and 300 mL 1.15M $Mg(NO_3)_2$?

11.60 What equal volumes of 0.900M solutions of $Ba(NO_3)_2$ and K_2SO_4 are needed to produce 50.0 g $BaSO_4$?

11.61 What is the molar concentration of Na_2SO_4 that results when 50.0 mL 0.350M H_2SO_4 is mixed with 75.0 mL 0.300M NaOH? Assume that the volumes are additive.

Additional Exercises

11.62   When one mole N_2 reacts with three moles H_2, two moles NH_3 and 92.6 kJ of heat are produced. (a) Calculate the masses of N_2 and H_2 required to produce 1.00×10^3 kJ of heat. (b) What mass of water can be heated from 0.0°C to 50.0°C, with the heat liberated when 84.2 g N_2 reacts with excess H_2? The specific heat of water is 4.184 J/(g·°C).

11.63   Calcium hydroxide, $Ca(OH)_2$ (slaked lime), is prepared by the following reactions:

$$CaCO_3 \rightarrow CaO + CO_2$$

$$CaO + H_2O \rightarrow Ca(OH)_2$$

(a) What mass of $Ca(OH)_2$ results when 544 g $CaCO_3$ is decomposed? (b) If 71.1% is the maximum overall yield of the above reactions, what mass of $Ca(OH)_2$ forms when 53.3 kg $CaCO_3$ decomposes?

11.64   Zinc blend, or zinc(II) sulfide ore, is one source of metallic zinc. Initially, the zinc sulfide is combined with oxygen to yield zinc(II) oxide and sulfur dioxide. The resulting zinc(II) oxide is then heated with carbon to produce free zinc metal and carbon monoxide.
(a) Write and balance both equations.
(b) Calculate the mass of zinc obtained from 6.23 metric tons zinc(II) sulfide, assuming a percent yield of 78.4%. One metric ton (t) equals 1000 kg.
(c) What mass of zinc forms when 65.8 g of zinc(II) sulfide combines with 33.9 g of oxygen, assuming 100% yield?

11.65   Consider the following aqueous reaction:

$$2KMnO_4 + 10KI + 8H_2SO_4 \rightarrow 6K_2SO_4 + 2MnSO_4 + 5I_2 + 8H_2O$$

Calculate the masses of I_2, K_2SO_4, and $MnSO_4$ produced when 7.80 g $KMnO_4$, 42.7 g KI, and 19.3 g H_2SO_4 are combined.

11.66   Consider the following reaction, in which sodium amide, $NaNH_2$, and nitrous oxide, N_2O, are heated.

$$2NaNH_2 + N_2O_5 \rightarrow NaN_3 + NH_3 + NaOH$$

(a) What is the maximum yield of NaN_3 when 18.64 g $NaNH_2$ combines with 10.61 g N_2O?
(b) What mass of excess reactant remains?
(c) How many grams of the limiting reactant must be added to totally react the excess reactant?

11.67   The percent yield of SF_4 in the following reaction is 66.9%.

$$3SCl_2 + 4NaF \rightarrow SF_4 + S_2Cl_2 + 4NaCl$$

(a) Calculate the masses of SCl_2 and NaF required to produce 37.8 g SF_4.
(b) If 250.99 g SCl_2 combines with 136.22 g NaF, what mass of SF_4 results?

11.68   Sulfuric acid, H_2SO_4, can be prepared from FeS_2 as follows:

$$4FeS_2 + 11O_2 \rightarrow 2Fe_2O_3 + 8SO_2$$

$$2SO_2 + O_2 \rightarrow 2SO_3$$

$$SO_3 + H_2O \rightarrow H_2SO_4$$

(a) What mass of sulfuric acid results when 24.2 kg FeS_2 combines with excess oxygen?
(b) If the percent yield of sulfuric acid is 71.4%, what mass of FeS_2 is required to produce 93.4 kg of sulfuric acid? (c) What mass of FeS_2 was initially present and what mass of sulfuric acid forms if the mass of SO_3 is 60.8 kg?

11.69   An excess amount of hydrochloric acid, HCl(aq), is added to a 1.000-g mixture of $CaCO_3$ and $CaSO_4$. The $CaCO_3$ combines with the HCl to produce $CaCl_2$, CO_2, and H_2O, but the $CaSO_4$ does not react with the HCl. If the mass of CO_2 produced is 0.303 g, what is the percent composition of the mixture?

11.70   One of the oxides of cobalt reacts with hydrogen gas, H_2, to produce Co and water. When 0.914 mol of this cobalt compound reacts with 5.54 g H_2, 108 g Co results. What is the formula of the oxide?

11.71   An impure sample of zinc, Zn, is treated with an excess amount of sulfuric acid, H_2SO_4, and $ZnSO_4$ and H_2 are the products. Calculate the percent of zinc in the impure sample if a 4.35-g sample produces 0.121 g of hydrogen gas.

11.72 When 0.750 g HBr(g) is bubbled into 100 g H_2O at 22.2°C inside of a Styrofoam cup calorimeter, the HBr dissolves and raises the temperature of the water to 24.1°C. Calculate the amount of heat, in kJ, released per mole of HBr, kJ/mol. Assume that the specific heat of the resulting solution is 4.18 J/(g °C), and that the calorimeter does not absorb any heat.

11.73 Oxalic acid, $H_2C_2O_4(s)$, reacts with two moles of sodium hydroxide solution, NaOH(aq), to produce sodium oxalate, $Na_2C_2O_4(aq)$, and water. (a) Write a balanced equation for the reaction. (b) What mass of sodium oxalate results when 5.07 g of oxalic acid is mixed with 40.5 mL of 2.50M NaOH? (c) What mass of sodium oxalate results when 321 g of oxalic acid combines with 2.65 L of 3.01M NaOH?

Notes and Calculations:

Chapter 11 Pretest Assignment

1.   Complete each of the following statements with the correct word, number, or phase.

   a. _____ is the study of mole, mass, energy, and volume relationships
   in chemical reactions.

   b. The _____ is the predicted amount of product(s) that forms in a
   chemical reaction.

   c. The _____ is the yield of product that actually forms in a reaction.

   d. The _____ is the reactant that runs out first.

2.   Consider the following reaction.

$$4FeS_2 + 11O_2 \rightarrow 2Fe_2O_3 + 8SO_2$$

   a. How many moles of SO_2 result when 5.97 mol O_2 reacts with excess FeS_2?

   b. What mass of Fe_2O_3 results when 11.9 g FeS_2 reacts with excess O_2?

3.   Consider the following reaction.

$$2BCl_3 + 3H_2 \rightarrow 2B + 6HCl$$

   a. What mass of H_2 exactly reacts with 91.6 g BCl_3?

   b. What is the total mass of products that result when 91.6 g BCl_3 reacts with H_2?

4.   Consider the combustion of octane.

$$C_8H_{18} + 12.5O_2 \rightarrow 8CO_2 + 9H_2O + 5450 \text{ kJ}$$

How much heat can be released from 5.0 g C_8H_{18}?

5.   What mass of lead(II) sulfide precipitates when 25.0 g $Pb(NO_3)_2$ reacts with 25.0 g $(NH_4)_2S$?

6.   What volume of 0.350M KOH is needed to exactly neutralize 100 mL 0.300M H_2SO_4?

CHAPTER 12

Gases

We previously learned in Chapter 4 that gases completely fill and take the shapes of their containers, are compressible, have the lowest average density, and are the least viscous of the three physical states. In Chapter 12 we will consider the principal properties of gases. To begin our study of gases we will take a brief look at the theory that is used to explain the properties of gases, the kinetic molecular theory.

WWWolfe 1
(See WWWolfe
section at the end of
the chapter.)

12.1 KINETIC MOLECULAR THEORY OF GASES

The behavior and properties of gases are theoretically explained using the **kinetic molecular theory** (KMT), literally the moving molecule theory. This theory is a model that explains the behavior of gases using generalizations about the random motion of the molecules or atoms that compose a gas. Some of the major assumptions of the kinetic molecular theory are:

1. All gases are composed of atoms or molecules that move rapidly and randomly in straight lines.
2. Individual atoms or molecules are widely separated from each other, and do not exert forces on other atoms or molecules, except when colliding. Nearly all of the volume of a gas is empty space.
3. Collisions of atoms or molecules with the walls of the container and with each other are perfectly elastic. This means there is no net loss of kinetic energy on colliding.
4. The average kinetic energy (KE = ½ mv^2) of the atoms or molecules in gases is proportional to the Kelvin temperature of the gas. The average energy of the molecules does not change unless the temperature changes.

A gas that behaves exactly according to the above assumptions is an **ideal gas**, i.e., one that exhibits perfect behavior. In actuality, no real gas behaves exactly as an ideal gas. However, real gases under conditions of low pressure and high temperature approach the behavior of ideal gases. Because the relationships of the properties for real gases are more complicated, we will concentrate on the perfect behavior of gases, realizing that our predictions are not totally correct for real gases. They are, however, for most purposes encountered in ordinary, everyday experiences. ❖

REVIEW EXERCISES

12.1 What are the main assumptions of the kinetic molecular theory?

12.2(a) What is an ideal gas?

(b) Why do chemists develop relationships for an ideal gas, when no real gas behaves exactly in this manner?

12.2 GAS LAWS

Gas laws are empirical relationships that relate the volume (V), pressure (P), temperature (T), and moles of gas particles (n).

Pressure

Gas pressure is defined as the force exerted by a gas on a unit area.

$$Pressure = \frac{force}{area} \qquad\qquad (1)$$

A force is exerted when the molecules in a gas sample hit the walls of the container. An increase in the number of collisions per second or in the force of impact by the molecules increases the pressure exerted by a gas.

Barometers and manometers are the two instruments used to measure the pressure of gases. A **barometer** is an instrument used to measure the pressure exerted by the atmosphere. A **manometer** is used to measure the pressure of isolated gas samples. Most scientific barometers and manometers use mercury to measure the pressure of gases. Mercury is a liquid metal that has a high density (13.6 g/cm^3). It is used because it does not readily evaporate, and smaller instruments can be constructed because of its high density.

Evangelista Torricelli (1608-1647), a student of Galileo, designed the first mercury barometer by filling a glass tube with liquid Hg, and then placing the open end of the tube vertically into a container of Hg. Some of the Hg initially spills out of the tube into the container of Hg. When the force exerted by the Hg column equals the force exerted by the atmosphere on the surface of the Hg in the container, no more mercury spills out (Fig. 12.1). If the atmospheric pressure increases, Hg is pushed up into the tube, and if the pressure decreases, mercury spills out of the tube into the Hg pool.

Torricelli measured atmospheric pressure in terms of the total height of Hg supported in the glass tube by the atmosphere. At sea level, on an average day, the atmosphere supports a column of Hg about 760 mm high. Today, atmospheric and gas pressures are still measured in terms of the height of mercury that a gas supports. Units of pressure most frequently employed are atmospheres (atm), millimeters of mercury (mm Hg), torr, and pascals (Pa). One atmosphere is defined as 760 mm Hg or 760 torr.

$$1.00 \text{ atm} = 760 \text{ torr} = 760 \text{ mm Hg}$$

Numerically, one mm Hg is equivalent to one torr (named for Torricelli).

$$1 \text{ torr} = 1 \text{ mm Hg}$$

We will most commonly encounter atmospheres and torr as the units of pressure in this textbook.

Because these units are not derived from the base SI units, they are not SI units. The SI unit for pressure is the pascal (Pa), which is a small unit of pressure. One pascal, 1 Pa, is derived from the SI unit of force, newton (1 (kg·m)/s^2) and the unit for area, meter squared,

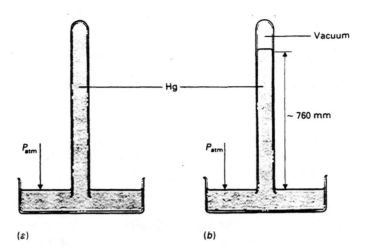

Figure 12.1 A barometer is an instrument used for measuring atmospheric pressure. One atmosphere supports 760 mm Hg in a vertical closed-end tube.

m². One atmosphere is equivalent to 101,325 Pa.

$$1 \text{ atm} = 101,325 \text{ Pa} = 101.325 \text{ kPa}$$

Because of the small size of the pascal, kilopascals (kPa) are most frequently encountered in chemistry. Table 12.1 summarizes the relationships between the many units of pressure used in chemistry.

Table 12.1 UNITS OF PRESSURE

Unit	Relationships
Atmosphere (atm)	1 atm = 760 torr
	1 atm = 760 mm Hg
	1 atm = 101,325 Pa
	1 atm = 101.325 kPa
Pascal (Pa)	1 Pa = 9.869×10^{-6} atm
	1 Pa = 7.501×10^{-3} torr
	1 Pa = 1×10^{-3} kPa
Torr or mm Hg	1 torr = 1.316×10^{-3} atm
	1 torr = 1.333×10^{2} Pa
	1 torr = 1.333×10^{-1} kPa

Example Problem 12.1 gives examples of how to interconvert pressure units, using the factor-label method.

Example Problem 12.1
Convert 796 torr to millimeters of Hg, atmospheres, and kilopascals.

Solution
1. What is unknown? mm Hg, atm, and kPa
2. What is known?   796 torr, 1 torr/1 mm Hg, 760 torr/1 atm, and 101,300 Pa/1 atm
3. Apply the factor-label method.

796 torr $\times$ 1 mm Hg/1 torr = **796 mm Hg**
796 torr $\times$ 1 atm/760 torr = **1.05 atm**
796 torr $\times$ 1 atm/760 torr $\times$ 101,300 Pa/atm $\times$ 1 kPa/1000 Pa = **106 kPa**

Given the number of torr, one immediately knows the number of millimeters of mercury because they are numerically equal. Converting to atmospheres is accomplished by multiplying by 1 atm/760 torr. Finally, changing to kPa requires that the pressure in torr is first converted to atm, and then converted to Pa and ultimately to kPa.
Exercise
Convert 0.233 atm to torr, mm Hg, and kPa. (177 torr, 177 mm Hg, 23.6 kPa)

The pressure exerted by an isolated gas sample is measured with a manometer. An open-ended manometer is pictured in Fig. 12.2; it is nothing more than a U-shaped tube filled with mercury. If the pressure of the gas sample, P_g, equals the pressure of the atmosphere, P_{atm}, then the level of the mercury is equal in either side of the U-tube. If the pressure of the gas sample is greater than atmospheric pressure, then the level of the mercury is higher on the side exposed to the atmosphere. As shown in Fig. 12.2, the level is x mm Hg higher on the right side; thus the pressure of the gas sample equals atmospheric pressure plus x mm Hg.

$$P_g = P_{atm} + x \text{ mm Hg} \quad (\text{when } P_g > P_{atm})$$

If the pressure of the gas sample is less than atmospheric pressure, then the level of the mercury is higher in the tube closest to the gas sample. The difference in height is subtracted from the atmospheric pressure to obtain the pressure of the gas sample for this case.

$$P_g = P_{atm} - x \text{ mm Hg} \quad (\text{when } P_g < P_{atm})$$

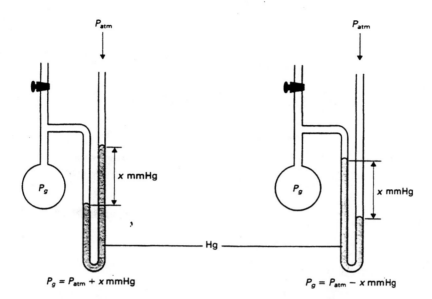

Figure 12.2 An open-ended manometer is used to measure the pressure of isolated gas samples, P_g. It is composed of a U-shaped tube that contains mercury. The pressure of a gas sample is calculated from the difference in height of the mercury column in either side of the tube and from the atmospheric pressure.

REVIEW EXERCISES

12.3 (a) Write a definition for pressure. (b) What units are used to measure the pressure of gases? (c) What instruments are used to measure pressure?

12.4 Convert each of the following to the new pressure units.

(a) 98.2 Pa = ? torr
(b) 2486 torr = ? atm
(c) 1.17 atm = ? kPa
(d) 915 atm = ? torr

12.4 (a) 0.737 torr, (b) 2.271 atm, (c) 119 kPa, (d) 6.95×10^5 torr

Boyle's Law

Boyle's law describes the relationship between the volume and pressure of an ideal gas at constant temperature and number of moles. Intuitively, it is easy to understand Boyle's law. As shown in Fig. 12.3, if we increase the external pressure on a gas sample, the volume decreases. Diminishing the external pressure allows the gas to expand and increase in volume. Therefore, a statement of **Boyle's Law** is the volume of a gas is inversely proportional to its pressure when the temperature and number of moles of gas are constant.

WWWolfe 2
(See WWWolfe
section at the end of
the chapter.)

   Mathematically, a statement of Boyle's law is as follows:

$$PV = k \text{ (at constant T and n)} \qquad (2)$$

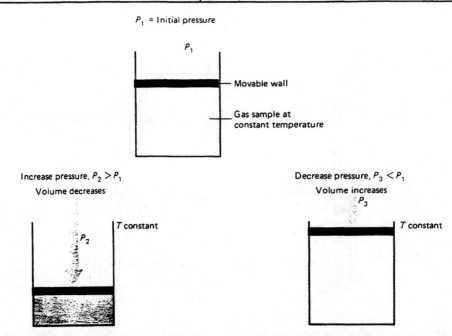

Figure 12.3 At constant temperature and number of moles, the volume of an ideal gas decreases if the pressure increases, and the volume increases if the pressure decreases. This inverse relationship is called Boyle's law.

in which P is the pressure of the gas, V is its volume, and k is a constant of proportionality.

To illustrate the inverse proportionality between the volume and pressure of an ideal gas, consider the data presented in Table 12.2. Initially, the pressure is 20 atm and the volume is 1.0 L. When the pressure is decreased to 10 atm (halved), the volume increases to 2.0 L (doubles). After decreasing the pressure to 5.0 atm, the volume increases to 4.0 L (doubles again). Notice that in each case, the product of the pressure times the volume remains 20 L·atm; P × V remains constant as long as no other factors (T, n, or other experimental factors) are changed. The P versus V inverse relationship is plotted in Fig. 12.4.

Table 12.2 Boyle's Law Relationship

P, atm	V, L	k, L·atm
20	1.0	20
10	2.0	20
5.0	4.0	20
4.0	5.0	20
2.0	10	20
1.0	20	20

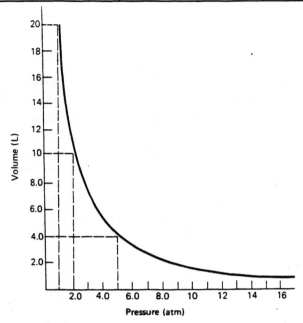

Figure 12.4 A gas initially occupies 20 L at 1.0 atm. When the pressure is increased to 2.0 atm, the volume decreases to 10 L. If the pressure is increased to 5.0 atm, the volume decreases to 4.0 L, one-fifth the initial volume.

A more useful expression of Boyle's law is:

$$P_1V_1 = P_2V_2 \tag{3}$$

in which P_1 is the initial pressure, V_1 is the initial volume, V_2 is the final volume after the pressure has been changed to P_2. A mathematical expression of Boyle's law allows us to calculate a new volume or pressure for an ideal gas after the pressure has changed. For example, what is the new volume of a gas that initially is in a 5.0-L cylinder under a pressure of 15 atm, when the pressure is decreased to 1.0 atm? Using the equation for Boyle's law, first rearrange it to isolate V_2 on one side:

$$\frac{P_1V_1}{P_2} = \frac{P_2V_2}{P_2}$$

After dividing by P_2 and changing the equation around, the equation becomes

$$V_2 = V_1 \times \frac{P_1}{P_2} \quad \textit{(Pressure factor)} \tag{4}$$

It is convenient to express the equation as above, in which the pressure terms are isolated from the initial volume. The ratio of pressures is sometimes called the *pressure factor* and is a conversion factor. Therefore, to solve the problem, we multiply the initial volume (V_1), 5.0 L, times the ratio of initial pressure to final pressure (P_1/P_2), 15 atm/1.0 atm.

$$V_2 = 5.0 \text{ L} \times \frac{15 \text{ atm}}{1.0 \text{ atm}} = 75 \text{ L}$$

With the decrease in pressure the volume expands to 75 L, exactly what we would expect for an inverse relationship, decreasing the pressure increases the volume.

Even if you forget the mathematical equation for Boyle's law, you can calculate the final volume by realizing that P and V are inversely related. Accordingly, the pressure factor must increase the magnitude of the initial volume if the pressure is decreased. In other words, the larger pressure must be written in the numerator, and the smaller pressure written in the denominator.

Figure 12.5 diagrams the procedure for calculating the final volume of an ideal gas after a pressure change. Also, study Example Problem 12.2 as another example of a Boyle's law problem.

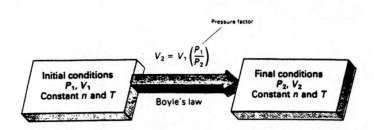

Figure 12.5 To calculate the final volume, V_2, of an ideal gas after the pressure is changed at constant temperature and number of moles, the initial volume, V_1, is multiplied by the pressure factor. The pressure factor P_1/P_2 is the conversion factor that expresses the ratio of the initial pressure, P_1, to the final pressure, P_2.

Example Problem 12.2
Calculate the final volume of He gas when the pressure on 375 mL He is increased from 428 torr to 1657 torr.

Solution
1. What is unknown?   mL He (final volume, V_2)
2. What is known?   375 mL (initial volume, V_1), 428 torr (initial pressure, P_1), and 1657 torr (final pressure, P_2).
3. Apply Boyle's law expression.

Instead of blindly plugging numbers into the expression, ask yourself, what is happening? In this problem, the pressure is increased; thus, the volume decreases. The pressure factor should be written with the smaller pressure divided by the larger pressure (P_1/P_2).

$$V_2 = V_1 \times \frac{P_1}{P_2} = 375 \text{ mL} \times \frac{428 \text{ torr}}{1657} = \textbf{96.9 mL}$$

After completing the problem, look at the answer and see if it is reasonable. A final volume of 96.9 mL is significantly smaller than the initial volume, exactly what we expect when the pressure is increased.

Exercise
Calculate the final volume of Ne gas when the pressure on 140 mL Ne is decreased from 900 torr to 375 torr. (336 mL)

We can use the kinetic molecular theory to explain Boyle's law. The pressure of a gas depends on the number of collisions per second on the walls of the container. If the volume of the gas is decreased, the inside area of the walls decreases and the number of collisions per second increase, thus the pressure increases (Fig. 12.6). However, if the volume of the gas increases, the area of the walls increases and the number of collisions per second decrease (Fig. 12.6).

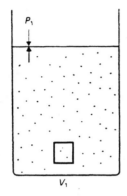
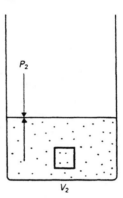

Figure 12.6 Pressure depends on the number of collisions of molecules per second with the walls of the container. If the volume of the container increases, V_1, the number of collisions per second decreases because of the larger area; thus, the pressure decreases. If the volume of the container decreases, V_2, the number of collisions per second increases; thus, the pressure increases.

Many phenomena may be explained by Boyle's law. For example, Boyle's law helps explain why liquids are drawn into hypodermic syringes (Fig. 12.7). When the plunger is withdrawn the pressure decreases inside of the syringe. Because the atmospheric pressure is higher than the pressure inside of the syringe, the atmospheric pressure pushes the liquid into the lower pressure region inside of the syringe. Boyle's law also explains the Heimlich maneuver. The Heimlich maneuver is the procedure used to dislodge food caught in the trachea (windpipe) of a person who is choking. If the abdomen is squeezed with a strong upward movement, the air in the lungs is compressed, which creates a large enough pressure to expel the food that blocks the trachea.

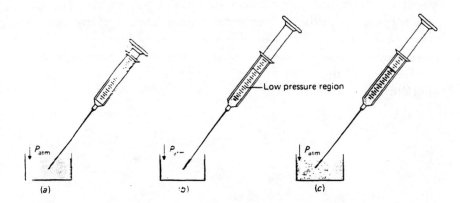

Figure 12.7 (a) The end of a syringe is placed below the surface of a liquid. (b) When the plunger is withdrawn, a low pressure region develops inside the syringe. (c) Because the pressure on the surface of the liquid, P_{atm}, is greater than the pressure inside the syringe, the liquid is forced into the syringe.

Charles' Law

Charles' law describes the relationship between the volume and Kelvin temperature of a gas at constant pressure and number of moles. If a gas sample is heated the average kinetic energy of the molecules increases–they move faster. Because they move faster, they hit the walls of the container more frequently and with a greater force of impact. Hence, if the pressure is to remain constant, the volume must increase (Fig. 12.8). Likewise, if the temperature is decreased, the volume decreases because the molecules slow down, hitting the walls less frequently and with less force.

Charles's law states that the volume of a gas is directly proportional to its Kelvin temperature when the pressure and number of moles are constant. Mathematically, a statement of Charles' law is as follows

$$\frac{V}{T} = k \text{ (at constant P and n)} \tag{5}$$

in which V is volume, T is the Kelvin temperature of the gas, and k is a proportionality constant. Now we are dealing with a direct relationship, one in which both variables (V and T) change in the same direction. Increase the temperature, and the volume increases, decrease the temperature and the volume decreases.

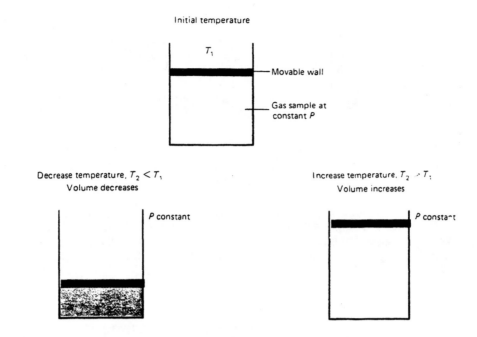

Initial temperature

T_1

— Movable wall

— Gas sample at constant P

Decrease temperature. $T_2 < T_1$
Volume decreases

P constant

Increase temperature. $T_2 > T_1$
Volume increases

P constant

Figure 12.8 If the pressure and number of moles of gas are constant, the volume of an ideal gas is directly proportional to its Kelvin temperature. Thus, if the temperature of a gas sample decreases, the volume decreases; and if the temperature increases the volume increases.

Figure 12.9 presents a representative graph of T versus V for an ideal gas. In this graph we see a linear relationship in which the volume increases as the temperature increases. Of special interest is the point where the line touches the temperature axis (point of zero volume), –273.15°C or absolute zero. Don't rashly jump to any false conclusions! It's fun to extrapolate data to see what might be expected above and below the range of collected data. Remember, we are describing ideal gases (they mainly exist in the minds of chemists). Gases, on cooling, liquefy before reaching 0 K.

Changing the Charles' law expression to a workable equation, we obtain

$$\frac{V_1}{T_1} = \frac{V_2}{T_2}$$

Rearranging to solve for the final volume, V_2, we obtain

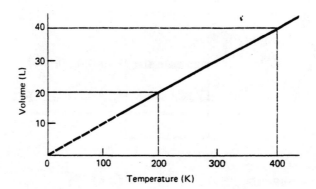

Figure 12.9 The volume of a gas sample is directly proportional to its Kelvin temperature. The graph shows the linear relationship between the volume and the Kelvin temperature of an ideal gas. If the Kelvin temperature of an ideal gas doubles from 200 to 400 K, the volume doubles from 20 to 40 L.

$$V_2 = V_1 \times \frac{T_2}{T_1} \text{ (Temperature factor)} \qquad (6)$$

Once again, the final volume of the gas is calculated by multiplying the initial volume of the gas times a conversion factor, the temperature factor. In contrast to the Boyle's law pressure factor, in which the initial pressure is divided by the final pressure, in the Charles' law temperature factor the final Kelvin temperature, T_2, is divided by the initial Kelvin temperature, T_1.

If an ideal gas initially occupies 25.4 L at 25.0°C, what is its final volume when the temperature is changed to 78.2°C? In this problem, the temperature is increased; consequently, the volume increases—a direct relationship. Before you apply the Charles' law relationship, the initial and final temperatures must be changed to Kelvin. Remember that a Kelvin temperature is calculated by adding 273.2 to the Celsius temperature:

$$T_1 = 25.0°C + 273.2 = 298.2 \text{ K}$$
$$T_2 = 78.2°C + 273.2 = 351.4 \text{ K}$$

Applying the Charles' law relationship

$$V_2 = V_1 \times \frac{T_2}{T_1} = 25.4 \text{ L} \times \frac{351.4 \text{ K}}{298.2 \text{ K}} = 29.9 \text{ L}$$

we find that the final volume of the gas sample is 29.9 L, an increase of 4.5 L from the initial volume. Figure 12.10 illustrates the procedure for calculating the final volume of an ideal gas after a temperature change.

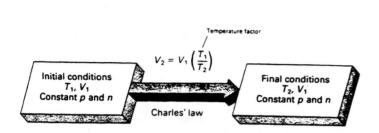

Figure 12.10 To calculate the final volume V_1 of a gas after the temperature changes at constant pressure, the initial volume V_1 is multiplied by the temperature factor. The temperature factor T_2/T_1 is the conversion factor that expresses the ratio between the final temperature T_2 and the initial temperature T_1.

Example Problem 12.3 shows another example of a Charles' law problem.

Example Problem 12.3

Calculate the final volume of a 178-mL gas sample of Xe when the temperature is decreased from 63.5°C to –155.3°C.

Solution

1. What is unknown?   Final volume, mL of V_2
2. What is known?   178 mL (initial volume, V_1), 63.5°C (initial temperature, T_1), –153.3°C (final temperature, T_2)
3. Convert Celsius temperatures to Kelvin.

$$T_1 = 63.5°C + 273.2 = 336.7 \text{ K}$$
$$T_2 = -155.3°C + 273.2 = 117.9 \text{ K}$$

4. Apply Charles' Law.

$$V_2 = V_1 \times \frac{T_2}{T_1} = 178 \text{ mL} \times \frac{117.9 \text{ K}}{336.7 \text{ K}} = \textbf{62.3 mL}$$

After the gas is cooled from 336.7 K to 117.9 K, the volume decreases to 62.3 mL, if the pressure and number of moles of gas remain constant.

Exercise

Calculate the final volume of a 500-mL gas sample of Kr when the temperature is increased from 15.5°C to 75.5°C. (604 mL)

Charles' law helps explain why hot air balloons ascend into the atmosphere. As the air in the balloon is heated, its volume increases, which lowers the density of the air. Recall that density is the ratio of mass to volume. If the volume of gas increases, its density decreases. As the density of air inside of the balloon decreases, the balloon becomes buoyant in the more dense air that surrounds it, and thus the balloon rises. By heating and cooling the air in the balloon, it rises and descends.

Combined Gas Law

Boyle's and Charles' laws are mathematically combined to yield the **combined gas law**.

$$V_2 = V_1 \times \frac{P_1}{P_2} \times \frac{T_2}{T_1} \tag{7}$$

In the combined gas law equation, two conversions factors, the pressure and temperature factors, are used to adjust the initial volume to the final volume:

$$V_2 = V_1 \times \frac{P_1}{P_2} \times \frac{T_2}{T_1}$$

Pressure factor   Temperature factor

If we multiply each side of this equation by (P_2/T_2), we obtain another expression of the combined gas law equation:

$$\frac{P_1 V_1}{T_1} = \frac{P_2 V_2}{T_2} \tag{8}$$

Combined gas law

With the combined gas law, it is not necessary to deal with the gas laws individually. If temperature is constant ($T_1 = T_2$), the temperature terms cancel, leaving Boyle's law

$$V_2 = V_1 \times \frac{P_1}{P_2} \times \frac{T_2}{T_1} = V_1 \times \frac{P_1}{P_2}$$

Boyle's law

In a similar manner, if the pressure is constant ($P_1 = P_2$), the pressure terms cancel, leaving the Charles' law expression. Prove this to yourself.

If the volume is constant ($V_1 = V_2$), the volume terms cancel, giving us a third gas law, called **Gay-Lussac's law**. This states that pressure is directly proportional to the Kelvin temperature at constant volume and number of moles. An illustration of Gay-Lussac's law is the variation in pressure in the tires of an automobile. During the winter, the pressure decreases and air must be added to obtain the proper inflation. During the summer, the pressure increases and air should be removed.

When both pressure and temperature changes are made on a gas, the final volume depends on the direction and magnitude of the two changes. For example, if the pressure is increased and the temperature is decreased, the final volume of the gas is smaller. Whenever the pressure is increased, the volume is decreased; in a similar manner, when the temperature is decreased the volume also decreases; both changes decrease the gas volume. Exactly the opposite occurs if the pressure is decreased and the temperature is increased, the volume of the gas increases.

Example Problems 12.4 and 12.5 provide illustrations of the application of the combined gas law. Use Fig. 12.11 as a guide to solving combined gas law problems in which the pressure and temperature are changed.

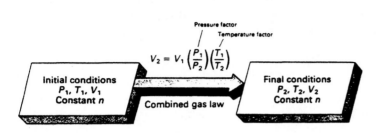

Figure 12.11 To calculate the final volume V_2 of a gas after temperature and pressure changes at constant number of moles, the initial volume V_1 is multiplied by both the pressure factor P_1/P_2 and the temperature factor T_2/T_1.

Example Problem 12.4

A balloon filled with He has a volume of 5.2 L at 44°C and 718 torr. What volume does the He occupy at standard temperature and pressure (STP), 273 K (0°C) and 1.00 atm (760 torr)?

Solution

1. What is unknown?   Final volume, V_2 in liters
2. What is known?   5.2 L, V_1; 44°C, T_1; 718 torr, P_1; 273 K, T_2; and 1.00 atm, P_2
3. Change the given units to kelvins and atmospheres.

$$T_1 = 44°C + 273 = 317 \text{ K}$$
$$P_1 = 718 \text{ torr} \times 1.00 \text{ atm}/760 \text{ torr} = 0.945 \text{ atm}$$

T_1 is changed to kelvins, and P_1 is changed to atmospheres so that the units cancel in the combined gas law equation.

3. Apply the combined gas law.

$$V_2 = V_1 \times \frac{P_1}{P_2} \times \frac{T_2}{T_1} = 5.2 \text{ L} \times \frac{0.945 \text{ atm}}{1.00 \text{ atm}} \times \frac{273 \text{ K}}{317 \text{ K}} = \textbf{4.2 L}$$

Is our answer reasonable? Pressure is increased and temperature is decreased. An increase in P decreases the volume, and a decrease in T also decreases the volume; accordingly, the final volume is less than the initial volume.

Exercise

A balloon filled with Ne has a volume of 10 L at 100°C and 705 torr. What volume does the Ne occupy at standard temperature and pressure (STP), 273 K (0°C) and 1.00 atm (760 torr)? (6.8 L)

Example Problem 12.5

A sample of hydrogen gas occupies a volume of 444 mL at 0°C and 593 torr. What must be the final temperature of the gas if, after changing the pressure to 291 torr, the gas occupies 1.88 L?

Solution

In this problem, instead of solving for a new volume, the final temperature is requested, given the pressure and volume changes. Rearrange the general form of the combined gas law and solve for the final temperature, T_2.

$$\frac{P_1 V_1}{T_1} = \frac{P_2 V_2}{T_2}$$

Multiply each side by T_1 and then by T_2 to get

$$P_1 V_1 T_2 = P_2 V_2 T_1$$

and divide both sides by $P_1 V_1$ to get

$$T_2 = T_1 \times \frac{P_2}{P_1} \times \frac{V_2}{V_1}$$

1. What is unknown? T_2 (final temperature) in K
2. What is known?   0°C, T_1; 444 mL, V_1; 1.88 L, V_2; 593 torr, P_1; and 291 torr, P_2
3. Change T_1 to kelvins, and V_1 to liters.

$$T_1 = 0°C + 273 = 273 \text{ K}$$
$$V_1 = 444 \text{ mL} \times 1 \text{ L}/1000 \text{ mL} = 0.444 \text{ L}$$

4. Apply the combined gas law.

$$T_2 = 273 \text{ K} \times \frac{291 \text{ torr}}{593 \text{ torr}} \times \frac{1.88 \text{ L}}{0.444 \text{ L}} = \textbf{567 K} = \textbf{294°C}$$

After the original hydrogen sample is heated to 567 K and the pressure is decreased to 291 torr, it expands to 1.88 L.

Exercise

A sample of hydrogen gas occupies a volume of 825 mL at 433 K and 950 torr. What must be the final temperature of the gas if, after changing the pressure to 775 torr, the gas occupies 1.25 L? (535 K)

REVIEW EXERCISES

12.5 Write a mathematical expression for each of the following.

(a) Boyle's law
(b) Charles' law
(c) Combined gas law

12.6 Distinguish between an inverse and direct proportion by sketching a graph for each.

12.7 Calculate the final volume of an ideal gas, if it occupies initially 4.00 L at a pressure of 12.0 atm and the pressure is changed to 8.75 atm.

12.8 What is the final volume of a gas that initially occupies 81.2 mL at 43.1°C when the temperature is increased to 84.6°C?

12.9 An ideal gas occupies 0.385 L at STP. What volume will it occupy at 653 torr and 4.31×10^2 K?

12.7 5.49 L; 12.8 91.9 mL; 12.9 0.707 L

Avogadro's Law

So far in our discussion of gases, the number of moles of particles within the gas sample has been constant. We did not want any of the gas to escape or additional gas added during the time the pressure and temperature were varied. Now let's consider what happens when the number of moles of gas are varied, at constant P and T.

WWWolfe 3
(See WWWolfe section at the end of the chapter.)

Amedeo Avogadro was the first to hypothesize that if the pressure and temperature of a gas are constant, its volume is directly proportional to the number of moles of gas molecules contained in the gas. Mathematically, this is expressed as follows

$$V = kn \qquad\qquad (9)$$
Avogadro's Law

in which V is volume, n is number of moles, and k is a proportionality constant. A balloon is a good illustration of Avogadro's law. A balloon expands when air is added to it (moles of air increase), and it contracts when air escapes (moles of air decreases).

An important relationship develops from Avogadro's law. If equal volumes of different gases are compared, they must contain the same number of moles of particles. Let's compare equal volumes of He(g) and Ne(g). Using the equation for Avogadro's law, we obtain the following two relationships

$$V_{He} = kn_{He} \quad \text{and} \quad V_{Ne} = kn_{Ne}$$

Because the volumes are equal ($V_{He} = V_{Ne}$), then:

$$kn_{He} = kn_{Ne}$$

At the same temperature and pressure the proportionality constants, k, in the equations are equal; therefore, the constants can be divided out of the equation, leaving:

$$n_{He} = n_{Ne}$$

Thus, the number of moles of He gas equals the number of moles of Ne gas, if equal volumes are compared at the same temperature and pressure.

Avogadro's law may be stated as follows: Equal volumes of different gases contain the same number of particles if their pressures and temperatures are the same. At standard conditions (STP) of 1.00 atm and 273 K, 1.00 mol of an ideal gas occupies 22.4 L. This volume is called the **molar volume** of an ideal gas.

$$\text{Molar volume}_{STP} = 22.4 \text{ L/1.00 mol}$$

The molar volume of an ideal gas is a conversion factor that allows us to calculate volume and mole relationships for gases (Fig. 12.12). To illustrate this, let's calculate the number of moles of Ne gas contained in a 1.00 L container at 273 K and 1.00 atm (STP).

$$n_{Ne} = 1.00 \cancel{L} \times 1.00 \text{ mol}/22.4 \cancel{L} = 0.0446 \text{ mol}$$

At STP, 0.0446 mol Ne is contained in a volume of 1.00 L. Any 1.00-L sample of an ideal gas at STP would give the same result.

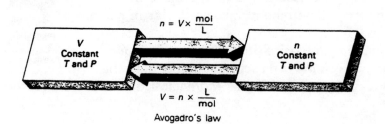

Avogadro's law

Figure 12.12 Avogadro's law calculations require the use of the molar gas volume, 22.4 L/mol at STP. The molar volume of a gas is the conversion factor that expresses the ratio between the volume and number of moles of an ideal gas.

Example Problem 12.6 shows another illustration of Avogadro's law.

Example Problem 12.6
What volume does a sample of 8.40 g of Ar gas occupy at STP?

Solution
1. What is unknown? Liters, L, Ar
2. What is known?   8.40 g Ar, 1.00 mole Ar/40.0 g, and 22.4 L Ar/1.00 mol Ar
3. Apply Avogadro's law.

$$V = 8.40 \cancel{\text{ g Ar}} \times \frac{1.00 \cancel{\text{ mol Ar}}}{40.0 \cancel{\text{ g Ar}}} \times \frac{22.4 \text{ L Ar}}{1.00 \cancel{\text{ mol Ar}}} = \textbf{4.70 L Ar}$$

First, we convert the mass of Ar to moles, using the molar mass, and then we calculate the number of liters by applying the molar volume relationship. We found that 8.4 g Ar occupy 4.70 L when the temperature is 273 K and the pressure is 1.00 atm.

Exercise
What volume does a sample of 8.40 g of CH_4 gas occupy at STP? (11.8 L)

What if the gas is not at standard conditions? We first calculate the volume the gas occupies at standard conditions, and then change to the desired set of conditions by applying the combined gas law. Example Problem 12.7 gives an illustration of mole-volume relationships at nonstandard conditions. ❖

Example Problem 12.7
What volume does 0.255 g Xe gas occupy at 298 K and 0.543 atm?

Solution
1. What is unknown? Liters, L, Xe at 298 K and 0.543 atm
2. What is known?   0.255 g Xe, 1 mol Xe/131 g Xe, 298 K, and 0.543 atm
3. Calculate the volume of Xe at STP.

It is not necessary to solve this problem in two steps, but for illustrative purposes we will find the volume at STP and then correct the volume to the stated conditions.

$$V_{STP} = 0.255 \text{ g Xe} \times \frac{1 \text{ mol Xe}}{131 \text{ g Xe}} \times \frac{22.4 \text{ L Xe}}{1 \text{ mol Xe}} = 4.36 \times 10^{-2} \text{ L Xe at STP}$$

4. Apply the combined gas law.
We now use the combined gas law to convert from STP conditions of 1 atm (P_1) and 273 K (T_1) to the desired conditions of 0.543 atm (P_2) and 298 K (T_2).

$$V_2 = V_{STP} \times \frac{P_1}{P_2} \times \frac{T_2}{T_1} = 4.36 \times 10^{-2} \text{ L} \times \frac{1.00 \text{ atm}}{0.543 \text{ atm}} \times \frac{298 \text{ K}}{273 \text{ K}} = 8.76 \times 10^{-2} \text{ L}$$

We find that our 0.255-g sample of Xe occupies 8.76×10^{-2} L (87.6 mL) at 298 K and 0.543 atm.

Exercise
What volume does 1.00 g O_2 gas occupy at 310 K and 1.44 atm? (0.552 L)

REVIEW EXERCISES
12.10 Write two different statements of Avogadro's law.

12.11 Calculate the number of moles of gas molecules contained in each of the following volumes at STP.

(a) 4.59 L N_2
(b) 0.107 L O_2
(c) 3.11 mL F_2

12.12 At STP, what volume would each of the following gases occupy?

(a) 99.4 g H_2
(b) 0.066 g He
(c) 321 mg CO

12.13 Calculate the mass of 12.11 L of radon gas, Rn, at STP.

12.14 What volume does 216.4 g of $F_2(g)$ occupy at 5.27 atm and 27.6°C?

12. 11 (a) 0.205 mol N_2, (b) 0.00476 mol O_2, (c) 1.39 × 10^{-4} F_2; 12.12 (a) 105 L H_2, (b) 0.37 L He, (c) 0.257 L CO; 12.13 120 g Rn; 12.14 26.7 L F_2

12.3 IDEAL GAS EQUATION

Boyle's Law, Charles' Law, and Avogadro's Law are mathematically combined to give a relationship for P, V, T and n of an ideal gas. This relationship is called the **ideal gas equation**. It is expressed as follows

$$PV = nRT \qquad\qquad (10)$$

in which P is pressure, V is volume, T is temperature, n is moles, and R is the ideal gas constant. Rearranging the equation and solving for R, we find the numerical value of R.

$$\frac{PV}{nT} = \frac{nRT}{nT}$$

Therefore

$$R = \frac{PV}{nT}$$

If we select a gas sample of 1.00 mol, we know that at STP conditions the volume of an ideal gas is 22.4 L. Substituting these numbers into the equation we get

$$R = \frac{1.00 \text{ atm} \times 22.4 \text{ L}}{1.00 \text{ mol} \times 298 \text{ K}} = 0.0821 \text{ (L·atm)/(mol·K)}$$

Thus, the value of R is 0.0821 (L·atm)/(mol·K) for ideal gases.

To use the ideal gas equation, we must adjust our units so that they cancel the units in the ideal gas constant or change the units of the constant, R.

Given three variable properties of a gas and the ideal gas equation, the fourth variable may be calculated. When solving such a problem, it is best to algebraically rearrange the ideal gas equation, isolating the unknown variable on one side. For example, if P, V, and T are known, rearrange the equation and solve for n. Thus we have

$$PV = nRT$$

and we divide both sides by RT

$$\frac{PV}{RT} = \frac{nRT}{RT}$$

which gives

$$n = \frac{PV}{RT} \qquad\qquad (11)$$

When the equation is successfully rearranged, the units cancel, leaving only the desired units, moles.

$$n = \frac{L \times atm}{\dfrac{L \times atm}{mol \times K} \times K} = \frac{1}{\dfrac{1}{mol}} = mol$$

Example Problems 12.8 and 12.9 show how the ideal gas equation is used to calculate unknown properties of ideal gases.

Example Problem 12.8
What volume does 2.2 mol of N_2 occupy at 440 K and 3.6 atm?

Solution
1. What is unknown? Volume, L
2. What is known?   n = 2.2 mol N_2, T = 440K, P = 3.6 atm, and R = 0.0821 L·atm/mol·K
3. Rearrange the ideal gas equation.

$$\frac{PV}{P} = \frac{nRT}{P}$$

$$V = \frac{nRT}{P} \tag{12}$$

4. Substitute known values into the equation.
All units given in this problem correspond to those in the ideal gas constant, so it is only necessary to substitute the numbers into the equation, and solve for V.

$$V = \frac{2.2 \text{ mol } N_2 \times 0.0821 \text{ L·atm/mol·K} \times 440 \text{ K}}{3.6 \text{ atm}} = \mathbf{22 \text{ L } N_2}$$

When 2.2 mol of an ideal gas is found at 440 K and 3.6 atm, it occupies 22 L.

Exercise
What volume does 5.9 g of Cl_2 occupy at 391 K and 2.66 atm? (1.0 L)

Example Problem 12.9
Calculate the temperature of a 0.390-mol sample of He that occupies 9850 mL under a pressure of 631 torr.

Solution
1. What is unknown?   T in kelvins
2. What is known?   n = 0.390 mol He, V = 9850 mL, and P = 631 torr
3. Change given units to those that correspond to the units of the ideal gas constant.
Because the ideal gas constant is expressed in L·atm/mol·K, the volume must be converted to liters and the pressure to atmospheres.

$$V = 9850 \text{ mL} \times 1 \text{ L}/1000 \text{ mL} = 9.850 \text{ L}$$

$$P = 631 \text{ torr} \times 1.00 \text{ atm}/760 \text{ torr} = 0.830 \text{ atm}$$

4. Rearrange and substitute into the ideal gas equation.

$$\frac{PV}{nR} = \frac{nRT}{nR}$$

$$T = \frac{PV}{nR}$$

$$T = \frac{0.830 \text{ atm} \times 9.850 \text{ L}}{0.390 \text{ mol He} \times 0.0821 \text{ (L·atm)}/\text{(mol·K)}} = \textbf{255 K}$$

At 255 K and 631 torr, 0.390 mol He occupies 9850 mL.

Exercise

What is the temperature of a 100-g sample of SF_6 that occupies 18.0 L and exerts a pressure of 1.35 atm? (432 K)

REVIEW EXERCISES

12.15 Calculate the numerical value for the ideal gas constant, R, in (L·torr)/(mol·K).

12.16 What volume does 2.06 mol Ne occupy at 33.1 atm and 285 K?

12.17 Calculate the temperature, in Celsius, of 0.391 mol of an ideal gas that occupies 1.10 L under a pressure of 7.84 atm.

12.18 How many moles of Ar are contained in a sample that has a measured volume of 78.4 mL under a pressure of 956 torr and a temperature of –15°C?

12.15 62.4 (L·torr)/(mol·K); 12.16 1.46 L; 12.17 –4°C; 12.18 0.00466 mol Ar

Molecular Masses and Densities of Gases

Modification of the ideal gas equation allows us to find the molecular mass of a gas. You should recall that the number of moles of a substance (n) is calculated by dividing its mass in grams (m) by the molar mass in grams per mole (MM), which is the mass of one mole (g/mol):

$$\text{Moles (n)} = \frac{m}{MM} = \frac{g}{\dfrac{g}{mol}}$$

Therefore, we can substitute m/MM into the ideal gas equation for n as follows:

$$PV = nRT$$

$$PV = \frac{m}{MM}RT \qquad\qquad (13)$$

Rearranging, and isolating molar mass, MM, we have

$$MM = \frac{mRT}{PV} \qquad (14)$$

Molar masses are found by determining their masses at a known set of conditions and applying the above equation. Example Problem 12.10 shows such a calculation.

Example Problem 12.10

A 61.5-g sample of an unknown gas occupies 37.2 L at 313 K and 0.924 atm. What is the molar mass of the unknown gas?

Solution
1. What is unknown?   g/mol of gas, MM
2. What is known?   61.5 g, 37.2 L, 313 K, 0.924 atm, and R = 0.0821 L·atm/mol·K
3. Apply the modified form of the ideal gas equation.

$$MM = \frac{mRT}{PV} = \frac{61.5\ g \times 0.0821\ (L·atm)/(mol·K) \times 313\ K}{0.924\ atm \times 37.2\ L} = \textbf{46.0 g/mol}$$

The molar mass of this unknown gas is 46.0 g/mol.

Exercise
A 95.0-g sample of an unknown gas occupies 63.2 L at 375 K and 1.98 atm. What is the molar mass of the unknown gas? (23.4 g/mol)

We can also use the ideal gas equation to calculate the density, d, of a gas. The density of a gas is the ratio of its mass (m) to volume (V).

$$d = \frac{m}{V} \qquad (15)$$

The most frequently used units for the densities of gases are g/L or g/dm^3. By using the modified form of the ideal gas equation, we can solve for g/V or the density of the gas.

$$PV = \frac{m}{MM}RT$$

$$d = \frac{m}{V} = \frac{P\,MM}{RT} \qquad (16)$$

Consequently, the density of the gas only depends on its molecular mass at a constant T and P. Example Problem 12.11 shows how the density of Cl_2 is calculated.

Example Problem 12.11

Calculate the density of Cl_2 gas at 315 K and 1.15 atm.

Solution

1. What is unknown? d of Cl_2 (g/L)
2. What is known? Cl_2 gas, T = 315 K, P = 1.15 atm, and MM = 71.0 g Cl_2/mol Cl_2
3. Substitute the known values into the equation.

$$d = \frac{P \cdot MM}{RT} = \frac{1.15 \text{ atm} \times 71.0 \text{ g } Cl_2/\text{mol } Cl_2}{0.0821 \text{ (L·atm)/(mol·K)} \times 315 \text{ K}} = \textbf{3.16 g/L}$$

The density of Cl_2 is 3.16 g/L at 315 K and 1.15 atm.

Exercise

Calculate the density of H_2 at 150 K and 1.33 atm. (0.218 L)

REVIEW EXERCISES

12.19 Calculate the molecular mass of a 0.148-g sample of an unknown gas that occupies 30.0 mL at 26°C and 813 torr.

12.20 Calculate the density of silicon tetrafluoride gas, SiF_4, at 152°C and 643 torr.

12.19 113 g/mol; 12.20 2.52 g/L

WorldWideWolfe CHEMISTRY LINKS

Connect to WorldWideWolfe at

http://www.mindspring.com/~drwolfe/WWWolfe_hcc_1025_links.htm

and link to the following sites.

Gases

1. Behavior of Gases This page covers the full range of topics that we will discuss regarding gases: Boyle's, Charles', Gay Lussac, and the combined gas laws. It the goes over the ideal gas equation and the important of the ideal gas constant, R.

Gases Covers the full range of what you need to know about the properties of gases. It has Learning Objectives, Before you start, Lecture Notes, and References and Resources.

Gas - The Basics This is an introduction to the gas phase.

2. Boyle's and Charles' Laws A discussion of Boyle and Charles' law with practice problems.

3. Avogadro's Law and the Ideal Gas Law Besides a discussion of Avogadro's law and the ideal gas equation, practice problems are presented.

SUMMARY

The properties of gases are explained theoretically by the **kinetic molecular theory**, which is a set of assumptions that concerns the behavior of atoms and molecules that make up an ideal gas.

Ideal gas laws explain relationships between volume, pressure, temperature, and number of moles of gas particles in ideal gas samples. **Boyle's law** states that the volume of an ideal gas is inversely proportional to the applied pressure at constant temperature and number of moles. **Gas pressure** is the force that gas particles exert on the walls of their containers. Pressure is measured in atmospheres, kilopascals, and torr, in which 1 atm = 760 torr = 101 kPa.

Charles' law states that the volume of a gas is directly proportional to its Kelvin temperature at constant pressure and number of moles. **Avogadro's law** states that the volume of a gas is directly proportional to the number of moles of gas at constant pressure and temperature, or stated another way, at a constant set of conditions, equal volumes of ideal gases contain the same number of molecules. At standard temperature and pressure (273 K and 1 atm), the volume of 1.00 mole of an ideal gas is 22.4 L.

Various mathematical expressions are derived from the gas laws. Two of the most important ones are the **combined gas law**

$$\frac{P_1 V_1}{T_1} = \frac{P_2 V_2}{T_2}$$

which is used to calculate the final set of conditions, given the initial conditions, and the **ideal gas equation**:

$$PV = nRT$$

in which one of the four gas variables can be calculated, given the other three. R in the equation is the ideal gas constant, 0.0821 (L·atm)/(mol·K).

KEY TERMS

absolute zero

atmosphere

barometer

direct proportion

ideal gas

inverse proportion

kinetic molecular theory

kinetic energy

manometer

mm Hg

partial pressure

pascal

pressure

STP

torr

STUDY GUIDELINES

After completing Chapter 12, you should be able to

1. List and discuss the principal assumptions of the kinetic molecular theory
2. State the properties of ideal gases
3. State a definition for pressure, and give three examples of the units most commonly used to measure pressure
4. Convert any given pressure unit to any other pressure unit.
5. State in words and as a mathematical expression: (1) Boyle's law, (2) Charles' law, and (3) Avogadro's law
6. Calculate the final pressure, volume, or temperature of an ideal gas, given the initial and final set of conditions
7. Provide an explanation for the fact that equal volumes of ideal gases at the same pressure and temperature contain the same number of particles
8. State the molar volume of a gas at STP, and use it to find the mass or number of moles of an ideal gas
9. Calculate the density or molecular mass of a gas, given all required information and the molar gas constant
10. Use the ideal gas equation to find unknown properties of gases (P, V, n, or T)

EXERCISES

12.21 Define each of the following terms: kinetic molecular theory, kinetic energy, ideal gas, pressure, pascal, mm Hg, torr, atmosphere, barometer, manometer, inverse proportion, direct proportion, absolute zero, STP.

Kinetic Molecular Theory

12.22 Use the kinetic molecular theory to completely explain each of the following.
(a) Gases are the most compressible state of matter.
(b) Two nonreacting gases can be mixed in any proportions.
(c) The volume of a gas increases when heated.
(d) Gases always take the shape of their container.
(e) Molecules that compose gases do not settle to the bottom of their containers on standing.

12.23 Why do gases exhibit more ideal properties as their pressures are decreased and their temperatures are increased?

12.24 (a) What causes an increase in the average kinetic energy of the particles in a gas?
(b) What would happen to gas particles if their collisions with each other and the walls of the container were not perfectly elastic?

Pressure

12.25 (a) How is gas pressure defined?
(b) What is the SI unit for pressure?

12.26 Explain how a mercury barometer measures atmospheric pressure.

12.27 Why could a barometer also be used as an altimeter, a device for measuring the height above the ground?

12.28 (a) How is a manometer constructed? (b) How is the pressure of a gas sample measured with a manometer?

12.29 For each of the following in Fig. 12.13, determine the pressure of the gas sample if the atmospheric pressure is 752 torr.

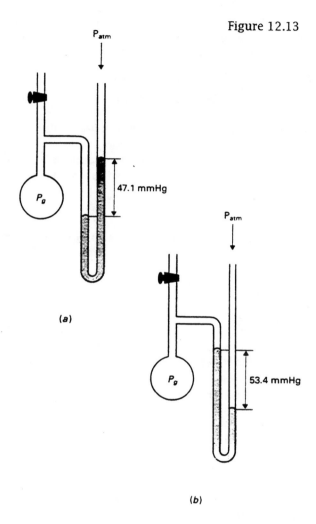

Figure 12.13

(a)

(b)

12.30 Account for the fact that, even at sea level, atmospheric pressure is constantly changing.

12.31 Convert 4.04×10^3 kilopascals to
(a) Pa   (b) torr
(c) atm   (d) mm Hg.

12.32 Change 2.953 atm to
(a) torr   (b) Pa
(c) kPa.

12.33 Convert 784 mm Hg to

(a) torr   (b) atm
(c) Pa   (d) kPa.

12.34   Change 9282 torr to
(a) atm,   (b) Pa
(c) kPa.

12.35   Perform the following pressure
conversions.
(a) 5.49 atm = ? torr
(b) 0.0944 torr = ? Pa
(c) 6.26×10^3 torr = ? atm
(d) 0.00912 kPa = ? torr
(e) 1726 torr = ? mm Hg

12.36   A unit of pressure in the United States
system is pounds per square inch,
abbreviated lbs/in^2 or psi. Standard
atmospheric pressure, in this system, is
14.7 lbs/in^2.
(a) Convert standard atmospheric
pressure to lbs/ft^2.
(b) Calculate the pressure, in torr, inside
of a tire with an internal pressure of 29.0
psi.

Boyle's Law

12.37   Correctly state Boyle's law, including
what variables are constant.

12.38   Using the mathematical statement of
Boyle's law, PV = k, calculate the volume
of a gas for each of the following
pressures, if k equals 0.910 L·atm.
(a) 2.51 atm   (b) 6.10 atm
(c) 0.0449 atm   (d) 327 torr
(e) 93.8 kPa

12.39   Consider the following graph of P versus
V in Fig. 12.14 to answer the following
questions.
(a) What is the volume of the gas at 6.0
atm?
(b) At what pressure will the gas occupy a
volume of 30.0 L?
(c) At an infinite pressure (if that were
possible), what should happen to the gas
volume?
(d) What pressure change is required to
change the volume of the gas from 1.0 to
5.0 L?

Figure 12.14

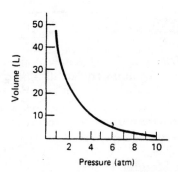

12.40   What is the final volume of an ideal gas, if
initially it occupies 9.5 L at a pressure of
0.89 atm, and the following pressure
changes are made?
(a) 2.0 atm   (b) 1.0 atm
(c) 25 atm   (d) 97 kPa
(e) 812 torr

12.41   A sample of N_2 gas occupies 73.5 cm^3 at
296 atm. What volume does it occupy at
standard atmospheric pressure?

12.42   If a sample of Ne gas occupies 7.77 L at
683 torr, what volume will it occupy at 109
kPa?

12.43   Initially, a Ne gas sample occupies 33.72 L
at 763.4 torr. Calculate the volume it
occupies under each of the following
pressures.
(a) 0.7903 atm   (b) 0.7903 torr
(c) 0.7903 Pa   (d) 0.7903 kPa

12.44   What is the final pressure that would have
to be exerted on 1204 mL H_2 at 1.000 atm
to change its volume to each of the
following?
(a) 1000 mL   (b) 340.5 mL
(c) 40.00 L   (d) 6.130 L

12.45   A 71-L He tank contains compressed
helium at 59 atm; how many 1.2 L
balloons can be filled with the He in the
cylinder, assuming that atmospheric
pressure is exactly 1 atm?

Charles' Law

12. 46   Correctly state Charles' law, and indicate
which variables are held constant.

12.47   Using the mathematical statement of
Charles' law, V/T = k, calculate the volume

of an ideal gas at each of the following temperatures, if it is known that k = 0.0821 L/K.
 (a) 418 K   (b) 35.2°C
 (c) 0.0°C   (d) –98.2°C
 (e) 107°C

12.48 Consider the following graph of T versus V data in Fig. 12.15 to answer each of the following questions.
 (a) At what temperature will the gas occupy 30.0 L?
 (b) At what temperature will the gas occupy 25.0 L?
 (c) What volume does the gas occupy at –10.0°C?
 (d) What temperature change is required to change the volume of the gas from 20 L to 30 L?

Figure 12.15

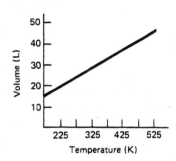

12.49 Why does no simple relationship exist between the volume of an ideal gas and its temperature in degrees Celsius?

12.50 What is the final volume of a gas that initially occupies 9.35 L at 282 K, when the temperature is changed to each of the following?
 (a) 149 K   (b) 596 K
 (c) 298°C   (d) –65°C?

12.51 Calculate the volume of O_2 gas that initially occupies 1.175 L at 200.0°C after the temperature is changed to 462.9 K.

12.52 What temperature would an ideal gas, initially occupying 5.74 L at 10.0°C, have to be changed to for it to occupy?
 (a) 10.0 L   (b) 6.00 L
 (c) 15.2 L

12.53 (a) Theoretically, what volume would a 125-L sample of He gas at 273 K occupy by decreasing its temperature to 10.0 K?
 (b) What pressure is required to decrease the volume of the 125-L He sample to the same volume that results when the He is cooled to 10.0 K, if initially the gas sample is at 1.00 atm?

Combined Gas Law

12.54 What happens to the volume of a gas sample when each of the following pressure and temperature changes are made?
 (a) P increased, T decreased
 (b) P decreased, T increased
 (c) Small P increase, large T increase
 (d) Large P decrease, small T decrease

12.55 What volumes do each of the following gas samples occupy when the conditions are changed to STP?
 (a) V_1 = 5.90 L, T_1 = 58°C, P_1 = 7.61 atm
 (b) V_1 = 279 cm^3, T_1 = –16°C, and P_1 = 806 torr
 (c) V_1 = 0.446 L, T_1 = 227 K, and P_1 = 446 kPa
 (d) V_1 = 577 L, T_1 = 203°C, and P_1 = 83.7 kPa.

12.56 For each of the following, calculate the final volume the gas occupies.
 (a) V_1 = 0.619 L V_2 = ? L
 T_1 = 444 K T_2 = 822 K
 P_1 = 1.24 atm P_2 = 9.49 atm
 (b) V_1 = 524 mL V_2 = ? L
 T_1 = –91°C T_2 = –43.4°C
 P_1 = 118 kPa P_2 = 0.652 atm
 (c) V_1 = 1.75 L V_2 = ? mL
 T_1 = 30.8°C T_2 = 310 K
 P_1 = 476 torr P_2 = 418 kPa
 (d) V_1 = 6.32 L V_2 = ? cm^3
 T_1 = –75°C T_2 = –10.4°C
 P_1 = 752 torr P_2 = 0.857 atm

12.57 Calculate the final pressure of each of the following gases when the stated volume and temperature changes are made.
 (a) V_1 = 89.6 L V_2 = 43.8 L
 T_1 = 23.5°C T_2 = 52.2°C
 P_1 = 1.79 atm P_2 = ? atm
 (b) V_1 = 2041 L V_2 = 4.53 L
 T_1 = 666 K T_2 = –52.9°C
 P_1 = 42.1 kPa P_2 = ? Pa
 (c) V_1 = 62.8 L V_2 = 77.4 L
 T_1 = –23 °F T_2 = 35 °F
 P_1 = 912 torr P_2 = ? torr
 (d) V_1 = 0.236 cm^3 V_2 = 1.72 L
 T_1 = 193 K T_2 = 723 K

P$_1$ = 164 kPa   P$_2$ = ? atm

12.58   If 562 L of an ideal gas is prepared at 701 torr and 512°C and then pumped into a 2.53-L steel tank at 35.0°C, what pressure will the tank have to withstand?

Avogadro's Law

12.59 Calculate the number of moles of ideal gas in each of the following samples at STP.
(a) 372 mL   (b) 2.09 L
(c) 0.00410 cm^3 (d) 2.551 mm^3
(e) 8.22 m^3

12.60 Find the volumes occupied by each of the following gases at STP.
(a) 1.94 g NH$_3$
(b) 4.21 × 10^{-4} g SO$_3$
(c) 21.9 mg CF$_4$
(d) 1.09 g Xe
(e) 351.3 kg O$_3$

12.61 Calculate the masses of each of the following gases, given their volumes at STP.
(a) 0.0304 L N$_2$O   (b) 148 L HCl
(c) 0.916 m^3 C$_2$H$_2$ (d) 6.311 mL UF$_6$
(e) 5.390 cm^3 Kr

12.62 What volume would each of the following gases occupy at 799 torr and 333 K?
(a) 492 g H$_2$
(b) 5.44 kg ClF
(c) 0.001011 mg SO$_2$

12.63   Calculate the volume of each of the following gases at the stated conditions:
(a) 21.5 g He at 247 K and 1.824 atm
(b) 0.553 mol O$_2$ at 808 K and 642 torr
(c) 931 mg Cl$_2$ at 164°C and 92.4 kPa
(d) 9.34 kg H$_2$S at 2.04°C and 0.917 atm

12.64 Calculate the density, in grams per liter, of each of the following gases at standard conditions.
(a) Cl$_2$ (b) CO$_2$
(c) Xe   (d) C$_3$H$_8$
(e) C$_2$FCl$_3$

Ideal Gas Equation

12.65 Solve the ideal gas equation, PV = nRT, for each of the following variables: (a) P, (b) n, (c) T, and (d) V, and show that the units cancel to give the correct units of the dependent variable.

12.66 Use the factor-label method to calculate the value of the ideal gas constant, R, with the following set of units.

(a) (mL·atm)/(mol·K)
(b) (cm^3·torr)/(mmol·K)
(c) (kPa·dL)/(mol·K)
(d) (m^3·torr)/(mol·K)

12.67 What volume, in liters, do each of the following gases occupy at the stated conditions?
(a) 2.36 mol CO$_2$ at 711 K & 1.73 atm
(b) 0.0889 mol He at 555 torr & 89.4°C
(c) 0.466 mol N$_2$O at 1247 torr & 301 K

12.68 Calculate the number of moles of gas molecules in each of the following gas samples.
(a) 2.98 L F$_2$ at 0.104 atm and 64.7°C
(b) 29.4 mL Cl$_2$ at 397 kPa and 9.06°C
(c) 0.00228 m^3 SO$_2$ at 840.4 K and 932 torr.

12.69 Calculate the pressures, in atm, exerted by each of the following gases.
(a) 1.18 mol H$_2$Te occupying 3.85 L at 587 K
(b) 212 mmol SiF$_4$ occupying 193 mL at −4.92°C
(c) 0.00299 mol NF$_3$ occupying 1.08 dm^3 at 107.4 K

12.70 Calculate the mass of each of the following gas samples.
(a) N$_2$ that occupies 2.17 L at 743 torr and 21.6°C
(b) Kr that occupies 81.2 cm^3 at −31.4°C and 0.515 atm
(c) F$_2$ that occupies 0.0112 m^3 at 243 kPa and 319 K

12.71   What volume does each of the following occupy at the stated conditions?
(a) 0.394 g Ar at 25.1°C and 791 torr
(b) 191.2 mg OF$_2$ at 1.04 atm and −115°C
(c) 481 kg NO at 112 kPa and 304 K

12.72 Calculate the density in grams per liter of SF$_6$ at 176°C and 0.499 atm.

12.73   Calculate the density in grams per liter of NF$_3$ at −111.5°C and 790.4 torr.

12.74 If 22.6 g of a gas sample occupies 17.9 L at 0.863 atm and 311 K, what is the molecular mass of the gas?

12.75   Calculate the molecular mass of 275 g of a gas that occupies 39.7 L at 125 kPa and −8.50°C.

Chapter 12 Pretest Assignment

1.   Complete each of the following statements with the correct word, number, or phase.

   a. _____ is the unit that measures the force exerted on an area.

   b. A(n) _____ is the instrument used to measure the pressure of the
   atmosphere.

   c. One atmosphere equals _____ torr.

   d. _____ Law is the relationship between the volume and Kelvin
   temperature of an ideal gas at constant pressure and number of moles.

   e. Boyle's law states that the volume of an ideal gas is _____
   proportional to it pressure at constant temperature and number of moles.

   f. Avogadro's law states that the volume of an ideal gas is _____
   _____

   g. _____ is the equation that shows the combined gas law.

   h. _____ is the ideal gas equation.

2.   A gas initially occupies 12.5 L at 890 torr, what volume does this gas occupy after the pressure is
   changed to 0.455 atm?

3.   A 23.4-L sample of an ideal gas is initially at 30.0°C. What volume will this gas occupy after the
   temperature is changed to 0.0°C?

4.   A 100-mL sample of He has a pressure of 1.33 atm at 50.1°C. What volume will this He sample
   occupy when the pressure is changed to 994 torr and the temperature is changed to 81.6°C?

5.   What is the volume of a 54.9-g sample of CO_2 that exerts a pressure of 12.1 atm at 298 K?

6.   What is the density of Kr at 100°C and 1232 torr?

Appendix A

Review of Math Skills

A.1 ALGEBRAIC OPERATIONS

Algebra is an area of mathematics that deals with equations and equalities. Generally, equations are solved to determine the value of an unknown quantity. This is accomplished by applying the most basic rule of algebra: **Isolate the unknown quantity in an equation by mathematically treating both sides of the equation in the same way.** An equation is unchanged as long as whatever is done to one side of the equation is also done to the other side. Consider the following equation:

$$x - 10 = 12$$

If the same number is added to both sides of the equation, the equality remains unchanged. Therefore, if 10 is added to both sides of the equation, the unknown value, x, is isolated on the left side (-10 plus 10 equals zero). On the right side, 10 is added to 12, giving 22; hence, the value of the unknown, x, is 22.

$$
\begin{array}{r}
x - 10 = 12 \\
\underline{+10 \quad +10} \\
x = 22
\end{array}
$$

Always check the answer by substituting the value obtained back into the equation. Checking the above example shows: $22 - 10 = 12$.

The above equation belongs to a general class of equations having the form

Type 1: $\qquad\qquad x + m = n$

where x is the unknown quantity and m and n are known quantities. To solve Type 1 equations, m is either added or subtracted to isolate x by itself on one side of the equation. See Example Problem 1.

Example Problem 1

Solve the following equation: $x + 23 = -100$.

Solution

To solve this equation, subtract 23 from both sides.

$$
\begin{array}{r}
x + 23 = -100 \\
\underline{-23 \quad\quad -23} \\
\boldsymbol{x = -123}
\end{array}
$$

Check the answer: $-123 + 23 = -100$.

Type 2 equations are solved by multiplying and dividing appropriate quantities to isolate the unknown value. Type 2 equations have the general form

Type 2:
$$mx = n \quad \text{or} \quad \frac{x}{m} = n$$

In the first equation, x is found by dividing both sides of the equation by m.

$$\frac{mx}{m} = \frac{n}{m} \quad \text{or} \quad x = \frac{n}{m}$$

In the second equation, x is determined by multiplying both sides by m.

$$m\left(\frac{x}{m}\right) = mn \quad \text{or} \quad x = mn$$

In the study of chemistry, we use both multiplication and division of numbers to solve equations. Consider the following equation:

$$\frac{ax}{m} = n$$

To solve for x in an equation of this form, multiply each side of the equation by m/a, then cancel a/m on the left side, yielding $x = mn/a$.

$$\frac{m}{a} \times \frac{ax}{m} = \frac{mn}{a}$$

Example Problem 2 shows how to solve a Type 2 equation.

Example Problem 2
Solve the following equation for x:

$$\frac{5x}{3} = -20$$

Solution
Multiply both sides of the equation by 3/5, thereby canceling the 5/3 on the left side of the equation and isolating x.

$$\frac{3}{5} \times \frac{5x}{3} = \frac{3}{5}(-20)$$

$$x = \frac{3}{5}(-20)$$

$$x = -12$$

Check the answer:

$$\frac{5 \times (-12)}{3} = -20$$

Many algebraic equations are a combination of Type 1 and Type 2 equations. Isolating the unknown quantity in this type of equation requires both addition and multiplication. To illustrate, let's solve the following equation for x:

$$a(x - m) = n$$

First divide each side by a, and then add m to both sides.

$$\frac{a(x - m)}{a} = \frac{n}{a}$$

$$x - m = \frac{n}{a}$$

$$\underline{+m} = \underline{+m}$$

$$x = \frac{n}{a} + m$$

If possible, when you solve such equations, initially remove all terms that can be eliminated from the side of the equation containing the unknown quantity by multiplying and dividing. Finally, add or subtract the remaining terms, leaving the unknown quantity by itself.

In other mixed equations the opposite procedure should be followed: Add and subtract first, and then multiply and divide (see Example Problem 3).

Example Problem 3
Solve for x:

$$\frac{18}{x} + 7 = 13$$

Solution
Subtract 7 from both sides of the equation.

$$\frac{18}{x} + 7 = 13$$

$$\underline{-7} = \underline{-7}$$

$$\frac{18}{x} = 6$$

Multiply both sides of the equation by x, and then divide the resulting equation by 6, giving the answer 3.

$$x \frac{18}{x} = 6x$$

$$18 = 6x$$

$$\frac{18}{6} = \frac{6x}{6}$$

$$\boldsymbol{x = 3}$$

Solving more complex equations involves applying the same general principles: Rearrange the equation and isolate the unknown quantity through additive and multiplicative operations. However, the number of operations needed to solve these equations increases as the equations become more complex. Consider the more involved equation in Example Problem 4. ❖

Example Problem 4
Solve the following equation for x:

$$\frac{a+1}{x+b} = \frac{m}{n}$$

Solution
1. Multiply both sides of the equation by $(x + b)$.

$$(x+b) \times \frac{a+1}{x+b} = (x+b) \times \frac{m}{n}$$

$$a+1 = (x+b) \times \frac{m}{n}$$

2. Multiply both sides by n/m.

$$\frac{n}{m} \times (a+1) = (x+b) \times \frac{m}{n} \times \frac{n}{m}$$

$$\frac{n}{m} \times (a+1) = x+b$$

3. Subtract b from both sides of the equation.

$$\frac{n}{m} \times (a+1) - b = x+b-b$$

This yields

$$\boldsymbol{x = \frac{n}{m} \times (a+1) - b}$$

A.2 SCIENTIFIC NOTATION

Exponential Numbers

Extremely small and extremely large numbers are often encountered in chemistry. Numbers such as

$$0.0000000000005 \text{ and } 6{,}000{,}000{,}000{,}000{,}000{,}000{,}000$$

are commonplace in chemical applications. Numbers in this form are unwieldy and awkward to deal with. Consequently, large and small numbers are ordinarily expressed exponentially or in a special exponential system called **scientific notation.**

Before considering the specifics of scientific notation, let's review some basic principles concerning exponential numbers. An exponent is a number or symbol written as a superscript to the right of a base number (or symbol) indicating how many times the base number is multiplied by itself. For instance, 10^3 is $10 \times 10 \times 10$, 2^6 is $2 \times 2 \times 2 \times 2 \times 2 \times 2$, and a^4 is $a \times a \times a \times a$. The exponent of a number is called the **power**, and the number being raised to the power is termed the **base**. We will restrict our discussion to numbers with base 10. Table 1 lists examples of exponential numbers with base 10.

You must obey a couple of simple rules when you multiply and divide exponential numbers (addition and subtraction are discussed later). When multiplying exponential numbers with the same bases, add the exponents. For example, the product of 10^6 and 10^8 is

$$10^6 \times 10^8 = 10^{6+8} = 10^{14}$$

TABLE I POWERS OF TEN

Exponential number	Meaning
10^0	1 (all numbers to the zero power are 1)
10^1	10
10^2	$10 \times 10 = 100$
10^3	$10 \times 10 \times 10 = 1000$
10^4	$10 \times 10 \times 10 \times 10 = 10{,}000$
10^{-1}	$1/10 = 0.1$
10^{-2}	$1/10 \times 1/10 = 0.01$
10^{-3}	$1/10 \times 1/10 \times 1/10 = 0.001$
10^{-4}	$1/10 \times 1/10 \times 1/10 \times 1/10 = 0.0001$

The explanation for adding exponents when multiplying is straightforward: 10^6 is $10 \times 10 \times 10 \times 10 \times 10 \times 10$, and 10^8 is $10 \times 10 \times 10 \times 10 \times 10 \times 10 \times 10 \times 10$; hence, $10^6 \times$

10^8 equals $(10 \times 10 \times 10 \times 10 \times 10 \times 10) \times (10 \times 10 \times 10 \times 10 \times 10 \times 10 \times 10 \times 10)$, or 10^{14}.

When dividing numbers with the same base, subtract the exponent in the denominator from the exponent in the numerator. Thus, the quotient of 10^5 divided by 10^4 is

$$\frac{10^5}{10^4} = 10^{5-4} = 10^1$$

or, without using exponential notation,

$$\frac{100,000}{10,000} = 10$$

Scientific Notation

Numbers are expressed in **scientific notation** by separating them into two factors: (1) decimal factor and (2) exponential factor. Examples of numbers expressed in scientific notation are

$$1.234 \times 10^9$$

$$9.87 \times 10^{-3}$$

$$3.0 \times 10^{59}$$

In each example, the first number (1.234, 9.87, and 3.0) is the decimal factor. By convention, the decimal factor is always given a value equal to or greater than 1 and less than 10. The decimal factor is multiplied by the exponential factor, 10 to some power.

To convert numbers to scientific notation, adjust the decimal point so that the decimal factor has a value equal to or greater than 1 and less than 10, and, depending on how many places the decimal point is moved and in what direction, give the appropriate power to the base, 10, so as not to change the value of the number.

To illustrate, let's change 23,000 to scientific notation. First, we adjust the decimal point to give a number between 1 and 10. To accomplish this, we move the decimal point four places to the left, giving the number 2.3000. For each place to the left we move the decimal point, we add 1 to the exponent of 10^0 (10^0 equals 1; by definition any number to the zero power is 1). So $23,000 \times 10^0$ is the same as $23,000 \times 1$ or just 23,000. Therefore, the exponent of 10^0 is increased by 4 to 10^{0+4} or 10^4.

$$23,000. \times 10^0 \text{ converts to } 2.3000 \times 10^4$$

The exponent is increased because each time the decimal point is moved to the left, it is the same as dividing the number by 10, or decreasing the value by a factor of 10, and in order not to change the number, it has to be multiplied by 10. If a number is multiplied and divided by 10 at the same time, this is the same as multiplying by 1 (10/10 = 1), which does not change the value of the number.

When large numbers are converted to scientific notation, the decimal point is moved to the left, thus increasing the value of the exponent. When numbers smaller than 1 are changed to scientific notation, the opposite is true—the decimal point is moved to the right, decreasing the value of the exponent.

How is 0.00000091 expressed in scientific notation? First, move the decimal point 7 places to the right, giving the value 9.1 for the decimal factor. In order not to change the numerical value of the number, 7 is subtracted from the exponent, 0 (10^0), giving −7 as the exponent. Thus

$$0.00000091 \text{ becomes } 9.1 \times 10^{-7}$$

Each time the decimal is moved one place to the right, the magnitude of the number is increased by 10; at the same time, it must be divided by 10 so the value remains constant. Study the Example Problem 5 to understand better how to change numbers to scientific notation.

Example Problem 5
Change each number to scientific notation.
(a) 390,000,000,000,000,000; (b) 0.0000000000000000000072

Solution
(a) Move the decimal point 17 places to the left, giving 3.9.

$$390,000,000,000,000,000 \text{ gives } 3$$

Add 17 to the exponent.
$$3.9 \times 10^{0+17} = \mathbf{3.9 \times 10^{17}}$$

(b) Move the decimal point 22 places to the right, giving 7.2.

$$0.0000000000000000000072 \text{ gives } 7.2$$

Subtract 22 from the exponent.

$$7.2 \times 10^{0-22} = \mathbf{7.2 \times 10^{-22}}$$

To change a number expressed in scientific notation to a nonexponential number, the operation is reversed. If the exponent is positive, move the decimal point to the right, and if the exponent is negative, move the decimal point to the left. For example, to change 1.75×10^5 to nonexponential form:

$$1.75000 \times 10^5 \text{ gives } 175,000 \times 10^0 = 175,000 \times 1 = 175,000$$

Each time the decimal is moved to the right, the value of the number is increased by a factor of 10; to keep the value of the number the same, 1 is subtracted from the exponent. In changing from scientific notation to nonexponential form, the exponential factor is changed to 10^0, or 1, which is not written. In Example Problem 6, two numbers are converted from scientific notation to nonexponential form.

Example Problem 6

Change each number to nonexponential form: (a) 1.19×10^{-7}; (b) 6.50×10^{6}.

Solution

(a) Since the exponent is –7, move the decimal point 7 places to the left and add 7 to the exponent in order not to change the value of the number.

$$6.19 \times 10^{-7} \text{ gives } 0.000000119 \times 10^{-7+7}$$

or

0.000000119

(b) Since the exponent is +6, move the decimal point 6 places to the right and subtract 6 from the exponent in order not to change the value of the number.

$$6.500000 \times 10^{6} \text{ gives } 6{,}500{,}000. \times 10^{6-6}$$

or

6,500,000

Arithmetic Operations: Multiplication and Division

Arithmetic operations on numbers expressed in scientific notation are handled the same way as operations on any exponential numbers. The only difference is that the proper operation must be performed on the decimal factor at the same time that the appropriate exponent operation is calculated.

To review: **When multiplying, add exponents; when dividing, subtract exponents**. For example: What is the product of $(3 \times 10^{4}) \times (2 \times 10^{6})$? It is easier to separate the decimal factors from the exponential factors, giving

$$(3 \times 2) \times (10^{4} \times 10^{6})$$

Multiply the decimal factors, and then add the exponents,

$$3 \times 2 = 6 \text{ and } 10^{4+6} = 10^{10}$$

to obtain the correct answer,

$$6 \times 10^{10}$$

Dividing numbers expressed in scientific notation is carried out in a similar manner except that the decimal factors are divided and the exponents are subtracted. Example Problem 7 illustrates multiplication and division of numbers expressed in scientific notation.

Example Problem 7

Simplify the following expression:

$$\frac{8 \times 10^{12}}{4 \times 10^{15}} \times 1.5 \times 10^{-3}$$

Solution

1. First divide 8×10^{12} by 4×10^{15}.

$$\frac{8}{4} \times 10^{12-15} = 2 \times 10^{-3}$$

Separate the factors 8 and 4 from the exponential factor and divide: $8/4 = 2$. Then subtract the exponents, 12 and 15, yielding -3.

2. Multiply the resulting number, 2×10^{-3}, by 1.5×10^{-3}.

$$2 \times 1.5 \times 10^{-3 +(-3)} = \mathbf{3 \times 10^{-6}}$$

Multiply the decimal factors, 2 and 1.5, obtaining the product 3. Add the exponents, -3 and -3, giving -6. The same answer is obtained if 8×10^{12} is multiplied by 1.5×10^{-3} and the product is divided by 4×10^{15}.

Arithmetic Operations: Addition and Subtraction

To complete our study of numbers expressed in scientific notation, we turn our attention to addition and subtraction operations. Again, one general rule prevails for both operations: **Only numbers with the same exponent can be added or subtracted.**

What is the sum of 1×10^3 (1000) and 1×10^2 (100)? To add these numbers, both exponents must be the same. Therefore, either the 3 is changed to 2 or the 2 is changed to 3. Generally, it is best to change the smaller exponent to a larger exponent, as we shall see. If the exponent is increased by 1 (1×10^2), the decimal factor is divided by 10 (move the decimal point to the left):

$$1. \times 10^2 \text{ gives } 0.1 \times 10^{2+1} = 0.1 \times 10^3$$

Now that both exponents are the same, the two numbers can be added:

$$0.1 \times 10^3 + 1 \times 10^3 = 1.1 \times 10^3 = 1100$$

When adding numbers in scientific notation, the decimal factors are added and the exponent of the answer remains the same (do not add the exponents).

In the above example, if the smaller exponent was not changed to a larger exponent, the resulting answer would not have been in scientific notation initially. Commonly, answers obtained after arithmetic operations are not in scientific notation; in other words, the decimal factor is not between 1 and 10. Whenever this case is encountered, it is necessary to change the answer back to scientific notation. Let's consider one final example problem that illustrates manipulation of numbers in scientific notation. ❖

Example Problem 8

Evaluate the following, and express the final answer in scientific notation:

$$\frac{3 \times 10^7}{1.5 \times 10^{-2}} - (7.5 \times 10^8) + (1.25 \times 10^{10})$$

Solution

1. Divide (3×10^7) by (1.5×10^{-2}).

$$\frac{3}{1.5} = 2 \quad \text{and} \quad \frac{10^7}{10^{-2}} = 10^{7-(-2)} = 10^9$$

This yields

$$2 \times 10^9$$

2. Because the next operation is subtraction and the numbers have different exponents, we must change one of the exponents. Change the exponent in 7.5×10^8 to 10^9.

$$7.5 \times 10^8 \text{ gives } 0.75 \times 10^{8+1} = 0.75 \times 10^9$$

Subtract this from the first number.

$$2 \times 10^9 - 0.75 \times 10^9 = 1.25 \times 10^9$$

3. Finally, add the last number, 1.25×10^{10}, after the exponents are changed to the same value.

$$1.25 \times 10^9 \text{ gives } 0.125 \times 10^{9+1} = 0.125 \times 10^{10}$$

and

$$0.125 \times 10^{10} + 1.25 \times 10^{10} = \mathbf{1.375 \times 10^{10}}$$

A.3 GRAPHING

A **graph** is a convenient means for displaying and observing trends in data. Frequently, in chemistry, collected data are graphed to show patterns in the data.

Graphing involves placing or "plotting" data points on graph paper and drawing a smooth curve or straight line through the plotted points. Regular graph paper is printed with evenly spaced horizontal and vertical lines for this purpose. All data are plotted between two perpendicular axes, called the x and y axes. Normal graphing convention defines x as the horizontal axis and y as the vertical axis. In mathematics, the x axis is called the **abscissa,** and the y axis is termed the **ordinate.**

The first step in graphing data is to scale the axes, i.e., to place appropriate values along each axis to accommodate all data points. It is a good practice to use as much of the graph paper as possible. If the x values range from 0 to 100, 0 is placed at the left side and 100 is placed as far to the right as possible, considering the magnitude of each division on the x axis. The size of each division depends on the collected data. For example, if the data values are measured to the nearest 0.5 unit, the scale should allow room so that values like 23.5 or 73.5 can be easily plotted.

After each axis is scaled, data points (ordered pairs) are plotted on the graph to correspond to each data pair, i.e., each x and y value. This is accomplished by moving across the x axis to the correct value, and then rising vertically until the y value is reached. At the intersection a mark is made, and in many cases is labeled with the x and y values. All data points are plotted in a similar manner before the graph is drawn.

A common error is to connect the plotted points with a jagged line, as in the children's game of "connect the dots" (Fig. A.1a). Data points are not always connected directly. Instead, a straight edge or french curve is used to draw the best–fitting line through the maximum number of data points. Usually some points do not fall exactly on the line since experimental errors are present in all measurements (Fig. A.1*b*).

Example Problem 9 illustrates the above procedures. .

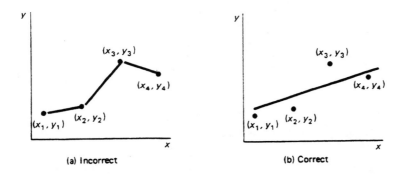

(a) Incorrect   (b) Correct

Figure A.1 (a) The improper way to construct a graph. Always draw the smooth curve or straight line that best fits the data points. (b) The correct way to construct a graph.

Example Problem 9

On a recent auto trip on an interstate highway the following distance and time data were collected:

Time, hr	Distance, mi
0.5	25
1.0	50
2.0	100
3.0	150

Plot a graph of the time and distance data, with time on the *x* axis and distance on the *y* axis.

Solution

Time values range from 0.5 to 3.0 hr. To include all values, scale the *x* axis from 0 to 4 hr in 0.5-hr intervals. Scale the *y* axis from 0 to 200 mi. It is a common practice to scale the axis above and below the range of collected data values.

Once the axes are scaled, plot each data pair. First, plot the (0.5 hr, 25 mi) point by moving horizontally to 0.5 hr. and then rising vertically to the 25–mi line. Plot all other data pairs in a similar fashion (Fig. A.2).

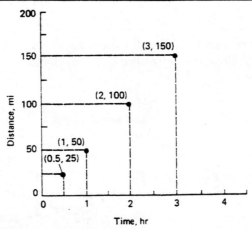

Figure A.2 Plotted points with correctly scaled axes.

It is apparent that the points are aligned in a linear fashion, or in a straight line. Using a ruler, draw a straight line through all plotted points, as in Fig. A.3.

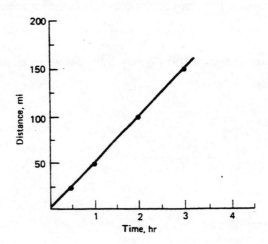

Figure A.3 Complete graph of distance traveled in miles versus time in hours.

If you examine the graph plotted in Example Problem 9 carefully, you can readily extract additional information. The graph shows a straight–line, or linear, relationship between the variables of time and distance. For each unit interval of the trip, the same amount of distance was traveled. No matter what hour interval is considered, 50 mi is traversed (check this for yourself. The change in distance per interval is constant in the above graph –50 mi/hr. All linear relationships have this common characteristic, called the **slope,** or **rate** of change of the y variable for a unit change in the x variable. To compute the slope of the line, select two data points on the lines determine the change in y values, and divide this factor by the corresponding change in x values. Verify the fact that the change is 50 mi/hr in the above graph.

Slopes of linear relationships are either positive, as above, or negative. A **positive slope** shows that for each increase in the variable plotted on the x axis there is a resulting increase in the y variable. In our example, an increase in time traveled produces an increase in distance. A **negative slope** shows that for each increase in the x variable, there is a resulting decrease in the y variable. Figure A.4 shows linear relationships with both positive and negative slopes.

Only four data pairs were collected for our theoretical auto trip in Example Problem 9. Nevertheless, the distance traveled at any interval can be determined by correctly reading the graph. How far did the auto travel in 2.5 hr? Find 2.5 hr on the x axis, and draw a perpendicular line from this point to the line plotted on the graph. Then draw a horizontal line from the intersection of the vertical line to the y axis. The point where it meets the axis is the distance traveled in 2.5 hr (125 mi). Reverse the above procedure to find time elapsed for a given distance traveled. For example, how long did it take to travel 75 mi?

In many cases, the limits of the data are extended, especially when there is a good fit between the line and the data points. Continuing the line on the graph above and below the range of collected data points is called **extrapolation.** Extrapolation is justified when there is a good reason to believe that the trend extends beyond the observed data. Extending the graph in Example Problem 9 to 4 hr shows that the auto would have traveled 200 mi in 4 hr (Fig. A.5). ·

Nonlinear relationships are also frequently encountered in chemistry. As the name implies, a **nonlinear relationship** is characterized by a graph that is not a straight line. Instead, the data points are connected by a curved line. Figure A.6 presents examples of nonlinear relationships.

All graphs, no matter what type, are interpreted in the same way. Ask yourself the following questions when you are interpreting a graph: What general trends are found? How are the variables changing (increasing or decreasing) with respect to each other? What special characteristics are there? What are the limits of the variables? ❖

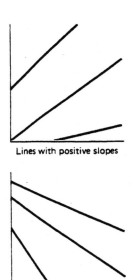

Lines with positive slopes

Lines with negative slopes

Figure A.4 Slopes of lines

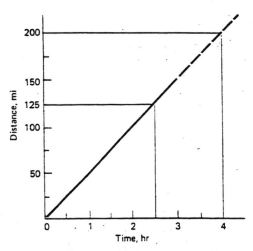

Figure A.5 Extrapolation of the distance versus time data shows that in 4 hr a total distance of 200 mi is traveled.

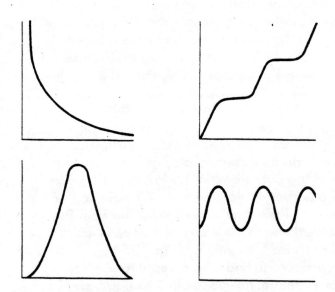

Figure A.6 Four types of nonlinear relationships are shown.

EXERCISES

Equations

1. Solve each of the following equations for x:
   (a) $x - 55 = -47$ (b) $125 = 83 + x$
   (c) $110 = -x - 78$ (d) $-9x = -94$

2. Solve each of the following equations for z:
   (a) $1/(z - 9) = 12.4$
   (b) $z/(2z + 5) = 1/12$
   (c) $(a + b)(z + 2) = (n + 1)/m$
   (d) $(a + 2)/(b - z) = 1/(n + 1)$

3. If $m = 25$ and $n = 9$, solve, for x:
   (a) $x = 5m - 3n + 2$
   (b) $x = 5(m - 3)n + 2$
   (c) $x = (5m - 3n) + 2$
   (d) $x = 5m - (3n + 2)$

4. Solve the following equations for x:
   (a) $5x = 512$ (b) $x/13 = 6.44$
   (c) $16x + 5 = 6x$ (d) $10x/30 = 12$
   (e) $(2x - 10)/8 = 63$

5. Solve the following equations for y:
   (a) $a/2(ny - m) = 1$
   (b) $(a + b)/(y + m) = n + 10$
   (c) $3a + b = 4y/5 + n$
   (d) $6/y + 2/y = a/b$

6. If $a = 25$, $b = 6$, $m = 3$, and $n = -1$, calculate the value of y in each equation in Exercise 5.

Scientific Notation

7. Change the following numbers to scientific notation:
   (a) 0.00049139
   (b) 120,000,000,000
   (c) 0.0000000013511
   (d) 0.0000000000000000000105

8. Change the following numbers to nonexponential form:
   (a) 3.11×10^{-3} (b) 2.90×10^{-2}
   (c) 7.7742×10^{8} (d) 8.001×10^{12}

9. Change the following numbers in exponential form to scientific notation:
   (a) 0.000436×10^{6} (b) 1215×10^{4}
   (c) 0.0001001×10^{-8} (d) 979×10^{-4}
   (e) $6,361,000 \times 10^{-10}$

10. Add the following numbers:
    (a) $(4.75 \times 10^{5}) + (7.11 \times 10^{5})$
    (b) $(8.33 \times 10^{-3}) + (1.20 \times 10^{-3})$
    (c) $(9.355 \times 10^{7}) + (1.722 \times 10^{9})$
    (d) $(2.109 \times 10^{35}) + (9.64 \times 10^{33})$
    (e) $(3.400 \times 10^{20}) + (4.230 \times 10^{18}) +$
    $$(5.011 \times 10^{19})$$

11. Subtract the following numbers:
    (a) $(4.38 \times 10^{4}) - (7.17 \times 10^{4})$
    (b) $(9.921 \times 10^{-13}) - (7.22 \times 10^{-14})$
    (c) $(2.55 \times 10^{45}) - (5.690 \times 10^{47})$
    (d) $(6.131 \times 10^{-34}) - (1.7492 \times 10^{-36})$

12. Find the product for each:
    (a) $(1.75 \times 10^3) \times (2.44 \times 10^8)$
    (b) $(3.54 \times 10^{54}) \times (9.82 \times 10^{96})$
    (c) $(1.11 \times 10^3) \times (5.35 \times 10^{23}) \times$
$$(7.44 \times 10^{28})$$

13. Find the quotient for each:
    (a) $\dfrac{4.175 \times 10^{-17}}{9.329 \times 10^{-24}}$
    (b) $\dfrac{5.67 \times 10^{91}}{1.05 \times 10^{-22}}$
    (c) $\dfrac{6.85 \times 10^7}{(2.79 \times 10^{-4}) \times (6.113 \times 10^{18})}$

14. Perform the indicated operations:
    (a) $\dfrac{1.42 \times 10^{-26} - (5.44 \times 10^{-6})}{1.56 \times 10^{-24}}$
    (b) $\dfrac{(6.788 \times 10^{57}) - (8.54 \times 10^{56})}{5.93 \times 10^{58}}$

Graphing

15. Graph the following data on a full sheet of graph paper.

x	y
10	36
25	81
40	126
55	171
80	246

(a) What type of relationship is plotted? (b) What y value corresponds to an x value of 70? (c) What x value corresponds to a Y value of 56? (d) Extrapolate the line to determine the expected y value corresponding to an x value of 100. (e) What is the slope of the line?

16. Plot the following data, with Fahrenheit temperatures on the x axis and Celsius temperatures on the y axis.

Temperature, °F	Temperature, °C
–40	–40
0	–17.8
40	4.4
80	26.7
120	48.9

(a) What is the slope of the line? (b) Using the graph, determine what Celsius temperature corresponds to each of the following Fahrenheit temperatures: 98.6°F, 75°F, –25°F, and 135°F.

17. (a) On a full sheet of graph paper, plot years on the x axis and the approximate population of the United States on the y axis, given the following data:

Year	Population (millions)
1940	130
1950	150
1960	175
1970	205
1980	225
1990	245

(b) Is this a linear function? Explain.
(c) What was the approximate population of the United States in 1945? (d) Extrapolate the population data to the year 2000. What is the expected population of the United States in the year 2000?

18. For each of the following graphs, explain what happens to the variable written on the vertical axis when the variable listed on the horizontal axis is increased across its full range.

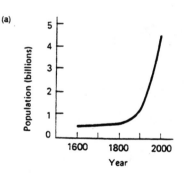

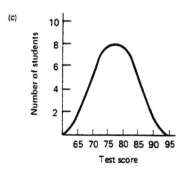

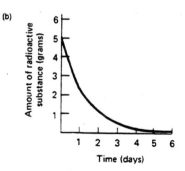

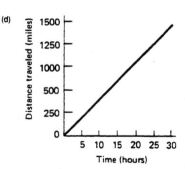

Figure A.7

Appendix B

Physical Constants and Conversion Factors

B.1 PHYSICAL CONSTANTS

Unified atomic mass unit (u or amu)

$1\ u = 1.66057 \times 10^{-27}\ kg = 1.66057 \times 10^{-24}\ g$
$6.022045 \times 10^{23}\ u = 1.000000\ g$

Avogadro's number $\qquad N = 6.022045 \times 10^{23}$ entities/mol

Electron mass $\qquad m_e = 9.10953 \times 10^{-28}\ g = 5.48580 \times 10^{-4}\ u$

Electron charge $\qquad e = -1.6022 \times 10^{-19}\ C$

Faraday's constant $\qquad F = 9.6485 \times 10^4\ C/mol$

Ideal gas constant $\qquad R = 0.082057\ (L \cdot atm)/(mol \cdot K)$
$R = 8.3144\ J/(mol\ K)$
$R = 8.3144\ (Pa \cdot dm^3)/(mol \cdot K)$

Molar volume (ideal gas), STP $\qquad V_{STP} = 22.4\ L/mol$

Neutron mass $\qquad m_{n^\circ} = 1.67495 \times 10^{-24}\ g = 1.00866\ u$

Proton mass $\qquad m_p{}^+ = 1.67265 \times 10^{-24}\ g = 1.00728\ u$

Speed of light $\qquad c = 2.997925 \times 10^8\ m/s$

B.2 UNIT CONVERSION FACTORS

Mass
$1\ g = 10^{-3}\ kg$
$1\ mg = 10^{-6}\ kg$
$1\ lb = 0.453592\ kg = 453.592\ g$
$1\ kg = 2.205\ lb$
$1\ oz = 28.349523\ g$
$1\ u = 1.66057 \times 10^{-27}\ kg$
1 metric ton, $t = 1000\ kg$
1 metric ton, $t = 2204.6\ lb$

Length
$1\ cm = 10^{-2}\ m$
$1\ mm = 10^{-3}\ m$
$1\ nm = 10^{-9}\ m$
$1\text{Å} = 10^{-10}\ m = 0.10\ nm = 100\ pm$
$1\ in = 2.54 \times 10^{-2}\ m = 2.54\ cm$
$1\ cm = 10\ mm = 0.39370\ in$
$1\ mi = 1.609\ km$
$1\ yd = 0.9144\ m$

Time
$1\ day = 8.64 \times 10^4\ s$
$1\ hr = 3.60 \times 10^3\ s$
$1\ ms = 10^{-3}\ s$

Temperature
$0°C = 273.15\ K$
$0°F = 255.37\ K$
$-273.15°C = 0\ K$
$-459.67°F = 0\ K$

Volume
$1\ L = 10^{-3}\ m^3$
$1\ L = 1.057\ qt$
$1\ qt = 0.9463\ L$
$1\ cm^3 = 10^{-6}\ m^3$
$1\ mL = 1\ cm^3$
$1000\ mL = 1\ L$

Energy
$1\ cal = 4.184\ J$
$1\ cal = 2.612 \times 10^{19}\ eV$
$1\ erg = 10^{-7}\ J$
$1\ erg = 2.3901 \times 10^{-8}\ cal$
$1\ J = 0.23901\ cal$

Pressure
$1\ atm = 101{,}325\ Pa = 101.325\ kPa$
$1\ atm = 760\ mmHg = 760\ torr$
$1\ atm = 14.70\ lb/in^2$
$1\ torr = 1\ mmHg$
$1\ torr = 133.322\ Pa$
$1\ bar = 1 \times 10^5\ Pa$

Appendix C

Polyatomic Ions and Their Formulas

Ion	Name	Ion	Name
AlO_3^{3-}	Aluminate	IO_3^-	Iodate
AsO_4^{3-}	Arsenate	IO_2^-	Iodite
AsO_3^{3-}	Arsenite	IO^-	Hypoiodite
BiO_3^{3-}	Bismuthate	MnO_4^-	Permanganate
BO_3^{3-}	Borate	MnO_4^{2-}	Manganate
BrO_3^-	Bromate	NH_4^+	Ammonium
BrO_2^-	Bromite	NO_3^-	Nitrate
BrO^-	Hypobromite	NO_2^-	Nitrite
CO_3^{2-}	Carbonate	O_2^{2-}	Peroxide
HCO_3^-	Hydrogencarbonate	OCN^-	Cyanate
$C_2O_4^{2-}$	Oxalate	OH^-	Hydroxide
$C_2H_3O_2^-$	Acetate	PO_4^{3-}	Phosphate
CN^-	Cyanide	PO_3^{3-}	Phosphite
HCO_2^-	Formate	PO_2^{3-}	Hypophosphite
ClO_4^-	Perchlorate	$P_2O_7^{2-}$	Pyrophosphate
ClO_3^-	Chlorate	SCN^-	Thiocyanate
ClO_2^-	Chlorite	SeO_4^{2-}	Selenate
ClO^-	Hypochlorite	SeO_3^{2-}	Selenite
CrO_4^{2-}	Chromate	SiO_3^{2-}	Silicate
$Cr_2O_7^{2-}$	Dichromate	SnO_4^{4-}	Stannate
GaO_3^{3-}	Gallate	SO_4^{2-}	Sulfate
GeO_4^{4-}	Germanate	SO_3^{2-}	Sulfite
GeO_3^{4-}	Germanite	$S_2O_3^{2-}$	Thiosulfate
H^-	Hydride	TeO_6^{6-}	Tellurate
IO_4^-	Periodate	TeO_3^{6-}	Tellurite

Appendix D

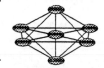

Answers to Selected Exercises

CHAPTER 1

1.15   (a) Geochemist, (b) organic chemist, (c) biochemist, (d) physical or inorganic chemist, (e) analytical chemist

1.24   A philosopher deals with problems primarily through the use of logic; a scientist conducts controlled systematic experiments based on observable phenomena

CHAPTER 2

2.17   (a) Fact, (b) theory, (c) theory
2.20   (a) 564 miles, (b) 3.5 gallons
2.21   (a) 480 seconds, (b) 0.693 years, (c) 0.9 centuries, (d) 432 dozen
2.23   (a) 300 seconds, (b) 51.0 seconds, (c) 4,500 seconds, (d) 267,840 seconds
2.24   (b) 219,000 hours, (d) 788,400,000 seconds
2.25   (a) 1.101 years, (b) 1.782 decades, (d) 10.6 days
2.27   (a) 256 drams, (b) 7000 grains, (c) 0.03657 drams
2.29   (a) 68 cents, (b) 9.16 dozen, (c) 11 cents
2.30   (a) 27 miles/gallon, (d) 51.45 dollars
2.31   (a) 0.27 dollars, (b) 0.0079 dollars
2.33   (a) 2,365,200,000, (b) 7.5 decades, (c) 27,375 days
2.34   (a) 40 rods/furlong, (c) 0.3636 rods
2.37   (a) 3,700,000,000 miles (3,696,192,000 miles)
      (b) 5,900,000,000,000 miles (5.8657×10^{12} miles)
2.39   (a) 365,000,000 acres (365,440,000 acres)
      (b) 15,900,000,000,000 ft^2 (1.5919×10^{13} ft^2)
      (c) 2,290,000,000,000,000 in^2 (2.2923×10^{15} in^2)

CHAPTER 3

3.30   The precision is not good because of the wide range of values, which indicates a high degree of uncertainty
3.31   (a) Analytical balance, (c) small graduated cylinder
3.32   If the thermometer is in the sun, the temperature reading will be too high
3.34   (a) 5, (b) 7, (c) 2, (g) 6, (i) 1
3.35   (a) 4, (b) 0, (c) 8, (g) 0, (i) 5
3.36   (a) 2×10^1, (b) 1×10^2, (c) 9×10^{-2}, (g) 1×10^{-3}, (i) 5×10^{-8}
3.37   (a) 194.6, (c) 962.2, (e) 9.996×10^{11}
3.38   (c) 9.00×10^4, (e) 9.0000×10^4
3.39   (a) 4.8 g, (b) 43.87 mL, (d) 756.87 m
3.40   (a) 97.3 mL, (c) 0.034 g
3.41   (b) 5.9×10^3 s^2, (c) 54 cm^2
3.42   (a) 6.6 g/mL, (c) 1×10^{20} m/s
3.43   (a) 7.4×10^3, (b) 0.286
3.48   (b) 16.69 m, (c) 4.3×10^5 cm, (f) 7.46×10^4 km
3.49   (a) 2×10^3 m, (b) 1.5×10^6 in, (d) 9.0×10^7 mm, (f) 7.820×10^{-1} Mm.

3.50   (a) 0.00048 km, (b) 1.12×10^4 mm, (c) 1.8 m
3.53   59 kg, 170 cm, 94 cm, 76 cm, 89 cm
3.54   Your weight would be much greater
3.55   (b) 0.074 g, (c) 9711.5 kg, (f) 4.52×10^{11} Mg, (h) 8.395×10^{10} cg
3.56   (b) 1.754×10^8 mg, (d) 5.4581×10^5 cg, (e) 3.82×10^9 ng
3.57   (a) 284 K, (c) 37.6 K
3.58   (a) -1.9×10^2°C, (d) 2948°C
3.59   (b) -60.94°C, (c) 796.7°C
3.60   (a) 172°F, (d) -220.0°F
3.61   (c) 1540.3°F, (d) -458.07°F
3.62 -40°C $= -40$°F
3.65   (a) 1.1×10^2 cm^3, (b) 0.11 dm^3
3.67   (b) 0.000012 m^3, (c) 73570 μL, (f) 0.012 m^3
3.69   (a) 0.670 m^3, (b) 2.386×10^4 cm^3
3.70   (a) 13.0 g/mL, (c) 0.942 g/mL
3.71   (b) 3.32×10^3 g, (e) 6×10^3 g, (f) 4.10×10^3 g
3.72   (a) 358 mL, (c) 1.43×10^3 mL, (d) 1.40×10^4 mL
3.73   (b) 1.29 kg/m^3, (c) 0.0805 lb/ft^3
3.75   1.59 g/mL
3.77   1.65 g/mL
3.78 1.9×10^5 g
3.80   (a) 0.0786 g^{-1}, (b) 78.6 m^2, (c) 0.408
3.81   (a) 9.32×10^{-9} Mg, (b) 2.445×10^{-8} m^3, (c) 3.22×10^{10} pm, (d) 179°F, (e) 9.561×10^5 cg,
        (f) 1.63 kg/dm^3, (g) 25 K, (h) 4.51×10^{-10} m^3
3.83   (a) 118.3 cm^3, (b) 17 g
3.86   (a) 893 km/h, (b) 248 m/s, (c) 0.000248 mm/ns
3.87   13.9 g/cm^3
3.90   (a) 1.2×10^2 in^3, (b) 0.0020 m^3
3.94 6.77×10^{13} particles
3.95   0.00014 cm^3

CHAPTER 4

4.34   Physical: (a), (i); chemical: (d), (j), (o)
4.35   Physical: (d), (i); chemical: (c), (g)
4.37   Physical: yellow color, solid state, melting point, boiling point; chemical: burns in air
4.40   (a) Vegetable oil, (d) molasses
4.41   (a) Solid, (b) gas, (d) solid and liquid, (i) gas and liquid, (j) gas
4.44   (a) Solution, (b) element, (c) heterogeneous mixture
4.45   Pure substance: (g); Mixture: (a), (e), (h), (k)
4.55   (a) Sodium 2, oxygen 1; (d) lithium 2, carbon 1, oxygen 3; (f) rubidium 1, hydrogen 2, phosphorus 1,
        oxygen 4; (g) aluminum 1, oxygen 3, hydrogen 3; (i) xenon 1, platinum 1, chlorine 6
4.56   (b) Element
4.58   Homogeneous: (a), (d), (e); heterogeneous: (c), (g)
4.59   (b) Distill: evaporate the alcohol from the water
4.60   (a) 2, (b) 2, (c) 2, (d) 3
4.63   (a) 13.2 J
4.65   (a) Composition, (d) condition, (e) position
4.66   (a) Bunsen burner flame, (e) neither
4.67   (a) 38.5 J, (d) 3.4×10^5 kJ
4.69   0.32 J/(g °C)
4.70 8.57×10^5 J
4.73   For 1.00 kg of water, 3.14×10^5 J are released. For 1.00 g of water, 314 J are released
4.75 8.4×10^2 °C
4.78   Potential energy of water to kinetic energy (mechanical energy) of the turbine to kinetic energy of the
        generator to electric energy

4.79   (b) 6.1×10^{24} mg

4.80   (a) 1.4×10^{11} J

4.81   343 m/s

4.85   Heat will flow from $O_2(l)$ into $N_2(l)$ increasing the temperature of $N_2(l)$ and decreasing the temperature of $O_2(l)$

4.86   0.871 J/(g °C)

4.88   (b) 1.27×10^3 J/°C

4.89 5.45×10^3 J

4.91 7.9×10^3 J

4.92   (a) 0.44 J/(g °C), (b) –3.79 kJ

4.93   (a) 0.37 J/(g °C), (b) –1.44 kJ

CHAPTER 5

5.29   Since the neutron has no charge, it could not be detected by the methods used to study charged particles

5.31   (a) 1 g/6.022×10^{23} u, (b) 1.673×10^{-24} g/p$^+$

5.33

	Atomic Symbol	Mass number	No. of number	No. of protons	No. of neutrons	No. of electrons
(a)	^{3}H	1	3	1	2	1
(e)	^{40}Ar	18	40	18	22	18
(h)	^{81}Br	35	81	35	46	35
(l)	^{195}Pt	78	195	78	117	78

5.34

	Protons	Neutrons	Electrons
(a)	46	62	46
(c)	22	26	22

5.35   (b) $^{127}_{53}$I

5.40   151.96 u

5.43   (a) 63.55 u

5.48   When an electron moves from a higher energy level to a lower energy level, a quantum of energy is released. This discrete packet of energy is associated with a line in the spectrum

5.52   (a) 2, (c) 4, (e) 14, (g) 3, (i) 0

5.55   (b) $1s^2 2s^2 2p^2$, (e) $1s^2 2s^2 2p^6 3s^2 3p^6 4s^1$, (f) $1s^2 2s^2 2p^6 3s^2 3p^6 4s^2 3d^{10}$,(i) $1s^2 2s^2 2p^6 3s^2 3p^6 4s^2 3d^{10} 4p^4$

5.57   (a) $5s^1$, (c) $4s^2 4p^1$, (f) $5s^2 5p^2$

5.58   (a) N, (c) P, (g) Rb

5.61   (a) Mg; (c) Y, Zr, Nb, Mo; (f) H, He, Li, Be

5.62   (a) $1s \, 2s^2 2p^6$ (c) $1s^2 2s^2 2p^6$

5.63   (a) [Xe] $6s^2 4f^{14} 5d^{10} 6p^2$

5.64   (a) $5s^2 5p^3$; (b) 3;

5.65   Filled d subshell and filled valence s subshell

5.68

	Protons	Neutrons	Electrons
(a)	84	124	84
(c)	72	108	72

5.69   (a) ^{129}Xe, ^{132}Xe; (c) ^{25}Mg, ^{26}Mg

5.70   (a) $1s^2 2s^2 2p^6 3p^1$

5.73   0.6 mile

5.74   Decreases by a factor of 9

5.76   30.0 u

5.79   (a) Chromium would be expected to have the electronic configuration $4s^2 3d^4$; however it is $4s^1 3d^5$; (b) The actual configuration has one more e$^-$ in the 3d and one less e$^-$ in the 4s. (c) The configuration in part (a) is at a lower energy than that in part (b)

5.86 1.22×10^{-23} cm^3

CHAPTER 6

6.16   Properties of the elements are periodic functions of their atomic number
6.17   (a) Alkali metals, (e) transition metals, (f) halogens, (g) alkaline earth metals, (i) nitrogen-phosphorus group, (k) lanthanide series
6.19   (a) s^1, (b) s^2p^5, (f) s^2p^3
6.21   Metal: (c), (f), (h); nonmetal: (b); metalloid: (a)
6.22   (a) Nonmetal
6.23   (a) Be, (b) Sn
6.24   (a) (1) 3, (3) 1, (4) 2; (b) (1) 3–, (3) 1–, (4) 2–
6.25   (a) (1) 1, (2) 2, (3) 3, (4) 3; (b) (1) 1+, (2) 2+, (3) 3+, (4) 3+
6.26   (a) 2+, (b) 3–, (d) 2–, (h) 1+, (i) 1–
6.27   (c) Ba → Ba^{2+} + 2e⁻; (d) Cs → Cs^+ + e⁻
6.28   (a) Ne, (b) Ne, (f) Kr
6.29   874 kJ/mol
6.30   (a) Sn, (c) Rb
6.31   (a) C, (c) Ca
6.32   (a) Rn, (c) Po, (e) N, (g) Ne, H
6.33   Element 118 would be a noble gas. (a) Nonmetal, (c) poor conductor of electricity (d) colorless, (g) does not form stable ions
6.34   (a) Fr, (d) Se, (e) Te, (g) Ra, (i) Zn.
6.37   (a) Ionization energy increases as atomic number increases. (b) Third row ionization energies are higher
6.39   0.25 nm, 1.53 g/cm³ (actual values)
6.40   The nuclear charge of 2+ readily attracts the two 1s electrons, which are not shielded
6.41   Element 120 would be a highly radioactive alkaline earth metal. It would be a dense, high-melting solid, and a good conductor of electricity. It will be larger than Ra and have a lower ionization energy than Ra. It would form a 2+ ion
6.43   The $3p^4$ electron in S must pair up with another 3p electron. This requires energy (pairing energy) which is released when the electron is removed from the S atom
6.45   (a) $1s^22s^22p^63s^23p^64s^23d^{10}4p^65s^24d^{10}5p^66s^2$; (b) $1s^22s^22p^63s^23p^64s^23d^{10}4p^65s^24d^{10}5p^6$; (c) Xe; (d) Ba^{2+} is smaller than Xe
6.47   (a) 3p, (b) 5s
6.49   1687 K, 2.33 kg/L
6.50   Tc is a radioactive metal; thus, it is a good conductor of heat and electricity, has high melting point and boiling points, a has a high density
6.53   (a) solid, nonconductor, low density

CHAPTER 7

7.35   The atomic mass in grams
7.36   (a) 10.81 g B, (d) 72.59 g Ge
7.37 2×10^4 centuries
7.38

Element	No. of moles	No. of atoms	Mass, g
(a) B	1.00	6.02×10^{23}	10.8
(d) Zr	2.000	1.204×10^{24}	182.4
(a) Sn	10.0	6.02×10^{24}	1.19×10^3

7.39   (a) 3.71×10^{-4} mol K, (e) 2.23×10^3 mol K
7.40   (a) 0.0533 mol As, (c) 9.64×10^{-5} mol Ni
7.41   (a) 3.21×10^{22} atoms As, (c) 5.81×10^{19} atoms Ni
7.42   (a) 284 g Ar, (c) 2.141×10^8 g Na
7.43   (a) 2.90×10^{22} atoms Pb, (d) 6.1781×10^{19} atoms Ra
7.44   (a) 0.835 mol Xe, (b) 6.8 mol Cu
7.45   (a) 42 g Kr, (c) 0.0646 g Ge
7.46   (a) 3×10^1 g Fe, (b) 5.01×10^{-13} g Fe, (c) 6.59×10^{-20} g Fe, (d) 9.274×10^{-23} g Fe
7.48   (a) 3.62×10^{-4} mol Re, (b) 1.132×10^{25} Pd, (c) 2×10^{-24} mol Hf, (d) 0.2424 mg Bi, (e) 56.5 kg Nb
7.50   (b), (d), (a), (c)

7.51   (a) 207 g/mol IBr, (d) 520 g/mol Cl_4, (e) 102 g/mol S_2F_2, (h) 194 g/mol $H_2S_2O_8$

7.52   (a) 219.9 g/mol P_4O_6, (c) 175.8 g/mol OBr_2, (f) 90.01 g/mol $H_2C_2O_4$

7.53

	Compound	No. of moles	No. of molecules	Mass, g
(a)	SO_2	1.000	6.022×10^{23}	64.05
(d)	H_2SO_3	0.0100	6.02×10^{21}	0.820
(f)	$AlCl_3$	0.262	1.58×10^{23}	34.9

7.54   (a) 0.232 g ClO_2, (e) 0.1021 g N_2O_4

7.55   (a) 1.1×10^{23} molecules, H_2O_2, (b) 2.931×10^{20} molecules, ClF_3

7.56   (a) 8.207 mol O, (c) 1.23×10^{-4} mol O

7.57   (a) 0.75 g H, (b) 7.43×10^{-4} g H, (c) 15.83 g H, (d) 2745.1 g H

7.60   (c) > (d) > (a) > (b)

7.61   (a) 99.0 g/mol CuCl, (c) 189 g/mol $Zn(NO_3)_2$, (e) 400 g/mol $Fe_2(SO_4)_3$

7.62   (a) 0.44 mol $NaClO3$, (b) 0.002257 mol $Ca_3(PO_4)_2$

7.63   (a) 763 g TiO_2, (b) 2.90×10^3 g K_2SnCl_6, (c) 0.001337 g PbC_2O_4

7.64   (a) 5.60×10^{22} formula units, $MgSiO_3$, (b) 7.1×10^{24} formula units, $Hg_2(NO_2)_2$, (c) 1.409×10^{23} formula units, $NH_4C_2H_3O_2$

7.65   (a) 0.788% H, 99.2% I, (c) 61.2% Hg, 38.8% I, (e) 70.4% Os, 29.6% O

7.66   (a) 24.74% K, 34.77% Mn, 40.49% O; (c) 59.89% Ba, 12.21% H. 27.91% O; (e) 11.1% N 3.200% H, 41.27% Cr. 44.44% O

7.67   (a) 87.1% Ag, (d) 65.4% Ag

7.69   (a) 36.07% H_2O, (c) 33.69% H_2O

7.71   (a) FeS_2, (d) SiI_4, (f) Ce_3S_4

7.72   (a) KCN, (b) PbC_2O_4, (e) Li_2CO_3

7.73 CrO_3

7.75 CNH_4

7.77 $N_3H_{12}PO_4 = (NH_4)_3PO_4$

7.79 $C_{12}H_{24}$

7.82 $B_{20}H_{16}$

7.84 $C_{12}H_{24}O_2$

7.87   (a) 11.8 g $NaNO_2$ in 387 g H_2O

7.88   (a) 12 g HCl solution, (c) 508 g HCl solution

7.90 2.40×10^2 g solution

7.92   2.25% m/m

7.94   (a) 1.72 g $Mg(NO_3)_2$ diluted to 50.0 mL, (b) 0.6863 g NH_3 diluted to 210.0 mL

7.95   (a) 8.006M $(NH_4)_2SO_4$, (d) 5.720×10^{-4} M HBr

7.96   (a) 1.42M C_2H_6O, (d) 0.316 M NH_4Cl

7.97   (a) 16M HNO_3

7.98   (a) 1.77 L

7.99   (a) 0.255 mol particles

7.101   (a) 3.3M; (b) 0.058M; (c) 2.34M; (d) 0.176M

7.103   308.6 mL

7.106   (a) 29.13 g Na_3PO_4

7.108 $Mg_2Si_3H_4O_{10}$

7.110 $C_7H_5O_3SN$

7.112   (a) 294 cm^3 IF_5, (b) 194 mol F, (c) 10.93 cm^3 IF_5

7.115   (a) 3.4×10^2 g 24 carat Au, (b) 1.0×10^{24} Au

7.116 1.3×10^{-14} g C

7.118   (a) 2.22% H, (b) 1.46 g C, 0.0874 g H, 0.729 g N. 1.66 g O

7.119   (a) 63.54 g/mol, (b) copper

7.121 2.732×10^{26} atoms

7.122   (a) C_5H_7N, (b) 1.2×10^{20} $C_{10}H_{14}N_2$

7.123   (a) 70.3%, (b) 501 mL, (c) 0.0896M

CHAPTER 8

8.37   (a) Sodium bromide, (d) barium phosphide, (f) lead sulfide, (g) silver bromide

8.40   (a) Dinitrogen oxide, (b) phosphorus trifluoride, (d) xenon tetrafluoride, (f) arsenic pentafluoride, (g) iodine trifluoride

8.41   (a) Diiodine tetroxide, (b) Potassium sulfide, (d) tetriodine nonoxide, (f) calcium iodide

8.46   A N atom has five valence electrons, which is very unstable. It can obtain a noble gas configuration by sharing three electrons with another N atom

8.48   The ionic bond in NaCl, as is found in all ionic compounds, has some degree of covalent character

8.51   Noble gases form relatively few compounds, most of which contain only bonds with highly electronegative atoms such as oxygen or a halogen

8.52   (b) Sn, (c) Fr, (d) Al

8.53   (a) P > As > Sb, (b) B > Be > Li

8.54   (a) Ar, (b) Ne, (d) Kr, (g) Ar, (h) Ne

8.55   (a) $1s^2 2s^2 2p^6 3s^2 3p^6 4s^2 3d^{10} 4p^6$, (b) $1s^2 2s^2 2p^6 3s^2 3p^6$, (e) $1s^2 2s^2 2p^6 3s^2 3p^6 4s^2 3d^{10} 4p^6 5s^2 4d^{10} 5p^6$, (g) $1s^2 2s^2 2p^6 3s^2 3p^6$

8.56   (a) Se^{2-}, (b) N^{3-}

8.57   (a)

$$K\cdot \ + \ :\overset{\cdot\cdot}{O}: \ + \ \cdot K \longrightarrow 2K^+ + [:\overset{\cdot\cdot}{\underset{\cdot\cdot}{O}}:]^{2-}.$$

(b)

$$:\overset{\cdot\cdot}{Br}\cdot \ + \ Mg \ + \ \cdot\overset{\cdot\cdot}{Br}: \longrightarrow Mg^{2+} + 2[:\overset{\cdot\cdot}{\underset{\cdot\cdot}{Br}}:]^-.$$

(c)

$$:\overset{\cdot\cdot}{O}\cdot + \cdot Al + \cdot\overset{\cdot\cdot}{O}: \ + \ \cdot Al + \overset{\cdot\cdot}{O}: \longrightarrow 2Al^{3+} + 3[:\overset{\cdot\cdot}{\underset{\cdot\cdot}{O}}:]^{2-}.$$

8.58   (a) $Na^+ \ [:\overset{\cdot\cdot}{\underset{\cdot\cdot}{I}}:]^-$

(b) $Mg^{2+} \ 2[:\overset{\cdot\cdot}{\underset{\cdot\cdot}{Br}}:]^-$

(d) $2Rb^+ \ [:\overset{\cdot\cdot}{\underset{\cdot\cdot}{S}}:]^{2-}$

(e) $3Ba^{2+} \ 2[:\overset{\cdot\cdot}{\underset{\cdot\cdot}{N}}:]^{3-}$

8.59   (a) Al_2O_3, (b) SrS, (c) $MgBr_2$, (f) Li_2Se

8.63   (a) 1s, 5p, (b) 5p, 4p, (d) 2p, 3p, (g) 2p, 1s

8.64   (a) Polar, (b) nonpolar, (d) polar

8.66   (a)

$$
\begin{array}{c}
:\overset{\cdot\cdot}{Br}: \\
| \\
:\overset{\cdot\cdot}{Br}{-}\underset{\,}{C}{-}\overset{\cdot\cdot}{Br}: \\
| \\
:\overset{\cdot\cdot}{Br}:
\end{array}
$$

(b) $:\overset{\cdot\cdot}{\underset{\cdot\cdot}{F}}{-}\overset{\cdot\cdot}{\underset{\cdot\cdot}{O}}{-}\overset{\cdot\cdot}{\underset{\cdot\cdot}{F}}:$

(d)

$$
\begin{array}{c}
:\overset{\cdot\cdot}{F}: \\
| \\
:\overset{\cdot\cdot}{\underset{\cdot\cdot}{F}}{-}P{-}\overset{\cdot\cdot}{\underset{\cdot\cdot}{F}}:
\end{array}
$$

(f)

$$
\begin{array}{c}
:\overset{\cdot\cdot}{Cl}{-}N{-\!-\!-}N{-}\overset{\cdot\cdot}{Cl}: \\
\ \ \ \ |\ \ \ \ \ \ \ | \\
:\overset{\cdot\cdot}{Cl}: \ :\overset{\cdot\cdot}{Cl}:
\end{array}
$$

(i) $H{-}\overset{\cdot\cdot}{\underset{\cdot\cdot}{O}}{-}\overset{\cdot\cdot}{\underset{\cdot\cdot}{O}}{-}H$

8.67   (a) $[:\overset{\cdot\cdot}{\underset{\cdot\cdot}{O}}{-}H]^-$

(f) $[:\overset{\cdot\cdot}{\underset{\cdot\cdot}{O}}{-}\overset{\cdot\cdot}{\underset{\cdot\cdot}{O}}:]^{2-}$

8.68   (a)

$$
\begin{array}{c}
\ \ \ H \ \ H \\
\ \ \ | \ \ \ | \\
H{-}C{-}C{-}H \\
\ \ \ | \ \ \ | \\
\ \ \ H \ \ H
\end{array}
$$

8.69   (a)   H—O—C—O—H (with O double-bonded above central C)

8.71   (b) PF_5, (e) SF_6

8.72   (a) $\left[H-O-\overset{:\overset{..}{O}:}{C}=O: \right]^{2-} \longleftrightarrow \left[H-O-\overset{\overset{..}{O}}{C}-\overset{..}{O}: \right]^{2-}$

8.74   (a) Pyramidal, (b) angular, (c) tetrahedral, (e) linear, (g) linear
8.75   (a) Angular, (c) trigonal planar, (e) tetrahedral
8.77   (a) 3, (b) 1
8.78   Carbon is a smaller atom that is more electronegative than the larger silicon atom; therefore, C
         will form a stronger, shorter bond with O
8.79   (a) . . . are *not* always . . .; (c) . . . are *smaller* for single . . .; (e) . . . sulfur *trioxide*; (g) . . . is *shared*
         by fluorine...

8.80   (a)   :P=P: :P—P: :P—P:
                | | ‖   ‖   (P₄ tetrahedron)
                :P=P: :P—P:

         (b) P_4 is nonpolar because each phosphorus atom has the *same* electronegativity *and* the lone
         pairs of electrons are symmetrically distributed

8.82   (a)
                H   O   H
                | ‖ |
            H—C—C—C—H
                | |
                H   H

         (b) The two terminal carbon atoms are tetrahedral. The central carbon is trigonal planar. (c) It is
         not possible to draw an equivalent structure for acetone with a different placement of the double
         bond so there can be no resonance

         (d)
                H   H   H
                | | |
            H—C—C—C=O:
                | |
                H   H

8.83   (a) $Na^+ [:\overset{..}{O}—H]^-$

8.85   (a) $\left[H-\overset{\overset{..}{O}}{C}-\overset{..}{O}: \right]^- \longleftrightarrow \left[H-C=\overset{:\overset{..}{O}:}{} \right]^-$

         (b) A pair of electrons is spread out over the carbon and two oxygen atoms.

         (c) $\left[H-C\overset{\displaystyle O}{\underset{\displaystyle O}{\diagup\hspace{-0.3em}\diagdown}} \right]^-$

8.86   (a) The C—C bond is shorter and stronger than the Si—Si bond. The bond order is one for both C—C and Si—Si. (c) N—N has a bond order of one and is longer and weaker than N=N, which has a bond order of two

8.88   (a)

$$H—\overset{\overset{\displaystyle H}{|}}{\underset{..}{N}}—\overset{..}{\underset{..}{O}}—H$$

8.90   (a) $:\overset{..}{S}=C=\overset{..}{N}^- \longleftrightarrow :\overset{..}{\underset{..}{S}}—C\equiv N:^- \longleftrightarrow :S\equiv C—\overset{..}{\underset{..}{N}}:^-$

(b) The sulfur-carbon and carbon-nitrogen bonds are best described as double bonds. However, since nitrogen is more electronegative than sulfur, the second structure could contribute significantly, making the sulfur-carbon bond closer to a single bond and the carbon-nitrogen closer to a triple bond

8.92 $H—\overset{\overset{..}{\underset{..}{I}}:\overset{..}{\underset{..}{I}}:}{\underset{}{C}}=\overset{}{\underset{}{C}}—H$, $:\overset{..}{\underset{..}{I}}—\overset{\overset{..}{\underset{..}{I}}:\overset{H}{}}{\underset{}{C}}=\overset{}{\underset{}{C}}—H$, $H—\overset{\overset{..}{\underset{..}{I}}:\overset{H}{}}{\underset{}{C}}=\overset{}{\underset{}{C}}—\overset{..}{\underset{..}{I}}:$

CHAPTER NINE

9.31   (a) F 0, (c) Mg +2, S –2, (e) N +5, O –2, (g) Al +3, S –2
9.32   (a) +6, (d) +4, (g) +3
9.34   (a) K +1, Cr +6, O –2; (c) Na +1, U +6, O –2; (e) Ca +2, H +1, S –2; (g) K +1, V +5, O –2; (i) Cu +2, C +2, N –3
9.36   (a) Carbon dioxide, (b) dinitrogen monoxide, (c) carbon tetrachloride, (d) phosphorus tribromide
9.37   (a) Tin(II) bromide, (b) cobalt(III) nitride, (c) lead(II) sulfide, (d) copper(I) phosphide, (e) mercury(II) oxide
9.38   (a) $FeBr_3$, (e) MgO, (h) Sn_3S_2, (j) Rb_3P
9.39   (a) Tl_2O_3, (b) UO_2, (c) Au_2O, (d) Mo_2O_5, (e) Mn_2O_7
9.40   Ammonium acetate, phosphate, permanganate, cyanide, carbonate, chromate, hydroxide, sulfide; magnesium acetate, phosphate, permanganate, cyanide, carbonate, chromate, hydroxide, sulfide; aluminum acetate, phosphate, permanganate, cyanide, carbonate, chromate, hydroxide, sulfide
9.41 $Ca(OH)_2$, $Ca(C_2H_3O_2)_2$, $CaSO_4$, $Ca(ClO_3)_2$, $CaSeO_4$, Ca_3N_2; $Al(OH)_3$, $Al(C_2H_3O_2)_3$, $Al_2(SO_4)_3$, $Al(ClO_3)_3$, $Al_2(SeO_4)_3$, AlN; $Pb(OH)_4$, $Pb(C_2H_3O_2)_4$, $Pb(SO_4)_2$, $Pb(ClO_3)_4$, $Pb(SeO_4)_2$, Pb_3N_4
9.43   (a) $(NH_4)_2SeO_4$, (b) $(NH_4)_2SO_3$, (d) NH_4IO_4, (f) NH_4HCO_3, (h) NH_4ClO
9.44   (a) $LiC_2H_3O_2$, (b) $Zn(C_2H_3O_2)_2$, (e) $Ga(C_2H_3O_2)_3$
9.45   (a) Hydrobromic acid, (b) hydroiodic acid
9.46   (a) Boric acid, (b) hypochlorous acid, (c) iodic acid, (d) arsenic acid, (e) carbonic acid, (f) perbromic acid
9.48   (a) Periodic acid, (b) acetic acid, (e) hydrocyanic acid
9.50   (a) Hydrogensulfite, sulfurous acid; (b) hydrogenphosphite, phosphorous acid
9.51   (a) Na +1, H +1, F –1; (b) Na +1, S +5, O –2, H +1; (c) Na +1, B +3, F –1
9.55   (a) Chromium(III) phosphate hexahydrate, (b) Gallium(III) oxide monohydrate, (c) Indium(III) perchlorate octahydrate
9.56   (a) $Na_3BO_3 \cdot 4H_2O$, (d) $Hg(BrO_3)_2 \cdot 2H_2O$
9.57   (1) Ammonium sulfide, (2) antimony(III) iodide, (3) arsenic acid, (4) arsenic(III) oxide, (5) barium chromate, (6) beryllium selenite, (7) bismuth(IV) chloride, (8) boron nitride, (9) bromine dioxide, (10) Cadmium(II) bromate, (11) calcium hypochlorite, (12) disulfur decafluoride, (13) cerium(III) hydroxide, (14) cesium hydrogencarbonate, (15) dichlorine heptoxide, (16) chromium(III) sulfite, (17) cobalt(III) fluoride, (18) copper(II) selenate, (19) gallium(III) chloride, (20) germanium(IV) sulfide, (21) hydrogen cyanide, (22) hydrocyanic acid, (23) iodic acid, (24) iodine pentafluoride,

(25) iridium(III) sulfide

9.58 (1) $TiCl_3$, (2) WBr_6, (3) $ZnCrO_3$, (4) ZrI_4, (5) $(NH_4)_2SO_3$, (6) NaOH, (7) $MgSO_4$, (8) $Ba(BrO)_2$, (9) Cs_2HPO_4, (10) $BiBr_3$, (11) CuClO, (12) $Al(NO_3)_3$, (13) Fe_3As_2, (14) $Pb(ClO_3)_4$, (15) Li_2HPO_3, (16) MnO, (17) HgTe, (18) MoI_4, (19) $Ni(HCO_3)_3$, (20) N_2O_4, (21) PdSi, (22) $OsSO_4$, (23) $LiClO_3$, (24) H_3PO_2, (25) P_4S_7

9.60 (a) $Mg_3(PO_3)_2 \cdot 5H_2O$, (b) magnesium phosphate pentahydrate

9.62 27.7% W, 72.3% Br

9.65 The functional group or lack thereof

9.66 (a) 7, (b) 4, (c) 10, (d) 2, (e) 8

9.67 (a)

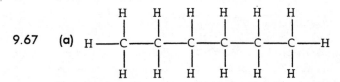

(c)

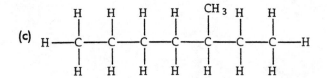

9.68 (a) Hexane, (c) octane

9.69 (a) 2,2,4-Trimethylpentane, (c) 3-ethyloctane, (e) 3,5-dimethyl-5-ethyldecane

9.70 (a) $CH_3CH_2CH(CH_3)CH_2CH_2CH_2CH_3$, (c) $CH_3CH_2CH(CH_3CH_2)CH(CH_3) CH_2CH_2CH_2CH_2CH_2CH_3$ (e) $CH_3C(CH_3)_2C(CH_3)_2CH_2CH_2CH_3$

9.73 (a) cyclooctane, (b) methylcycloheptane

9.74 $2n$

9.75 (a) $CH_3CH_2CH=CH_2$, (d) $CH_2=CHCH=CH_2$, $CH_3CH=C=CH_2$

9.76 (a) 12, (b) 18, (c) 12, (d) 6

9.77 1-pentene, (cis and trans)-2-pentene, 2-methyl-1-butene, 2-methyl-2-butene, 3-methyl-1-butene, cyclopentane, methylcyclobutane, 1,1-dimethylcyclpropane, 1,2-dimethylcyclopropane, ethylcyclopropane

9.78 (a) C_nH_{2n-2}; (b) C_nH_{2n-2}

9.79 1,2-Diethylbenzene, 1,3-diethylbenzene, 1,4-diethylbenzene

9.80 (b) 1,2,3-trimethylbenzene, 1,2,4-trimethylbenzene, 1,3,5-trimethylbenzene

9.82 (a) —CHO, (b) —COOH, (c) —NH_2

9.83 (a) Alcohol, ester, halide, acid; (b) Halide, amine, aldehyde, ether; (c) Ether, ketone, amide, amine, double bond

9.84 (a) $CH_3CH_2CH_2CH_2OH$; (b) CH_3CH_2CHO; (c) $CH_3CH_2CH_2COOH$

CHAPTER 10

10.21 (a) Two moles of gaseous sulfur trioxide when heated produce two moles of gaseous sulfur dioxide and one mole of gaseous oxygen. (b) One mole of liquid mercury and one mole of chlorine gas produce one mole of mercury(II) chloride

10.22 (a) 1, 5, 2; (c) 1, 1, 2; (d) 1, 2, 1, 2; (f) 1, 1, 1; (g) 1, 2, 2, 3

10.23 (a) 2, 13, 8, 10 or 1, 13/2, 4, 5; (b) 1, 3, 1, 3; (c) 2, 2, 4, 1; (d) 3, 2, 1, 3, 3; (e) 2, 5, 2, 4

10.24 (a) 2, 15, 3, 3, 6; (b) 3, 4, 3, 1; (c) 2, 2, 1, 1, 1, 4; (d) 3, 8, 9, 4; (e) 1, 1, 1, 2; (f) 2, 15, 14, 6; (k) 1, 6, 6, 2, 1, 3, 6

10.25 (a) $NaBr(aq) + AgNO_3(aq) \rightarrow NaNO_3(aq) + AgBr(s)$.
(b) $Al(OH)_3(aq) + 3HNO_3(aq) \rightarrow Al(NO_3)_3(aq) + 3H_2O$
(c) $Cl_2(g) + 2RbI(aq) \rightarrow 2RbCl(aq) + I_2(s)$
(d) $2Fe(C_2H_3O_2)_3(aq) + 3Na_2S(aq) \rightarrow 6NaC_2H_3O_2(aq) + Fe_2S_3(s)$

(e) $SiF_4(g) + 2H_2O \rightarrow SiO_2(s) + 4HF(aq)$

(f) $MnO_2(s) + 4HCl(aq) \rightarrow MnCl_2 + Cl_2(g) + 2H_2O$

(g) $N_2O_4(g) \rightarrow 2NO_2(g)$

(h) $Ca_3P_2 + 6H_2O \rightarrow 3Ca(OH)_2 + 2PH_3(g)$

(i) $2AgNO_3(s) \rightarrow 2Ag(s) + 2NO_2(g) + O_2(g)$

(j) $2Al + 3CuSO_4 \rightarrow 3Cu + Al_2(SO_4)_3$

10.26   (a) Decomposition: (g), (i); single replacement: (c), (j); metathesis: (a), (b), (d), (e), (h); none of these: (f), (b) oxidation-reduction (p), (r), (s)

10.28   (a) C, O_2; (b) S, O_2; (e) P_4, H_2

10.29   (a) K_2O, (b) BaO

10.30   (a) CO_2, (b) SO_2, (d) SO_3

10.31   (a) $MgCO_3$, (b) $KClO_3$, (c) $KHCO_3$, (d) $Ba(NO_2)_2 \cdot H_2O$, (f) $NaNO_3$

10.33

	Oxidation	**Reduction**
(a)	Li	HCl
(b)	Si	F_2
(c)	H_2	Cl_2
(d)	ZnS	O_2

10.34   (a) $Na + H_2O \rightarrow NaOH + \frac{1}{2}H_2$; (b) $Ca + 2HCl \rightarrow CaCl_2 + H_2$; (d) $Br_2 + 2RbI \rightarrow 2RbBr + I_2$

10.37   Soluble: (a), (e); insoluble: (b), (c), (d), (f)

10.38   (a) $NiCl_2(aq) + Ca(OH)_2(aq) \rightarrow CaCl_2(aq) + Ni(OH)_2(s)$

(b) $Hg(C_2H_3O_2)_2(aq) + 2K_2CO_3(aq) \rightarrow 2KC_2H_3O_2(aq) + HgCO_3(s)$

(c) $H_3PO_4(aq) + 3AgNO_3(aq) \rightarrow Ag_3PO_4(s) + 3H_2O(l)$

(d) $3H_2SO_3(aq) + 2Al(OH)_3(aq) \rightarrow Al_2(SO_3)_3(s) + 6H_2O(l)$

10.39   (a) $2AgNO_3(aq) + CuCl_2(aq) \rightarrow 2AgCl(s) + Cu(NO_3)_2(aq)$

(b) $(NH_4)_2S(aq) + Hg(C_2H_3O_2)_2(aq) \rightarrow HgS(s) + 2NH_4C_2H_3O_2(aq)$

(c) $2KOH(aq) + H_2SO_4(aq) \rightarrow K_2SO_4(aq) + 2H_2O(l)$

(d) $2HNO_3(aq) + BaCO_3(s) \rightarrow Ba(NO_3)_2(aq) + CO_2(g) + H_2O(l)$

(e) $3NaHCO_3(s) + H_3PO_4(aq) \rightarrow Na_3PO_4(aq) + CO_2(g) + 3H_2O(l)$

(f) $H_2SO_4(aq) + Cu(OH)_2(s) \rightarrow CuSO_4(aq) + 2H_2O(l)$

(g) $HBr(aq) + Pb(NO_3)_2(aq) \rightarrow PbBr_2(s) + HNO_3(aq)$

(h) $Ca(NO_3)_2(aq) + K_2SO_4(aq) \rightarrow CaSO_4(s) + 2KNO_3(aq)$

(i) $NH_4NO_3(aq) + Zn_3(PO_4)_2(s) \rightarrow NR$

(j) $Na_2CO_3(s) + HClO_4(aq) \rightarrow NaClO_4(aq) + CO_2(l) + H_2O(l)$

(k) $SnS(s) + 2HBrO(aq) \rightarrow Sn(BrO)_2(aq) + H_2S(g)$

10.41   (a) −47.7 kJ, (b) 36°C

10.43   (a) $C_6H_6 + 15/2 O_2 \rightarrow 6CO_2 + 3H_2O$, (c) −1910 kJ

10.44   (a) Endothermic, (c) exothermic

10.47   (a) ... produce *basic* solutions ...; (b) ... *Most inorganic* ...; (c) ... *can be used* ...; (d) ... insoluble except those of alkali metals and ammonium; (e) ... into liquid water *does not react.*

10.48   (a) $N_2 + 3H_2 \rightarrow 2NH_3$, (b) $4NH_3 + 5O_2 \rightarrow 4NO + 6H_2O$

10.49   (1) $CaCO_3 \rightarrow CaO + CO_2$

(2) $CO_2 + NH_3 + H_2O + NaCl \rightarrow NaHCO_3 + NH_4Cl$

(3) $2NaHCO_3 \rightarrow Na_2CO_3 + CO_2 + H_2O$

(4) $CaO + 3C \rightarrow CaC_2 + CO$

10.50   (a) 1, 5, 1, 3, 5; (c) 2, 7, 3, 2, 7, 3

CHAPTER 11

11.20

	$N_2(g)$	+	**$O_2(g)$**	→	**$2NO(g)$**
Molecules	5 molecules		5 molecules		10 molecules
Molecules	6.02×10^{23}		6.02×10^{23}		1.20×10^{24}
Moles	5.0 mol		5.0 mol		10. mol
Mass, g	14.0 g		16.0 g		30.0 g
Mass g	9.10 g		10.4 g		19.5 g

11.22 (a) 1 mol CaF_2, (b) 78 g CaF_2, (c) 40 g Ca + 38 g F_2 = 78 g CaF_2

11.24 (a) 5.0 mol $AlCl_3$, (b) 5.3 mol $AlCl_3$

11.25 $\dfrac{1\ mol\ C_5H_{12}}{5\ mol\ CO_2}$, $\dfrac{1\ mol\ C_5H_{12}}{6\ mol\ H_2O}$, $\dfrac{8\ mol\ O_2}{5\ mol\ CO_2}$, $\dfrac{5\ mol\ O_2}{6\ mol\ H_2O}$

11.27 (a) 0.22 mol Fe_2O_3, 0.88 mol SO_2; (b) 14.6 mol Fe_2O_3, 58.2 mol SO_2; (c) 1.491 mol Fe_2O_3, 5.964 mol SO_2; (d) 0.00362 mol Fe_2O3, 0.0145 mol SO_2; (e) 6.27×10^{-4} mol Fe_2O_3, 2.51×10^{-3} mol SO_2

11.28 (a) 820 g O_2; (b) 0.0190 mol O_2; (c) 50.6 mol KCl, 75.9 mol O_2; (d) 1.01 g $KClO_3$

11.30 (a) 1.76×10^3 g Cu, (d) 3.02×10^8 g Cu

11.31 (a) 0.3548 g Ag, (c) 0.00579 g Ag

11.33 (a) 1.89 g CH_4, (b) 1.721×10^4 g Cl_2, (c) 4.42×10^{-4} g CH_4, (d) 8.343×10^4 g CH_4, 1.475×10^6 g Cl_2

11.35 (a) 278.5 g XeF_4; (b) 0.382 g XeF_4; (c) 1.324×10^{-3} g H_2O; (d) 1.25×10^{-3} g $XeOF_4$; 1.47×10^{-3} g Xe, 8.96×10^{-4} g HF, 2.68×10^{-4} g O_2

11.37 (a) $2KNO_3 \rightarrow 2KNO_2 + O_2$;
(b) $\dfrac{2\ mol\ KNO_3}{2\ mol\ KNO_2}$, $\dfrac{2\ mol\ KNO_3}{1\ mol\ O_2}$, $\dfrac{2\ mol\ KNO_2}{1\ mol\ O_2}$
(c) 489.1 g KNO_2, (d) 753.1 g O_2

11.39 $Sb_2S_3 + 3Fe \rightarrow 2Sb + 3FeS$
(b) 28.9 g Fe, (c) 6.79×10^4 g Sb, (d) 7.110 g Sb_2S_3, 3.507 g Fe

11.40 (a) $2H_2(g) + O_2(g) \rightarrow 2H_2O(g) + 136$ kcal; (b) 2.89 g H_2, 22.9 g O_2; (c) 834 kJ, (d) 52.1 kJ

11.42 (a) 50.3 kJ, (b) 0.0129 g C_2H_4, (c) 87.5 kJ, (d) 0.229 g C_2H_4

11.44 (a) $CaCO_3 + 178$ kJ $\rightarrow CaO + CO_2$
(b) $CaCO_3 + 42.5$ kcal $\rightarrow CaO + CO_2$

11.45 22.4 kJ

11.46 –30 kJ/mol

11.47 (a) 127 g HI, (b) 1033 g HI, (c) 2.3 g I_2

11.49 (a) 1179 g Na_2SO_4, (b) 31.7 g Na_2SO_4, (c) 7.24×10^5 g HCl, (d) 5.8×10^2 g NaCl

11.51 (a) 74.5 g NaCN, (b) 213 g N_2

11.52 (a) 18.7 g C_6H_5Cl, (b) 55.6%, (c) 2.66 g C_6H_5Cl, (d) 5.77 g C_6H_6

11.54 (a) 3.44 g $CaCN_2$, (b) 3.94×10^4 g $CaCN_2$

11.55 (a) 0.464 g $FeCO_3$, (b) 0.721 g $FeCO_3$

11.56 (a) 0.176 g CO_2

11.57 (a) 6.10 mL, (b) 12.2 mL

11.58 (a) 0.988 g $NaNO_3$, (b) 0.912 g $NaNO_3$

11.60 238 mL

11.63 (a) 403 g $Ca(OH)_2$, (b) 2.81×10^4 g $Ca(OH)_2$

11.65 31.2 g I_2, 25.7 g K_2SO_4, 7.43 g $MnSO_4$

11.67 (a) 162 g SCl_2, 87.8 g NaF; (b) 58.6 g SF_4

11.69 68.9% $CaCO_3$, 31.1% $CaSO_4$

11.70 Co_2O_3

11.72 –85 kJ/mol

11.73 (b) 6.78 g $Na_2C_2O_4$, (c) 478 g $Na_2C_2O_4$

Chapter 12

12.29	(a) 799 torr, (b) 699 torr
12.31	(a) 4.04×10^6 Pa, (b) 3.03×10^4 torr
12.32	(a) 2244 torr
12.33	(a) 784 torr, (c) 1.05×10^5 Pa
12.34	(c) 1237 kPa
12.36	(a) 2.12×10^3 b/ft^2, (b) 1.50×10^3 torr
12.38	(a) 0.362 L, (e) 0.983 L
12.41	2.18×10^4 cm^3
12.44	(a) 1.204 atm, (b) 3.536 atm
12.48	(a) 325 K, (b) 275 K, (c) 27 L, (d) 125 K
12.50	(a) 4.94 L, (b) 19.8 L, (c) 18.9 L, (d) 6.90 L
12.52	(a) 493 K
12.54	(a) V decreases, (c) V increases
12.55	(a) 37.0 L, (c) 2.36 L
12.56	(a) 0.150 L, (c) 271 mL
12.57	(a) 4.02 atm, (c) 838 torr
12.59	(a) 0.0166 mol, (d) 1.14×10^{-7} mol
12.60	(a) 2.55 L, (e) 1.64×10^5 L
12.61	(a) 0.0597 g N_2O, (c) 1.06×10^3 g C_2H_2
12.62	(b) 2.60×10^3 L
12.64	(a) 3.16 g/L, (b) 1.96 g/L
12.65	(a) $P = nRT/V$, (b) $n = PV/(RT)$
12.66	(a) 82.1 (mL · atm)/(mol · K), (c) 83.2 (kPa · dL)/(mol · K)
12.67	(a) 79.6 L
12.68	(b) 0.00498 mol
12.69	(c) 0.0244 atm
12.70	(a) 2.46 g N_2
12.72	1.98 g/L
12.74	37.3 g/mol

APPENDIX A

1.	(a) 8, (b) 42, (c) –188, (d) 10.44
2.	(a) 9.081, (b) 0.50, (c) $[(n + 1)/m(a + b)] - 2$, (d) $b - [(a + 2)(n + 1)]$
3.	(a) 100, (b) 992, (c) 100, (d) 96
4.	(a) 102.4, (b) 83.72, (c) –0.50, (d) 36, (e) 257
5.	(a) $(2 + am)/an$, (b) $[(a + b)/(n + 10)] - m$, (c) $(3a + b - n)(5/4)$, (d) $8b/a$
6.	(a) –3.08, (b) 0.444, (c) 102.5, (d) 1.92
7.	(a) 4.9139×10^{-4}, (b) 1.2×10^{11}, (c) 1.3511×10^{-9}, (d) 1.05×10^{-20}
8.	(a) 0.00311, (b) 0.0290, (c) 777,420,000, (d) 8,001,000,000,000
9.	(a) 4.36×10^2, (b) 1.215×10^7, (c) 1.001×10^{-12}, (d) 9.79×10^{-2}, (e) 6.361×10^{-4}
10.	(a) 1.186×10^6, (b) 9.53×10^{-3}, (c) 1.8156×10^9, (d) 2.2054×10^{35}, (e) 3.9434×10^{20}
11.	(a) -2.79×10^4, (b) 9.199×10^{-13}, (c) -5.6645×10^{47}, (d) 6.1135×10^{-34}
12.	(a) 4.27×10^{11}, (b) 3.4763×10^{151}, (c) 4.4182×10^3
13.	(a) 4.4753×10^6, (b) 5.4×10^{113}, (c) 4.0164×10^{-8}
14.	(a) 9.0971×10^{-3}, (b) 0.10007
15.	(e) 3
16.	(a) 0.56; (b) 37°C, 24°C, –32°C, 57°C

Glossary

Absolute zero the lowest possible temperature, 0 K or –273.15°C

Accuracy how close a measured value is to the actual value

Acid a substance that donates H^+ to water (the Arrhenius definition); a proton donor (the Brønsted-Lowry definition)

Acid anhydride a substance that reacts with water to produce an acidic solution, a nonmetal oxide

Acid-base indicator a dye that changes color depending on the pH of a solution

Actinide series the 14 elements that come after actinium, Ac, on the periodic table; elements with atomic numbers 90-103

Activated complex a high-energy intermediate species produced in chemical reactions as a result of the collision of the reactant molecules

Activation energy the minimum energy needed to produce the activated complex at the transition state; the minimum energy required for a reaction to occur

Actual yield the mass of product obtained in a chemical reaction

Aerobic able to take place in the presence of oxygen gas, O_2

Alcohol an organic compound that has an —OH group bonded to a hydrocarbon group

Aldehyde an organic compound that has a —CHO, a carbonyl group and H atom, bonded to a hydrocarbon chain or ring

Alkali metals group IA elements: Li, Na, K, Rb, Cs, and Fr

Alkaline earth metals group (2) IIA elements: Be, Mg, Ca, Sr, Ba, and Ra

Alkane a hydrocarbon in which all C—C bonds are single bonds; a saturated hydrocarbon

Alkene an unsaturated hydrocarbon that has at least one C—C double bond

Alkyl group a substituent group that results when one H atom is removed from a nonaromatic hydrocarbon, for example, methyl, CH_3— ; ethyl, C_2H_5—; etc.

Alkyne an unsaturated hydrocarbon that has at least one C—C triple bond

Allotropes different forms of the same element, e.g. graphite and diamond, two distinct forms of carbon

Alloy a solution of metals

Alpha particle a high-energy helium nucleus, He^{2+}, emitted by some heavy nuclides when undergoing radioactive decay

Amalgam the solution that results when a metal solute is dissolved in liquid mercury

Amide an organic compound with a N atom bonded to a carbonyl C atom, $—CONH_2$, —CONHR, or—$CONR_2$.

Amine an organic compound with one or more alkyl groups, R, bonded to an N atom; RNH_2, R_2NH, or R_3N

Amino acid an organic compound that contains both an amino group and a carboxylic acid group; amino acids combine to produce proteins

Amorphous solid a solid whose structure lacks the long-range order of crystalline solids

Ampere (A) a unit of electric current; the amount of coulombs of charge per second

Amphiprotic term used to describe a substance that can both donate and accept protons

Amphoteric term used to describe a substance that can react with either H^+ or OH^-, thus behaving as either an acid or base, depending on the conditions

Anaerobic able to take place without the presence of oxygen, O_2; the opposite of aerobic

Anion a negative ion; one with extra electrons

Anode the electrode where oxidation occurs in electrochemical cells

Antimatter a form of matter that has properties opposite to "regular" matter; if antimatter contacts regular matter, the two annihilate each other and are transformed totally into energy

Aqueous solution a solution in which water is the solvent

Aromatic hydrocarbon an organic compound that contains a benzene ring or has benzenelike properties

Atmosphere (atm) a unit of pressure equivalent to 101 kPa; the amount of pressure necessary to support a column of mercury 760 mmHg high

Atom a tiny, neutral particle composed of protons, neutrons, and electrons that is the smallest unit that retains the chemical properties of an element

Atomic mass (atomic weight) the average mass of the naturally occurring isotopes of an element compared with ^{12}C

Atomic mass unit (see unified atomic mass unit)

Atomic number the number of protons in the nucleus of an atom; the positive charge on the nucleus of an atom

Atomic size a measure of the relative size of an atom; the average distance from the nucleus to the valence electron, normally measured as half the distance between two bonded nuclei

Atomic weight (see atomic mass)

Avogadro's number the number of particles in 1 mol, 6.022×10^{23}

Balance a laboratory instrument used to measure the mass of objects

Barometer a device used to measure atmospheric pressure

Base a substance that increases the OH^- concentration when dissolved in water (Arrhenius definition); a proton acceptor (Brønsted-Lowry definition)

Base units one of the seven fundamental SI units of measurement from which all other SI units are derived

Beta particle a high-energy electron emitted by a nucleus undergoing one type of radioactive decay

Binary acid an acid with a H atom bonded to a nonmetal, HX

Binary compound a compound composed of two different elements

Boiling point the temperature at which the vapor pressure of a liquid equals the applied pressure; when the boiling point is reached, bubbles of the liquid's vapor form throughout the liquid

Boiling-point elevation the increase in boiling temperature of a solvent after a nonvolatile solute is added

Bond the primary force of attraction that holds atoms together in molecules and lattice structures

Bonding electrons electrons attracted by two nuclei; shared electrons

Bond length the average distance between the nuclei of two bonded atoms

Calorie (cal) a unit of thermal (heat) energy; 1 cal = 4.184 J

Calorimeter a laboratory instrument used to measure heat transfers in chemical and physical changes

Carbohydrate a class of biologically important compounds that includes sugars and starches

Carbonyl group a functional group in organic chemistry that consists of a C atom doubly bonded to an O atom, C=O; aldehydes and ketones both have carbonyl groups with no other functional groups in their structures

Carboxyl group the functional group in organic acids; it consists of a C atom with a doubly bonded O atom, C=O, and an —OH group attached, —COOH

Catalyst a substance that increases the rate of a chemical reaction by lowering its activation energy; generally, a catalyst is fully recovered after the reaction

Cathode the electrode where reduction occurs in electrochemical cells

Cation an ion with a positive charge; one that forms when an atom or group of atoms loses electrons

Celsius temperature scale a temperature scale that is displaced 273.15 degrees from the Kelvin temperature scale; water's boiling point is 100°C (373 K), and its freezing point is 0°C (273 K)

Centi a prefix attached to units that decrease their magnitude by 1/100 ×

Chalcogen a name applied to group 16 (VIA) elements: O, S, Se, Te, and Po

Chemical bond the force of attraction between atoms in compounds

Chemical change a change in which the composition of a substance is altered; also called a chemical reaction

Chemical equation an expression of symbols, formulas, and coefficients that describes mass, volume, and mole relationships in specific chemical reactions; in chemical equations the reactants are written to the left of an arrow, and the products are written to the right of the arrow

Chemical equilibrium a closed chemical system in which the forward and reverse reaction rates are equal

Chemical family a group of chemical elements with similar properties listed in a vertical column on the periodic table

Chemical formula a combination of chemical symbols with appropriate subscripts that indicate the ratio of atoms in molecules and formula units

Chemical group a vertical column of elements in the periodic table; elements in a chemical group have similar outer electronic configurations

Chemical kinetics the study of the rates and mechanisms of chemical reactions

Chemical nomenclature a system of rules and guidelines for writing unique names for each element and compound

Chemical property a property that describes a chemical change that a substance undergoes

Chemical symbol either one or two letters used to represent an element; normally, these letters are the beginning letters of the modern or classical name of the element

Chemistry the study of matter and its interactions

Coefficient a number or algebraic quantity preceding a variable, unknown quantity, or chemical formula

Colligative property a property of a solution that depends on the number of dissolved solute particles, rather than their type, e.g., freezing-point depression, boiling-point elevation, and vapor pressure lowering

Collision theory a theory that attempts to explain the rates of chemical reactions in terms of the number of effective collisions of reactants that take place in a specified time interval

Combination reaction a reaction in which two or more reactants are chemically combined to produce a single product

Composition the amount and type of components in a sample of matter

Compound a pure substance composed of two or more different elements that have been combined chemically

Concentrated the term applied to describe solutions in which a large quantity of solute is dissolved in a solvent

Condensation the process in which a vapor changes to a liquid

Conversion factor a fraction that expresses the equality of one set of units to the value of another set of units, for example, 1 cal/4.184 J

Coordinate covalent bond a covalent bond that results when one atom contributes both electrons in the formation of the bond

Coulomb (C) a unit of electric charge; the amount of charge that passes in an electric circuit when one ampere flows for one second

Covalent bond a chemical bond that results when electrons are shared between two nuclei; the overlap of atomic orbitals from two different atoms

Critical mass the minimum mass of a fissionable element, like U, that is necessary to sustain a nuclear fission reaction

Cryogenics the branch of physics that deals with the study of very low temperatures and their effects

Crystalline solid a solid with atoms, ions, and molecules arranged in an orderly, regular, three-dimensional pattern

Data the information collected when conducting an experiment

Decomposition reaction a reaction in which a single reactant is broken down to two or more products

Deliquescence the property of various solids to absorb moisture from the air, and then dissolve in this added water

Density the mass to volume ratio of a substance

Derived units SI units obtained by combining two or more of the seven base units

Diatomic molecule a molecule that contains two atoms, for example, Br_2, O_2, and HF.

Dilute the term used to describe solutions with a small quantity of solute per amount of solvent; the opposite of concentrated

Dipole (electric) case in which a charge separation is found in a molecule; the positive center of charge does not correspond with the negative center

Dipole-dipole interactions attractive intermolecular forces that exist among polar covalent substances

Dispersion force the attractive intermolecular force existing in all molecules as a result of momentary induced dipoles; this force is most important in molecules that do not have other types of intermolecular forces

Dissociation the separation of a larger chemical species into smaller ones, generally the separation of ions in salts entering solution

Distillation a chemical separation procedure in which one component is selectively vaporized and condensed to remove it from other substances

Double bond a covalent bond in which four electrons are shared between two nuclei

Dynamic equilibrium an equilibrium that results when the rates of two opposing processes are equal

Effective collision a collision between two reactant particles that results in the formation of the products; the colliding particles must possess the proper amount of energy and be properly oriented

Efflorescence the loss of water by hydrated salts

Electrolyte a substance that exists as ions when dissolved in solution

Electrolytic cell a container in which substances are decomposed by passing a direct electric current through them

Electron the low-mass, negatively charged particle found in atoms outside the nucleus; it has a mass of 0.000549 u

Electronegativity the property of atoms to attract electrons in chemical bonds

Electronic configuration the arrangement and population of electrons in specific energy levels (shells), sublevels (subshells), and orbitals in atoms

Electron shells (energy levels) regions of space about the nucleus where electrons reside; they are subdivided into smaller regions called sublevels and orbitals

Electron spin the property of electrons to appear as if they are spinning on an axis

Element a pure substance that cannot be decomposed by chemical means

Empirical formula a formula that expresses the simplest ratio of atoms in a compound; also known as the simplest formula

Endothermic a term used to describe a chemical process in which heat flows from the surroundings to the observed system; applied to reactions in which heat is absorbed

End point the point at which the indicator changes color during a titration, indicating that the titration has been completed

Energy the ability to do work or produce a change

Enthalpy a quantity that is used to predict the heat flow in chemical reactions, the difference in enthalpy of products and reactants is equal to the amount of heat liberated or absorbed

Enzyme a high-molecular-mass protein structure

within living systems that catalyzes chemical reactions (see protein)

Equilibrium (see chemical equilibrium)

Equivalence point the point in an acid-base titration at which the number of moles of H^+ equals the number of moles of OH^-; the point in a redox titration in which the number of electrons lost by the reducing agent equals those gained by the oxidizing agent

Equivalent mass for acids and bases, the mass of a substance that gives up or takes in 1 mol of H^+ or electrons

Ester a class of organic compounds that results when an organic acid combines with an alcohol; esters have the general formula RCOOR'

Ether a class of organic compounds with two hydrocarbon groups bonded to an O atom, R—O—R'

Evaporation the process whereby surface molecules of liquids break free of the intermolecular forces that hold them in the liquid and enter the vapor phase

Exothermic term used to describe a chemical process in which heat flows from a system to the surroundings; applied to reactions in which heat is liberated

Faraday (*F*) the quantity of charge possessed by one mole of electrons, 96,485 C

Fission (see nuclear fission)

Fluorescence the property of a substance to release visible light after being excited by other energy types

Force a push or a pull

Formula an expression used to represent the type and number of atoms in a molecule or ion

Formula mass the sum of the atomic masses of all atoms in a particular formula unit

Freezing point the temperature at which a liquid changes states and becomes a solid

Freezing-point depression the decrease in the freezing point of a solvent after the addition of a solute

Functional group a group of atoms that gives an organic molecule its characteristic chemical and physical properties, e.g., carbonyl group, carboxyl group, or alcohol group

Fusion (see nuclear fusion)

Galvanic cell an electrochemical cell that produces an electric current from spontaneous redox reactions, also called a voltaic cell or battery

Gamma ray a high-energy radiation form released by unstable nuclei during radioactive decay

Gas constant (R) the numerical constant that relates volume, pressure, temperature, and moles in the ideal gas equation, $PV = nRT$; the numerical value is 0.082056 (L·atm)/(mol·K)

Group a vertical column in the periodic table denoted by either a number from 1 to 18 or a roman numeral followed by the letter A or B.; sometimes chemical groups are called families

Half-life the amount of time for one-half of the reactants in a chemical reaction to change to products or for one-half of the radioactive nuclei to decay to a new nuclide

Half-reaction a pseudoreaction that represents either the oxidation or reduction part of a redox reaction; half-equations are written to represent half-reactions; for example, $Cu^{2+} + 2e^- \rightarrow Cu$

Halide ion the negative ion produced when a halogen atom takes in an electron; for example, F^-, Cl^-, Br^-, or I^-

Halogen an element that belongs to group 17 (VIIA) in the periodic table: F, Cl, Br, I, and At

Heat a form of kinetic energy that, when transferred to an object not undergoing a state change, increases its temperature

Heat capacity the amount of heat required to increase the temperature of a fixed amount of substance (usually one mole or one gram) by one Kelvin

Heat (Enthalpy) of fusion the amount of heat needed to change a fixed amount of solid to liquid at a constant temperature

Heat (Enthalpy) of vaporization the amount of heat required to change a fixed amount of liquid to vapor at a constant temperature

Heterogeneous composed of two or more distinct: components; applied to types of matter with: more than one observable phase

Homogeneous mixture a mixture of pure substances that has the same composition throughout; a solution

Homologous series a group of similar compounds in which one member differs from the one preceding and the one following by a fixed amount; e.g., CH_2

Hydrate a chemical species, generally a salt, that has bonded water molecules, for example, $CuSO_4 \cdot 5H_2O$

Hydration addition of water to another substance

Hydration energy the energy released when solute particles are surrounded by water molecules in the solution process

Hydride an ionic or covalent binary compound of hydrogen; examples of ionic hydrides are LiH and CaH_2, and examples of covalent hydrides are NH_3 and SiH_4

Hydrocarbon an organic compound composed only of C and H atoms; includes the alkanes, alkenes, alkynes, and aromatic hydrocarbons

Hydrocarbon derivative an organic compound with at least one other atom beside C and H; each group of hydrocarbon derivative is characterized by a functional group

Hydrogen bond the dipole-dipole interaction between molecules that have a H atom bonded to F, O, or N.; the strongest intermolecular force in liquids

Hydrolysis a chemical reaction in which the water molecule is split

Hydronium ion ion that results when a hydrogen ion combines with water, $H^+ + H_2O$ or H_3O^+ (hydronium ion); a hydrated proton

Hygroscopic a term used to describe salts that take up and retain moisture without dissolving

Hypothesis a tentative guess based on previously collected facts that is proposed to explain regularities in data

Ideal gas a nonexistent gas that behaves exactly as predicted by the ideal gas law; some real gases approach ideal gas behavior at low pressures and high temperatures

Ideal gas equation the equation that expresses the relationship of pressure, volume, temperature, and number of moles of an ideal gas, $PV = nRT$

Immiscible the term used to describe two or more liquids that are not soluble in each other; they are identified by observing two or more layers

Inert atmosphere an environment of stable gases such as helium, argon, or nitrogen that will not enter into a chemical reaction

Inert gases the old name for the noble gases

Inhibitor a substance that decreases the rate of chemical reactions by increasing the activation energy

Intermolecular forces attractive forces among molecules that are responsible for holding molecules in a particular physical state; the primary intermolecular forces are London dispersion forces, dipole-dipole interactions, hydrogen bonds, ionic bonds, covalent bonds, and metallic bonds

International System of Units (SI) a system of measurement units based on the metric system and is used by scientists throughout the world

International Union of Pure and Applied Chemistry Nomenclature System (IUPAC System) a set of rules used to assign a unique name to any chemical compound

Ion a charged atom or group of atoms (see anion and cation)

Ionic bond a chemical bond in which electrons are transferred from a metal to a nonmetal or polyatomic ion, resulting in the formation of ionic species

Ionization a process by which a substance is changed to ions

Ionization energy the amount of energy required to remove the most loosely held electron from a neutral gaseous atom

Ionizing radiation radiation that produces ions as it traverses matter

Isoelectronic a term used to describe different chemical species with the same electronic configuration; for example, the F in NaF is isoelectronic to Ne

Isomers compounds with the same molecular formula but different structures

Isotopes atoms with the same atomic number but different mass numbers

Joule (J) a unit of energy, equivalent to 0.239 calorie; 1 cal = 4.184 J

Kelvin temperature scale a temperature scale in which the zero point is absolute zero, the lowest possible temperature; each degree is 1/273.16 of the temperature of the triple point of water

Ketone an organic compound with a carbonyl group bonded to two hydrocarbon groups, RCOR'

Kilo a prefix that is placed in front of units to increase their magnitude 1000 ×

Kinetic energy the energy possessed by moving bodies; it equals one-half the mass of an object times its velocity squared, $KE = \frac{1}{2}mv^2$

Lanthanides (lanthanide series) the 14 elements in the periodic table directly following lanthanum, La; elements 58 through 71; also called the rare earths

Law of conservation of mass the law that states that mass cannot be created or destroyed in normal chemical changes

Law of constant composition the law that states that the mass ratios of elements within a compound are fixed

Le Chatelier's principle the principle that states that when an equilibrium system is changed, the equilibrium attempts to absorb the change and return to a state of equilibrium

Lewis structure formula that shows the valence electrons in a molecule as dots and dashes

Lewis symbol symbol of an element that shows the valence electrons as dots

Limiting reagent (limiting reactant) the reactant that determines the maximum amount of products produced; when all of it is consumed, the reaction ceases even though the other reactants are still present

Lipids a class of biologically important compounds that include triacylglycerols, steroids, waxes, and prostaglandins

Liter (L) a non-SI unit of volume, equivalent to the SI unit 1 dm^3

Logarithm of a number the exponent of 10 (common logarithm) that gives a quantity equal to the number; for example, log 1000 = 3, because $10^3 = 1000$

London dispersion force (see dispersion force)

Malleable term used to describe the property of

substances that enables them to be hammered and shaped into different forms, a characteristic property of metals

Manometer a laboratory instrument used to measure gas pressure

Mass the measure of the quantity of matter in an object

Mass number the total number of protons and neutrons (nucleons) in an atom

Matter anything that has mass and occupies space

Mechanism (see reaction mechanism)

Melting point the temperature at which a solid changes to a liquid, and the solid and liquid exist in equilibrium; the same temperature as the freezing point

Metal a substance that is a good conductor of heat and electricity, readily loses electrons to form cations, is malleable, is ductile, and has a shiny, metallic appearance

Metalloid an element with properties different from those of metals or nonmetals; examples of metalloids are B. Si, Ge, and As

Metathesis reaction a double replacement reaction

Meter (m) SI unit of length; 1 m = 39.37 in

Metric system the decimal system of measurement from which the International System (SI) was derived

Milli a prefix placed in front of a unit to diminish its size to 1/1000 × the original unit

Millimeter of Hg (mmHg) a unit of pressure equal to X of an atmosphere; 1 atm = 760 mmHg (also see torr)

Miscible term used to describe the property of two or more mutually soluble liquids

Mixture a combination of two or more pure substances; two types of mixtures exist: (1) homogeneous mixtures, or solutions; and (2) heterogeneous mixtures, those with more than one identifiable phase

Molality (m) a unit of solution concentration that relates moles of solute to kilograms of solvent, mol (solute)/kg (solvent)

Molarity (M) a unit of solution concentration that relates moles of solute to liters of solution, mol (solute)/L (solution)

Molar mass the mass of one mole of a substance

Molar volume the volume of one mole of a substance under a fixed set of conditions

Mole (mol) the SI unit for the amount of a substance; a mole of substance contains 6.022×10^{23} particles

Molecular formula a formula that indicates the type and exact number of atoms in a molecule

Molecular geometry the three-dimensional shape of a molecule; it indicates the position of each atom relative to all other atoms in the molecule

Molecular mass the sum of all the atomic masses of atoms in a molecule

Molecule the most fundamental unit in a covalent

compound that retains the chemical properties of the compound; molecules are composed of atoms that are chemically combined

Monomer the molecular structure or structures that combine to produce polymers

Monosaccharides simple sugars that combine to yield all other carbohydrates; most naturally occurring monosaccharides contain three to seven C atoms

Multiple covalent bonds covalent bonds with more than two shared electrons; includes double and triple bonds

Neutralization the combination of an acid and base to yield a salt and often water

Neutron a particle in the nucleus of an atom possessing no electric charge; its mass, 1.008665 u, is slightly larger than that of a proton

Noble gases group 18 (VIIIA) elements, including He, Ne, Ar, Kr, Xe, and Rn

Nomenclature (see chemical nomenclature)

Nonelectrolyte a substance that does not ionize when dissolved

Nonmetals elements on the right side of the periodic table that possess filled or nearly filled outer electronic configurations and have chemical and physical properties opposite to the metals

Nonpolar covalent bond a bond in which electrons are shared equally; no separation of charge is found

Normal boiling point the temperature at which the vapor pressure of a liquid equals 760 torr

Nuclear fission a nuclear change in which a high-mass nucleus breaks up into two or more smaller fragments, releasing a large quantity of energy

Nuclear fusion a nuclear change in which two low-mass atoms are united to produce a higher-mass atom; a large amount of energy is released during nuclear fusion

Nucleic acid any one of a class of biologically important molecules that are composed of nucleotides, including deoxyribonucleic acids (DNAs) and ribonucleic acids (RNAs)

Nucleon a particle located in the nucleus, either a proton or a neutron

Nucleus the small, dense, positively charged region in the center of an atom; it contains the protons and neutrons

Orbital a region of space in an atom where a high probability exists for finding electrons; it is the smallest subdivision of an electron energy level, holding a maximum of two electrons

Ore the rock or mineral from which elements, commonly metals, can be extracted

Organic compound any C compound except those that exhibit properties of inorganic compounds;

the two principal classes are hydrocarbons and hydrocarbon derivatives

Oxidation a chemical change in which electrons are released; the addition of oxygen or the loss of hydrogen by a substance

Oxidation number a number assigned to atoms to assist in predicting chemical changes and writing chemical formulas

Oxide a binary compound of oxygen

Oxidizing agent a substance that brings about the oxidation of another substance by accepting electrons from it

Oxyacid an inorganic acid that contains one or more O atoms, for example, HNO_3, H_2SO_4, and $HClO_4$

Partial pressure the pressure exerted by an individual gas in a gaseous mixture

Parts per million (ppm) a unit of concentration that expresses the number of parts of solute per million total parts, parts(solute)/1,000,000 total parts

Pascal (Pa) the SI unit of pressure; 133.3 Pa = 1 torr

Percent (mass to volume) (% m/v) a unit of concentration that expresses the mass of solute per 100 mL of solution (mass(solute)/100 mL(solution))

Percent by mass (%m/m) a unit of concentration that expresses the mass of solute per 100 g of solution (mass(solute)/100 g(solution))

Percent by volume (% m/v) a unit of concentration that expresses the volume of solute per 100 mL of solution (volume(solute)/100 mL(solution))

Percent yield the actual yield of products in a chemical reaction divided by the theoretical yield, times 100; percent of the theoretically calculated yield actually obtained

Period a horizontal row in the periodic table

Periodic properties the chemical and physical properties that recur regularly with increasing atomic number

Peroxide a compound with an O—O single bond

pH the negative logarithm of $[H^+]$

Phase a homogeneous region of matter with observable boundaries

Physical change a change in physical properties of a substance with no change in composition

Physical property a property associated with an individual substance that can be described without referring to any other substance, e.g., color, size, mass, and density

Physical states various forms in which substances exist, depending on temperature, pressure, and intermolecular forces; solid, liquid, and gas

Polar covalent bond a bond in which electrons are shared unequally; there is a separation of charge

Polyatomic ion an ion containing more than one atom

Polymer a high-molecular-mass compound composed of long chains of repeating small bonded units (monomers)

Polyprotic acid an acid with the capacity to donate more than one H^+

Polysaccharides polymers of monosaccharides found in living systems, e.g., starch, cellulose, and glycogen

Positron a positively charged electron, e^+; a form of antimatter

Potential energy stored energy resulting from an object's position, condition, or composition

Precipitation a process whereby a solid, insoluble substance is produced in an aqueous reaction

Precision expresses how closely repeated measurements are grouped; describes the reproducibility of measurements

Pressure force applied to an area; gas pressure is measured in kilopascals, atmospheres, bars, and torr

Product the end result of a chemical reaction, written to the right of the arrow in a chemical equation

Property a physical or chemical characteristic used to identify a sample of matter

Proteins a class of biologically important molecules that are major structural and controlling agents in cells; chemically, they are amino acid polymers

Proton a positively charged particle within the nucleus of atoms; it has a mass of 1.007276 u

Radiation absorbed dose (rad) a measure of the amount of energy absorbed per gram of living tissue as a result of being exposed to ionizing radiation

Radioactive element an unstable element that emits matter-energy forms at a measurable rate

Radioactivity the emission of particles and energy forms by unstable nuclei

Random errors unidentifiable errors associated with all measurements

Rare earth elements (see lanthanides)

Rate constant the proportionality constant relating the rate of a chemical reaction to the concentration of one or more of the reactants raised to a power; k is the symbol for any rate constant

Reactant a substance initially present in a chemical reaction

Reaction mechanism a series of steps that occurs when the reactant molecules collide and form the products

Reaction rate the change in concentration, or pressure, of reactants or products over a unit time interval; how fast or how slowly a reaction proceeds

Real gas a gas, often at high pressures and low temperatures, that does not behave exactly in the manner predicted by the ideal gas laws

Redox a contraction meaning reduction and oxidation

Reducing agent a substance that brings about the reduction of another substance; a substance that undergoes oxidation

Reduction a chemical process whereby electrons are taken in; adding hydrogen to or removing oxygen from a substance results in the reduction of the substance

Replacement reaction a reaction whereby an element combines with a compound and displaces one of its components

Resonance exhibited by molecules with electron delocalization; is found in molecules with more than one correct Lewis structure

Reversible reaction a reaction in which the products can combine to re-form the reactants

Salt a substance that results when an acid combines with a base; salts are ionic substances composed mainly of combinations of metals and nonmetals or metals and polyatomic ions

Saturated hydrocarbon hydrocarbon with only C—C single bonds

Saturated solution a solution in which the maximum amount of solute is dissolved in a solvent for a particular set of conditions; the dissolved solute particles would be in equilibrium with undissolved solute, if present

Scale a laboratory instrument used to measure an object's weight; a series of marks on a line used to measure something

Scientific exponential notation the expression used to write large and small numbers as the product of decimal and exponential factors; the decimal factor has a numerical value between 1 and 10, and the exponential factor is a power of 10

Shell region within an atom with a specific energy where electrons exist; organized into subregions called subshells

Significant figures measured digits plus one estimated digit that together indicate the degree of uncertainty of a measurement

Simplest formula (see empirical formula)

Single bond a covalent bond with two electrons shared between two atoms

Solubility the amount of solute dissolved in a fixed amount of solvent at a specified temperature, usually measured in grams of solute per 100 mL of solvent

Solute the component of a solution present in smaller amount; the solid component in a solid-1iquid solution

Solution a homogeneous mixture of pure substances

Solvent the component of a solution present in larger amount; the liquid component of a solid- liquid solution

Specific gravity the ratio of the density of a substance to the density of water, a unitless ratio

Specific heat the amount of heat required to raise one gram of substance by one degree Kelvin

Spectator ion an ion not chemically changed in an aqueous reaction

Stable a term used to describe substances that do not tend to undergo spontaneous changes

Standard temperature and pressure (STP) when applied to gases, the conditions of 1 atm and 273 K (0°C)

Stoichiometry the study of quantitative relationships in chemical reactions and formulas

STP (see standard temperature and pressure)

Strong acid an acid that dissociates 100% in dilute aqueous solutions, adding a large quantity of H^+ to water

Strong base a base that dissociates 100% in dilute aqueous solution, adding a large quantity of OH^- to water

Structure the three-dimensional arrangement of the components of matter

Subliming point the temperature at which a solid changes to a vapor; solid-vapor transition point

Subshell (sublevel) a subdivision of an electron shell; the four primary sublevels are designated by the letters s, p, d, and f.

Surface tension a property of the surface of a liquid to act as if it has a membrane covering

Systematic errors correctable errors in measurement; they result from poor techniques and procedures, uncalibrated equipment, and human error

Temperature the measurement of the relative hotness of an object; it determines the direction of heat flow

Ternary compound a compound with three different elements

Theoretical yield the maximum obtainable yield of a chemical reaction predicted from stoichiometric relationships

Theory a unified set of hypotheses consistent with one another and with experimentally observable phenomena

Thermodynamics the study of energy and its transformation

Titration a laboratory procedure that determines the volume of one chemical needed to totally combine with another

Torr another name for the unit of pressure 1 mmHg; 760 torr = 1 atm

Transition metal a metal belonging to a chemical groups 3 to 12; those with a B designation

Transition state the high-energy condition that must be reached to produce the activated complex

Transmutation the conversion of one nuclide to another nuclide

Transuranium element an element on the periodic table that comes after U within the actinide series; elements 93 through 103 (Np to Lr)

Triacylglycerol (Triglyceride) an ester of three fatty

acids and glycerol; the most common form of lipids

Triple covalent bond a bond in which six electrons are shared between two atoms

Unified atomic mass with unit (u or amu) a mass equivalent to one-twelfth the mass of a ^{12}C atom $(1.666 \times 10^{-24}$ g); it is used to express the mass of individual atoms

Unsaturated hydrocarbon a hydrocarbon with double or triple bonds

Unsaturated solution a solution in which more solute can be dissolved, an equilibrium does not exist between dissolved and undissolved solute

Valence electron an electron in the outermost energy level of an atom

Vapor a substance in the gas phase

Vapor pressure of a liquid the pressure of a vapor above a liquid; this term normally refers to the equilibrium vapor pressure

Viscosity the resistance of a substance to flow, directly related to the strength of the substance's intermolecular forces

Volatile a term used to describe a liquid that evaporates readily at relatively low temperatures

Volt a unit of electromotive force (J/C); electrical potential difference

Voltaic cell (see galvanic cell)

Volume the space occupied by a mass

Weak acid an acid that dissociates to a small degree, producing few H^+ in solution

Weak base a base that dissociates to a small degree, producing few OH^- in solution

Weight the measure of the gravitational force of attraction on a mass

Index

Element Listing with Symbols, Atomic Numbers, and Atomic Masses

Element	Symbol	Atomic Number	Atomic Mass
Hydrogen	H	1	1.00794
Helium	He	2	4.002602
Lithium	Li	3	6.941
Beryllium	Be	4	9.01218
Boron	B	5	10.811
Carbon	C	6	12.0107
Nitrogen	N	7	14.00674
Oxygen	O	8	15.9994
Fluorine	F	9	18.9984
Neon	Ne	10	20.1797
Sodium	Na	11	22.98977
Magnesium	Mg	12	24.3050
Aluminum	Al	13	26.98154
Silicon	Si	14	28.0855
Phosphorus	P	15	30.97376
Sulfur	S	16	32.066
Chlorine	Cl	17	35.4527
Argon	Ar	18	39.948
Potassium	K	19	39.0983
Calcium	Ca	20	40.078
Scandium	Sc	21	44.9559
Titanium	Ti	22	47.867
Vanadium	V	23	50.9415
Chromium	Cr	24	51.9961
Manganese	Mn	25	54.9380
Iron	Fe	26	55.845
Cobalt	Co	27	58.9332
Nickel	Ni	28	58.6934
Copper	Cu	29	63.546
Zinc	Zn	30	65.39
Gallium	Ga	31	69.723
Germanium	Ge	32	72.61
Arsenic	As	33	74.9216
Selenium	Se	34	78.96
Bromine	Br	35	79.904
Krypton	Kr	36	83.80
Rubidium	Rb	37	85.4678
Strontium	Sr	38	87.62
Yttrium	Y	39	88.9059
Zirconium	Zr	40	91.22
Niobium	Nb	41	92.906
Molybdenum	Mo	42	95.94
Technetium	Tc	43	98
Ruthenium	Ru	44	101.07
Rhodium	Rh	45	102.905
Palladium	Pd	46	106.4
Silver	Ag	47	107.8682
Cadmium	Cd	48	112.411
Indium	In	49	114.82
Tin	Sn	50	118.710
Antimony	Sb	51	121.760
Tellurium	Te	52	127.60
Iodine	I	53	126.9045
Xenon	Xe	54	131.29
Cesium	Cs	55	132.905
Barium	Ba	56	137.34
Lanthanum	La	57	138.91
Cerium	Ce	58	140.1
Praseodymium	Pr	59	140.907
Neodymium	Nd	60	144.24
Promethium	Pm	61	147.0
Samarium	Sm	62	150.35
Europium	Eu	63	151.96
Gadolinium	Gd	64	157.25
Terbium	Tb	65	158.924
Dysprosium	Dy	66	162.5
Holmium	Ho	67	164.93
Erbium	Er	68	167.26
Thulium	Tm	69	168.934
Ytterbium	Yb	70	173.04
Lutetium	Lu	71	174.97
Hafnium	Hf	72	178.49
Tantalum	Ta	73	180.95
Tungsten	W	74	183.85
Rhenium	Re	75	186.2
Osmium	Os	76	190.2
Iridium	Ir	77	192.2
Platinum	Pt	78	195.09
Gold	Au	79	196.967
Mercury	Hg	80	200.59
Thallium	Tl	81	204.37
Lead	Pb	82	207.19
Bismuth	Bi	83	208.98
Polonium	Po	84	210
Astatine	At	85	210
Radon	Rn	86	222
Francium	Fr	87	223
Radium	Ra	88	226
Actinium	Ac	89	237
Thorium	Th	90	232.038
Protactinium	Pa	91	231.0
Uranium	U	92	238.0

Drew H. Wolfe, Ph. D
General Chemistry/Modern Chemistry
8/98

Periodic Table of the Elements

1 (IA)	2 (IIA)	3 (IIIB)	4 (IVB)	5 (VB)	6 (VIB)	7 (VIIAB)	8 (VIIIB)	9 (VIIIB)	10 (VIIIB)	11 (IB)	12 (IIB)	13 (IIIA)	14 (IVA)	15 (VA)	16 (VIA)	17 (VIIA)	18 (VIIIA)
1 H 1.0079																	2 He 4.0026
3 Li 6.941	4 Be 9.0122											5 B 10.811	6 C 12.011	7 N 14.007	8 O 15.999	9 F 18.998	10 Ne 20.183
11 Na 22.990	12 Mg 24.312											13 Al 26.981	14 Si 28.086	15 P 30.974	16 S 32.066	17 Cl 35.452	18 Ar 39.948
19 K 39.098	20 Ca 40.078	21 Sc 44.956	22 Ti 47.867	23 V 50.942	24 Cr 51.996	25 Mn 54.938	26 Fe 55.845	27 Co 58.933	28 Ni 58.693	29 Cu 63.546	30 Zn 65.39	31 Ga 69.723	32 Ge 72.61	33 As 74.922	34 Se 78.96	35 Br 79.904	36 Kr 83.80
37 Rb 85.468	38 Sr 87.62	39 Y 88.905	40 Zr 91.224	41 Nb 92.906	42 Mo 95.94	43 Tc (98)	44 Ru 101.07	45 Rh 102.90	46 Pd 106.42	47 Ag 107.87	48 Cd 112.40	49 In 114.82	50 Sn 118.71	51 Sb 121.75	52 Te 127.60	53 I 126.90	54 Xe 131.30
55 Cs 132.91	56 Ba 137.33	57 * La 138.91	72 Hf 178.49	73 Ta 180.95	74 W 183.85	75 Re 186.20	76 Os 190.23	77 Ir 192.22	78 Pt 195.09	79 Au 196.97	80 Hg 200.59	81 Tl 204.38	82 Pb 207.19	83 Bi 208.98	84 Po (210)	85 At (210)	86 Rn (222)
87 Fr (223)	88 Ra (226)	89 ** Ac (227)	104 Rf (261)	105 Db (262)	106 Sg (266)	107 Bh (264)	108 Hs (269)	109 Mt (268)	110 UUn (269)	111 UUu (272)	112 UUb (277)	113 UUt	114 UUq	115 UUp	116 UUh	117 UUs	118 UUo

* Lanthanide Series

58 Ce 140.12	59 Pr 140.91	60 Nd 144.24	61 Pm (147)	62 Sm 150.35	63 Eu 151.96	64 Gd 157.25	65 Tb 158.92	66 Dy 162.50	67 Ho 164.93	68 Er 167.26	69 Tm 168.93	70 Yb 173.04	71 Lu 174.97

** Actinide Series

90 Th 232.04	91 Pa (231)	92 U 238.03	93 Np (237)	94 Pu (242)	95 Am (243)	96 Cm (247)	97 Bk (249)	98 Cf (251)	99 Es (254)	100 Fm (253)	101 Md (256)	102 No (253)	103 Lr (257)

Drew H. Wolfe, Ph.D. General Chemistry/Modern Chemistry 8/98